D1108341

THE MODERN LIBRARY
OF THE WORLD'S BEST BOOKS

The Vicar
of Wakefield

and other writings

The publishers will be pleased to send, upon request, an illustrated folder setting forth the purpose and scope of THE MODERN LIBRARY, *and listing each volume in the series. Every reader of books will find titles he has been looking for, handsomely printed, in definitive editions, and at an unusually low price.*

OLIVER GOLDSMITH

The Vicar
of Wakefield

and other writings

EDITED, WITH AN INTRODUCTION AND NOTES, BY

Frederick W. Hilles

BODMAN PROFESSOR OF ENGLISH LITERATURE, YALE UNIVERSITY

THE MODERN LIBRARY · NEW YORK

FIRST MODERN LIBRARY EDITION, 1955

Library of Congress Catalog Card Number: 55-6394

Copyright, 1955, by Random House, Inc.

Random House IS THE PUBLISHER OF *The Modern Library*

BENNETT CERF · DONALD S. KLOPFER · ROBERT K. HAAS

Manufactured in the United States of America

by H. Wolff, New York

CONTENTS

INTRODUCTION

A couple of hundred years ago a young man whose name at that time meant nothing to the world wrote to a friend: "There will come a day, no doubt it will—I beg you may live a couple of hundred years longer only to see the day—when the Scaligers and Daciers will vindicate my character, give learned editions of my labours, and bless the times with copious comments on the text. . . . How will they bewail the times that suffered so much genius to lie neglected!" And after playfully describing his future fame he ended by coming down to hard reality, "here in a garret writing for bread, and expecting to be dunned for a milk score." The letter was written in the summer of 1758 by Oliver Goldsmith, who for well over a year had been leading the life of an underpaid journalist in London. He was to know what it is to be famous; during the last ten years of his life he was to be regarded as one of the two or three outstanding living authors. But there never was to to be a time when he could not speak of himself as "writing for bread, and expecting to be dunned."

Much that one reads about his early life is legendary. We do not even know—Goldsmith himself seems not to have known—just when he was born, but the work of modern scholars indicates that the date Dr. Johnson adopted, 1731, may after all have been the correct one. We know that he was one of a large family and that his father was rector of a small church in an Irish village. We know too something about his education. His first teacher thought him "impenetrably stupid," and throughout his school and college days he showed far more interest in social activities than in book learning. At Trinity College, Dublin, where he held a scholarship, he proved himself an undisciplined student, though finally, in 1749, he received the

B.A. Then for three years he led an unsettled life, planning at one time to go into the church, at another to become a lawyer, trying his hand at schoolteaching, and eventually deciding to be a doctor. In 1752 he set out for Edinburgh, where he was to study medicine. He never returned to his native land.

The picture he painted of Ireland is not a flattering one. "Conversation there is generally made up of a smutty toast or a baudy song." The young men that he knew spent their lives "hunting and drinking and swearing and getting bastards." It is clear that even in his early days Goldsmith was exceptionally thin-skinned. People interested him; he wished people to be interested in him; but was all too conscious that he was awkward and absurd in society. He resented being treated with "civil contempt" by those who in the eyes of the world were successful. We have his word for it that when he was in Ireland he was despised by most and hateful to himself, and when he departed he declared that he took with him nothing "except his brogue and his blunders." He did not seem to realize that he also took with him his outlook on life, his way of thinking. To the end of his days he remained an Irish Tory conservative.

He stayed at Edinburgh little more than a year, where, if we may trust the account he wrote to his favorite uncle, he spent the first winter "almost unknown to Every body Except some few who attend the Proffesors of Physick." He had an ugly, pock-marked face, and he was poor. Such a man, he wrote, "is society only for himself, and such society the world lets me enjoy in great abundance." No doubt he exaggerated. We know that before he left Edinburgh he was taken up by the Great as "the facetious Irish man," but sensing that they liked him more as a jester than as a companion, he "disdained so servile an employment."

In 1754 he moved to the continent to continue his medical studies at Leyden. "The great Albinus is still alive there, and 'twill be proper to go, though only to have it said that we have studied in so famous an university." But he was disappointed with his teachers and contemptuous of the natives, a contempt that keeps cropping out in his later writings. And here again he seems to have spent much of his time alone. "I generally detachd myself from all society and was wholy taken up in observing the face of the country." After ten months he left

Holland and made the Grand Tour, traveling through Flanders, France, Germany, Switzerland, and Italy. But unlike the sons of the wealthy Goldsmith made much of his tour alone and on foot, with empty pockets and "one clean shirt."

Returning to London in 1756, he spent several years trying various ways of earning a living. He was (perhaps) an actor. He was an assistant to an apothecary, a physician in the slums of the city, a corrector of the press for a printer, a teacher in a boys' school, a reviewer for the magazines, a translator of books from the French. He applied for a position as ship's hospital mate but was rejected. Finally—it would seem to us inevitably—he realized that he was an author by profession.

He described himself at this time as having "a pale melancholly visage with two great wrinkles between the eye brows, with an eye disgustingly severe and a big wig." He had not lost his self-consciousness. "I can neither laugh nor drink, have contracted an hesitating disagreeable manner of speaking, and a visage that looks ill-nature itself." This was written at a time when he was deeply in debt and obviously discouraged, after "some years struggling with a wretched being, with all that contempt which indigence brings with it, with all those strong passions which makes contempt insupportable."

A glimpse of his surroundings at this period of his life is given by Bishop Percy, who as a young vicar called on Goldsmith in 1759, finding him "in a wretched dirty room in which there was but one chair." Goldsmith, insisting that his visitor occupy the chair, seated himself on the window-ledge. "While they were conversing, some one gently rapped at the door, and being desired to come in, a poor little ragged girl of very decent behaviour entered, who, dropping a curtsie, said 'My mamma sends her compliments, and begs the favour of you to lend her a chamber-pot full of coals.' "

Percy's visit was made just as Goldsmith was emerging from obscurity. Within a year he was well known, in a limited circle, as a successful journalist and as author of *An Enquiry into the Present State of Polite Learning in Europe*. He met, and seems to have made a favorable impression on, one of the greatest living authors, Dr. Smollett, and was soon to meet an even greater, the author of *The Rambler*. It is to Percy that we turn for a story concerning the first meeting of Goldsmith and

Johnson. Goldsmith was host at a supper to which he had invited a number of literary men. Percy, who escorted Johnson, was "struck with the studied neatness of Johnson's dress; he had on a new suit of cloaths, a new wig nicely powdered, and every thing about him so perfectly dissimilar from his usual habits and appearance that his companion could not help inquiring the cause of this singular transformation. 'Why, sir,' said Johnson, 'I hear that Goldsmith, who is a very great sloven, justifies his disregard of cleanliness and decency by quoting my practice, and I am desirous this night to show him a better example.' "

Helped, it may be, by the friendship of Dr. Johnson, Goldsmith steadily moved towards general recognition. Even before he had put his name on a title page (the *Enquiry* had been anonymous), he was mentioned as one of the ablest writers of the day. That was early in 1762, the year in which he brought out in book form his Chinese letters under the title of *The Citizen of the World,* thus proving his abilities as an essayist, published his *Life of Nash,* which put him second only to Johnson among living biographers, and sold the manuscript of *The Vicar of Wakefield*. This too was the year in which he first met Boswell, and presumably Reynolds. Two years later The Club was organized, Goldsmith being one of the nine original members, along with Reynolds, Edmund Burke, and Dr. Johnson.

What brought him into "high reputation"—the phrase is Johnson's—was the publication, at the end of 1764, of *The Traveller*. Sir Joshua tells us that this poem "produced an eagerness unparalleled to see the author," and from this time on there are numerous eye-witness accounts of his behavior in society. The first impression he made on some was that he was a pedant. Many were struck by the fact that he was ill at ease and spoke clumsily. Almost everyone noticed that he wished to dominate the group and in an attempt to do so uttered paradoxical statements that were merely absurd. To Boswell on first meeting he seemed "a most impudent puppy," and Mrs. Thrale speaks of his "Impudence truly Irish." According to Sir Joshua, who was probably his closest friend, there was nothing that Goldsmith would not do to attract attention, "sing, stand upon his head, dance about the room." It was discovered that he was as imprudent in financial mat-

ters as in conversation, addicted to gambling and overly generous to those who asked him for money. He had been out
of Ireland for more than ten years, but he still carried with
him his brogue and his blunders. In new company he would
ask tactless questions or make embarrassingly revealing comments about his past life. His vanity—he would admire himself in a mirror or strut about in a new suit of clothes—was
often noted, as was his envy of anyone who was being praised.
Clearly he was "an ideot."

But along with all his absurdities was a genuineness which
inspired affection in his friends. Among the unpublished Boswell Papers there is a letter from Bennet Langton, an original
member of The Club, in which he refers to Goldsmith's "kind
and affectionate Spirit." "He has so much good nature," wrote
young James Northcote, who was studying painting in Sir
Joshua's studio, "and no conceit or affectation." Northcote's
introduction to Goldsmith deserves retelling. "When I came
into the room, Sir Joshua said, 'This is Dr. Goldsmith, who
you often wish'd to see. What was your reason for it?' and I
said, 'because he is a notable man.' Sir Joshua laugh'd and
said he should always be call'd the notable man." At that time
the word *notable* still signified one who was capable in business, a good manager. In the first paragraph of *The Vicar*
Mrs. Primrose is called a "notable" woman. It is the last word
that should at any time have been applied to Goldsmith.

One of Horace's odes (IV, xii) ends with an invitation to
forget business for a while, put serious thoughts aside, and
relax. *Dulce est desipere in loco:* there are times when it is
pleasant to play the fool. This was a sentiment close to Goldsmith's heart. Some of his absurdities can be explained by the
fact that he was deliberately clowning. "Come now," he would
say to Catherine Horneck, "and let us play the fool a little."
Unhappily what was to him playful or ludicrous was too
often completely misunderstood. At times this angered him;
he complained that whatever he said or whatever he did was
twisted so as to seem absurd, malicious, or foolish. "Sir, I
am as a lion baited with curs." At other times he laughed
about it. To Reynolds he wrote when in France, "As for the
meat of this country, I can scarce eat it, and though we pay
two good shillings an head for our dinner, I find it all so

tough that I have spent less time with my knife than my picktooth. I said this as a good thing at table, but it was not understood. I believe it to be a good thing." Two of the letters which he wrote to the Reynolds-Horneck-Bunbury-Baker circle have been included in this edition because of the light-hearted verse in them. They illustrate the side of Goldsmith which endeared him to his friends.

Little need be said of his life after the publication of *The Traveller.* He was now in a position to earn a comfortable living from his pen, but his habitual imprudence in money matters kept him continually in financial hot water. In 1765 he brought out a collected edition of his early essays. The next year saw the delayed publication of *The Vicar of Wakefield.* In 1768 he launched his first comedy, *The Good Natur'd Man,* and two years later published *The Deserted Village.* The first night of *She Stoops to Conquer* was 15 March, 1773, and almost exactly one year later, while he was still writing *Retaliation,* he died. In addition to the works mentioned he had steadily worked on a variety of potboilers, notably his histories (of Greece, of Rome, of England, of his own times) and the *History of the Earth and Animated Nature,* which was published in eight large volumes after his death. Writing for bread, and expecting to be dunned, he who had constantly attacked quacks hastened his death by putting his faith in a quack's cure for fever. "Of poor, dear Dr. Goldsmith," wrote Johnson to Boswell, "there is little to be told. He died of a fever, made, I am afraid, more violent by uneasiness of mind. His debts began to be heavy, and all his resources were exhausted. Sir Joshua is of opinion that he owed not less than two thousand pounds. Was ever poet so trusted before?"

The epitaph for the monument in Westminster Abbey was, as every reader of Boswell remembers, composed by Johnson in Latin. We of today who have little or no Latin, may prefer to read it in Croker's translation:

Of Oliver Goldsmith—
a Poet, Naturalist, and Historian,
who left scarcely any style of writing untouched,
and touched nothing that he did not adorn;
of all the passions,

whether smiles were to be moved or tears,
a powerful yet gentle master;
in genius, sublime, vivid, versatile;
in style, elevated, clear, elegant—
the love of companions,
the fidelity of friends,
and the veneration of readers,
have by this monument honoured the memory.
He was born in Ireland,
at a place called Pallas [in the parish] of Forney,
[and county] of Longford, on the 29th November, 1731.
Educated at [the University of] Dublin,
and died in London, 4th April, 1774.

Johnson's epitaph stresses Goldsmith's remarkable versatility as a writer, and one of the functions of this edition is to illustrate that versatility. A review of a recent life of Goldsmith concluded by asserting "that he didn't produce much, but that of what he did produce, one novel, one poem, and one play, will very likely outlive the work of many of his more fortunate contemporaries." That, doubtless, is the verdict of posterity, but it is questionable whether his fame today should rest merely on three short works. Goldsmith is one of the masters of English prose. To know him through his more famous works only, is to do him an injustice.

In the present edition his writings have been arranged in a roughly chronological order. This is not allowing him to put his best foot forward, but will enable those who are interested to determine whether or not there is any appreciable difference between his early and late styles of writing. The reviews and essays which comprise the first section were, except for the last one, written by an unknown Grub Street hack. The later poems and the plays were regarded, even when they first appeared, as the products of one of the most celebrated living authors.

As an essayist Goldsmith ranks with the best that England has produced. Johnson had taken the form perfected by Addison and Steele and had turned it admirably to his own uses. Goldsmith consistently praised *The Rambler*, but his own essays are very different in tone. In the development of the genre as well as in chronology they stand halfway between the polished Augustanism of Mr. Spectator at the beginning of the eighteenth century and the more sentimental personalized vehicle developed by Hazlitt and Lamb at the beginning of the nineteenth. What Goldsmith succeeded in doing is best described in the words he himself applied to one of his immediate predecessors: "he rather converses with all the ease of a cheerful companion than dictates, as other writers of this class have done, with the affected superiority of an author. He is the first writer since Bickerstaff who has been perfectly satirical yet perfectly good-natured, and who never for the sake of declamation represents simple folly as absolutely criminal. He has solidity to please the grave, and humour and wit to allure the gay."

Goldsmith as essayist is best seen in the individual letters making up *The Citizen of the World,* but the way in which he maintained a continuous narrative in the letters as a whole shows that even at that early time in his career he was well on the road to becoming a novelist. The plot, to be sure, could hardly be more flimsy, but the collected letters contain the ingredients of a typical novel, including tales within tales, and describing, as Smollett put it, "the knavery and foibles of life, with infinite humour and sagacity." There is much that is Dickensian about the odd characters that move in and out of Goldsmith's pages. At times the likenesses are striking. When, for example, we hear Beau Tibbs say, "You shall know,—but let it go no further,—a great secret—five hundred a year to begin with.— My Lord's word of honour for it—," the voice sounds strangely like the voice of Mr. Jingle.

But it is of course by *The Vicar of Wakefield* that Goldsmith must be judged as novelist. And it would be hard to name another novel which better exemplifies Goldsmith's remark that the "reputation of books is raised not by their freedom from defects but the greatness of their beauties." The extraordinary coincidences, the sharp contrast between black and white, the solemn disquisitions on government or the penal laws, the incredible ending—these we must put down as some of the hundred faults in the book. I suspect that Mark Twain was only one of many who have attempted to judge it as we judge "realistic" fiction. Scholars have sought to localize the home of the Primroses, which the Vicar tells us was seventy miles north of Wakefield. The fact is that the Primroses did not live in England at all—they lived in a never-never land of the author's creation. *The Vicar* is a prose-poem in which a highly delicate balance is maintained between obviously stylized bits of sentiment and the subtlest touches of humor. The book represents the vision of an artist and recalls a story told of J. M. W. Turner, who having planted his easel on the high ground overlooking Plymouth harbor, and while painting what he saw from there, was interrupted by a woman unknown to him. Looking over his shoulder, first at the painting and then at the scene, she is said to have remarked, "Well, it doesn't look *that* way to *me!*" "Madam," replied the painter, "don't you wish that it did?"

The same idyllic atmosphere, the same felicity of expression, the same gentle humor mixed with sentiment is to be found in *The Deserted Village,* the poem on which his reputation as poet rests. Recently T. S. Eliot has asserted that even if Goldsmith had written nothing else, this poem would have given him the right to be considered a major poet. Dr. Johnson, always a good judge of this sort of poetry, preferred *The Traveller,* and though it lacks the popular appeal of the other, *The Traveller* comes very near being perfect of its kind. It is an ideal example of the neoclassic ethic poem. Its balanced structure supports the statement which the poem as a whole is making. The balanced discussion (the friendliness or hostility of nature versus the follies or virtues of the natives) reënforces the theme of moderation. The sub-title is *A Prospect of Society.* In a poem which deals not with men but with Man the diction is appropriately generalized.

Goldsmith's plays are pitched in a far different key. They are, as is obvious from his essays on the theatre, written to bring back to the stage some of the qualities found in the exuberant comedy of an earlier period. One may argue as to the merits of *The Good Natur'd Man,* but there can be no question that *She Stoops to Conquer,* one of the very few eighteenth-century plays that still hold the boards, succeeds in doing what it was meant to do. "Did it make you laugh?" asked the playwright of a young man who had just seen it, and when the answer was an enthusiastic affirmative, "that is all I require." "Amusement of so pure a quality," wrote Virginia Woolf, "will never come our way again."

Different as the plays may be in tone from the sedateness of the principal poems or the controlled irony of the better essays or the quaint charm of the novel, they have in common with everything that Goldsmith wrote certain distinctive qualities. Goldsmith lived at a time when the first of all the commandments for the writer was, in Austin Dobson's ringing words, "Be thou clear." But Goldsmith's brand of clarity mingles with other elements. "Let us," he wrote in his first book, "instead of writing finely, try to write naturally." He is not of the genteel school. He cheerfully describes the Sprigginses and Blenkinsops with big bellies and pimples on their noses. But he describes them in a loving fashion. "A man blind of one eye," he wrote, "should always be painted in profile." The kindly nature that Langton refers to peeps out between the lines that he wrote. And never far below the surface is a vein of the comical. "On my conscience," he quoted with approval, "I believe we have all forgot to laugh in these days." *Sive risus essent movendi, sive lacrymae:* not only do we laugh when reading Goldsmith; his writings tend to bring the tear to the eye. Modern readers may find the pathetic passages cloying at times, but these times are rare; his melting sentiment, to quote Mr. Eliot once more, is "just saved by the precision of his language."

The reputation of many an author has remained high for a time and then sunk out of sight. With Goldsmith it has been a different story. The secret of his success will presumably remain a secret, but we do know that he was a lifelong student of the human heart ("study the people" was his advice to a fellow-poet) and that he early developed an ability to write, in Garrick's phrase, "like an angel." The uninitiated reader of today, confronted with a volume of writings that were produced two centuries ago, may echo what George Primrose has to say of Elizabethan dramatists: "Is it possible the present age can be pleased with that antiquated dialect, that obsolete humour, those over-charged characters?" Popular opinion has long since answered the question: witness the present volume.

EDITORIAL NOTE

The text of this edition differs slightly from all other editions of Goldsmith's works. The greater part of what he wrote appeared in various forms during his lifetime. Editors have usually, and quite naturally, adopted the final revisions, thus giving us the version which the author must have wished to preserve. But Goldsmith was not always happy in altering what he had written. More often than not, the changes which he made were substitutions of "correct" phrases for those which, though perhaps ungrammatical, have a freshness about them that pleases. The text of the present edition, then, is based on the earliest version of each selection and restores those phrases which, in Dr. Primrose's words, "have the print of nature still strong upon them." Some of the additions which Goldsmith made at a later date have been included, but these are set off within square brackets. An attempt has been made to preserve the original spelling with all its inconsistencies, but obvious misprints have been silently corrected, and some of the long paragraphs in the early essays have been split up. Considerable liberty has been taken with such quirks of the printer as the use of italics, initial capital letters, and punctuation.

The "official" biography is the so-called Percy memoir, based on materials collected by Bishop Percy and published as preface to Goldsmith's *Miscellaneous Works* in 1801. The standard life was written by Sir James Prior and published in 1837. Of the many shorter biographical studies, that by Austin Dobson (1891) is still the best. The standard edition of Goldsmith's works was edited by J. W. M. Gibbs and published in five volumes in 1885. Since that time important additions to the canon have appeared in two books, *New Essays,* edited by Ronald S. Crane (Chicago, 1927), and *The Collected Letters,* edited by Katharine C. Balderston (Cambridge, 1928). Numerous quotations from this edition of Goldsmith's letters have been incorporated in my introduction with the kind permission of Professor Balderston and the Cambridge University Press. An outstanding contribution to scholarship is *Les Sources Françaises de Goldsmith* (Paris, 1924) by A. L. Sells, and an excellent appraisal of Goldsmith's writings is included in the fourth chapter of Oliver Elton's *Survey of English Literature, 1730-1780* (London, 1928). Professor Crane's admirably complete bibliography of writings by and about Goldsmith is to be found in the second volume of the *Cambridge Bibliography of English Literature* (New York, 1941). A few of the more recent essays or monographs on Goldsmith follow:

Oswald Doughty: Introduction to Scholartis Press ed. of *The Vicar of Wakefield,* London, 1928

T. S. Eliot: Introduction to Haslewood Books ed. of Johnson's *London* and *Vanity of Human Wishes,* London, 1930; reprinted in *English Critical Essays, Twentieth Century* (World's Classics), London, 1933

Arthur Friedman: "Goldsmith's Contributions to the *Critical Review*" in *Modern Philology* for August, 1946

W. F. Gallaway, Jr.: "The Sentimentalism of Goldsmith" in *Pub. Mod. Lang. Assoc.* for December, 1933

F. W. Hilles: Introduction to American Everyman ed. of *The Vicar of Wakefield,* New York, 1951

D. W. Jefferson: "Observations on *The Vicar of Wakefield*" in *The Cambridge Journal* for July, 1950

H. E. MacDermot: "Goldsmith as a Talker" in *Queen's Quarterly* for Summer, 1944

E. L. McAdam: "Goldsmith the Good-natured Man" in *The Age of Johnson* (essays presented to C. B. Tinker), New Haven, 1949

Sir Joshua Reynolds: *Portraits,* ed. F. W. Hilles, New York, 1952

W. V. Reynolds: "Goldsmith's Critical Outlook" in *Review of English Studies* for April, 1938

R. W. Seitz: "The Irish Background of Goldsmith's Thoughts" in *Pub. Mod. Lang. Assoc.* for June, 1937

C. B. Tinker: "Figures in a Dream" in *The Good Estate of Poetry,*
   Boston, 1929
Virginia Woolf: "Oliver Goldsmith" in *The Captain's Death Bed,*
   London, 1950

The Vicar
of Wakefield

and other writings

Essays and Criticisms

[At the beginning of his literary career Goldsmith contributed a great number of essays to the various magazines of the time, but they were printed anonymously. When at the end of 1764 he suddenly became famous as author of *The Traveller,* he collected twenty-seven of the early essays and issued them under his own name in a small volume which appeared in 1765. The preface which follows was written for the collected edition. The five essays which in the present edition follow the preface were first published in *The Bee,* a weekly periodical which Goldsmith produced in the autumn of 1759. Then come two essays that were published in *The British Magazine* in 1760. The reviews (of Smollett, the novels, and Gray's *Odes*) had been published between May and September 1757 in *The Monthly Review,* and the articles on criticism and the stage are extracted from Goldsmith's first book, *An Enquiry into the Present State of Polite Learning in Europe,* 1759. The final essay in this section, on laughing and sentimental comedy, was written at the end of his life, and published in *The Westminster Magazine* at the beginning of 1773.]

THE PREFACE

The following essays have already appeared at different times, and in different publications. The pamphlets in which they were inserted being generally unsuccessful, these shared the common fate, without assisting the bookseller's aims or extending the writer's reputation. The public was too strenuously employed with their own follies to be assiduous in estimating mine, so that many of my best attempts in this way have fallen victims to the transient topic of the times, the Ghost in Cock Lane, or the siege of Ticonderago.

But though they have past pretty silently into the world, I can by no means complain of their circulation. The magazines and papers of the day have, indeed, been liberal enough in this respect. Most of these essays have been regularly reprinted twice or thrice a year, and conveyed to the public through the kennel of some engaging compilation. If there be a pride in multiplied editions, I have seen some of my labours sixteen times reprinted, and claimed by different parents as their own. I have seen them flourished at the beginning with praise, and signed at the end with the names of Philantos, Philalethes, Philaḷutheros, and Philanthropos. These gentlemen have kindly stood sponsors to my productions; and to flatter me more, have always past them as their own.

It is time, however, at last to vindicate my claims; and as these entertainers of the public, as they call themselves, have partly lived upon me for some years, let me now try if I cannot live a little upon myself. I would desire, in this case, to imitate that fat man who I have somewhere heard of in a shipwreck, who, when the sailors prest by famine, were taking slices from his posteriors to satisfy their hunger, insisted, with great justice, on having the first cut for himself.

Yet after all, I cannot be angry with any who have taken it into their heads to think that whatever I write is worth reprinting, particularly when I consider how great a majority will think it scarce worth reading. Trifling and superficial are terms of reproach that are easily objected, and that carry an air of penetration in the observer. These faults have been objected to the following essays; and it must be owned in some measure that the charge is true. However, I could have made them more metaphysical, had I thought fit; but I would ask whether in a short essay it is not necessary to be superficial? Before we have prepared to enter into the depths of a subject in the usual forms we have got to the bottom of our scanty page, and thus lose the honours of a victory by too tedious a preparation for the combat.

There is another fault in this collection of trifles which, I fear, will not be so easily pardoned. It will be alledged that the humour of them (if any be found) is stale and hackneyed. This may be true enough as matters now stand, but I may with great truth assert that the humour was new when I wrote it. Since that time, indeed, many of the topics which were first started here have been hunted down, and many of the thoughts blown upon. In fact, these essays were considered as quietly laid in the grave of oblivion; and our modern compilers, like sextons and executioners, think it their undoubted right to pillage the dead.

However, whatever right I have to complain of the public, they can as yet have no just reason to complain of me. If I have written dull essays, they have hitherto treated them as dull essays. Thus far we are at least upon par, and until they think fit to make me their humble debtor by praise, I am resolved not to lose a single inch of my self-importance. Instead, therefore, of attempting to establish a credit amongst them, it will perhaps be wiser to apply to some more distant correspondent; and as my drafts are in some danger of being protested at home, it may not be imprudent, upon this occasion, to draw my bills upon Posterity. Mr. Posterity:– Sir: Nine hundred and ninety-nine years after sight hereof, pay the bearer, or order, a thousand pounds worth of praise, free from all deductions whatsoever, it being a commodity that will then be very serviceable to him, and place it to the account of, &c.

ON THE USE OF LANGUAGE

The manner in which most writers begin their treatises on the Use of Language, is generally thus: "Language has been granted to man in order to discover his wants and necessities, so as to have them relieved by society. Whatever we desire, whatever we wish, it is but to cloath those desires or wishes in words, in order to fruition; the principal use of language therefore, say they, is to express our wants so as to receive a speedy redress."

Such an account as this may serve to satisfy grammarians and rhetoricians well enough, but men who know the world maintain very contrary maxims; they hold, and I think with some shew of reason, they hold that he who best knows how to conceal his necessities and desires is the most likely person to find redress, and that the true use of speech is not so much to express our wants as to conceal them.

When we reflect on the manner in which mankind generally confer their favours, we shall find that they who seem to want them least, are the very persons who most liberally share them. There is something so attractive in riches that the large heap generally collects from the smaller; and the poor find as much pleasure in encreasing the enormous mass, as the miser who owns it sees happiness in its encrease. Nor is there in this any thing repugnant to the laws of true morality. Seneca himself allows that in conferring benefits, the present should always be suited to the dignity of the receiver. Thus the rich receive large presents, and are thanked for accepting them. Men of middling stations are obliged to be content with presents something less, while the beggar, who may be truly said to want indeed, is well paid if a farthing rewards his warmest solicitations.

Every man who has seen the world and has had his *ups and downs in life,* as the expression is, must have frequently experienced the truth of this doctrine, and must know that to have much, or to seem to have it, is the only way to have more. Ovid finely compares a man of broken fortune to a falling column; the lower it sinks, the greater weight it is obliged to sustain. Thus, when a man has no occasion to borrow, he finds numbers willing to lend him. Should he ask his friend to lend him an hundred pounds, it is possible from the largeness of the demand he may find credit for twenty; but should he humbly only sue for a trifle, it is two to one whether he might be trusted for two pence. A certain young fellow at George's, whenever he had occasion to ask his friend for a guinea, used to prelude his request as if he wanted two hundred, and talked so familiarly of large sums that none could ever think he wanted a small one. The same gentleman, whenever he wanted credit for a new suit from his taylor, always made the proposal in laced cloaths; for he found by experience that if he appeared shabby on these occasions, Mr. Lynch had taken an oath against trusting, or what was every bit as bad, his foreman was out of the way and would not be at home these two days.

There can be no inducement to reveal our wants, except to find pity, and by this means relief; but before a poor man opens his mind in such circumstances, he should first consider whether he is contented to lose the esteem of the person he solicits, and whether he is willing to give up friendship only to excite compassion. Pity and friendship are passions incompatible with each other, and it is impossible that both can reside in any breast for the smallest space, without impairing each other. Friendship is made up of esteem and pleasure; pity is composed of sorrow and contempt; the mind may for some time fluctuate between them, but it never can entertain both together.

Yet let it not be thought that I would exclude pity from the human mind. There is scarce any who are not in some degree possessed of this pleasing softness; but it is at best but a short-lived passion, and seldom affords distress more than transitory assistance: With some it scarce lasts from the first impulse till the hand can be put into the pocket; with others it may continue for twice that space, and on some of extraordinary sensibility I have seen it operate for half an hour. But however, last as it will, it generally produces but beggarly effects; and where from this motive we give an halfpenny, from others we give always pound. In great distress we sometimes, it is true, feel the influence of tenderness strongly; when the same distress solicits a second time, we then feel with diminished sensibility, but like the repetition of an eccho, every new impulse becomes weaker, till at last our sensations lose every mixture of sorrow, and degenerate into downright contempt.

Jack Spindle and I were old acquaintance; but he's gone. Jack was bred in a compting-house, and his father dying just as he was out of his time, left him an handsome fortune, and many friends to advise with. The restraint in which he had been brought up, had thrown a gloom upon his temper, which some regarded as an habitual prudence, and from such considerations he had every day repeated offers of friendship. Those who had money were ready to offer him their assistance that way; and they who had daughters, frequently in the warmth of affection advised him to marry. Jack, however, was in good circumstances; he wanted neither money, friends, nor a wife, and therefore modestly declined their proposals.

Some errors in the management of his affairs and several losses in trade soon brought Jack to a different way of thinking; and he at last thought it his best way to let his friends know that their offers were at length acceptable. His first address was therefore to a scrivener who had formerly made him frequent offers of money and friendship at a time when, perhaps, he knew those offers would have been refused.

Jack, therefore, thought he might use his old friend without any ceremony, and as a man confident of not being refused, requested the use of an hundred guineas for a few days, as he just then had an occasion for money. "And pray, Mr. Spindle," replied the scrivener, "do you want all this money?" "Want it, Sir," says the other, "if I did not want it, I should not have asked it." "I am sorry for that," says the friend; "for those who want money when they come to borrow, will want money when they should come to pay. To say the truth, Mr. Spindle, money is money now-a-days. I believe it is all sunk in the bottom of the sea, for my part; and he that has got a little is a fool if he does not keep what he has got."

Not quite disconcerted by this refusal, our adventurer was resolved to apply to another, whom he knew to be the very best friend he had in the world. The gentleman whom he now addressed received his proposal with all the affability that could be expected from generous friendship. "Let me see, you want an hundred guineas; and pray, dear Jack, would not fifty answer?" "If you have but fifty to spare, Sir, I must be contented." "Fifty to spare! I do not say that, for I believe I have but twenty about me." "Then I must borrow the other thirty from some other friend." "And pray," replied the friend, "would it not be the best way to borrow the whole money from that other friend, and then one note will serve for all, you know. Lord, Mr. Spindle, make no ceremony with me at any time; you know I'm your friend, and when you chuse a bit of dinner or so.——You, Tom, see the gentleman down. You won't forget to dine with us now and then. Your very humble servant."

Distressed, but not discouraged at this treatment, he was at last resolved to find that assistance from love, which he could not have from friendship. Miss Jenny Dismal had a fortune in her own hands, and she had already made all the advances that her sex's modesty would permit. He made his proposal therefore with confidence, but soon perceived, *No bankrupt ever found the fair one kind.* Miss Jenny and Master Billy Galloon were lately fallen deeply in love with each other, and the whole neighbourhood thought it would soon be a match.

Every day now began to strip Jack of his former finery; his cloaths flew piece by piece to the pawnbroker's, and he seemed at length equipped in the genuine mourning of antiquity. But still he thought himself secure from starving; the numberless invitations he had received to dine, even after his losses, were yet unanswered; he was therefore now resolved to accept of a dinner because he wanted one; and in this manner he actually lived among his friends a whole week without being openly affronted. The last place I saw poor Jack was at the Rev. Dr. Gosling's. He had, as he fancied, just nicked the time, for he came in as the cloth was laying. He took a chair without being desired, and talked for some time without being attended to. He assured the company that nothing procured so good an appetite as a walk to White Conduit-house, where he had been that morning. He looked at the table-cloth, and praised the figure of the damask; talked of a feast where he had been the day before, but that the venison was over done. All this, however, procured the poor creature no invitation, and he was not yet sufficiently hardened to stay without being asked; wherefore, finding the gentleman of the house insensible to all his fetches, he thought proper at last to retire, and mend his appetite by a walk in the Park.

You then, O ye beggars of my acquaintance, whether in rags or lace; whether in Kent-street or the Mall; whether at the Smyrna or St. Giles's, might I advise as a friend, never seem in want of the favour which you solicit. Apply to every passion but pity, for redress. You may find relief from vanity, from self-interest, or from avarice, but seldom from compassion. The very eloquence of a poor man is disgusting; and that mouth which is opened even for flattery is seldom expected to close without a petition.

If then you would ward off the gripe of poverty, pretend to be a stranger to her, and she will at least use you with ceremony. Hear not my advice, but that of Offellus. If you be caught dining upon a halfpenny porrenger of pease soup and potatoes, praise the wholesomeness of your frugal repast. You may observe that Dr. Cheyne has prescribed pease broth for the gravel, hint that you are not one of those who are always making a god of your belly. If you are obliged to wear a flimsy stuff in the midst of winter, be the first to remark that stuffs are very much worn at Paris. If there be found some irreparable defects in any part of your equipage, which cannot be concealed by all the arts of sitting cross-legged, coaxing, or derning, say, that neither you nor Sampson Gideon were ever very fond of dress. Or if you be a philosopher, hint that Plato and Seneca are the taylors you choose to employ; assure the company that man ought to be content with a bare covering, since what now is so much the pride of some, was formerly our shame. Horace will give you a Latin sentence fit for the occasion,

Toga [quæ] defendere frigus quamvis crassa queat.[1]

In short, however caught, do not give up, but ascribe to the frugality of your disposition what others might be apt to attribute to the narrowness of your circumstances, and appear rather to be a miser than a beggar. To be poor, and to seem poor, is a certain method never to rise. Pride in the great is hateful, in the wise it is ridiculous; *beggarly pride* is the only sort of vanity I can excuse.

THE SAGACITY OF SOME INSECTS

To the Author of *The Bee:*

Sir,

Animals in general are sagacious in proportion as they cultivate society. The elephant and the beaver shew the greatest signs of this when united; but when man intrudes into their communities, they lose all their spirit of industry and testify but a very small share of that sagacity for which, when in a social state, they are so remarkable.

Among insects the labours of the bee and the ant have employed the attention and admiration of the naturalist; but their whole sagacity is lost upon separation, and a single bee or ant seems destitute of every degree of industry, is the most stupid insect imaginable, languishes for a time in solitude, and soon dies.

Of all the solitary insects I have ever remarked, the spider is the most sagacious; and its actions to me who have attentively considered them seem almost to exceed belief. This insect is formed by nature for a state of war, not only upon other insects but upon each other. For this state nature seems perfectly well to have formed it. Its head and breast are covered with a strong natural coat of mail, which is impenetrable to the attempts of every other insect, and its belly is inveloped in a soft pliant skin, which eludes the sting even of a wasp. Its legs are terminated by strong claws, not unlike those of a lobster, and their vast length, like spears, serve to keep every assailant at a distance.

Not worse furnished for observation than for an attack or a defence, it has several eyes, large, transparent, and covered with an horny substance, which however does not impede its vision. Besides this, it is furnished with a forceps above the mouth, which serves to kill or secure the prey already caught in its claws or its net.

Such are the implements of war with which the body is

immediately furnish'd; but its net to entangle the enemy seems what it chiefly trusts to, and what it takes most pains to render as complete as possible. Nature has furnished the body of this little creature with a glutinous liquid which, proceeding from the anus, it spins into a thread, coarser or finer as it chuses to contract or dilate its sphincter. In order to fix its thread when it begins to weave, it emits a small drop of its liquid against the wall, which hardening by degrees, serves to hold the thread very firmly. Then receding from the first point, as it recedes the thread lengthens, and when the spider has come to the place where the other end of the thread should be fixed, gathering up with its claws the thread which would otherwise be too slack, it is stretched tightly and fixed in the same manner to the wall as before.

In this manner, it spins and fixes several threads parallel to each other, which so to speak serve as the warp to the intended web. To form the woof, it spins in the same manner its thread, transversly fixing one end to the first thread that was spun and which is always the strongest of the whole web, and the other to the wall. All these threads being newly spun are glutinous, and therefore stick to each other wherever they happen to touch; and in those parts of the web most exposed to be torn, our natural artist strengthens them by doubling the threads sometimes sixfold.

Thus far naturalists have gone in the description of this animal; what follows is the result of my own observation upon that species of the insect called an *House-Spider*. I perceived, about four years ago, a large spider in one corner of my room, making its web; and though the maid frequently levelled her fatal broom against the labours of the little animal, I had the good fortune then to prevent its destruction; and, I may say, it more than paid me by the entertainment it afforded.

In three days the web was, with incredible diligence, completed; nor could I avoid thinking that the insect seemed to exult in its new abode. It frequently traversed it round, examined the strength of every part of it, retired into its hole and came out very frequently. The first enemy, however, it had to encounter was another and a much larger spider, which, having no web of its own and having probably exhausted all its stock in former labours of this kind, came to invade the property of its neighbour. Soon then a terrible encounter ensued, in which the invader seemed to have the victory, and the laborious spider was obliged to take refuge in its hole. Upon this I perceived the victor using every art to draw the enemy from his stronghold. He seemed to go off, but quickly returned; and when he found all arts vain, began to demolish the new web without mercy. This brought on another battle, and contrary to my expectations the laborious spider became conqueror and fairly killed his antagonist.

Now, then, in peaceable possession of what was justly its own, it waited three days with the utmost patience, repairing the breaches of its web and taking no sustenance that I could perceive. At last, however, a large blue fly fell into the snare, and struggled hard to get loose. The spider gave it leave to entangle itself as much as possible, but it seemed to be too strong for the cobweb. I must own I was greatly surprized when I saw the spider immediately sally out and in less than a minute weave a new net round its captive, by which the motion of its wings was stopped; and when it was fairly hampered in this manner, it was seized and dragged into the hole.

In this manner it lived in a precarious state, and nature seemed to have fitted it for such a life, for upon a single fly it subsisted for more than a week. I once put a wasp into the net; but when the spider came out in order to seize it as usual, upon perceiving what kind of an enemy it had to deal with, it instantly broke all the bands that held it fast, and contributed all that lay in its power to disengage so formidable an antagonist. When the wasp was at liberty, I expected the spider would have set about repairing the breaches that were made in its net, but those it seems were irreparable; wherefore the cobweb was now entirely forsaken, and a new one begun, which was completed in the usual time.

I had now a mind to try how many cobwebs a single spider could furnish; wherefore I destroyed this, and the insect set about another. When I destroyed the other also, its whole stock seemed entirely exhausted, and it could spin no more. The arts it made use of to support itself, now deprived of its great means of subsistence, were indeed surprising. I have seen it roll up its legs like a ball, and lie motionless for hours together, but cautiously watching all the time; when a fly happened to approach sufficiently near, it would dart out all at once, and often seize its prey.

Of this life, however, it soon began to grow weary, and resolved to invade the possession of some other spider, since it could not make a web of its own. It formed an attack upon a neighbouring fortification with great vigour, and at first was as vigorously repulsed. Not daunted, however, with one defeat, in this manner it continued to lay siege to another's web for three days, and at length, having killed the defendant, actually took possession. When smaller flies happen to fall into the snare, the spider does not sally out at once, but very patiently waits till it is sure of them; for, upon his immediately approaching, the terror of his appearance might give the captive strength sufficient to get loose. The manner then is to wait patiently, till by ineffectual and impotent struggles the captive has wasted all its strength, and then he becomes a certain and an easy conquest.

The insect I am now describing lived three years; every year it changed its skin and got a new set of legs. I have sometimes plucked off a leg, which grew again in two or three days. At first it dreaded my approach to its web, but at last it became so familiar as to take a fly out of my hand, and, upon my touching any part of the web, would immediately leave its hole, prepared either for a defence or an attack.

To complete this description, it may be observed, that the male spider is much less than the female, and that the latter are oviparous. When they come to lay, they spread a part of their web under the eggs, and then roll them up carefully as we roll up things in a cloth, and thus hatch them in their hole. If disturbed in their holes, they never attempt to escape without carrying this young brood in their foreceps away with them, and thus frequently are sacrificed to their paternal affection.

As soon as ever the young ones leave their artificial covering, they begin to spin, and almost sensibly seem to grow bigger. If they have the good fortune, when even but a day old, to catch a fly, they fall-to with good appetites; but they live sometimes three or four days without any sort of sustenance and yet still continue to grow larger, so as every day to double their former size. As they grow old, however, they do not still continue to encrease, but their legs only continue to grow longer; and when a spider becomes entirely stiff with age, and unable to seize its prey, it dies at length of hunger.

A CITY NIGHT-PIECE

Ille dolet vere qui sine teste dolet. Mart.[2]

The clock has struck two, the expiring taper rises and sinks in the socket, the watchman forgets the hour in slumber, the laborious and the happy are at rest, and nothing now wakes but guilt, revelry and despair. The drunkard once more fills the destroying bowl, the robber walks his midnight round, and the suicide lifts his guilty arm against his own sacred person.

Let me no longer waste the night over the page of antiquity or the sallies of cotemporary genius, but pursue the solitary walk where vanity, ever changing, but a few hours past walked before me, where she kept up the pageant, and now, like a froward child, seems hushed with her own importunities.

What a gloom hangs all around! the dying lamp feebly emits a yellow gleam; no sound is heard but of the chiming clock, or the distant watch-dog. All the bustle of human pride is forgotten, and this hour may well display the emptiness of human vanity.

There may come a time when this temporary solitude may be made continual, and the city itself, like its inhabitants, fade away, and leave a desart in its room.

What cities, as great as this, have once triumph'd in existence, had their victories as great as ours, joy as just and as unbounded as we, and with short-sighted presumption promised themselves immortality. Posterity can hardly trace the situation of some. The sorrowful traveller wanders over the awful ruins of others, and as he beholds, he learns wisdom, and feels the transience of every sublunary possession.

Here stood their citadel, but now grown over with weeds; there their senate-house, but now the haunt of every noxious reptile; temples and theatres stood here, now only an undistinguished heap of ruin. They are fallen, for luxury and avarice

17

first made them feeble. The rewards of state were conferred on amusing and not on useful members of society. Thus true virtue languished; their riches and opulence invited the plunderer, who, though once repulsed, returned again and at last swept the defendants into undistinguished destruction.

How few appear in those streets, which but some few hours ago were crowded; and those who appear no longer now wear their daily mask, nor attempt to hide their lewdness or their misery.

But who are those who make the streets their couch, and find a short repose from wretchedness at the doors of the opulent? These are strangers, wanderers, and orphans, whose circumstances are too humble to expect redress, and their distresses too great even for pity. Some are without the covering even of rags, and others emaciated with disease; the world seems to have disclaimed them; society turns its back upon their distress, and has given them up to nakedness and hunger. These poor shivering females have once seen happier days, and been flattered into beauty. They have been prostituted to the gay luxurious villain, and are now turned out to meet the severity of winter in the streets. Perhaps now lying at the doors of their betrayers they sue to wretches whose hearts are insensible to calamity, or debauchees who may curse, but will not relieve them.

Why, why was I born a man, and yet see the sufferings of wretches I cannot relieve! Poor houseless creatures! the world will give you reproaches, but will not give you relief. The slightest misfortunes, the most imaginary uneasinesses of the rich, are aggravated with all the power of eloquence and engage our attention, while you weep unheeded, persecuted by every subordinate species of tyranny, and finding enmity in every law.

Why was this heart of mine formed with so much sensibility! or why was not my fortune adapted to its impulse! Tenderness, without a capacity of relieving, only makes the heart that feels it more wretched than the object which sues for assistance.

But let me turn from a scene of such distress to the sanctified hypocrite, *who has been talking of virtue till the time of bed,* and now steals out to give a loose to his vices under the protection of midnight, vices more attrocious, because he attempts to conceal them. See how he pants down the dark alley, and with hastening steps fears an acquaintance in every face. He has passed the whole day in company he hates, and now goes to prolong the night among company that as heartily hate him. May his vices be detected; may the morning rise upon his shame; yet I wish to no purpose; villainy, when detected, never gives up, but boldly adds impudence to imposture.

A RESVERIE

Scarce a day passes in which we do not hear compliments paid to Dryden, Pope, and other writers of the last age, while not a month comes forward that is not loaded with invective against the writers of this. Strange, that our critics should be fond of giving their favours to those who are insensible of the obligation, and their dislike to these who, of all mankind, are most apt to retaliate the injury.

Even though our present writers had not equal merit with their predecessors, it would be politic to use them with ceremony. Every compliment paid them would be more agreeable, in proportion as they least deserved it. Tell a lady with an handsome face that she is pretty, she only thinks it her due; it is what she has heard a thousand times before from others, and disregards the compliment: but assure a lady, the cut of whose visage is something more plain, that she looks killing to-day, she instantly bridles up and feels the force of the well-timed flattery the whole day after. Compliments which we think are deserved, we only accept as debts, with indifference; but those which conscience informs us we do not merit, we receive with the same gratitude that we do favours given away.

Our gentlemen, however, who preside at the distribution of literary fame, seem resolved to part with praise neither from motives of justice or generosity; one would think, when they take pen in hand, that it was only to blot reputations, and to put their seals to the pacquet which consigns every new-born effort to oblivion.

Yet, notwithstanding the republic of letters hangs at present so feebly together; though those friendships which once promoted literary fame seem now to be discontinued; though every writer who now draws the quill seems to aim at profit as well as applause, many among them are probably laying in stores for immortality, and are provided with a sufficient stock of reputation to last the whole journey.

As I was indulging these reflections in order to eke out the present page, I could not avoid pursuing the metaphor of going a journey, in my imagination, and formed the following Resverie, too wild for allegory and too regular for a dream.

I fancied myself placed in the yard of a large inn in which there were an infinite number of waggons and stage-coaches, attended by fellows who either invited the company to take their places, or were busied in packing their baggage. Each vehicle had its inscription, shewing the place of its destination. On one I could read, *The pleasure stage-coach;* on another, *The waggon of industry;* on a third, *The vanity whim;* and on a fourth, *The landau of riches.* I had some inclination to step into each of these, one after another; but I know not by what means I passed them by, and at last fixed my eye upon a small carriage, Berlin fashion, which seemed the most convenient vehicle at a distance in the world; and, upon my nearer approach, found it to be *The fame machine.*

I instantly made up to the coachman, whom I found to be an affable and seemingly good-natured fellow. He informed me that he had but a few days ago returned from the temple of fame, to which he had been carrying Addison, Swift, Pope, Steele, Congreve, and Colley Cibber, that they made but indifferent company by the way, and that he once or twice was going to empty his berlin of the whole cargo. "However," says he, "I got them all safe home, with no other damage than a black eye which Colley gave Mr. Pope, and am now returned for another coachful." "If that be all, friend," said I, "and if you are in want of company, I'll make one with all my heart. Open the door. I hope the machine rides easy." "Oh! for that, sir, extremely easy." But still keeping the door shut, and measuring me with his eye, "Pray, sir, have you no luggage? You seem to be a good-natured sort of a gentleman; but I don't find you have got any luggage, and I never permit any to travel with me but such as have something valuable to pay for coach-hire." Examining my pockets, I own I was not a little disconcerted at this unexpected rebuff; but considering that I carried a number of the Bee under my arm, I was resolved to open it in his eyes and dazzle him with the splendor of the page. He read the title and contents, however, without any emotion, and assured me he had never heard of it before. "In short, friend," said he, now losing all his former respect, "you must not come in. I expect better passengers; but as you seem an harmless creature, perhaps if there be room left I may let you ride a while for charity."

I now took my stand by the coachman at the door, and since I could not command a seat, was resolved to be as useful as possible, and earn by my assiduity what I could not by my merit.

The next that presented for a place, was a most whimsical figure indeed.[3] He was hung round with papers of his own composing, not unlike those who sing ballads in the streets, and came dancing up to the door with all the confidence of instant admittance. The volubility of his motion and address prevented my being able to read more of his cargo than the word Inspector, which was written in great letters at the top of some of the papers. He opened the coach-door himself without any ceremony, and was just slipping in, when the coachman, with as little ceremony, pulled him back. Our figure seemed perfectly angry at this repulse and demanded gentleman's satisfaction. "Lord, sir!" replied the coachman, "instead of proper luggage, by your bulk you seem loaded for a West-India voyage. You are big enough, with all your papers, to crack twenty stage-coaches. Excuse me, indeed, sir, for you must not enter." Our figure now began to expostulate; he assured the coachman that though his baggage seemed so bulky, it was perfectly light, and that he would be contented with the smallest corner of room. But Jehu was inflexible, and the carrier of the inspectors was sent to dance back again, with all his papers fluttering in the wind. We expected to have no more trouble from this quarter, when in a few minutes the same figure changed his appearance, like harlequin upon the stage, and with the same confidence again made his approaches, dressed in lace and carrying nothing but a nosegay. Upon coming near, he thrust the nosegay to the coachman's nose, grasped the brass, and seemed now resolved to enter by violence. I found the struggle soon begin to grow hot, and the coachman, who was a little old, unable to continue the contest, so in order to ingratiate myself I stept in to his assistance, and our united efforts sent our literary Proteus, though worsted unconquered still, clear off, dancing a rigadoon and smelling to his own nosegay.

The person[4] who after him appeared as candidate for a place in the stage came up with an air not quite so confident, but somewhat however theatrical; and, instead of entering, made the coachman a very low bow, which the other returned and desired to see his baggage; upon which he instantly produced some farces, a tragedy, and other miscellany productions. The coachman, casting his eye upon the cargoe, assured him at present he could not possibly have a place, but hoped in time he might aspire to one, as he seemed to have read in the book of nature, without a careful perusal of which none ever found entrance at the temple of fame. "What," replied the disappointed poet, "shall my tragedy, in which I have vindicated the cause of liberty and virtue!"——"Follow nature," returned the other, "and never expect to find lasting fame by topics which only please from their popularity. Had you been first in the cause of freedom, or praised in virtue more than an empty name, it is possible you might have gained admittance; but at present I beg, sir, you will stand aside for another gentleman whom I see approaching."

This was a very grave personage,[5] whom at some distance I took for one of the most reserved and even disagreeable figures I had seen; but as he approached, his appearance improved, and when I could distinguish him thoroughly, I perceived that in spite of the severity of his brow he had one of the most good-natured countenances that could be imagined. Upon coming to open the stage door, he lifted a parcel of folios into the seat before him, but our inquisitorial coachman at once shoved them out again. "What, not take in my dictionary!" exclaimed the other in a rage. "Be patient, sir," replyed the coachman, "I have drove a coach, man and boy, these two thousand years; but I do not remember to have carried above one dictionary during the whole time. That little book which I perceive peeping from one of your pockets, may I presume to ask what it contains?" "A mere trifle," replied the author, "it is called the Rambler." "The Rambler!" says the coachman. "I beg, sir, you'll take your place. I have heard our ladies in the court of Apollo frequently mention it with rapture; and Clio, who happens to be a little grave, has been heard to prefer it to the Spectator, though others have observed that the reflections, by being refined, sometimes become minute."

This grave gentleman was scarce seated, when another,[6] whose appearance was something more modern, seemed willing to enter, yet afraid to ask. He carried in his hand a bundle of essays, of which the coachman was curious enough to inquire the contents. "These," replied the . gentleman, "are rhapsodies against the religion of my country." "And how can you expect to come into my coach, after thus chusing the wrong side of the question." "Ay, but I am right," replied the other; "and if you give me leave, I shall in a few minutes state the argument." "Right or wrong," said the coachman, "he who disturbs religion is a blockhead, and he shall never travel in a coach of mine." "If then," said the gentleman, mustering up all his courage, "if I am not to have admittance as an essayist, I hope I shall not be repulsed as an historian; the last volume of my history met with applause." "Yes," replied the coachman, "but I have heard only the first approved at the temple of fame; and as I see you have it about you, enter without further ceremony." My attention was now diverted to a crowd, who were pushing forward a person[7] that seemed more inclined to the *stage coach of riches;* but by their means he was driven forward to the fame machine, which he, however, seemed heartily to despise. Impelled, however, by their sollicitations, he steps up, flourishing a voluminous history, and demanding admittance. "Sir, I have formerly heard your name mentioned," says the coachman, "but never as an historian. Is there no other work upon which you may claim a place?" "None," replied the other, "except a romance; but this is a work of too trifling a nature to claim future attention." "You mistake," says the inquisitor, "a well-written romance is no such easy task as is generally imagined. I remember formerly to have carried Cervantes and Segrais, and if you think fit, you may enter." Upon our three literary travellers coming into the same coach, I listened attentively to hear what might be the conversation that passed upon this extraordinary occasion; when, instead of agreeable or entertaining dialogue, I found them grumbling at each other, and each seemed discontented with his companions. Strange! thought I to myself, that they who are thus born to enlighten the world, should still preserve the narrow prejudices of childhood, and, by disagreeing, make even the highest merit ridiculous. Were the learned and the wise to unite against the dunces of society instead of sometimes siding into opposite parties with them, they might throw a lustre upon each other's reputation, and teach every rank of subordinate merit, if not to admire, at least not to avow dislike.

In the midst of these reflections, I perceived the coachman, unmindful of me, had now mounted the box. Several were approaching to be taken in whose pretensions I was sensible were very just. I therefore desired him to stop and take in more passengers; but he replied as he had now mounted the box, it would be improper to come down; but that he should take them all, one after the other, when he should return. So he drove away, and, for myself, as I could not get in I mounted behind, in order to hear the conversation on the way.

To be continued.[8]

ON EDUCATION

To the author of *The Bee:*

Sir,

As few subjects are more interesting to society, so few have
been more frequently written upon than the education of
youth. Yet is it not a little surprizing that it should have been
treated almost by all in a declamatory manner? They have insisted largely on the advantages that result from it, both to the
individual and to society; and have expatiated in the praise
of what none have ever been so hardy as to call in question.

Instead of giving us fine but empty harangues upon this
subject, instead of indulging each his particular and whimsical
systems, it had been much better if the writers on this subject
had treated it in a more scientific manner, repressed all the
sallies of imagination, and given us the result of their
observations with didactic simplicity. Upon this subject the
smallest errors are of the most dangerous consequence; and
the author should venture the imputation of stupidity upon
a topic where his slightest deviations may tend to injure the
rising generation.

I shall therefore throw out a few thoughts upon this subject which have not been attended to by others, and shall dismiss all attempts to please while I study only instruction.

The manner in which our youth of London are at present
educated is some in free schools in the city, but the far greater
number in boarding schools about town. The parent justly
consults the health of his child and finds an education in the
country tends to promote this much more than a continuance
in town. Thus far they are right: if there were a possibility
of having even our free schools kept a little out of town, it
would certainly conduce to the health and vigour of perhaps
the mind as well as the body. It may be thought whimsical
but it is truth,—I have found by experience that they who

26

have spent all their lives in cities, contract not only an effeminacy of habit, but even of thinking.

But when I have said that the boarding schools are preferable to free schools, as being in the country, this is certainly the only advantage I can allow them; otherwise it is impossible to conceive the ignorance of those who take upon them the important trust of education. Is any man unfit for any of the professions, he finds his last resource in setting up school. Do any become bankrupts in trade, they still set up a boarding school, and drive a trade this way when all others fail; nay, I have been told of butchers and barbers who have turned schoolmasters; and more surprising still, made fortunes in their new profession.

Could we think ourselves in a country of civilized people—could it be conceived that we have any regard for posterity, when such are permitted to take the charge of the morals, genius, and health of those dear little pledges who may one day be the guardians of the liberties of Europe, and who may serve as the honour and bulwark of their aged parents? The care of children, is it below the state? is it fit to indulge the caprice of the ignorant with the disposal of their children in this particular? For the state to take the charge of all its children, as in Persia or Sparta, might at present be inconvenient; but surely with great ease it might cast an eye to their instructors. Of all members of society I do not know a more useful or a more honourable one than a schoolmaster; at the same time that I do not see any more generally despised or whose talents are so ill rewarded.

Were the salaries of school masters to be augmented from a diminution of useless sinecures, how might it turn to the advantage of this people— a people whom, without flattery, I may in other respects term the wisest and greatest upon earth. But while I would reward the deserving, I would dismiss those utterly unqualified for their employment: in short, I would make the business of a school master every way more respectable by encreasing their salaries and admitting only men of proper abilities.

There are already school masters appointed, and they have some small salaries; but where at present there is but one school master appointed, there should at least be two; and wherever the salary is at present twenty pounds, it should be an hundred. Do we give immoderate benefices to those who instruct ourselves, and shall we deny even subsistence to those who instruct our children? Every member of society should be paid in proportion as he is necessary; and I will be bold enough to say that school masters in a state are more necessary than clergymen, as children stand in more need of instruction than their parents.

But instead of this, as I have already observed, we send them to board in the country to the most ignorant set of men that can be imagined. But least the ignorance of the master be not sufficient, the child is generally consigned to the usher. This is generally some poor needy animal, little superior to a footman either in learning or spirit, invited to his place by an advertisement and kept there merely from his being of a complying disposition and making the children fond of him. "You give your child to be educated to a slave," says a philosopher to a rich man; "instead of one slave, you will then have two."

It were well, however, if parents, upon fixing their children in one of these houses, would examine the abilities of the usher as well as the master; for, whatever they are told to the contrary, the usher is generally the person most employed in their education. If then a gentleman upon putting out his son to one of these houses sees the usher disregarded by the master, he may depend upon it that he is equally disregarded by the boys; the truth is, in spite of all their endeavours to please, they are generally the laughing stock of the school. Every trick is played upon the usher; the oddity of his manners, his dress, or his language, is a fund of eternal ridicule; the master himself, now and then, cannot avoid joining in the laugh; and the poor wretch, eternally resenting this ill-usage, seems to live in a state of war with all the family. This is a very proper person, is it not, to give children a relish for learning? They must esteem learning very much, when they see its professors used with such ceremony. If the usher be despised the father may be assured his child will never be properly instructed.

But let me suppose that there are some schools without these inconveniences,—where the masters and ushers are men of learning, reputation, and assiduity. If there are to be found such, they cannot be prized in a state sufficiently. A boy will learn more true wisdom in a public school in a year than by a private education in five. It is not from masters, but from their equals, youth learn a knowledge of the world; the little tricks they play each other, the punishment that frequently attends the commission, is a just picture of the great world; and all the ways of men are practised in a public school in miniature. It is true a child is early made acquainted with some vices in a school; but it is better to know these when a boy than be first taught them when a man, for their novelty then may have irresistible charms.

In a public education boys early learn temperance; and if the parents and friends would give them less money upon their usual visits, it would be much to their advantage, since it may justly be said that a great part of their disorders arise from surfeit,— *plus occidit gula quam gladius.*[9] And now I am come to the article of health, it may not be amiss to observe that Mr. Locke and some others have advised that children should be inured to cold, to fatigue, and hardship from their youth; but Mr. Locke was but an indifferent physician. Habit, I grant, has great influence over our constitutions, but we have not precise ideas upon this subject.

We know that among savages and even among our peasants there are found children born with such constitutions that they cross rivers by swimming, endure cold, thirst, hunger, and want of sleep, to a surprizing degree; that when they happen to fall sick, they are cured, without the help of medicine, by nature alone. Such examples are adduced to persuade us to imitate their manner of education and accustom ourselves betimes to support the same fatigues. But had these gentlemen considered first [how many lives are lost in this ascetic discipline; had they considered] that those savages and peasants are generally not so long lived as they who have led a more indolent life; secondly, that the more laborious the life is, the less populous is the country: had they considered that what physicians call the *stamina vitæ* by fatigue and labour become rigid and thus anticipate old age; that the number who survive those rude trials, bears no proportion to those who die in the experiment. Had these things been properly considered, they would not have thus extolled an education begun in fatigue and hardships. Peter the Great, willing to inure the children of his seamen to a life of hardship, ordered that they should only drink sea water, but they unfortunately all died under the trial.

But while I would exclude all unnecessary labours, yet still I would recommend temperance in the highest degree. No luxurious dishes with high seasoning, nothing given children to force an appetite, as little sugared or salted provisions as possible, though never so pleasing; but milk, morning and night, should be their constant food. This diet would make them more healthy than any of those slops that are usually cooked by the mistress of a boarding school; besides, it corrects any consumptive habits, not unfrequently found amongst the children of city parents.

As boys should be educated with temperance, so the first, greatest lesson that should be taught them is to admire frugality. It is by the exercise of this virtue alone they can ever expect to be useful members of society. It is true lectures continually repeated upon this subject may make some boys, when they grow up, run into an extreme and become misers; but it were well had we more misers than we have among us. I know few characters more useful in society; for a man's having a larger or smaller share of money lying useless by him, no way injures the commonwealth; since, should every miser now exhaust his stores, this might make gold more plenty, but it would not encrease the commodities or pleasures of life; they would still remain as they are at present. It matters not, therefore, whether men are misers or not, if they be only frugal, laborious, and fill the station they have chosen. If they deny themselves the necessaries of life, society is no way injured by their folly.

Instead, therefore, of romances, which praise young men of spirit who go through a variety of adventures and at last conclude a life of dissipation, folly, and extravagance in riches and matrimony, there should be some men of wit employed to compose books that might equally interest the passions of our youth; where such an one might be praised for having resisted allurements when young, and how he at last became Lord

Mayor—how he was married to a lady of great sense, fortune, and beauty; to be as explicit as possible, the old story of Whittington, were his cat left out, might be more serviceable to the tender mind than either *Tom Jones, Joseph Andrews,* or an hundred others, where frugality is the only good quality the hero is not possessed of. Were our schoolmasters, if any of them have sense enough to draw up such a work, thus employed, it would be much more serviceable to their pupils than all the grammars and dictionaries they may publish these ten years.

Children should early be instructed in the arts from which they would afterwards draw the greatest advantages. When the wonders of nature are never exposed to our view, we have no great desire to become acquainted with those parts of learning which pretend to account for the phænomena. One of the ancients complains, that as soon as young men have left school and are obliged to converse in the world they fancy themselves transported into a new region: *Ut cum in forum venerint existiment se in aliam terrarum orbem delatos.*[10] We should early, therefore, instruct them in the experiments, if I may so express it, of knowledge, and leave to maturer age the accounting for the causes. But instead of that, when boys begin natural philosophy in colleges they have not the least curiosity for those parts of the science which are proposed for their instruction; they have never before seen the phænomena, and consequently have no curiosity to learn the reasons. Might natural philosophy, therefore, be made their pastime in school by this means it would in college become their amusement.

In several of the machines now in use there would be ample field both for instruction and amusement; the different sorts of the phosphorus, the artificial pyrites, magnetism, electricity, the experiments upon the rarefaction and weight of the air, and those upon elastic bodies, might employ their idle hours; and none should be called from play to see such experiments but such as thought proper. At first, then, it would be sufficient if the instruments and the effects of their combination were only shewn; the causes should be deferred to a maturer age, or to those times when natural curiosity prompts us to discover the wonders of nature. Man is placed in this world as a specta-

tor; when he is tired with wondering at all the novelties about
him, and not till then, does he desire to be made acquainted
with the causes that create those wonders.

What I have observed with regard to natural philosophy, I
would extend to every other science whatsoever. We should
teach them as many of the facts as were possible, and defer
the causes until they seemed of themselves desirous of knowing
them. A mind thus leaving school, stored with all the simple
experiences of science, would be the fittest in the world for the
college course; and though such a youth might not appear so
bright or so talkative as those who had learned the real principles and causes of some of the sciences, yet he would make a
wiser man, and would retain a more lasting passion for letters
than he who was early burdened with the disagreeable institution of effect and cause.

In history, such stories alone should be laid before them as
might catch the imagination: instead of this, they are too frequently obliged to toil through the four empires, as they are
called, where their memories are burdened by a number of
disgusting names that destroy all their future relish for our
best historians, who may be termed the truest teachers of
wisdom.

Every species of flattery should be carefully avoided; a boy
who happens to say a sprightly thing is generally applauded so
much that he happens to continue a coxcomb sometimes all his
life after. He is reputed a wit at fourteen, and becomes a blockhead at twenty. Nurses, footmen, and such, should therefore
be driven away as much as possible. I was even going to add
that the mother herself should stifle her pleasure or her vanity
when little master happens to say a good or a smart thing.
Those modest, lubberly boys who seem to want spirit [be-
come at length more shineing men; and at school] generally
go through their business with more ease to themselves and
more satisfaction to their instructors.

There has of late a gentleman appeared who thinks the study
of rhetoric essential to a perfect education.[11] That bold male
eloquence which often without pleasing convinces, is generally
destroyed by such institutions. Convincing eloquence however
is infinitely more serviceable to its possessor than the most
florid harangue, or the most pathetic tones that can be imag-

ined; and the man who is thoroughly convinced himself, who understands his subject and the language he speaks in, will be more apt to silence opposition than he who studies the force of his periods and fills our ears with sounds, while our minds are destitute of conviction.

It was reckoned the fault of the orators at the decline of the Roman empire, when they had been long instructed by rhetoricians, that their periods were so harmonious as that they could be sung as well as spoken. What a ridiculous figure must one of these gentlemen cut, thus measuring syllables and weighing words when he should plead the cause of his client! Two architects were once candidates for the building a certain temple at Athens; the first harangued the crowd very learnedly upon the different orders of architecture and shewed them in what manner the temple should be built; the other, who got up to speak after him, only observed that what his brother had spoken he could do; and thus he at once gained his cause.

To teach men to be orators is little less than to teach them to be poets; and for my part I should have too great a regard for my child to wish him a manor only in a bookseller's shop.

Another passion which the present age is apt to run into is to make children learn all things,—the languages, the sciences, music, the exercises, and painting. Thus the child soon becomes a *talker* in all, but a *master* in none. He thus acquires a superficial fondness for every thing and only shews his ignorance when he attempts to exhibit his skill.

As I deliver my thoughts without method or connection, so the reader must not be surprized to find me once more addressing schoolmasters on the present method of teaching the learned languages, which is commonly by literal translations. I would ask such if they were to travel a journey whether those parts of the road in which they found the greatest difficulties would not be most strongly remembered? Boys who, if I may continue the allusion, gallop through one of the ancients with the assistance of a translation, can have but a very slight acquaintance either with the author or his language. It is by the exercise of the mind alone that a language is learned; but a literal translation, on the opposite page, leaves no exercise for the memory at all. The boy will not be at the fatigue of remembering, when his doubts are at once satisfied by a glance of the eye; whereas, were every word to be sought from a dictionary, the learner would attempt to remember them, to save himself the trouble of looking out for it for the future.

To continue in the same pedantic strain tho' no school-master, of all the various grammars now taught in schools about town, I would recommend only the old common one, I have forgot whether Lily's or an emendation of him. The others may be improvements; but such improvements seem to me only mere grammatical niceties, no way influencing the learner, but perhaps loading him with trifling subtilties which, at a proper age, he must be at some pains to forget.

Whatever pains a master may take to make the learning of the languages agreeable to his pupil, he may depend upon it, it will be at first extreamly unpleasant. The rudiments of every language, therefore, must be given as a task, not as an amuse-ment. Attempting to deceive children into instruction of this kind is only deceiving ourselves; and I know no passion capable of conquering a child's natural laziness but fear. Solomon has said it before me; nor is there any more certain, tho' perhaps more disagreeable, truth than the proverb in verse, too well known to repeat on the present occasion. It is very probable that parents are told of some masters who never use the rod and consequently are thought the properest instructors for their children; but though tenderness is a requisite quality in an instructor, yet there is too often the truest tenderness in well-timed correction.

Some have justly observed that all passion should be banished on this terrible occasion; but, I know not how, there is a frailty attending human nature, that few masters are able to keep their temper whilst they correct. I knew a good-natured man who was sensible of his own weakness in this respect, and consequently had recourse to the following expedient, to prevent his passions from being engaged, yet at the same time administer justice with impartiality. When ever any of his pupils committed a fault, he summoned a jury of his peers,— I mean of the boys of his own or the next classes to him; his accusers stood forth; he had liberty of pleading in his own defence; and one or two more had a liberty of pleading against him; when found guilty by the panel, he was consigned to the footman who attended in the house, who had previous orders to use his punishment with lenity. By this means the master took off the odium of punishment from himself; and the footman, between whom and the boys there could not be even the slightest intimacy, was placed in such a light as to be shunned by every boy in the school.

And now I have gone thus far, perhaps you will think me some pedagogue, willing by a well-timed puff to encrease the reputation of his own school; but such is not the case. The regard I have for society, for those tender minds who are the objects of the present essay, such are the only motives I have for offering those thoughts, calculated not to surprize by their novelty or the elegance of composition, but merely to remedy some defects which have crept into the present system of school education. If this letter should be inserted, perhaps I may trouble you, in my next, with some thoughts upon an university education, not with an intent to exhaust the subject, but to amend some few abuses. I am, &c.

A REVERIE AT THE BOAR'S HEAD TAVERN

IN EASTCHEAP

There are few books I have ever read when young with greater pleasure than Cicero's treatise on Old Age. He places the infirmities naturally consequent on our decline in so pleasing a light that my youth was persuaded to wish for a state where every passion subsides and every mental excellence is refined. I am at last declined into the vale of years, but Cicero is no longer pleasing; no declamations can give pliancy to the rigid sinew, or increase the languid circulation. The improvements I make in wisdom only render me each day more sensible to the defects of my constitution. Nor am I so wholly devoted to mental enjoyments but I could wish to have my body come in for a share of the entertainment. With this in view, therefore, let me recur to the amusements of youth, endeavour to forget age and wisdom, and as far as innocence goes, be as much a boy as the best of them.

I won't sit preaching when under a fit of the gout and like the philosopher denying pain to be an evil. I am not so hardy as to quarrel with the executioner, even while under correction. I find myself no way disposed to make fine speeches while I am making wry faces. In a word, I drink when the fit is on, to make me insensible, and drink when it is over for joy that I feel pain no longer.

The character of old Falstaff, even with all his faults, gives me more consolation than the most studied efforts of wisdom. I here behold an agreeable old fellow forgetting age and shewing me the way to be young at sixty-five. Sure I am well able to be as merry, though not so comical as he. Is it not in my power to have, though not so much wit, at least as much vivacity? Age, care, wisdom, reflection begone! I give you to the winds. Let's have t'other bottle; here's to the memory of Shakespear, Falstaff, and all the merry men of Eastcheap.

Such were the reflections that naturally arose while I sat at the Boar's Head Tavern, still kept at East-cheap. Here, by a pleasant fire, in the very room where old Sir John Falstaff cracked his jokes, in the very chair that was sometimes honoured by prince Henry, and sometimes polluted by his immoral merry companions, I sat and ruminated on the follies of youth, wished to be young again, but was resolved to make the best of life while it lasted. I now considered myself as the only living representative of the old fat knight and transported my imagination back to the times when the prince and he gave spirit to the revel and made even debauchery not disgusting. The room also conspired to throw my reflections back into antiquity: the oak floor, the Gothic windows and the ponderous chimney-piece had all withstood the tooth of time and seemed co-eval with the gaberdine and trunk-hose.

The watchman had gone twelve; my companions had all stole off, and none now remained with me but the landlord. From him I could have wished to know the history of a tavern that had such a long succession of customers. I could not help thinking that an account of this kind would be a pleasing picture of the different manners of different ages, but my landlord could give me no information. He continued to doze and sot and tell a tedious story, as most other landlords usually do. Though he said nothing, yet he never was silent; one good joke followed another good joke, and the best joke of all was generally begun towards the end of a bottle. I found at last, however, his wine and his conversation by degrees operate. He insensibly began to alter his appearance. His cravat seemed quilled into a ruff and his breeches swelled out into a far-dingale. I now fancied him changing sexes, and as my eyes began to close in slumber I imagined my fat landlord actually converted into as fat a landlady. Sleep made but few changes in my situation however: the tavern, the apartment and the table continued as before; nothing suffered mutation but my host, who was fairly altered into a gentlewoman whom I knew to be Dame Quickly, mistress of this tavern in the days of Sir John, and the liquor we were drinking, which seemed converted into sack and sugar.

"My dear Mrs. Quickly," cried I (for I knew her perfectly well at first sight), "I am heartily glad to see you. How have you left Falstaff, Pistol, Doll Tearsheet and the rest of our friends below stairs? Brave and hearty, I hope?" "In good sooth," replied she, "he did deserve to live for ever here, for he maketh foul work on't where he hath flitted. Queen Proserpine and he have quarrelled for his attempting a rape upon her divinity, and were it not that she still had bowels of compassion, it more than seems he might have been now sprawling in Tartarus. Had he been contented with Helen, or Cleopatra, or me, we were all at his service, but nothing but a goddess would serve his turn, and he had the impudence even to say that he was resolved upon having a progeny of salamanders. Indeed he's a false man, and a vile man; and yet it would do one's heart good to hear him, he has always such a way with him; not that I think him handsome—no, that's wide of the mark; and yet he's very well for a man too."

I now found that spirits still preserve the frailties of the flesh, and that according to the laws of criticism and dreaming, ghosts have been known guilty of even more than platonic affection; wherefore as I found her too much moved on such a topic to proceed, I was resolved to change the subject; and desiring she would pledge me in a bumper, observed with a sigh that our sack was nothing now to what it was in former days. "Ah, Mrs. Quickly, those were merry times when you drew sack for prince Henry; men were twice as strong and twice as wise and much braver and ten thousand times more charitable than now. Those were the times! The battle of Agincourt was a victory indeed! Ever since that we have only been degenerating, and I have lived to see the day when drinking is no longer fashionable, when men wear clean shirts and women shew their necks and arms. All are degenerated, Mrs. Quickly; and we shall probably, in another century, be frittered away into beaus or monkeys. Had you been on earth to see what I have seen, it would congeal all the blood in your body (your soul I mean). Why, our very nobility now have the intolerable arrogance, in spite of what is every day remonstrated from the press; our very nobility, I say, have the assurance to frequent assemblies and presume to be as merry as the vulgar. Had you but continued upon earth to observe the changes that have happened, you would have long since been melted into a flood of tears. See, my very friends have scarce manhood enough to sit to it till eleven, and I only am left to make a night on't."

"Observe this apartment," interrupted my companion, "of neat device and excellent workmanship; in this room I have lived, child, woman, and ghost, more than three hundred years. I now and then migrate to the world below, to see and hear news of thy friends and mine of much note in both our estimation, but in this apartment is my walk. I am ordered by Pluto to keep an annual register of every transaction that passeth here, and I have whilom compiled three hundred tomes, which eftsoons may be submitted to thy regards."

"None of your whiloms or eftsoons, Mrs. Quickly, if you please," I replied. "I know you can talk every whit as well as I can; for, as you have lived here so long, it is but natural to suppose you should learn the conversation of the company. Believe me, dame, at best you have neither too much sense or too much language to spare, so give me both as well as you can. Let me hear, like an honest free-hearted ghost as you seem to be, some account of your own adventures while alive, and the revolutions of this tavern since your decease. But first, my service to you; old women should water their clay a little, now and then; and now to your story."

"The story of my own adventures," replied the vision, "is but short and unsatisfactory; for believe me, Mr. Rigmarole (she knew my name by intuition), believe me, a woman with a butt of sack at her elbow is never long-lived. Sir John's death afflicted me to such a degree that I sincerely believe, to drown sorrow, I drank more liquor myself than I drew for my customers; my grief was sincere, and the sack was excellent. The prior of a neighbouring convent (for our priors then had as much power as a Middlesex justice now), he I say it was who gave me a license for keeping a disorderly house, upon condition that I should never make hard bargains with the clergy, that he should have a bottle of sack every morning and the liberty of confessing which of my girls he thought proper in private. I had continued for several years to pay this tribute; and he, it must be confessed, continued as rigorously to exact it. I grew old insensibly. My customers continued, however, to compliment my looks while I was by, but I could hear them say I was wearing when my back was turned. The prior, however, still was constant, and so were half his convent; but one fatal morning he missed the usual beverage, for I had incautiously drank over-night the last bottle by myself. What will you have on't? The very next day Doll Tearsheet and I were sent to the house of correction, and accused of keeping *a low bawdy-house*. In short, we were so well purified there with stripes, mortification, and penance, that we were afterwards utterly unfit for worldly conversation; though sack would have killed me, had I stuck to it, yet I soon died for want of a drop of something comfortable, and fairly left my body to the care of the sexton and beadle.

"Such is my own history; but that of the tavern, where I have ever since been stationed, affords greater variety. In the history of this, which is one of the oldest in London, you may view the different manners, pleasures, and follies of men at different periods. You will find mankind neither better nor worse now than formerly; the vices of an uncivilized people are generally more detestable, though not so frequent as those in polite society. It is the same luxury, which formerly stuffed your alderman with plum-porridge, and now crams him with turtle; it is the same low ambition, that formerly induced a courtier to give up his religion to please his king, and now persuades him to give up his conscience to please his minister; it is the same vanity, that formerly stained our ladies' cheeks and necks with woad, and now paints them with carmine. Your ancient Briton formerly powdered his hair with red earth like brick-dust, in order to appear frightful; your modern Briton cuts his hair on the crown and plaisters it with hog's lard and flour, and this to make him look killing. It is the same vanity, the same folly, and the same vice, only appearing different, as viewed through the glass of fashion. In a word, all mankind are a——"

"Sure the woman is dreaming," interrupted I. "None of your reflections, Mrs. Quickly, if you love me; they only give me the spleen. Tell me your history at once. I love stories, but hate reasoning."

"If you please, then, Sir," returned my companion, "I'll read you an abstract, which I made of the three hundred volumes I mentioned just now. But without farther preface the revolutions of the Boar's-head-tavern are as follow.

"My body was no sooner laid in the dust, than the prior and several of his convent came to purify the tavern from the pollutions with which they said I had filled it. Masses were said in every room, reliques were exposed upon every piece of furniture, and the whole house washed with a deluge of holy water. My habitation was soon converted into a monastery: instead of customers now applying for sack and sugar, my rooms were crowded with images, reliques, saints, whores, and friars. Instead of being a scene of occasional debauchery, it was now filled with continual lewdness. The prior led the fashion, and the whole convent imitated his pious example. Matrons came hither to confess their sins and to commit new; virgins came hither who seldom went virgins away. Nor was this a convent peculiarly wicked; every convent at that period was equally fond of pleasure, and gave a boundless loose to appetite. The laws allowed it; each priest had a right to a favourite companion, and a power of discarding her as often as he pleased. The laity grumbled, quarrelled with their wives and daughters, hated their father-confessors—and maintained them in opulence and ease.— These, these were happy times, Mr. Rigmarole! these were times of piety, bravery, and simplicity!"

"Not so very happy, neither, good Madam; pretty much like the present; those that labour starve, and those who do nothing wear fine cloaths and live in luxury."

"In this manner the fathers lived for some years without molestation; they transgressed, confessed themselves to each other, and were forgiven. One evening, however, our prior keeping a lady of distinction somewhat too long at confession, her husband unexpectedly came upon them, and testified all the indignation which was natural upon such an occasion. The prior assured the gentleman that it was the devil who had put it into his heart; and the lady was very certain that she was under the influence of magic, or she could never have behaved in so unfaithful a manner. The husband, however, was not to be put off by such evasions, but summoned both before the tribunal of justice. His proofs were flagrant, and he expected large damages. Such, indeed, he had a right to expect, were the tribunals of those days constituted in the same manner as they are now. The cause of the priest was to be tried before an assembly of priests; and a layman was to expect redress only from their impartiality and candour. What plea, then, do you think the prior made to obviate this accusation? He denied the fact and challenged the plaintiff to try the merits of their cause by single combat. It was a little hard, you may be sure, upon the poor gentleman, not only to be made a cuckold, but to be obliged to fight a duel into the bargain; yet such was the justice of the times. The prior threw down his glove, and the injured husband was obliged to take it up, in token of his accepting the challenge.

"Upon this the priest supplied his champion, for it was not lawful for the clergy to fight; and the defendant and plaintiff, according to custom, were put in prison, both ordered to fast and pray, every method being previously used to induce both to a confession of the truth. After a month's imprisonment, the hair of each was cut, the bodies anointed with oil, the field of battle appointed and guarded by soldiers, while his majesty presided over the whole in person. Both the champions were sworn not to seek victory either by fraud or magic. They prayed and confessed upon their knees; and after these ceremonies, the rest was left to the courage and conduct of the combatants. As the champion whom the prior had pitch'd upon had fought six or eight times before upon similar occasions, it was no way extraordinary to find him victorious in the present combat. In short, the husband was discomfited; he was taken from the field of battle, stripp'd to his shirt, and after one of his legs were cut off, as justice ordained in such cases, he was hanged as a terror to future offenders.— These, these were the times, Mr. Rigmarole! you see how much more just, and wise, and valiant, our ancestors were than us!"

"I rather fancy, Madam, that the times then were pretty much like our own, where a multiplicity of laws give a judge as much power as a want of law, since he is ever sure to find among the number some to countenance his partiality."

"Our convent, victorious over their enemies, now gave a loose to every demonstration of joy. The lady became a nun, the prior was made a bishop, and three Wickliffites were burned in the illuminations and fire-works that were made upon the present occasion. King Henry V., who was one of the best princes that ever sat on the throne, was fond of burning those Wickliffites. There were few feasts or entertainments in which the people were not delighted with two or three roasted Wickliffites. 'Tis certain, if what was alleged against them be true, they deserved no mercy; they were magicians or witches, every one of them; they were sometimes seen eating dead bodies torn from the grave. Sir John Oldcastle, one of the chief of the sect, was particularly fond of human flesh. I need not mention their promiscuous copulations, their cursings, and their treasons; these are written in all the books that were written by the priests of those times; the laws took every method to extirpate them, promised them life in order to make them repent, and then burned them to prevent a relapse. Acton, Brown, and Beverly, men of distinction, and who, till they were detected of heresy, were famed for having lived virtuous and pious lives, were the three that were tied to the stake to give solemnity to the present rejoicing. The flames, as if willing to assist the cause of heaven, burned upon this occasion with more than ordinary fierceness; the mob looked on and huzza'd with great devotion; and the ladies that came to see the shew were greatly edified and improved.— These, these were the times, Mr. Rigmarole, when men were found zealous as well to burn others for religion as to suffer for it themselves!"

"Equally faulty they were with ourselves; they loved religion more than their fellow creatures, and we regard neither the one nor the other."

"Our convent now began to enjoy a very high degree of reputation. There was not one in London that had the reputation of hating heretics so much as ours. Ladies of the first distinction chose from our convent their confessors. In short, it flourished, and might have flourished to this hour, but for a fatal accident which terminated in its overthrow. The lady, whom the prior had placed in a nunnery, and whom he continued to visit for some time with great punctuality, began at last to perceive that she was quite forsaken. Secluded from conversation, as usual, she now entertained the visions of a devotee, found herself strangely disturbed, but hesitated in determining whether she was possessed by an angel or a demon. She was not long in suspense however; for upon vomiting a large quantity of crooked pins and finding the palms of her hands turned outwards, she quickly concluded that she was possessed by the devil. She soon lost entirely the use of speech; and when she seemed to speak, every body that was present perceived that the voice was not her own, but that of the devil within her. In short, she was bewitched; and all the difficulty lay in determining who it could be that bewitched her. The nuns and the monks all demanded the magician's name, but the devil made no reply; for he knew they had no authority to ask questions. By the rules of witchcraft, when an evil spirit has taken possession, he may refuse to answer any questions asked him, unless they are put by a bishop, and to these he is obliged to reply. A bishop, therefore, was sent for, and now the whole secret came out; the devil reluctantly owned that he was a servant of the prior, that by his command he resided in his present habitation, and that without his command he was resolved to keep in possession. The bishop was an able exorcist; he drove the devil out by force of mystical arms; the prior was arraigned for witchcraft; the witnesses were strong and numerous against him, not less than fourteen persons being by who heard the devil talk Latin. There was no resisting such a cloud of witnesses; the prior was condemned; and he who had assisted at so many burnings was burned himself in turn.—These were the times, Mr. Rigmarole! the people of those times were not infidels, as now, but sincere believers!"

"Equally faulty with ourselves; they believed what the devil, the father of lies, was pleased to tell them, and we seem resolved at last to believe neither God nor devil."

"After such a stain upon the convent it was not to be supposed it could subsist any longer; the fathers were ordered to decamp, and the house was once again converted into a tavern. The King conferred it on one of his cast mistresses; she was constituted landlady by royal authority; and as the tavern was in the neighbourhood of the court, and Mrs. Gleek was a very polite woman, it began to have more business than ever, and sometimes took not less than four shillings a day.

"But perhaps you are desirous of knowing what were the peculiar qualifications of women of fashion at that period; and in a description of the present landlady, you will have a tolerable idea of all the rest. Mrs. Gleek was the daughter of a nobleman, and received such an education in the country as became her quality, beauty, and great expectations. She could make shifts and hose for herself and all the servants of the family, when she was twelve years old. She knew the names of the four-and-twenty letters, so that it was impossible to bewitch her; and this was a greater piece of learning than any lady in the whole country could pretend to. Some were even pleased to ridicule her as a female pedant upon this account; it is true she was not a little vain of this qualification. She was always up early and saw breakfast served in the great hall by six o'clock. At this scene of festivity she generally improved good humour by telling her dreams, relating stories of spirits, several of which she herself had seen, and one of which she was reported to have killed with a black-hafted knife. From hence she usually went to make pastry in the larder, and here she was followed by her sweethearts, who were much helped on in conversation by struggling with her for kisses. About ten, miss generally went to play hot-cockles and blindman's-buff in the parlour; and when the young folks (for they seldom played at these diversions when grown old) were tired of such amusements, the gentlemen entertained miss with the history of their greyhounds, bear-baitings and victories at cudgel-playing. If the weather was fine they ran at the ring [and] shot at butts, while miss held in her hand a ribbon, with which she adorned the conqueror. She was not taught to breakfast upon tea and such slops, but could dispatch a toast and tankard at a meal. Her mental qualifications were exactly fitted to her external accomplishments. Before she was fifteen she could tell the story of Jack the Giant Killer, could name every mountain that was inhabited by fairies, knew a witch at first sight, and could repeat four Latin prayers without a prompter. Her dress was perfectly fashionable; her arms and her hair were completely covered; a monstrous ruff was put round her neck, so that her head seemed like that of John the Baptist placed in a charger. None of your tawdry silks, but honest home-spun grey adorned her person. In short, when completely equipped, her appearance was so very modest that she discovered little more than her nose.— Those were the times, Mr. Rigmarole! when every lady that had a good nose might set up for [a] beauty, when every woman that could tell stories might be cried up for a wit!"

"I am as much displeased at those dresses which conceal too much as at those which discover too much. I am equally an enemy to a female dunce or a female pedant."

"You may be sure that miss chose an husband with qualifications resembling her own; she pitched upon Mr. Gleek, a courtier equally remarkable for hunting and drinking, who had given several proofs of his virility among the daughters of his tenants and domestics. They fell in love at first sight, for such was the gallantry of the times, were married, came to court, and madam appeared with superior qualifications. The king was struck with her beauty. All property was at the king's command; the husband was obliged to resign all pretensions in his wife to the sovereign, whom God had anointed to commit adultery where he thought proper. The king loved her for some time; but at length, repenting of his misdeeds and instigated by his father confessor from a principle of conscience, removed her from his levee to the bar of a tavern, and took a new mistress in her stead. Let it not surprize you to behold the mistress of a king degraded to so humble an office. It is true we see modern ladies of the same profession adorned with rank and precedence, but kings at the time of which I am speaking had generally new mistresses every night. As the ladies had no mental accomplishments, a good face was enough to raise them to the royal couch; and she who was this day a royal mistress, might the next, when her beauty palled upon enjoyment, be doomed to infamy and want.

"Under the care of Mrs. Gleek the tavern grew into great reputation; the courtiers had not yet learned to game, but they paid it off by drinking: drunkenness is ever the vice of a barbarous, and gaming of a luxurious age. They had not such frequent entertainments as the moderns have, but were more expensive and more luxurious in those they had. All their fooleries were more elaborate, and more admired by the great and the vulgar than now. A courtier has been known to spend his whole fortune at a single feast, a king to mortgage his dominions to furnish out the frippery of a tournament. There were certain days appointed for riot and debauchery, and to be sober at such times was reputed a crime. Kings themselves set the example; and I have seen monarchs, in this room, drunk before the entertainment was half concluded.— These were the times, Sir, when kings kept mistresses and got drunk in public; they were too plain and simple in those happy times to hide their vices and act the hypocrite, as now."

"Lord! Mrs. Quickly" (interrupting her), "I expected to have heard a story, and here are you going to tell me I know not what of times and vices! Prithee, let me entreat thee, once more, to waive reflections, and give thy history without deviation."

"No lady upon earth," continued my visionary correspondent, "knew how to put off her damaged wine or women with more art than she. When these grew flat, or those paltry, it was but changing the names; the wine became excellent, and the girls agreeable. She was also possessed of the engaging leer, the chuck under the chin, winked at a double entendre, could nick the opportunity of calling for something comfortable, and perfectly understood the discreet moments when to withdraw. The gallants of those times pretty much resembled the bloods of ours; they were fond of pleasure, but quite ignorant of the art of refining upon it; thus a court bawd of those times resembled the common low-lived harridan of a modern bagnio. Witness, ye powers of debauchery, how often I have been present at the various appearances of drunkenness, riot, guilt, and brutality! A tavern is a true picture of human infirmity; in history we find only one side of the age exhibited to our view; but, in the accounts of a tavern, we see every age equally absurd and equally vicious.

"Upon this lady's decease, the tavern was for some time untenanted until the king was pleased to appoint old James Talbot to this honourable situation. This Talbot from a private centinel, by his courage and his conduct in numberless battles, had obtained at last a colonel's commission and was reckoned the most valiant soldier of his time; from several wounds however he was at last rendered incapable of following his master to the field; wherefore he was considered as a piece of useless lumber, which is thrown aside to rot in a corner. Soldiers then fought while their vigour remained in defence of their country, and in old age were obliged to beg their bread thro' those kingdoms which their valour had saved. But this was not entirely the case of colonel Talbot; for, after numberless sollicitations, he was preferred to be the host of this tavern.

"Of all places in the world Talbot was the most unfit for his new situation; he was unable to attend his customers with proper alertness, because he was lame; and as he had been only taught to fight in his youth, in his old age he could not learn to flatter. A few old soldiers came now and then, when they had money, to talk over their former campaigns; and when they had none James Talbot gave them his liquor for nothing. As the trade of the house began to diminish, on account of his incapacity for his present business, so its emolument furnished him with a scanty subsistence; small however as it was, a few of his old companions in war were welcome to his table; that generosity he had learned in forty campaigns still stuck by him and might at last have made him a bankrupt, had this not been anticipated by the following circumstance.

"As he usually enquired after the success of his old master, King Henry, he was one day informed of the battle of Tewksbury, where Edward, who usurped the crown, having gained a complete victory, secured the kingdom to himself. He was informed of the unhappy state of the Prince of Wales, who was taken prisoner upon this occasion, that Edward demanded, in an imperious tone, how he durst presume to enter his kingdom; to which the prince replied with intrepidity that he had come to rescue his own and his father's crown from usurpers.

"Old Talbot heard this part of the story with pleasure; he loved the prince, and had carried him in his arms when a child round the camp an hundred times; he therefore rejoiced in such early proofs of magnanimity. When he came to be told how Edward dashed the gauntlet in the prince's face, the tears started into his eyes, and he could scarce contain; but when he was informed how Clarence, Hastings, and Grey fell upon him, unarmed as he was, and plunged their swords in his breast, the disabled soldier could contain no longer, but laying his hand upon his sword, cried out in an agony, 'Old James Talbot, where wer't thou?' This expression, trifling as it was, cost the old man his life; he was that moment confined in prison, and the next dragged to execution.— These were the times! Were we to read an history of Negroeland, could it furnish any occurrences more truly detestable?

"The tavern was after this successively occupied by adventurers, bullies, pimps, and gamesters. Towards the conclusion of the reign of Henry VII, gaming was more universally practised in England than even now. Kings themselves have been known to play off at Primero not only all the money and jewels they could part with, but the very images in churches. The last Henry played away, in this very room, not only the four great bells of St. Paul's Cathedral, but the fine image of St. Paul which stood upon the top of the spire, to Sir Miles Partridge, who took them down the next day and sold them by auction. Have you, then, any cause to regret being born in the times you now live, or do you still believe that human nature continues to run on declining every age? If we observe the actions of the busy part of mankind, your ancestors will be found infinitely more gross, servile, and even dishonest, than you. If, forsaking history, we only trace them in their hours of amusement and dissipation, we shall find them more sensual, more entirely devoted to pleasure, and infinitely more selfish.

"The last hostess of note I find upon record, was Jane Rouse. She was born among the lower ranks of the people; and by frugality and extreme complaisance, contrived to acquire a moderate fortune; this she might have enjoyed for many years, had she not unfortunately quarrelled with one of her neighbours, a woman who was in high repute for sanctity thro' the whole parish. In the times of which I speak, two women seldom quarrelled that one did not accuse the other of witchcraft, and she who first contrived to vomit crooked pins was sure to come off victorious. The scandal of a modern tea-table differs widely from the scandal of former times; the fascination of a lady's eyes at present is regarded as a compliment; but if a lady, formerly, should be accused of having witchcraft in her eyes, it were much better, both for her soul and body, that she had no eyes at all.

"In short, Jane Rouse was accused of witchcraft. The circumstances were plain against her; she had quarrelled with her neighbour, and that neighbour vomited pins. You will think I jest when I assure you that such a circumstance was sufficient in any court of justice then subsisting to burn half the women in the parish. Jane made the best defence she could, but all to no purpose. She was taken from her own bar to the bar of the Old Bailey, condemned, and executed accordingly.— These were times indeed, when even women could not scold in safety!

"Since her time the tavern underwent several revolutions, according to the spirit of the times or the disposition of the reigning monarch. It was this day a brothel and the next a conventicle for enthusiasts. It was one year noted for harbouring whigs and the next infamous for a retreat to tories. Some years ago it was in high vogue, but at present it seems declining. This only may be remarked in general, that whenever taverns flourish most the times are then most extravagant and luxurious."

"Lord! Mrs. Quickly!" interrupted I, "you have really deceived me. I expected a romance, and here you have been this half hour giving me only a description of the spirit of the times; if you have nothing but tedious remarks to communicate, seek some other hearer. I am determined to hearken only to stories."

I had scarce concluded when my eyes and ears seemed opened to my landlord, who had been all this while giving me an account of the repairs he had lately made, and was now got into the story of the crack'd glass in the dining-room.

THE ADVENTURES OF A STROLLING PLAYER

To the Authors of *The British Magazine*:

Gentlemen,

I went some days ago to take a walk in St. James's Park, about the hour in which company leave it in order to go to dinner. There were but few in the walks, and those who staid seemed by their looks rather more willing to forget that they had an appetite than gain one. I sat down on one of the benches at the other end of which was seated a man in very shabby cloaths but such as appeared once to have been fashionable; in short I could perceive in his figure somewhat of the gentleman, but gentility (to speak like Milton) shorn of its beams.

We continued to groan, to hem, and to cough, as usual upon such occasions, and at last ventured upon conversation. "I beg pardon, Sir," cried I, "but I think I have seen you before; your face is familiar to me." "Yes, Sir," replied he with the most perfect solemnity of look, "I have a good familiar face, as my friends tell me. I am as well known, Sir, in every town in England as the dromedary or live crocodile. You must understand, Sir, that I have been these sixteen years Merry Andrew to a puppet-shew; last Bartholomew Fair my master and I quarreled, beat each other, and parted, he to sell his puppets to the pincushion-makers in Rosemary-lane and I to starve in St. James's-Park, as you see."

"I am sorry, Sir," said I, "that a person of your appearance should labour under any difficulties." "O, Sir," returned he, "my appearance is very much at your service; but though I cannot boast of eating much, yet there are few that are merrier; if I had twenty thousand a year I should be very merry; and thank the fates! though not worth a groat, I am no way sorrowful. If I have threepence in my pocket, I never refuse to be my three halfpence; and if I have no money I never scorn to be treated by any that are kind enough to pay my reckoning.

51

What think you, Sir, of a steak and a tankard? You shall treat me now, and I will treat you again, when I find you in the park in love with eating and without money to bribe the cook's-shop for a dinner."

As I never refuse a small expense for the sake of a merry companion, we instantly adjourned to a neighbouring ale-house, and in a few moments had a frothing tankard and a smoking steak spread on the table before us. It is impossible to express how much the sight of such good cheer improved my companion's vivacity. "I like this dinner, Sir," says he, "for three reasons: first because I am naturally fond of beef, secondly because I am hungry, and thirdly and lastly because I get it for nothing; no meat eats so sweet as that for which we do not pay."

He therefore now fell to and his appetite seemed to correspond with his inclination. After dinner was over he observed that the steak was tough: "and yet, Sir," returns he, "bad as it was, it seemed a rump steak to me. O, the delights of poverty and a good appetite! We beggars are the very fondlings of nature; the rich she treats like an arrant step-mother; they are pleased with nothing; cut a steak from what part you will and it is insupportably tough; dress it up with pickles—even pickles cannot procure them an appetite, while the whole creation is filled with good things for the beggar; Calvert's butt out-tastes champagne, and Sedgeley's home-brewed excels tokay. Joy, joy, my blood! tho' our estate lies no where, we have fortunes wherever we go. If an inundation sweeps away half the ground of Cornwall, I am content—I have no lands there; if the stocks sink, that gives me no uneasiness—I am no Jew. Let us drink and I'll tell you my history and adventures; let us have another tankard; for, ah, how charming a tankard looks when full!

"You must know, then, that I am very well descended; my family has made some noise in the world: my mother cried oysters and my father beat a drum. I am told we have even had some trumpeters among our ancestors. Many a nobleman cannot shew so respectful a genealogy, but that is neither here nor there. I was their only child, the darling of their age and the pledge of their mutual love. My father designed to breed me up to his own employment, which was that of drummer to a puppet-shew, and the whole employment of my younger years was being interpreter to Punch and King Solomon in all his glory. But though my father was very fond of instructing me in beating all the marches and points of war, I made no very great progress because I naturally had no ear for music; so at the age of fifteen I went and listed for a soldier. I naturally hated to beat the drum, and I soon found that I disliked carrying a musquet also; neither the one trade nor the other were to my taste, for I was naturally fond of being a gentleman; besides I was obliged to obey a captain; he has his will, I have mine, and you have yours; now I very reasonably concluded that it was much more comfortable for a man to obey his own will than that of another.

"The life of a soldier soon, therefore, gave me the spleen. I asked leave of my captain to quit the service; but as I was tall and strong, he thanked me for my kind intentions and said because he had a regard for me that I should stay. I wrote to my father a very dismal penitent letter and desired that he would raise money to pay for my discharge; but the good man was as fond of drinking as I was (Sir, my service to you), and those who are fond of drinking never pay for other people's discharges; in short, he never answered my letter. What could be done? If I have not money, said I to myself, to pay for my discharge, I must find an equivalent some other way to procure my liberty; and that must be by running away. I deserted, and that answered my purpose every bit as well as if I had bought my discharge.

"Well, I was now fairly rid of my military employment. I sold my soldier's cloaths, bought worse, and in order not to be overtaken took the most unfrequented roads possible. One evening as I was entering a village I perceived a man, whom I afterwards found to be the curate of the parish, thrown from his horse in a miry road, and almost smothered in the mud. He desired my assistance. I gave it and drew him out with some difficulty. He thanked me for my trouble and was going off, but I followed him home, for I loved always to have a man thank me at his own door. The curate asked an hundred questions; as whose son I was, from whence I came, and whether I would be faithful. I answered him greatly to his satisfaction and gave myself one of the best characters in the world for sobriety (Sir, I have the honour of drinking your health), discretion, and fidelity. To make a long story short, he wanted a servant and hired me. With him I lived but two months; we did not much like each other. I was fond of eating, and he gave me but little to eat; I loved a pretty girl, and the old woman, my fellow-servant, was ill-natured and ugly. As they endeavoured to starve me between them, I made a pious resolution to prevent their committing murder. I stole the eggs as soon as they were laid. I emptied every unfinished bottle that I could lay my hands on; whatever eatable came in my way was sure to disappear,—in short, they found I would not do, so I was discharged one morning and paid three shillings and sixpence for two months wages.

"While my money was getting ready I employed myself in preparations for my departure. Two hens were hatching in an outhouse. I went and took the eggs from habit, and not to separate the parents from the children, I lodged hens and all in my knapsack. After this piece of frugality, I returned to receive my money, and with my knapsack on my back and a staff in my hand, I bid adieu, with tears in my eyes, to my old benefactor. I had not gone far from the house when I heard behind me the cry of 'Stop thief!' but this only increased my dispatch; it would have been foolish to stop, as I knew the voice could not be levelled at me. But, hold, I think I passed those two months at the curate's without drinking. Come, the times are dry, and may this be my poison, if I ever spent two more pious, stupid months in all my life!

"Well, after travelling some days, whom should I light upon but a company of strolling players. The moment I saw them at a distance my heart warmed to them. I had a sort of natural love of every thing of the vagabond order. They were employed in settling their baggage, which had been overturned in a narrow way. I offered my assistance, which they accepted, and we soon became acquainted so well that they took me as a servant. This was a paradise to me; they sung, they danced, drank, eat, and travelled all at the same time. By the blood of the Mirabels, I thought I had never lived till then. I grew as merry as a grig, and laughed at every word that was spoken. They liked me as much as I liked them. I was a very good figure, as you see, and tho' I was poor, I was not modest.

"I love a straggling life above all things in the world; sometimes good, sometimes bad; to be warm to-day and cold to-morrow, to eat when I can get it and drink when—(the tankard is out)—it stands before me. We arrived that evening at Tenterden, and took a large room at the Greyhound, where we resolved to exhibit Romeo and Juliet, with the funeral procession, the grave, and the garden scene. Romeo was to be performed by a gentleman from the Theatre-Royal, in Drury Lane, Juliet by a lady who had never appeared on any stage before, and I was to snuff the candles: all excellent in our way. We had figures enough, but the difficulty was to dress them. The same coat that served Romeo, turned with the blue lining outwards, served for his friend Mercutio; a large piece of crape sufficed at once for Juliet's petticoat and pall; a pestle and mortar from a neighbouring apothecary's answered all the purposes of a bell, and our landlord's own family, wrapped in white sheets, served to fill up the procession. In short, there were but three figures among us that might be said to be dressed with any propriety,—I mean the nurse, the starved apothecary, and myself. Our performance gave universal satisfaction; the whole audience were enchanted with our powers, [and Tenterden is a town of taste].

"There is one rule by which a strolling player may be ever secure of success; that is, in our theatrical way of expressing it, to make a great deal of the character. To speak and act as in common life is not playing, nor is it what people come to see; natural speaking, like sweet wine, runs glibly over the palate and scarce leaves any taste behind it, but being high in a part resembles vinegar which grates upon the taste, and one feels it while he is drinking. To please in town or country the way is to cry, wring, cringe into attitudes, mark the emphasis, slap the pockets and labour like one in the falling sickness; that is the way to work for applause; that is the way to give universal satisfaction.

"As we received much reputation for our skill on this first exhibition, it was but natural for me to ascribe part of the success to myself. I snuffed the candles, and let me tell you that without a candle-snuffer the piece would lose half its embellishments. In this manner we continued a fortnight and drew tolerable houses, but the evening before our intended departure we gave out our very best piece, in which all our strength was to be exerted. We had great expectations from this and even doubled our prices, when behold one of the principal actors fell ill of a violent fever. This was a stroke like thunder to our little company. They were resolved to go in a body to scold the man for falling sick at so inconvenient a time, and that too of a disorder that threatened to be expensive. I seized the moment and offered to act the part myself in his stead. The case was desperate; they accepted my offer, and I accordingly sat down, with the part in my hand and a tankard before me (Sir, your health), and studied the character which was to be rehearsed the next day and played soon after.

"I found my memory excessively helped by drinking. I learned my part with astonishing rapidity and bid adieu to snuffing candles ever after. I found that nature had designed me for more noble employments, and I was resolved to take her when in the humour. We got together in order to rehearse; and I informed my companions—masters now no longer—of the surprising change I felt within me. 'Let the sick man,' said I, 'be under no uneasiness to get well again. I'll fill his place to universal satisfaction; he may even die if he thinks proper. I'll engage that he shall never be missed.' I rehearsed before them, strutted, ranted, and received applause. They soon gave out that a new actor of eminence was to appear, and immediately all the genteel places were bespoke. Before I ascended the stage, however, I concluded within myself that as I brought money to the house I ought to have my share in the profits. 'Gentlemen,' said I addressing our company, 'I don't pretend to direct you; far be it from me to treat you with so much ingratitude; you have published my name in the bills with the utmost good-nature, and as affairs stand, cannot act without me; so, gentlemen, to shew you my gratitude, I expect to be paid for my acting as much as any of you; otherwise I declare off. I'll brandish my snuffers and clip candles as usual.' This was a very disagreeable proposal, but they found that it was impossible to refuse it; it was irresistible, it was adamant; they consented, and I went on in King Bajazet, my frowning brows bound with a stocking stuffed into a turban, while on my captiv'd arms I brandished a jack-chain. Nature seemed to have fitted me for the part. I was tall and had a loud voice;

my very entrance excited a clap of universal applause. I looked round on the audience with a smile and made a most low and graceful bow, for that is the rule among us. As it was a very passionate part I invigorated my spirits with three full glasses (the tankard is almost out) of brandy. By Alla! it is inconceivable how I went through it. Tamerlane was but a fool to me, though he was sometimes loud enough too, yet still I was louder than him; but then, besides, I had attitudes in abundance; in general I kept my arms folded up thus, upon the pit of my stomach; it is the way at Drury-Lane and has always a fine effect. The tankard would sink to the bottom before I could get through the whole of my merit; in short, I came off like a prodigy; and such was my success that I could ravish the laurels even from a sirloin of beef. The principal gentlemen and ladies of the town came to me, after the play was over, to compliment me upon my success; one praised my voice, another my person. 'Upon my word,' says the squire's lady, 'he will make one of the finest actors in Europe. I say it, and I think I am a good judge.' Praise in the beginning is agreeable enough, and we receive it as a favour; but when it comes in great quantities we regard it only as a debt which nothing but our merit could extort; instead of thanking them, I internally applauded myself. We were desired to give our piece a second time; we obeyed, and I was applauded even more than before.

"At last we left the town in order to be at an horse-race at some distance from thence. I shall never think of Tenterden without tears of gratitude and respect. The ladies and gentlemen there, take my word for it, are very good judges of plays and actors. Come, let us drink their healths, if you please, Sir. We quitted the town, I say; and there was a wide difference between my coming in and my going out. I entered the town a candle-snuffer, and I quitted it an hero! Such is the world; little to-day, and great to-morrow. I could say a great deal more upon that subject—something truly sublime, upon the ups and downs of fortune; but it would give us both the spleen, and so I shall pass it over.

"The races were ended the day before we arrived at the next town, which was no small disappointment to our company; however, we were resolved to take all we could get. I played capital characters there too, and came off with my usual brilliancy. I sincerely believe I should have been the first actor of Europe, had my growing merit been properly cultivated; but there came an unkindly frost, which nipped me in the bud and levelled me once more down to the common standard of humanity. I played Sir Harry Wildair; all the country ladies were charmed; if I but drew out my snuff-box, the whole house was in a roar of rapture; when I exercised my cudgel, I thought they would have fallen into convulsions.

"There was here a lady who had received an education of nine months in London, and this gave her pretensions to taste which rendered her the indisputable mistress of the ceremonies wherever she came. She was informed of my merits; every body praised me, yet she refused at first going to see me perform. She could not conceive, she said, any thing but stuff from a stroller; talked something in praise of Garrick, and amazed the ladies with her skill in enunciations, tones, and cadences. She was at last, however, prevailed upon to go; and it was privately intimated to me what a judge was to be present at my next exhibition. However, no way intimidated, I came on in Sir Harry, one hand stuck in my breeches, and the other in my bosom, as usual at Drury-Lane; but instead of looking at me, I perceived the whole audience had their eyes turned upon the lady who had been nine months in London; from her they expected the decision which was to secure the general's truncheon in my hand or sink me down into a theatrical letter-carrier. I opened my snuff-box, took snuff; the lady was solemn, and so were the rest. I broke my cudgel on Alderman Smuggler's back; still gloomy, melancholy all; the lady groaned and shrugged her shoulders. I attempted, by laughing myself, to excite at least a smile; but the devil a cheek could I perceive wrinkled into sympathy. I found it would not do. All my good-humour now became forced; my laughter was converted into hysteric grinning, and while I pretended spirits, my eye shewed the agony of my heart; in short, the lady came with an intention to be displeased, and displeased she was; my fame expired, and—*the tankard is no more!*"

REVIEW OF SMOLLETT'S "HISTORY
OF ENGLAND"

When the historian relates events far removed from the age
in which he writes, when evidence is become scarce, and authorities are rendered doubtful from the obscurities which
time has thrown upon them, he ought, above all things, to be
careful that his narration be as amply authenticated as the
nature of his researches will allow. Strictly speaking, the eye-
witness alone should take upon him to transmit facts to posterity; and as for the historians, the copyists, the annotators,
who may follow him, if possessed of no new and genuine materials, instead of strengthening they will only diminish the
authority of their guide; for, in proportion as history removes
from the first witnesses, it may recede also from truth; as, by
passing thro' the prejudices or the mistakes of subsequent compilers, it will be apt to imbibe what tincture they may chance to
give it. The *later* historian's only way, therefore, to prevent the
ill effects of that decrease of evidence which the lapse of years
necessarily brings with it, must be by punctually referring to
the spring-head from whence the stream of his narration flows,
which at once will cut off all appearance of partiality or mis-
representation. As in law the rectitude of a person's character
is not alone sufficient to establish the truth of a fact, so in
history not merely the writer's testimony, be our opinion of his
veracity ever so great, but collateral evidence also is required
to determine every thing of a questionable nature. The funda-
mental materials for the general history of any country are the
public records, ancient monuments, and original historians of
that country; and in proportion as they are slighted by the
compiler, these venerable originals themselves may fall into
neglect and possibly in the end even into irretrievable oblivion:
—and when *they* are gone, in vain may we look for an enlight-

ening ray to guide us thro' the darkness of antiquity; we must then be content with the uncertain gleam with which an erroneous or partial leader is pleased to conduct us.

There were of old, and still are, indolent readers who turn to an author with the design rather of killing than improving their time; and who, scared at the serious face of instruction, are rather attracted by the lively, florid stile of a Florus than the more substantial disquisitions of a Polybius. With such readers every step an historian takes towards determining the weight of evidence or the degrees of credibility, is an excursion into the regions of dulness; but while the writer proceeds in his narrative without reflection, they continue to read without reflecting; and his history enlightens them just as much as a romance would have done, for they are equally unconcerned about truth in either.

Truth should be the main object of the historian's pursuit; *elegance* is only its ornament; if, therefore, we see a writer of this class plume himself upon his excelling in the last, and at the same time slighting the evidences that ought to ascertain and support the first, suspicion will naturally arise, and the author's credit will sink in proportion.

With respect to the history now before us the compiler does not pretend to have discovered any hidden records or authentic materials that have escaped the notice of former writers, or to have thrown such lights upon contested events or disputed characters as may serve to rectify any mistaken opinions mankind may have entertained with respect to either. His care is rather to disburthen former histories of those tedious vouchers and proofs of authenticity which, in his opinion, only serve to swell the page and exercise the reader's patience. He seldom quotes authorities in support of his representations; and if he now and then condescends to cite the testimony of former writers, he never points to the page, but leaves the sceptical reader to supply any defect of this kind by an exertion of that industry which the author disdains; and thus on the veracity of the relator are we to rest our conviction, and accept his own word for it that he has no intention to deceive or mislead us.

That this author, however, has no such design, may be fairly presumed from his declining all attempts to bias us by any remarks of his own. Determined to avoid all *useless disquisitions,* as his plan professes, he steers wide indeed of that danger and avoids all *disquisition* as *useless.* A brief recital of facts is chiefly what the public is to expect from this performance. But, with submission, we think the ingenious author might have afforded us something more. He has undoubted ability; and he well knows that a moderate interspersion of manly and sensible observations must have greatly enlivened his work and would hardly have been deemed superfluous by such readers as have any turn for reflection.

With respect to the stile of this historian, it is in general clear, nervous, and flowing; and we think it impossible for a reader of taste not to be pleased with the perspicuity and elegance of his manner. But what he seems principally to value himself upon, and what his patronizers chiefly mention in praise of his performance, are the Characters he has summed up at the close of every reign. Here, however, we cannot entirely fall in with the ingenious Doctor's admirers.—But we forbear to enlarge, and shall therefore proceed to enable our readers, in some measure, to judge for themselves, by a few specimens, taken from such parts of the history as, we apprehend, the author's friends will think we do him no injustice in selecting. . . .

We shall conclude with the following summary of the qualifications required in an historian. His learning, says Bayle, should be greater than his genius, and his judgment stronger than his imagination. In private life, he should have the character of being free from party, and his former writings ought always to have shewn the sincerest attachment to truth. I ask several questions, says the same author: who the historian is? of what country? of what principles? for it is impossible but that his private opinions will almost involuntarily work themselves into his public performances. His stile also should be clear, elegant, and nervous. And lastly, to give him a just boldness of sentiment and expression, he should have a consciousness of these his superior abilities.—As to the first requisites, how far our author is possessed of them his former productions will abundantly demonstrate; but in the last, he seems to have fallen short of none of his predecessors.

BRIEF NOTICES OF NEW NOVELS

1. *The Impetuous Lover, or, the Guiltless Parricide; shewing to what lengths love may run, and the extreme folly of forming schemes for futurity. Written under the instructions and at the request of one of the interested parties. By A. G. Esq. . . .*

We shall select from the beginning (and it is but reasonable to suppose the author puts the best leg foremost) a short speci-men of this performance. "No sooner *wou'd he* have repeated the name, and thereby recalled before his eyes the *lovely she,* than the whole *flux* of his imagination *bending* again to his beloved Iris, he would condemn his very suspicions as *founda-tionless,* in that it was impossible for nature itself to form a second so masterly a being as the exquisite Iris." We may add,—or the exquisite author of *The Impetuous Lover.*

2. *The History of Two Persons of Quality, taken from Memoirs written in the Reign of Edward IV by William St. Pierre, Esq., who was educated with the Earl of *** and afterwards gover-nor to the son of that Nobleman. . . .*

Who these persons of quality were our author does not inform us; however, we can well excuse the omission. The hero, like most other heroes of romance, is wholly employed in making love, the heroine, in returning his addresses with equal ardour; the hero kills his man, the heroine, too, in her way dispatches every swain that meets her eyes; the hero has a certain noble-ness in his manner, the heroine a peculiar delicacy in hers. What pity so much excellence has not found a better historian!

3. *True Merit True Happiness, exemplified in the entertaining and instructive Memoirs of Mr. S——. . . .*

A translation from a French novel entitled *Memoires & Avantures d'un Bourgeois.* It concludes, as they all do: "Thus, before I was thirty years of age, I saw myself completely happy, beloved by my family, and more especially so by a wife whose lover I am as well as husband. From that happy moment no misfortunes have intervened to intercept our tranquility. Our family has received the additional increase of several children, and I have now six alive, all well provided for and thriving in the world."— Reader, if thou hast ever known such perfect happiness as these romance-writers can so liberally dispense, thou hast enjoyed greater pleasure than has ever fallen to our lot. How deceitful are these imaginary pictures of felicity! and, we may add, how mischievous too! The young and the ignorant lose their taste of present enjoyment by opposing to it those delusive daubings of consummate bliss they meet with in novels; and, by expecting more happiness than life can give, feel but the more poignancy in all its disappointments.

4. *The History of Cleanthes, an Englishman of the highest Quality, and Celemene, the illustrious Amazonian Princess: Interspersed with a variety of most entertaining Incidents and surprizing turns of Fortune and a particular Account of that famous Island so much talked of but hitherto so little known. Written by a Person well acquainted with all the principal Characters from their Original. . . .*

By the title-page some readers may be induced to search into this performance for hidden satire or political allegory, but it contains nothing more than an harmless tale, loaded with uninteresting episodes and professedly wrote in the manner and stile of the old romances—equally improbable indeed with the wildest of them but falling far short of their glowing imagery and strong colouring, which often captivate the fancy of *young* readers especially, and please in spite of sense and reason.

5. *The Mother-in-Law, or the Innocent Sufferer, interspersed with
   the uncommon and entertaining Adventures of Mr. Hervey
   Faulconer. . . .*

This performance seems to come from the same hand which
obliged us with the *Guiltless Parricide*.[12] For instance: "Madam
having the proverb of her side, escaped only with a bruise
or two upon her legs and one shoulder; but her husband, poor
man, looked more like a spectre than a living person when
he appeared, for his head was most confoundedly broken
against the iron ketch in the ceiling of the landau, besides
several severe bruises which lay concealed under the weightier
calamity to his noddle; but these failed not to remind him of
them soon after the dressing of his skull, by an almost inability
to walk for a few days after." The story contains the adventures of a couple of true *lovyers* in indigent circumstances, the
lady obliged to go to service, the gentleman in quest of fortune to the East Indies. After some vicissitudes they at length
meet again, wallow in riches, and the lady lives to this day
under her husband's *wing,* as we are told, in Gloucestershire.
Where we shall leave them in the full enjoyment of all the
felicity that a bounteous *author* can bestow.

6. *The Fair Citizen, or the real Adventures of Miss Charlotte
   Bellmour. Written by herself. . . .*

As Miss Bellmour is now happily married to the very agreeable Mr. Frankly, we would not interrupt her present felicity
by any strictures upon her authorship. But we must beg leave
to offer her one hint at parting, which she may profit from
if she does not too much mistake her talents—viz., that one
good pudding is worth fifty modern romances.

REVIEW OF GRAY'S "ODES"

As this publication seems designed for those who have formed their taste by the models of antiquity, the generality of readers cannot be supposed adequate judges of its merit; nor will the poet, it is presumed, be greatly disappointed if he finds them backward in commending a performance not entirely suited to their apprehensions. We cannot, however, without some regret behold those talents so capable of giving pleasure to all, exerted in efforts that, at best, can amuse only the few; we cannot behold this rising poet seeking fame among the learned, without hinting to him the same advice that Isocrates used to give his scholars, *study the people*. This study it is that has conducted the great masters of antiquity up to immortality. Pindar himself, of whom our modern lyrist is an imitator, appears entirely guided by it. He adapted his works exactly to the dispositions of his countrymen. Irregular, enthusiastic, and quick in transition,—he wrote for a people inconstant, of warm imaginations, and exquisite sensibility. He chose the most popular subjects, and all his allusions are to customs well known, in his days, to the meanest person.

His English imitator wants those advantages. He speaks to a people not easily impressed with new ideas, extremely tenacious of the old, with difficulty warmed, and as slowly cooling again. How unsuited then to our national character is that species of poetry which rises upon us with unexpected flights, where we must hastily catch the thought or it flies from us, and, in short, where the reader must largely partake of the poet's enthusiasm in order to taste his beauties. To carry the parallel a little farther, the Greek poet wrote in a language the most proper that can be imagined for this species of composition; lofty, harmonious, and never needing rhyme to heighten the numbers. But for us, several unsuccessful experiments seem to prove that the English cannot have Odes in blank verse; while, on the other hand, a natural imperfection attends those which are composed in irregular rhymes; the similar sound often recurring where it is not expected and not being found where it is, creates no small confusion to the reader, who, as we have not seldom observed, beginning in all the solemnity of poetic elocution, is by frequent disappointments of the rhyme at last obliged to drawl out the uncomplying numbers into disagreeable prose.

It is by no means our design to detract from the merit of our author's present attempt; we would only intimate that an English poet, one whom the Muse has *mark'd for her own,* could produce a more luxuriant bloom of flowers by cultivating such as are natives of the soil, than by endeavouring to force the exotics of another climate; or, to speak without a metaphor, such a genius as Mr. Gray might give greater pleasure and acquire a larger portion of fame, if, instead of being an imitator, he did justice to his talents and ventured to be more an original. These two Odes, it must be confessed, breathe much of the spirit of Pindar; but then they have caught the seeming obscurity, the sudden transition, and hazardous epithet, of his mighty master; all which, though evidently intended for beauties, will probably be regarded as blemishes by the generality of his readers. In short, they are in some measure a representation of what Pindar now appears to be, though perhaps not what he appeared to the states of Greece when they rivalled each other in his applause and when Pan himself was seen dancing to his melody.

In conformity to the antients, these Odes consist of the strophe, antistrophe, and epode, which, in each Ode, are thrice repeated. The strophes have a correspondent resemblance in their structure and numbers; and the antistrophe and epode also bear the same similitude. The poet seems, in the first Ode particularly, to design the epode as a complete air to the strophe and antistrophe, which have more the appearance of recitative. There was a necessity for these divisions among the antients, for they served as directions to the dancer and musician; but we see no reason why they should be continued among the moderns; for instead of assisting, they will but perplex the musician, as our music requires a more frequent transition from the air to the recitative than could agree with the simplicity of the antients.

The first of these poems celebrates the Lyric Muse. It seems the most laboured performance of the two; but yet we think its merit is not equal to that of the second. It seems to want that regularity of plan upon which the second is founded; and though it abounds with images that strike, yet, unlike the second, it contains none that are affecting. . . .

The second Ode "is founded on a tradition current in Wales, that Edward the first, when he compleated the conquest of that country, ordered all the Bards that fell into his hands to be put to death." The author seems to have taken the hint of this subject from the fifteenth Ode of the first book of Horace. Our poet introduces the only surviving bard of that country in concert with the spirits of his murdered brethren, as prophetically denouncing woes upon the conqueror and his posterity. The circumstances of grief and horror in which the bard is represented, those of terror in the preparation of the votive web, and the mystic obscurity with which the prophecies are delivered, will give as much pleasure to those who relish this species of composition as any thing that has hitherto appeared in our language, the Odes of Dryden himself not excepted. . . .

UPON CRITICISM

. . . There are still some men, whom fortune has blessed with affluence, to whom the muse pays her morning visit, not like a creditor, but a friend: to this happy few, who have leisure to polish what they write, and liberty to chuse their own subjects, I would direct my advice, which consists in a few words: *Write what you think, regardless of the critics.* To persuade to this, was the chief design of this essay. To break, or at least to loosen those bonds, first put on by caprice, and afterwards drawn hard by fashion, is my wish. I have assumed the critic only to dissuade from criticism.

There is scarce an error of which our present writers are guilty, that does not arise from this source. From this proceeds the affected obscurity of our odes, the tuneless flow of our blank verse, the pompous epithet, laboured diction, and every other deviation from common sense, which procures the poet the applause of the connoisseur; he is praised by all, read by a few, and soon forgotten.

There never was an unbeaten path trodden by the poet, that the critic did not endeavour to reclaim him, by calling his attempt innovation. This might be instanced in Dante, who first followed nature, and was persecuted by the critics as long as he lived. Thus novelty, one of the greatest beauties in poetry, must be avoided, or the connoisseur will be displeased. It is one of the chief privileges, however, of genius to fly from the herd of imitators by some happy singularity; for should he stand still, his heavy pursuers will at length come up and fairly dispute the victory.

The ingenious Mr. Hogarth used to assert that every one, except the connoisseur, was a judge of painting. The same may be asserted of writing; the public in general set the whole piece in the proper point of view; the critic lays his eye close to all its minutenesses and condemns or approves in detail. And this may be the reason why so many writers at present are apt to appeal from the tribunal of criticism to that of the people.

From a desire in the critic of grafting the spirit of ancient languages upon the English, has proceeded of late several disagreeable instances of pedantry. Among the number, I think we may reckon blank verse. Nothing but the greatest sublimity of subject can render such a measure pleasing; however, we now see it used upon the most trivial occasions; it has particularly found its way into our didactic poetry, and is likely to bring that species of composition into disrepute for which the English are deservedly famous.

Those who are acquainted with writing know that our language runs almost naturally into blank verse. The writers of our novels, romances, and all of this class who have no notion of stile naturally hobble into this unharmonious measure. If rhymes, therefore, be more difficult, for that very reason I would have our poets write in rhyme. Such a restriction upon the thought of a good poet often lifts and encreases the vehemence of every sentiment; for fancy, like a fountain, plays highest by diminishing the aperture. But rhymes, it will be said, are a remnant of monkish stupidity, an innovation upon the poetry of the ancients. They are but indifferently acquainted with antiquity who make the assertion. Rhymes are probably of older date than either the Greek or Latin dactyl and spondé. The Celtic, which is allowed to be the first language spoken in Europe, has ever preserved them, as we may find in the Edda of Iceland and the Irish carrols still sung among the original inhabitants of that island. Olaus Wormius gives us some of the Teutonic poetry in this way, and Pantoppidan, bishop of Bergen, some of the Norwegian; in short, this jingle of sounds is almost natural to mankind; at least it is so to our language, if we may judge from many unsuccessful attempts to throw it off.

I should not have employed so much time in opposing this erroneous innovation, if it were not apt to introduce another in its train, I mean a disgusting solemnity of manner into our poetry; and, as the prose writer has been ever found to follow the poet, it must consequently banish in both all that agreeable trifling which, if I may so express it, often deceives us into instruction. Dry reasoning, and dull morality, have no force with the wild fantastic libertine. He must be met with smiles, and courted with the allurements of gaiety. He must be taught to believe that he is in pursuit of pleasure, and surprized into reformation. The finest sentiment and the most weighty truth may put on a pleasing face, and it is even virtuous to jest when serious advice must be disgusting. But instead of this, the most trifling performance among us now assumes all the didactic stiffness of wisdom. The most diminutive son of fame, or of famine, has his *we* and his *us,* his *firstlys* and his *secondlys* as methodical, as if bound in cowhide, and closed with clasps of brass. Were these Monthly Reviews and Magazines frothy, pert, or absurd, they might find some pardon; but to be dull and dronish is an encroachment on the prerogative of a folio.

These pamphlets should be considered as pills to purge melancholly; they should be made up in our splenetic climate to be taken as physic, and not so as to be used when we take it. Some such law should be enacted in the republic of letters as we find take place in the house of commons. As no man there can shew his wisdom, unless first qualified by three hundred pounds a year, so none here should profess gravity, unless his work amounted to three hundred pages.

However, by the power of one single monosyllable, our critics have almost got the victory over humour amongst us. Does the poet paint the absurdities of the vulgar; then he is *low*; does he exaggerate the features of folly, to render it more thoroughly ridiculous, he is then very *low*. In short, they have proscribed the comic or satyrical muse from every walk but high life, which, though abounding in fools as well as the humblest station, is by no means so fruitful in absurdity. Among well-bred fools we may despise much, but have little to laugh at; nature seems to present us with an universal blank of silk, ribbands, smiles, and whispers; absurdity is the poet's game, and good breeding is the nice concealment of absurdities. The truth is, the critic generally mistakes humour for wit, which is a very different excellence. Wit raises human nature above its level; humour acts a contrary part, and equally depresses it. To expect exalted humour is a contradiction in terms; and the critic, by demanding an impossibility from the comic poet, has, in effect, banished new comedy from the stage. But to put the same thought in a different light:

When an unexpected similitude in two objects strikes the imagination, in other words, when a thing is *wittily* expressed, all our pleasure turns into admiration of the artist who had fancy enough to draw the picture. When a thing is *humourously* described, our burst of laughter proceeds from a very different cause; we compare the absurdity of the character represented with our own, and triumph in our conscious superiority. No natural defect can be a cause of laughter, because it is a misfortune to which ourselves are liable; a defect of this kind changes the passion to pity or horror; we only laugh at those instances of moral absurdity to which we are conscious we ourselves are not liable. For instance, should I describe a man as wanting his nose, there is no humour in this, as it is an accident to which human nature is subject, and may be any man's case; but should I represent this man without his nose, as extremely curious in the choice of his snuff-box, we here see him guilty of an absurdity of which we imagine it impossible for ourselves to be guilty, and therefore applaud our own good sense on the comparison. Thus, then, the pleasure we receive from wit turns on the admiration of another; that we feel from humour centers in the admiration of ourselves. The poet, therefore, must place the object he would have the subject of humour in a state of inferiority; in other words, the subject of humour must be low.

The solemnity worn by many of our modern writers is, I fear, often the mask of dulness; for certain it is, it seems to fit every author who pleases to put it on. By the complexion of many of our late publications, one might be apt to cry out with Cicero, *Civem mehercule non puto esse qui his temporibus ridere possit.* On my conscience, I believe we have all forgot to laugh in these days. Such writers probably make no distinction between what is praised and what is pleasing, between those commendations which the reader pays his own discernment and those which are the genuine result of his sensations.

As our gentlemen writers have it therefore so much in their power to lead the taste of the times, they may now part with the inflated stile that has for some years been looked upon as fine writing, and which every young writer is now obliged to adopt if he chuses to be read. They may now dispense with loaded epithet and dressing up of trifles with dignity. For to use an obvious instance, it is not those who make the greatest noise with their wares in the streets that have the most to sell. Let us, instead of writing finely, try to write naturally. Not hunt after lofty expressions to deliver mean ideas, nor be for ever gaping when we only mean to deliver a whisper.

OF THE STAGE

Our theatre may be regarded as partaking of the shew and decoration of the Italian opera with the propriety and declamation of French performance. Our stage is more magnificent than any other in Europe, and the people in general fonder of theatrical entertainment. But as our pleasures, as well as more important concerns, are generally managed by party, the stage is subject to its influence. The managers and all who espouse their side are for decoration and ornament; the critic and all who have studied French decorum are for regularity and declamation. Thus it is almost impossible to please both parties, and the poet by attempting it finds himself often incapable of pleasing either. If he introduces stage pomp, the critic consigns his performance to the vulgar; if he indulges in recital and simplicity, he is accused of insipidity or dry affectation.

From the nature therefore of our theatre and the genius of our country, it is extremely difficult for a dramatic poet to please his audience. But happy would he be were these the only difficulties he had to encounter; there are many other more dangerous combinations against the little wit of the age. Our poet's performance must undergo a process truly chymical before it is presented to the public. It must be tried in the manager's fire, strained through a licenser, and purified in the review or the news-paper of the day. At this rate before it can come to a private table it may probably be a mere *caput mortuum* and only proper entertainment for the licenser, manager, or critic himself. But it may be answered that we have a sufficient number of plays upon our theatres already, and therefore there is no need of new ones. But are they sufficiently good? And is the credit of our age nothing? Must our present times pass away unnoticed by posterity? We are desirous of leaving them liberty, wealth, and titles, and we can have no recompence but their applause. The title of Learned given to an age is the most glorious applause, and shall this be disregarded? Our reputation among foreigners will quickly be discontinued when we discontinue our efforts to deserve it, and shall we despise their praise? Are our new absurdities, with which no nation more abounds, to be left unnoticed? Is the pleasure such performances give upon the perusal to be entirely given up? If these are all matters of indifference, it then signifies nothing whether we are to be entertained with the actor or the poet, with fine sentiments or painted canvas, or whether the dancer, or the carpenter, be constituted master of the ceremonies.

But they are not matters of indifference. Every age produces new follies and new vices, and one absurdity is often displaced in order to make room for another. The dramatic poet, however, who should be, and has often been, a firm champion in the cause of virtue, detects all the new machinations of vice, levels his satire at the rising structures of folly, or drives her from behind the retrenchments of fashion. Thus far then the poet is useful; but how far the actor, that dear favourite of the public, may be so is a question next to be determined.

As the poet's merit is often not sufficient to introduce his performance among the public with proper dignity, he is often obliged to call in the assistance of decoration and dress to contribute to this effect. By this means a performance which pleases on the stage often instructs in the closet, and for one who has seen it acted, hundreds will be readers. The actor then is useful by introducing the works of the poet to the public with becoming splendor; but when these have once become popular I must confess myself so much a sceptic as to think it would be more for the interests of virtue if such perform-ances were read, not acted, made rather our companions in the closet than on the theatre. While we are readers every moral sentiment strikes us in all its beauty, but the love scenes are frigid, tawdry, and disgusting. When we are spec-tators all the persuasives to vice receive an additional lustre. The love scene is aggravated, the obscenity heightened, the best actors figure in the most debauched characters, while the parts of dull morality, as they are called, are thrown to some mouthing machine, who puts even virtue out of countenance by his wretched imitation. The principal performers find their interest in chusing such parts as tend to promote, not the benefit of society but their own reputation, and in using arts which inspire emotions very different from those of morality. How many young men go to the playhouse speculatively in love with the rule of right, but return home actually enamour'd of an actress?

I have often attended to the reflections of the company upon leaving the theatre; one actor had the finest pipe, but the other the most melodious voice; one was a bewitching creature, another a charming devil; and such are generally our acquisitions at the play-house. It brings to my remembrance an old lady who being passionately fond of a famous preacher went every Sunday to church, but, struck only with his graceful manner of delivery, disregarded and forgot the truths of his discourse.

But it is needless to mention the incentives to vice which are found at the theatre or the immorality of some of the performers. Such impeachments, though true, would be regarded as cant, while their exhibitions continue to amuse. I would only infer from hence that an actor is chiefly useful in introducing new performances upon the stage, since the reader receives more benefit by perusing a well-written play in his closet than by seeing it acted. I would also infer that to the poet is to be ascribed all the good that attends seeing plays, and to the actor all the harm.

But how is this rule inverted on our theatres at present? Old pieces are revived, and scarce any new ones admitted; the actor is ever in our eye, and the poet seldom permitted to appear; the public are again obliged to ruminate those hashes of absurdity which were disgusting to our ancestors, even in an age of ignorance; and the stage, instead of serving the people, is made subservient to the interests of an avaricious few. We must now tamely see the literary honours of our country suppressed that an actor may dine with elegance; we must tamely sit and see the celestial muse made a slave to the histrionic dæmon.

We seem to be pretty much in the situation of travellers

at a Scotch inn, vile entertainment is served up, complained of and sent down, up comes worse and that also is changed, and every change makes our wretched cheer more unsavoury. What must be done? Only sit down contented, cry up all that comes before us, and admire even the absurdities of Shakespear.

Let the reader suspend his censure. I admire the beauties of this great father of our stage as much as they deserve, but could wish for the honour of our country, and for his honour too, that many of his scenes were forgotten. A man blind of one eye should always be painted in profile. Let the spectator who assists at any of these new revived pieces only ask himself whether he would approve such a performance if written by a modern poet; if he would not, then his applause proceeds merely from the sound of a name and an empty veneration for antiquity. In fact, the revival of those pieces of forced humour, far fetch'd conceit, and unnatural hyperbole which have been ascribed to Shakespear is rather gibbeting than raising a statue to his memory; it is rather a trick of the actor who thinks it safest acting in exaggerated characters and who by out-stepping nature chuses to exhibit the ridiculous outré of an harlequin under the sanction of this venerable name.

What strange vamp'd comedies, farcical tragedies, or what shall I call them, speaking pantomimes, have we not of late seen. No matter what the play may be, it is the actor who draws an audience. He throws life into all; all are in spirits and merry, in at one door and out at another; the spectator, in a fool's paradise, knows not what all this means till the last act concludes in matrimony. The piece pleases our critics because it talks old English, and it pleases the galleries because it has fun. True taste, or even common sense, are out of the question.

But great art must be sometimes used before they can thus impose upon the public. To this purpose a prologue written with some spirit generally precedes the piece, to inform us that it was composed by Shakespear or old Ben, or somebody else who took them for his model. A face of iron could not have the assurance to avow dislike; the theatre has its partizans who understand the force of combinations, trained up to vociferation, clapping of hands, and clattering of sticks; and tho' a man might have strength sufficient to overcome a lion in single combat, by an army even of mice he may run the risk of being eaten up marrow-bones and all.

I am not insensible that third nights are disagreeable drawbacks upon the annual profits of the stage. I am confident it is much more to the manager's advantage to furbish up all the lumber which the good sense of our ancestors, but for his care, had consign'd to oblivion; it is not with him therefore but with the public I would expostulate; they have a right to demand respect, and sure those new revived plays are no instances of the manager's deference.

I have been informed that no new play can be admitted upon our theatre unless the author chuses to wait some years, or to use the phrase in fashion, till it comes to be played in turn. A poet thus can never expect to contract a familiarity with the stage, by which alone he can hope to succeed, nor can the most signal success relieve immediate want. Our Saxon ancestors had but one name for a wit and a witch. I will not dispute the propriety of uniting those characters then; but the man who under the present discouragements ventures to write for the stage now, whatever claim he may have to the apellation of a wit, at least he has no right to be called a conjuror.

Yet getting a play on even in three or four years is a privilege reserved only for the happy few who have the arts of courting the manager as well as the muse, who have adulation to please his vanity, powerful patrons to support their merit, or money to indemnify disappointment. The poet must act like our beggars at Christmas, who lay the first shilling on the plate for themselves. Thus all wit is banished from the stage, except it be supported by friends or fortune, and poets are seldom over-burthened with either.

I am not at present writing for a party but above theatrical connections in every sense of the expression. I have no particular spleen against the fellow who sweeps the stage with the besom or the hero who brushes it with his train. It were a matter of indifference to me whether our heroines are in keeping or our candle-snuffers burn their fingers, did not such make a great part of public care and polite conversation. It is not these but the age I would reproach; the vile complexion of the times, when those employ our most serious thoughts and seperate us into parties whose business is only to amuse our idlest hours. I cannot help reproaching our meanness in this respect; for our stupidity and our folly will be remembered when even the attitudes and eye brows of a favourite actor shall be forgotten. . . .

ON THE THEATRE:

A Comparison between Laughing and Sentimental Comedy

The theatre, like all other amusements, has its fashions and its prejudices, and when satiated with its excellence mankind begin to mistake change for improvement. For some years tragedy was the reigning entertainment, but of late it has entirely given way to comedy, and our best efforts are now exerted in these lighter kinds of composition. The pompous train, the swelling phrase, and the unnatural rant are displaced for that natural portrait of human folly and frailty, of which all are judges because all have sat for the picture.

But as in describing nature it is presented with a double face, either of mirth or sadness, our modern writers find themselves at a loss which chiefly to copy from, and it is now debated whether the exhibition of human distress is likely to afford the mind more entertainment than that of human absurdity.

Comedy is defined by Aristotle to be a picture of the frailties of the lower part of mankind, to distinguish it from tragedy, which is an exhibition of the misfortunes of the great. When comedy therefore ascends to produce the characters of princes or generals upon the stage, it is out of its walk, since low life and middle life are entirely its object. The principal question therefore is whether in describing low or middle life an exhibition of its follies be not preferable to a detail of its calamities. Or in other words, which deserves the preference, the weeping sentimental comedy so much in fashion at present or the laughing and even low comedy which seems to have been last exhibited by Vanbrugh and Cibber?

It we apply to authorities, all the great masters in the dramatic art have but one opinion. Their rule is, that as tragedy displays the calamities of the great, so comedy should excite our laughter by ridiculously exhibiting the follies of the lower part of mankind. Boileau, one of the best modern critics, asserts that comedy will not admit of tragic distress.

> Le comique, ennemi des soupirs et des pleurs,
> N'admet point dans ses vers de tragiques doleurs.[13]

Nor is this rule without the strongest foundation in nature, as the distresses of the mean by no means affect us so strongly as the calamities of the great. When tragedy exhibits to us some great man fallen from his height and struggling with want and adversity, we feel his situation in the same manner as we suppose he himself must feel, and our pity is increased in proportion to the height from whence he fell. On the contrary, we do not so strongly sympathize with one born in humbler circumstances and encountering accidental distress, so that while we melt for Belisarius we scarce give halfpence to the beggar who accosts us in the street. The one has our pity, the other our contempt. Distress, therefore, is the proper object of tragedy, since the great excite our pity by their fall, but not equally so of comedy, since the actors employed in it are originally so mean that they sink but little by their fall.

Since the first origin of the stage, tragedy and comedy have run in distinct channels and never till of late encroached upon the provinces of each other. Terence, who seems to have made the nearest approaches, yet always judiciously stops short before he comes to the downright pathetic; and yet he is even reproached by Cæsar for wanting the *vis comica*. All the other comic writers of antiquity aim only at rendering folly or vice ridiculous, but never exalt their characters into buskined pomp or make what Voltaire humourously calls a *Tradesman's Tragedy*.

Yet, notwithstanding this weight of authority and the universal practice of former ages, a new species of dramatic composition has been introduced under the name of *sentimental* comedy, in which the virtues of private life are exhibited rather than the vices exposed, and the distresses rather than the faults of mankind make our interest in the piece. These comedies have had of late great success, perhaps from their novelty and also from their flattering every man in his favourite foible. In these plays almost all the characters are good and exceedingly generous; they are lavish enough of their *tin* money on the stage, and though they want humour have abundance of sentiment and feeling. If they happen to have faults or foibles, the spectator is taught not only to pardon but to applaud them, in consideration of the goodness of their hearts, so that folly instead of being ridiculed is commended, and the comedy aims at touching our passions without the power of being truly pathetic; in this manner we are likely to lose one great source of entertainment on the stage, for while the comic poet is invading the province of the tragic muse, he leaves her lovely sister quite neglected. Of this however he is noway solicitous, as he measures his fame by his profits.

But it will be said that the theatre is formed to amuse mankind and that it matters little, if this end be answered, by what means it is obtained. If mankind find delight in weeping at comedy, it would be cruel to abridge them in that or any other innocent pleasure. If those pieces are denied the name of comedies, yet call them by any other name, and if they are delightful they are good. Their success, it will be said, is a mark of their merit, and it is only abridging our happiness to deny us an inlet to amusement.

These objections however are rather specious than solid. It is true that amusement is a great object of the theatre, and it will be allowed that these sentimental pieces do often amuse us; but the question is, whether the true comedy would not amuse us more. The question is, whether a character supported throughout a piece with its ridicule still attending would not give us more delight than this species of bastard tragedy, which only is applauded because it is new.

A friend of mine, who was sitting unmoved at one of these sentimental pieces, was asked how he could be so indifferent. "Why, truly," says he, "as the hero is but a tradesman, it is indifferent to me whether he be turned out of his counting-house on Fish-street Hill, since he will still have enough left to open shop in St. Giles's."

The other objection is as ill-grounded; for though we should give these pieces another name, it will not mend their efficacy. It will continue a kind of *mulish* production with all the defects of its opposite parents and marked with sterility. If we are permitted to make comedy weep, we have an equal right to make tragedy laugh, and to set down in blank verse the jests and repartees of all the attendants in a funeral procession.

But there is one argument in favour of sentimental comedy which will keep it on the stage in spite of all that can be said against it. It is, of all others, the most easily written. Those abilities that can hammer out a novel are fully sufficient for the production of a sentimental comedy. It is only sufficient to raise the characters a little, to deck out the hero with a ribband or give the heroine a title, then to put an insipid dialogue without character or humour into their mouths, give them mighty good hearts, very fine cloaths, furnish a new sett of scenes, make a pathetic scene or two, with a sprinkling of tender melancholy conversation through the whole, and there is no doubt but all the ladies will cry and all the gentlemen applaud.

Humour at present seems to be departing from the stage, and it will soon happen that our comic players will have nothing left for it but a fine coat and a song. It depends upon the audience whether they will actually drive those poor merry creatures from the stage, or sit at a play as gloomy as at the Tabernacle. It is not easy to recover an art when once lost; and it would be but a just punishment that, when by our being too fastidious we have banished humour from the stage, we should ourselves be deprived of the art of laughing.

The Citizen of the World

OR, LETTERS FROM A CHINESE PHILOSOPHER RESIDING IN LONDON
TO HIS FRIENDS IN THE EAST

[*The Citizen of the World,* published in 1762 in two small volumes, is a collection of "Chinese Letters" which first appeared in a daily newspaper, *The Public Ledger,* from January 1760 to August 1761. Goldsmith took advantage of the contemporary interest in the orient and was influenced by such books as Montesquieu's *Lettres Persanes,* which satirized European customs by having a foreigner describe them. The text of the present edition is based on the newspaper version, but the numbering of the letters and the descriptive headings derive from the first collected edition, corrected where necessary.]

LETTER ONE

Introduction. A character of the Chinese Philosopher.

To Mr. **** Merchant in London.

Sir, *Amsterdam, Oct. 21, 1759*
Yours of the 13th instant, covering two bills, one on Messrs. R. and D. value 478 1. 10s. and the other on Mr.****, value 285 1. duly came to hand, the former of which met with honour, but the other has been trifled with, and I am afraid will be returned protested.

The bearer of this is my friend, therefore let him be yours. He is a native of Honan in China, and one who did me signal services when he was a mandarine and I a factor at Canton. By frequently conversing with English there, he has learned some of the language, though intirely a stranger to your manners and customs. I am told he is a philosopher, I am sure he is an honest man; and that to you will be the best recommendation, next to the consideration of his being my friend. I am, Sir, yours, &c.

LETTER TWO

The arrival of the Chinese in London. His motives for the journey. Some description of the streets and houses.

From Lien Chi Altangi to ****, *Merchant in* Amsterdam.

Friend of my heart,   *London.*
May the wings of peace rest upon thy dwelling, and the shield of conscience preserve thee from misery and vice; for all thy favours accept my gratitude and esteem, the only tributes a poor philosophic wanderer like me can return; sure fortune is resolved to make me unhappy when she gives others a power of testifying their friendship by actions and leaves me only words to express the sincerity of mine.

I am perfectly sensible of the delicacy by which you endeavour to lessen your own merit and my obligations. By calling your late instances of friendship only a return for former favours, you would induce me to accept of ten times the equivalent.

The services I did you when at Canton, when I was the emperor's first slave, justice, humanity, and my office bade me perform; those you have done me since my arrival at Amsterdam, no laws obliged you to, no justice required, and even half your favours would have been greater than my most sanguine expectations.

The sum of money therefore which you privately conveyed into my baggage, when I was leaving Holland, and which I was ignorant of till my arrival in London, I must beg leave to return. You have been bred a merchant, and I was educated a scholar. You consequently love money better than I. You can find pleasure in superfluity, I am perfectly contented with what is sufficient; take therefore what is yours, it may give you some pleasure, even though you have no occasion to use it; my happiness it cannot improve, for I have already all that I want.

My passage by sea from Rotterdam to England was more painful to me than all the journies I ever made on land. I have traversed the immeasurable wilds of Mogul Tartary;

felt all the rigours of Siberian skies; have had my repose an hundred times disturbed by invading savages, and have seen without shrinking the desart sands rise like a troubled ocean all around me; but against these calamities I was armed with resolution. But in my passage to England, though nothing occurred that gave the mariners any uneasiness, yet to one who was never at sea before, all was a subject of astonishment and terror. To find the land disappear, to see our ship mount the waves quick as an arrow from the Tartar bow, to hear the wind howling through the cordage, and to feel a sickness which depresses even the spirits of the brave; these were unexpected distresses, and consequently assaulted me when off my guard.

You men of Europe think nothing of a voyage by sea. With us of China, a man who has been from sight of land is regarded upon his return with admiration ever after. I have known some provinces where there is not even a name for the ocean. What a strange people therefore am I got amongst, who have founded an empire on this unstable element, who build cities upon billows that rise higher than the mountains of Taskuti, and give laws to kingdoms beneath the equator.

Such accounts as these, I must confess it was, that first gave me a desire to see England, that indeed induced me to undertake a journey of seven hundred painful days, in order to examine their opulence, buildings, sciences, arts and manufactures. Judge then how great was my disappointment on entering London to see no signs of that opulence so much talked of abroad; wherever I turn, I am presented with a gloomy solemnity in the houses, the streets and the inhabitants; none of that beautiful gilding which makes a principal ornament in Chinese architecture. The streets of Pekin are sometimes strewed with gold leaf; very different are those of London: in the midst of their streets a great lazy puddle moves muddily along; heavy laden machines with wheels of unweildy thickness crowd up every passage; so that a stranger, instead of finding time for observation, is often happy if he has time to escape from being crushed to pieces.

The houses borrow very few ornaments from architecture; their chief decoration seems to be a paltry piece of painting, hung out at their doors or windows, which at once evinces their vanity and their poverty: their vanity, in each having one of those pictures exposed to public view; and their poverty, in being unable to get them better painted. The fancy of their painters also is equally deplorable in this respect. You'll scarce believe me when I assure you that I have seen five black lions and three blue boars in less than a circuit of half a mile; and yet you know that animals of these colours are no where to be found except in such wild imaginations.

From these circumstances in their buildings and from the dismal looks of some of the inhabitants, I am induced to conclude that the nation is actually poor; and that like the Persians, they make a splendid figure every where but at home. The proverb of Xixofou is that a man's riches may be seen in his eyes; if we judge by this rule of the English, there is not a poorer nation under the sun.

I have been here but two days, so will not be hasty in my decisions; such letters as I shall write to Fipsihi in Moscow I beg you'll endeavour to forward with all diligence; I shall send them open, in order that you may take copies or translations, as you are equally well acquainted with the Dutch and Chinese languages. Dear friend, think of my absence with regret, for I sincerely regret yours; even while I write, I lament our separation. Adieu.

LETTER THREE

The description of London continued. The luxury of the English. Its benefits. The fine gentleman. The fine lady.

From Lien Chi Altangi, to the care of Fipsihi, resident in Moscow; to be forwarded by the Russian caravan to Fum Hoam, first president of the ceremonial academy at Pekin in China.

Think not, O thou guide of my youth, that absence can impair my respect, or interposing trackless desarts can blot your reverend figure from my memory. The farther I travel I feel the pain of separation with more reluctance; those ties that bind me to my native country, and you, are still unbroken, while by every remove, I only drag a greater length of chain.

Could I find aught worth transmitting from so remote a

region as this to which I have wandered, I should gladly send it; but instead of this, you must be contented with a renewal of my former professions, and an imperfect account of a people with whom I yet am but superficially acquainted. The remarks of a man who has been but three days in the country can only be those obvious circumstances which force themselves upon the imagination: I consider myself here as a newly created Being introduced into a new world; every object strikes with wonder and surprise. The imagination, still unsatiated, seems the only active principle of the mind. The most trifling occurrence gives pleasure, till the gloss of novelty is worn away. Nor till we have ceased wondering can we possibly grow wise; it is then we call the reasoning principle to our aid, and compare those objects with each other which we before examined without reflection.

Behold me then in London, gazing at the strangers, and they at me; it seems they find somewhat absurd in my figure; and had I been never from home it is possible I might find an infinite fund of ridicule in theirs; but by long travelling I am taught to laugh at folly alone, and to find nothing truly ridiculous but [villainy and] vice.

When I had just quitted my native country, and crossed the Chinese wall, I thought every deviation from the customs and manners of China was a departing from nature: I smiled at the blue lips and red foreheads of the Tongusas. I could hardly contain when I saw the Daures dress their heads with horns, the Ostiacs powder their hair with red earth, and the Calmuck beauties trick out in all the finery of sheep-skin. But I soon perceived that the ridicule lay not in them but in me, and that I falsely condemned others for absurdity, because they happened to differ from my standard of perfection, which was founded in prejudice or partiality.

I find no pleasure therefore in taxing the English with departing from nature in their external appearance, which is all I yet know of their character; it is possible they only endeavour to improve her simple plan, since every extravagance in our dress proceeds from a desire of becoming more beautiful than nature made us; this is so harmless a vanity that I not only pardon but approve it. A desire to be more excellent than others is what actually makes us so, and as thousands find a livelihood in society by such appetites, none but the ignorant inveigh against them.

You are not insensible, most reverend Fum Hoam, what numberless trades, even among the Chinese, subsist by the harmless pride of each other. Your nose-borers, feet-swathers, tooth-stainers, eye brow pluckers, would all want bread, should their neighbours want vanity. Those vanities, however, employ much fewer hands in China than in England; a fine gentleman, or a fine lady, here dressed up to the fashion, seem scarcely to have a single limb or feature as nature has left it. They call in to their assistance fancy on every occasion, and think themselves finest when they most depart from what they really are.

To make a fine gentleman several trades are required, but chiefly a barber; you have undoubtedly heard of the Jewish champion all whose strength lay in his hair. One would think that the English were for placing all wisdom there. In order to appear a wise man, nothing more is requisite than to borrow hair from the heads of all his neighbours and clap it like a bush on his own: the distributors of their laws stick on such quantities that it is almost impossible, even in idea, to distinguish between their heads and their hair.

Those whom I have been now describing affect the gravity of the lion: those I am going to describe more resemble the tricks of the monkey. The barber, who still seems master of the ceremonies, cuts their hair not round the edges as with us, but close to the crown; and then with a composition of meal and hog's lard, plaisters the whole in such a manner as to make it impossible to distinguish whether he wears a cap or a plaister; to make the picture more perfectly striking, conceive the tail of some beast, a pig's tail for instance, appended to the back of his head, and reaching down to that place where other tails are generally seen to begin; thus betailed and bepowdered, he fancies he improves in beauty, dresses up his hard-featured face in smiles, and attempts to look hideously tender. Thus equipped, he is qualified to make love, and hopes for success more from the powder on the outside of his head than the sentiments within.

Yet when you consider what sort of a creature the fine lady

is, to whom he pays his addresses, it is not strange to find
him thus equipped in order to please her. She is herself every
whit as fond of powder, and tails, and ribbands, and hog's lard
as he: to speak my secret sentiments, most reverend Fum, the
ladies here are horridly ugly; I can hardly endure the sight of
them; they no way resemble the beauties of China; the Europeans have a quite different idea of beauty from us; when I
reflect on the small footed perfections of thy charming daughter, how is it possible I should have eyes for any other personal excellence. How very broad her face; how very short
her nose; how very little her eyes; how very thin her lips;
and how very black her teeth; the snow on the tops of Bao
is not fairer than her cheek; and her eye-brows are as small
as the thread of the finest silk. Here a lady with such perfections would be frightful. The Dutch and Chinese beauties, I
own, have some resemblance, but the English ladies are entirely different; red cheeks, big eyes, and teeth of a most
odious whiteness are every where to be seen; and then such
masculine feet as actually serve *some* of them for walking!

Yet uncivil as nature has been, they seem resolved to outdo
her in unkindness; they use white powder, blue powder, and
black powder, but never red powder, as among the Tartars, in
their hair.

They paint their faces not less than the Calmucks and stick
on, with spittle, little black patches on every part of the face,
except only the tip of the nose, which I never see with a
patch on it. You'll have a better idea of their manner of
placing these spots, when I have finished a map of an English
face patch'd up to the fashion, which perhaps I shall shortly
send to add to your curious collection of beasts, medals, and
monsters.

Thus far I have seen, and I have now one of their own
authors before me, who tells me something strange and which
I can hardly believe. His words are to this effect: "Most ladies
in this country have two faces; one face to sleep in, and
another to shew in company: the first face is generally reserv'd
for the husband and family at home, the other put on to
please strangers abroad; [the family face is often indifferent
enough, but the out-door one looks something better;] this
last is always made at the toilet, where whim, the looking-glass,

and the toad-eater sit in council and settle the complexion of the day."

I can't ascertain the truth of this remark; however, they seem to me to act upon very odd principles upon another occasion, since they wear more cloaths within doors than without; and a lady who seems to shudder at a breeze in her own apartment appears half naked in public. Adieu.

LETTER FOUR

English pride. Liberty. An instance of both. News papers. Politeness.

To the same.

The English seem as silent as the Japonese, yet vainer than the inhabitants of Siam. Upon my arrival I attributed their reserve to modesty which I now find had its origin in pride. Condescend to address them first and you are sure of their acquaintance; stoop to flattery and you conciliate their friendship and esteem. They bear hunger, cold, fatigue, and all the miseries of life without shrinking; danger only calls forth their fortitude; they even exult in calamity; but contempt is what they cannot bear. Contempt an Englishman fears more than death; he often flies to death as a refuge from its pressure; and dies when he fancies the world has ceased to esteem him.

This pride seems the source not only of their national vices, but of their national virtues also. An Englishman is taught to love his king as his friend, but to acknowledge no other master than the laws of his country. He despises those nations who, that one may be free, are all content to be slaves; who first lift a tyrant into terror, and then shrink beneath his power as if delegated from heaven. Liberty is ecchoed in all their assemblies, and thousands might be found ready to offer up their lives for the sound, though perhaps not one of all that thousand understands its meaning. The lowest mechanic however looks upon it as his duty to be a watchful guardian of his country's freedom, and often uses a language that might seem haughty, even in the mouth of the great emperor who claims kindred with the moon.

A few days ago, as I was passing by one of their prisons, I could not avoid stopping, in order to listen to a dialogue which

I thought might afford me some entertainment. The conversation was carried on between a debtor through the grate of his prison, a porter [who had stopped to rest his burthen] and a soldier at the window. The subject was a threatened invasion from France, and all seemed extreamly anxious how to rescue their country from impending danger. "For my part," cries the prisoner, "the greatest of my apprehension is for our freedom; if the French should conquer, what would become of English liberty. My dear Friends, liberty is the Englishman's prerogative; we must preserve that at the expence of our lives, of that the French shall never deprive us; it is not to be expected that men who are slaves themselves would preserve our freedom should they happen to conquer." "Ay, slaves," cries the porter, "they are all slaves, fit only to carry burthens every one of them. Before I would stoop to slavery, may this be my poison (and he held the goblet in his hand) may this be my poison— but I would sooner list for a soldier."

The soldier taking the goblet from his friend, with much awe fervently cried out, "Not our liberties but our religion would suffer by such a change: Ay, our religion, my friends; for may the Devil sink me into flames," (such was the solemnity of his adjuration) "if the French should come over, what would then become of our religion?" So saying, instead of a libation, he applied the goblet to his head, and confirmed his sentiments with every ceremony of sincere devotion.

In short, every man here pretends to be a politician; and even the fair sex are sometimes found to mix the severity of national altercation with the blandishments of love [and often become conquerors by more weapons of destruction than their eyes].

In order to indulge this universal propensity, each day there appears several broad leaves of paper, written all over with politics and hieroglyphics, and in order to see these, the tradesmen leave their shops with a curiosity not unlike that with which our artizans of China run out to see the emperor giving a spectacle of paper kites. When the populace have sufficiently gazed at one paper, there is another clapped up in its stead, and instead of a lanthorn at the tail, as in China, they sometimes furnish their papers with an eclipse or a blazing star.

But you must not imagine that they who compile these

papers have any actual knowledge of the politics or the government of the state they live in; they only collect their materials from the oracle of some coffee-house, which the oracle himself has gathered the night before from a beau at a gaming-table, who has himself pillaged his knowledge from a great man's porter, who has had his information from the great man's gentleman, who himself has invented the whole story for his own amusement the night preceding.

The English in general seem fonder of gaining the esteem than the love of those they converse with: this gives a formality to their amusements; their gayest conversations have something too wise for innocent relaxation; though in company you are seldom disgusted with the absurdity of a fool, you are seldom lifted into rapture by those strokes of vivacity which give instant pleasure, however they may pall upon recollection.

What they want, however, in gaiety, they make up by politeness. I know you smile at hearing me praise the English for their politeness: you who have heard very different accounts from the missionaries at Pekin, and have seen such a different behaviour in their merchants and seamen at Canton. But I must still repeat it, the English seem more polite than any of their neighbours: their great art in this respect lies in their endeavouring, while they oblige, to lessen the force of the favour. Other countries are fond of obliging strangers, but then they seem desirous that you should be sensible of the obligation. The English confer their kindness with an air of indifference, and give away benefits which they seem to despise.

Walking a few days ago between an English and a Frenchman into the suburbs of the city, we were overtaken by a heavy shower of rain. I was unprepared; but they had each large coats, which defended them from what seemed to me a perfect inundation. The Englishman seeing me shrink from the weather, accosted me thus: "Psha, man, what dost shrink at? here, take this coat; I don't want it; I find it no way useful to me; I had as lief be without it." The Frenchman began to shew his politeness in turn. "My dear friend," cries he, "why wont you oblige me by making use of my coat; you see how well it defends me from the rain; I should not chuse to part with it to others, but to such a friend as you, I could even part with my skin to do him service."

From such minute instances as these, most reverend Fum Hoam, I am sensible your sagacity will collect instruction. The volume of nature is the book of knowledge; and he becomes most wise who makes the most judicious selection. Adieu.

Lien Chi Altangi

LETTER FIVE

English passion for politics. A specimen of a news paper. Characteristic of the manners of different countries.

To the same.

I have already informed you of the singular passion of this nation for politics. An Englishman, not satisfied with finding by his own prosperity the contending powers of Europe properly balanced, desires also to know the precise value of every weight in either scale. To gratify this curiosity a leaf of political instruction is served up every morning with tea: When our politician has sufficiently feasted upon this, he repairs to a coffee-house, in order to ruminate upon what he has read and encrease his collection; from thence he proceeds to the ordinary, enquires what news, and treasuring up every acquisition at the tavern, he learns more, and carefully adds it to the rest, from whence he retires home, full of the important advices of the day. Awaking next morning, he finds the instructions of yesterday a collection of absurdity or palpable falshood. This one would think a mortifying repulse in the pursuit of wisdom; yet our politician no way discouraged, hunts on, in order to collect fresh materials and to be again disappointed.

I have often admired the commercial spirit which prevails over Europe; have been surprised to see them carry on a traffic with productions that an Asiatic stranger would deem entirely useless. It is a proverb in China that an European suffers not even his spittle to be lost; the maxim, however, is not sufficiently strong; since they sell even their Lies to great advantage, and every nation drives a considerable trade in this commodity with their neighbours.

For instance, suppose I am an English dealer in this way. I have only to ascend my work-house and manufacture a turbulent speech averred to be spoken in the senate, a report supposed to be dropt at court, a piece of scandal that strikes at a popular Mandarine, a secret treaty between two neighbouring powers, a piece of murder, a piece of criticism, and an horse race. When finished, these goods are baled up and consigned to my factor abroad, who sends me in return two battles, three sieges, an inundation, and a shrewd letter filled with dashes —— blanks   and stars **** of double meaning.

Thus you perceive that a single news paper is the joint manufacture of Europe; and he who would peruse it with a philosophical eye could perceive in every paragraph something characteristick of the nation to which it belongs. A map does not exhibit a more distinct view of the boundaries and situation of every country than its news does a picture of the genius and the morals of its inhabitants. The superstition and erroneous delicacy of Italy, the formality of Spain, the cruelty of Portugal, the fears of Austria, the confidence of Prussia, the levity of France, the avarice of Holland, the pride of England, the absurdity of Ireland, and the national partiality of Scotland, are all conspicuous in those diurnal publications.

But, perhaps, you may find more satisfaction in a real news paper than in my description of one; I shall therefore produce a specimen of a news paper, which may serve at once to exhibit the manner of writing and distinguish the characters of the various nations by which it is compos'd.

ITALY. We have had lately dug up here a curious Etruscan monument, though broke in two in the raising. The characters, it is true, are scarce visible; but Gimeracci, the learned antiquary, supposes it to have been erected in honour of Picus, one of the Latin kings, as one of the lines may be plainly distinguished to begin with a P. It is hoped this discovery will produce something valuable, as the literati of our twelve academies are deeply engaged in the disquisition.

PISA. Since father Fudgi, prior of St. Gilbert's, has gone to reside at Rome, no miracles have been performed at the shrine of St. Gilbert; the devout begin to grow uneasy, and some begin actually to fear that St. Gilbert has forsaken them [with the reverend father].

LUCCA. The administrators of our serene republic have

frequent conferences upon the part they shall take in the present commotions of Europe. Some are for sending a body of their troops, [consisting of one company of foot and six horsemen,] to make a diversion in favour of the empress-queen; and others are as strenuous asserters of the Prussian interest: what turn these debates may take, time only can discover. However, certain it is we shall send, at the opening of next campaign, seventy-five armed men, a commander in chief, and two drums of great experience.

SPAIN. Yesterday the new king shewed himself to his subjects, and after having staid half an hour in his balcony, retired to the royal apartment. The night concluded on this extraordinary occasion with illuminations, and other demonstrations of joy.

The queen is very beautiful and reckoned one of the first wits in Europe: she had a glorious opportunity of displaying the readiness of her invention and skill in repartee at court a few nights ago. The duke of Lerma, coming up to her with a low bow and a smile, and presenting her a nosegay set with diamonds, "Madam," cries he, "I'm your most obedient humble servant." "Oh, Sir," replies the queen (without any prompter or the least hesitation), "I'm very proud of the very great honour you do me." Upon which she made a low curtesy, and all the courtiers fell a laughing at the readiness of her reply.

LISBON. Yesterday we had an *auto da fé*, at which were burned three young women that were heretics, one of them of exquisite beauty, two Jews, and an old woman convicted of being a witch: One of the friars, who attended this last, reports that he saw the devil fly out of her at the stake in the shape of a flame of fire. The populace behaved on this occasion with great good humour, and sincere devotion.

Our *merciful Sovereign* has been for some time past recovered of his fright: though so atrocious an attempt deserved to exterminate half the nation, yet he has been graciously pleased to spare the lives of his subjects, and not above two hundred have been broke upon the wheel or otherwise executed upon this occasion.

VIENNA. We have received certain advices that a party of twenty thousand Austrians, having attacked a much superior body of Prussians, put them all to flight and took the rest prisoners of war.

BERLIN. We have received certain advices that a party of twenty thousand Prussians, having attacked a much superior body of Austrians, put them to flight and took a great number of prisoners, with their military chest, cannon, and baggage.

Though we have not succeeded this campaign to our wishes, yet when we think of him who commands us, we rest in security: while we sleep, our king is watchful for our safety.

PARIS. We shall soon strike a signal blow. We have seventeen flat-bottom'd boats at Havre. The people are in excellent spirits, and our ministers make no difficulty of raising the supplies.

We are all undone; the people are discontented to the last degree; the ministers are obliged to have recourse to the most rigorous methods to raise the expences of the war.

Our distresses are great; but madam Pompadour continues to supply our king, who is now growing old, with a fresh lady every night. His health, thank heaven, is still pretty well; nor is he in the least unfit, as was reported, for any kind of royal amusement. He was so frighted at the affair of Damien,[14] that his physicians were apprehensive lest his reason should suffer, but that wretch's tortures soon composed the kingly terrors of his breast.

ENGLAND. There was a great concourse of nobility this season at Newmarket. The French are preparing to invade us from Havre. Those, however, are only the efforts of a sinking nation, for Admiral Hawke has come up with them and drubbed them heartily. There will be a great route this evening at the house of her grace the Dutchess of Birmingham. [Wanted: an usher to an academy.—N.B. He must be able to read, dress hair, and must have had the small pox.[15]]

DUBLIN. We hear that there is a benevolent subscription on foot among the nobility and gentry of this kingdom, and that there is five hundred pounds already actually on foot, in order to encourage Black and All Black and the Padderen mare.[16] They are to start on the Curragh.

We hear from Germany that Prince Ferdinand has gained a complete victory, and has taken twelve kettle drums, five standards, and four waggons of ammunition prisoners of war.

The match between Laughin O'Swiney, Esq. and Miss Cicely Morrogho, who were married in our last, is entirely broke off.

EDINBURGH. We are positive when we say that Saunders M'Gregor, who was lately executed for horse-stealing, is not a Scotchman, but born in Carrickfergus.

LETTER EIGHT

The Chinese deceived by a prostitute, in the streets of London.

To the same.

How insupportable! oh thou partaker of heavenly wisdom, would be this separation, this immeasurable distance from my friends, were I not able thus to delineate my heart upon paper, and to send thee daily a map of my mind. For this invention I honour the manes of that great emperor who first instituted marks to represent our ideas, who humaniz'd mankind and taught that the most holy was to come from the west.

I am every day better reconciled to the people among whom I reside, and begin to fancy that in time I shall find them more opulent, more charitable, and more hospitable than I at first imagined. I begin to learn somewhat of their manners and customs, and to see reasons for several deviations which they make from us, from whom all other nations derive their politeness as well as their original.

In spite of taste, in spite of prejudice, I now therefore begin to think their women tolerable; I can now look on a languishing blue eye without disgust, and pardon a set of teeth, even though whiter than ivory. I now begin to fancy there is no universal standard for beauty in this city. The truth is, the manners of the ladies are so very open and so vastly engaging that I am inclined to pass over the more glaring defects of their persons, in consideration of the more solid, yet latent beauties of the mind; what tho' they want black teeth or are deprived of the allurements of feet no bigger than my thumb, yet still they have souls, my friend, such souls, so free, so pressing, so hospitable, and so engaging——I have received more invitations in the streets of London from the sex in one night than I have met with at Pekin in twelve revolutions of the moon.

Every evening as I return home from my usual solitary

excursions, I am met by several of those well disposed daughters of hospitality, at different times and in different streets,
richly dressed, and with minds not less noble than their appearance. You know that nature has indulged me with no very
agreeable figure; yet are they too generous to object to my
homely appearance; they feel no repugnance to my broad face
and flat nose. No, they perceive that I am a stranger, and
that alone is a sufficient recommendation. They even seem
to think it their duty to do the honours of their country by
every act of complaisance in their power to bestow. One takes
me under the arm and in a manner forces me along; another
catches me round the neck and desires to partake in this office
of hospitality; while a third, kinder still, invites me to refresh
my spirits with a glass of wine. Wine is in England reserved
only for the rich, yet here even wine is given away to the
stranger!

A few nights ago, one of those generous creatures, dressed
all in white and flaunting like a meteor by my side, attended
me home to my own apartment. She seemed charmed with
the elegance of the furniture and the convenience of my situation. (And well indeed she might, for I have hired an apartment for not less than two shillings of their money every
week.) But her civility did not rest here; for at parting, being
desirous to know the hour, and perceiving my watch out of
order, she kindly took it to be repaired by a relation of her
own, which you may imagine will save me some expence, while
it costs her nothing. I shall have it back in a few days when
mended and am preparing a proper speech expressive of my
gratitude upon the occasion: "Celestial excellence," will I say,
"I am happy in having found out, after many painful adventures, the land of innocence, and a people of humanity: I may
rove into other climes, and converse with nations yet unknown,
but where shall I meet a soul of such purity as that which resides in thy breast! Sure thou hast been nurtured by the bill of
the Shin Shin, or suck'd the breasts of the provident Gin
Hiung. The melody of thy voice could rob the Chong Fou of
her whelps, or inveigle the Boh Chou that lives amidst the
waters. Thy servant shall ever retain a sense of thy favours;
and one day boast of thy virtue, sincerity, and truth, among
the daughters of China."

LETTER NINE

The licentiousness of the English, with regard to women. A character of a woman's man.

To the same.

I have been deceived! she whom I fancied a daughter of Paradise has proved to be one of the infamous disciples of Lao. What I have lost is but a trifle; what I have gain'd is the consolation of having at last discovered a deceiver. I once more, therefore, relax into my former indifference with regard to the English ladies, they once more begin to appear disagreeable in my eyes. Thus is my whole time passed in forming conclusions which the next minute's experience may probably destroy; one moment becomes a comment on the preceding, and serves to teach me rather humility than wisdom.

Their laws and religion forbid the English to keep more than one woman. I therefore concluded that prostitutes were banished from society. I was deceived; every man here keeps as many wives as he can maintain; the laws are [cemented with blood,] praised and disregarded. The very Chinese, whose religion allows him two wives, takes not half the liberties of an Englishman in this particular. The English laws may be compared to the books of the Sybils; they are held in great veneration, but seldom read or seldomer understood; even those who pretend to be their guardians dispute about the meaning of many of them, and confess their ignorance of others. The law therefore which commands them to have but one wife is strictly observed only by those for whom one is more than sufficient, or by such as have not money to buy two. As for the rest, they violate it publicly, and some glory in its violation. They seem to think like the Persians that they give evident marks of manhood by encreasing their seraglio. A mandarine therefore here generally keeps four wives, a gentleman three, and a stage-player two. As for the magistrates, the country justices and squires are employed in debauching young virgins, for the town, and the city justices are employed in sending them to the house of correction. Thus they play into each others hands and make work for each other.

From such a picture you will be apt to conclude that he who

employs four ladies for his amusement has four times as much constitution to spare as he who is contented with one; that a Mandarin is much cleverer than a gentleman, and a gentleman than a player; and yet it is quite the reverse; a Mandarine is frequently supported on spindle shanks, appears emaciated by luxury, and is obliged to have recourse to variety, merely from the weakness, not the vigour of his constitution, and the number of his wives is the most equivocal symptom of his virility.

Beside the country squires, there are also another set of men whose whole employment consists in corrupting beauty, wherever they are admitted; these the silly part of the fair sex call amiable; the more sensible part of them, and all the men, however, give them the title of abominable. You will probably demand what are the talents of a man who is thus caressed by the majority of the opposite sex; what talents or what beauty is he possessed of superior to the rest of his fellows. To answer you directly, he has neither talents or beauty, but then he is possessed of impudence and assiduity. With these two qualifications men of all ages and all kinds of person and face may commence admirers. I have even been told of men who made professions of expiring for love when all the world could perceive they were going to die of old age: and what is more surprising still, such men in the decline of life are generally most infamously successful.

As we sometimes, however, talk in China of the twelve beatitudes of Confucius, the three excellencies of Quangti, or the five tranquilities of Lao, permit me to recite the ten perfections of a Dangler, the appelation by which creatures of this character are distinguished from men.

He employs three hours each morning in dressing his head, by which is understood only his hair.

He is a professed admirer, not of any particular lady, but of the whole sex.

He is to suppose every lady has caught cold every night, which gives him an opportunity of calling to see how she does the next morning.

He is upon all occasions to shew himself in very great pain for the ladies; if a lady drops even a pin, he is to fly in order to present it to her.

He never speaks to a lady without advancing his mouth to

her ear, by which he frequently addresses more senses than one.

Upon proper occasions he looks excessively tender. This is performed by laying his hand upon his heart, shutting his eyes, and shewing his teeth.

He is excessively fond of dancing a minuet with the ladies, by which is only meant walking round the floor eight or ten turns with his hat on, affecting great gravity, and sometimes looking tenderly on his partner.

He never affronts any man himself, and never resents an affront from another.

He has an infinite variety of small talk upon all occasions, and laughs when he has nothing more to say.

Such is the killing creature who prostrates himself to the sex till he has undone them; all whose submissions are the effects of design, and who to please the ladies almost becomes himself a lady.

LETTER TWELVE

The funeral solemnities of the English. Their passion for flattering epitaphs.

To the same.

From the funeral solemnities of the Daures, who think themselves the politest people in the world, I must make a transition to the funeral solemnities of the English, who think themselves as polite as they. The numberless ceremonies which are used here when a person is sick appear to me so many evident marks of fear and apprehension. Ask an Englishman, however, whether he is afraid of death, and he boldly says no; but see his behaviour in circumstances of approaching sickness and you will find his actions give his assertions the lie.

The Chinese are very sincere in this respect; they hate to die, and they confess their terrors: a great part of their life is spent in preparing things proper for their funeral; a poor artizan shall spend half his income in providing himself a tomb twenty years before he wants it; and denies himself the necessaries of life, that he may be amply provided for when he shall want them no more.

People of distinction here really deserve pity, for they die in circumstances of the most extreme distress. It is an established rule never to let a man know that he is dying: physicians are sent for, the clergy are called, and every thing passes in mute solemnity round the sick bed; the patient is in agonies, looks round for pity, yet not a single creature will say that he is dying. If he is possessed of fortune, his relations entreat him to make his will, as it will restore the tranquillity of his mind. He is desired to undergo the rites of the church, for decency requires it. His friends take their leave only because they don't care to see him in pain. In short, an hundred stratagems are used to make him do what he might have been induced to perform only by being told: *Sir, you are past all hopes, and had as good think decently of dying.*

Besides all this, the chamber is darkened, the whole house ecchoes to the cries of the wife, the lamentations of the children, the grief of the servants, and the sighs of friends. The bed is surrounded with priests and doctors in black, and flambeaux emit a yellow gloom, instead of the light of day. Where is the man, how intrepid soever, that would not shrink at such a gloomy solemnity? For fear of affrighting their expiring friends, the English practise all that can fill them with terror. Strange effect of human prejudice thus to torture merely from mistaken tenderness!

You see, my friend, what a strange contradiction there is in the tempers of those islanders; when prompted by ambition, revenge, or disappointment, they meet death with the utmost resolution; the very man who in his bed would have trembled at the aspect of a doctor, shall go with intrepidity to attack a bastion, or deliberately nooze himself up in a halter.

The passion of the Europeans for magnificent interments is equally strong with that of the Chinese. When a tradesman dies, his frightful face is painted up by an undertaker and he is placed in a proper situation to receive company; and this is called lying in state. To this disagreeable spectacle all the idlers in town flock, and learn to loath the wretch dead whom they despised when living. In this manner you see some who would have refused a shilling to save the life of their dearest friend, bestow thousands on adorning their putrid carcass. I have been told of a fellow who grown rich by the price of blood, ordered a magnificent funeral, left it in his will that he should lie in state, and thus involuntarily gibbeted himself into infamy, who might have otherwise quietly retired into oblivion.

When the person is buried, the next care is to make his epitaph; they are generally reckoned the best which flatter most; such relations therefore who have received most benefits from the defunct discharge this friendly office and express their joy in the warmest strains of monumental gratitude. When we read those monumental histories of the dead, it may be justly said that *all men are equal in the dust;* for they all appear equally remarkable for being the most sincere Christians, the most benevolent neighbours, and the honestest men of their time.[17] To go thro' an European cemetery one would be apt to wonder how mankind could have so basely degenerated from such excellent ancestors; every tomb pretends to claim your reverence and regret; some are praised for piety in those inscriptions who never entered the temple until they were dead; some are praised for being excellent poets, who were never mentioned when living except for their dulness; others for sublime orators, who were never known except by their impudence; and others still for military atchievements, who were never in any other skirmishes but those of drink. Some even make epitaphs for themselves, and bespeak the readers good will. It were indeed to be wish'd that every man would early learn in this manner to make his own; that he would draw it up in terms as flattering as possible; and that he would make it the employment of his whole life to deserve it!

I have not yet been in a place called Westminster Abbey, but soon intend to visit it. There I am told I shall see justice done to deceased merit; none, I am told, are permitted to be buried there but such as have adorned as well as improved mankind. There no intruders by the influence of friends or fortune presume to mix their unhallowed ashes with philosophers, heroes, and poets. I am told nothing but true merit has a place in that awful sanctuary: the guardianship of the tombs is committed to several reverend priests, who are never guilty for a superior reward of taking down the names of good men to make room for others of equivocal character, who never prophane the sacred walls with pageants that posterity cannot know or shall blush to own.

I ever was of opinion that sepulchral honours of this kind should be considered as a national concern and not trusted to the care of the priests of any country, how respectable soever; but from the conduct of the reverend personages, whose disinterested patriotism I have been now describing, I am taught to retract my former sentiments. It is true, the Spartans and the Persians made a fine political use of this sepulchral vanity; they permitted none to be thus interred who had not fallen in the vindication of their country; a monument thus became a real mark of distinction, it nerved the heroe's arm with tenfold vigour; for he surely must fight without fear who only fights for a grave.—Adieu.

LETTER THIRTEEN

An account of Westminster Abbey.

From the same.

I am just returned from Westminster-abbey, the place of sepulture for the philosophers, heroes, and kings of England. What a gloom do monumental inscriptions and all the venerable remains of deceased merit inspire! Imagine you behold a temple marked with the hand of antiquity, solemn as religious awe, [adorned with all the magnificence of barbarous profusion,] dim windows, fretted pillars, long colonades, and dark cielings. Think then, O my friend, what were my sensations at being introduced to such a scene. I stood in the midst of the temple and threw my eyes round on the walls which were filled with the statues, the inscriptions, and the monuments of the dead.

Alas, I said to myself, how does pride attend the puny child of dust even to the grave! Even I, humble as I am, possess more consequence in the present scene than the greatest dead heroe of them all; they have toiled for an hour to gain a transient immortality and are at length retired to the grave, where they have no attendant but the worm, none to flatter but the epitaph. Yet it is the duty of every good government to turn this silly pride to its own advantage, to grow strong in the aggregate from the weakness of every individual.

As I was indulging such reflections, a gentleman dressed in black, perceiving me to be a stranger, came up, entered into conversation, and politely offered to be my instructor and guide through the temple. "If any monument," said he, "should particularly excite your curiosity, I shall endeavour to satisfy your questions as far as I am able." I accepted with thanks the gentleman's offer, adding that I was come to observe the policy, the wisdom, and the justice of the English, in conferring rewards upon deceased merit. "If adulation like this," continued I, "be properly conducted, as it can no ways injure those who are flattered, so it may be a glorious incentive to those who desire to be flattered. If none but the truly great have a place in this awful repository, a temple like this will give the finest lessons of morality and be a strong incentive to true ambition. I am told that none have a place here but characters of the most distinguished merit." The man in black seemed impatient at my observations, so I discontinued my remarks, and we walked on together to take a view of every particular monument in order as it lay.

As the eye is naturally caught by the finest monuments, I could not avoid being particularly curious about one which to me appeared more beautiful than ordinary. "That," said I to my guide, "I take to be the tomb of some very great man indeed. By the peculiar excellence of the workmanship and the magnificence of the design this must be a trophy raised to the memory of some king who has saved his country from ruin, or law-giver who reduced his fellow-citizens from anarchy into just subjection——" "It is not requisite," replied my companion smiling, "to have such qualifications in order to have a very fine monument here. More humble abilities will suffice." "What, I suppose then the gaining two or three battles or the taking half a score towns is thought a sufficient qualification?" "Gaining battles, or taking towns," replied the man in black, "are very pretty things; but a gentleman may have a very fine monument here without ever seeing a battle or a siege." "This then is the monument of some poet, I presume, of one whose wit has gained him immortality?" "No, sir," replied my guide, "the gentleman who lies here never made verses; and as for wit, he despised it in others because he had none himself." "Pray tell me then in a word," said I peevishly, "what is the great man who lies here particularly remarkable for?" "Remarkable, sir!" said my companion; "why, sir, the gentleman that lies here is remarkable, very remarkable—— for a tomb in Westminster-abbey." "But how the plague has he got here? I fancy he could never bribe the guardians of the temple to give him a place. Was he not ashamed to be seen among company, where even moderate merit would look like infamy?" "I suppose," replied the man in black, "the gentleman was rich, his friends consequently told him he was great and he readily believed them; the guardians of the temple, as they got by the self-delusion, were ready to believe him; so he paid his money for a fine monument; and the workman, as you see, has made him one. Think not, however, that this gentleman is singular in his desire of being buried among the great; there are several others in the temple who, hated and shunned by the great while alive, have come here, however, fully resolved to keep them company now they are dead."

As we walked along to a particular part of the temple, "there," says the gentleman, pointing with his finger, "that is the poets corner; there you see the monuments of Shakespear, and Milton, and Prior, and Drayton." "Drayton," I replied, "I never heard of him before, but I have been told of one Pope; is he there?" "It is time enough," replied my guide, "these hundred years; he is not long dead, people have not done hating him yet." "Strange," cried I, "can any be found to hate a man whose life was wholly spent in entertaining and instructing his fellow creatures!" "Yes," says my guide, "they hate him for that very reason. There are a set of men called answerers of books, who take upon them to watch the republic of letters, and distribute reputation by the sheet; they somewhat resemble the eunuchs in a seraglio, who are incapable of giving pleasure themselves, and hinder those that would. These answerers have no other employment but to cry out *Dunce,* and *Scribbler,* to praise the dead and revile the living, to grant a man of confessed abilities some small share of merit, to applaud twenty blockheads in order to gain the reputation of candour, and to revile the moral character of the man whose writings they

cannot injure. Such wretches are kept in pay by some mercenary bookseller, or more frequently the bookseller himself
takes this dirty work off their hands, as all that is required is to
be very abusive and very dull; every Poet of any genius is sure
to find such enemies; he feels, though he seems to despise their
malice; they make him miserable here, and in the pursuit of
empty fame, at last he gains solid anxiety."

"Is this the case with every poet I see here?" "Yes, with
every mother's son of them, except he happen'd to be born a
mandarine. If he has much money, he may buy reputation
from your book answerers, as well as a monument from the
guardians of the temple."

"But are there not some men of distinguished taste, as in
China, who are willing to patronize men of real merit and
soften the rancour of malevolent dulness?"

"I own there are many," replied the man in black, "but, alas!
Sir, the book answerers croud about them and call themselves
the writers of books; the patron has not abilities to distinguish;
thus poets are kept at a distance, while their enemies eat up all
their rewards at the mandarine's table."

Leaving this part of the temple, we made up to an iron gate,
thro' which my companion told me we were to pass in order to
see the monuments of the kings. Accordingly I marched up
without further ceremony and was going to enter, when a
person who held the gate in his hand told me I must pay first.
I was surprised at such a demand and asked the man whether
the people of England kept a *shew?* Whether the paltry sum he
demanded was not a national reproach? Whether it was not
more to the honour of the country to let their magnificence or
their antiquities be openly seen, than thus meanly to tax a
curiosity which tended to their own honour? "As for your
questions," replied the gate-keeper, "to be sure they may be
very right, because I don't understand them, but as for that
there three-pence, I farm it from one, who rents it from another, who hires it from a third, who leases it from the guardians of the temple." I expected upon paying here to see something extraordinary, since what I had seen for nothing filled
me with so much surprize; but in this I was disappointed; there
was little more to be seen within than black coffins, rusty armour, tatter'd standards, and some few slovenly figures in wax.

I was sorry I had paid, but I comforted myself by considering it would be my last payment. A person attended us, who without once blushing told an hundred lies; he talked of a lady who died by pricking her finger, of a king with a golden head, and twenty such pieces of absurdity; "Look ye there, gentlemen," says he, pointing to an old oak chair, "there's a curiosity for ye; in that chair the kings of England were crowned, you see also a stone underneath,[18] and that is Jacob's pillow." I could see no curiosity either in the oak chair or the stone; could I, indeed, behold one of the old kings of England seated in the one, or Jacob's head laid upon the other, there might be something curious in the sight; but as it was, there was no more reason for my surprize than if I should pick a stone from their streets and call it a curiosity, because one of their kings happened to tread upon it as he passed that way.

From hence our conductor led us through several dark walks and winding ways, uttering lies, talking to himself, and flourishing a wand which he held in his hand. He reminded me of the black magicians of Kobi. After we had been almost fatigued with the variety of objects, he at last desired me to consider attentively a certain suit of armour, which seemed to shew nothing remarkable. "This armour," said he, "belonged to general Monk." "Very surprising, that a general should wear armour." "And pray," added he, "observe this cap, this is general Monk's cap." "Very strange, indeed, very strange, that a general should have a cap also! Pray friend, what might this cap have cost originally?" "That, Sir," says he, "I don't know, but this cap is all the wages I have for my trouble." "A very small recompence, truly," said I. "Not so very small," replied he, "for every gentleman puts some money into it, and I spend the money." "What, more money! still more money!" "Every gentleman gives something, sir." "I'll give thee nothing; the guardians of the temple should pay you your wages, friend, and not permit you to squeeze thus from every spectator. When we pay our money at the door to see a shew, we never give more as we are going out. Sure the guardians of the temple can never think they get enough. Shew me the gate; if I stay longer, I may probably meet with more beggars."

Thus leaving the temple precipitately, I returned to my

lodgings, in order to ruminate over what was great and to despise what was mean in all that I had seen.

LETTER SEVENTEEN

Of the war now carried on between France and England, with its frivolous motives.

From the same.

Were an Asiatic politician to read the treaties of peace and friendship that have been annually making for more than an hundred years among the inhabitants of Europe, he would probably be surpriz'd how it should ever happen that christian princes could quarrel among each other. Their compacts for peace are drawn up with the utmost precision and ratified with the greatest solemnity; to these each party promises a sincere and inviolable obedience, and all wears the appearance of open friendship and unreserved reconciliation.

Yet, notwithstanding those treaties, the people of Europe are almost continually at war. There is nothing more easy than to break a treaty ratified in all the usual forms, and yet neither party be the aggressor. One side, for instance, breaks a trifling article by mistake; the opposite party upon this makes a small but premeditated reprisal; this brings on a return of greater from the other; both sides complain of injuries and infractions; war is declar'd; they beat, are beaten; some two or three hundred thousand men are killed, they grow tired, leave off just where they began; and so sit cooly down to make new treaties.

The English and French seem to place themselves foremost among the champion states of Europe. Though parted by a narrow sea, yet are they entirely of opposite characters; and from their vicinity are taught to fear and admire each other. They are at present engaged in a very destructive war, have already spilled much blood, are excessively irritated against each other, and all upon account of one side's desiring to wear greater quantities of *furs* than the other.[19]

The pretext of the war is about some lands a thousand leagues off; a country cold, desolate, and hideous; a country belonging to a people who were in possession for time immemorial. The savages of Canada claim a property in the country in dispute; they have all the pretensions which long possession can confer. Here they had reigned for ages without rivals in dominion, and knew no enemies but the prowling bear or insidious tyger; their native forests produced all the necessaries of life, and they found ample luxury in the enjoyment. In this manner they might have continued to live to eternity, had not the English been informed that those countries produced furs in great abundance. From that moment the country became an object of desire; it was found that furs were things very much wanted in England; the ladies edged some of their cloaths with furs, and muffs were worn both by gentlemen and ladies. In short, furs were found indispensably necessary for the good of the state: and the king was consequently petitioned to grant the country of Canada and all the savages belonging to it to the subjects of England, in order to have the people supplied with proper quantities of this necessary commodity.

So reasonable a request was immediately complied with, and large colonies were sent abroad to procure furs and take possession of the country. The French who were equally in want of furs (for they were fond of muffs and tippets as well as the English) made the very same request to their monarch and met with the same gracious reception. Wherever the French landed, they called the country their own; and the English took possession wherever they came, upon the same equitable pretensions. The harmless savages made no opposition; and could the intruders have agreed together, they might peaceably have shared this desolate country between them. But they quarrelled about the boundaries of their settlements, about grounds and rivers to which neither side could shew any other right than that of power, and which neither could occupy but by usurpation. Such is the contest that no honest man can heartily wish success to either party.

The war has continued for some time with various success. At first the French seemed victorious; but the English have of late dispossessed them of the whole country in dispute. Think not, however, that success on one side is the harbinger of peace: on the contrary, both parties must be heartily tired to effect even a temporary reconciliation. It should seem the business of the victorious party to offer terms of peace; but there are many in England who, encouraged by success, are for still protracting the war.

The best English politicians, however, are sensible that to keep their present conquests would be rather a burthen than an advantage to them, rather a diminution of their strength than an encrease of power. It is in the politic as in the human constitution; if the limbs grow too large for the body, their size, instead of improving, will diminish the vigour of the whole. The colonies should always bear an exact proportion to the mother country; when they grow populous, they grow powerful, and by becoming powerful, they become independent; thus subordination is destroyed, and a country is swallowed up in the extent of its own dominions. The Turkish empire would be more formidable, were it less extensive— were it not for those countries which it can neither command nor give entirely away, which it is obliged to protect but from which it has no power to exact obedience.

Yet, obvious as these truths are, there are many Englishmen who are for transplanting new colonies, for peopling the desarts of America with the refuse of their countrymen, and (as they express it) with the waste of an exuberant nation. And who are those unhappy creatures who are to be thus sent over? Not the sickly, for they are unwelcome guests abroad as well as at home; nor the idle, for they would starve as well behind the Appalachian mountains as in the streets of this metropolis. This refuse is composed of the laborious and enterprising, of men who can be serviceable to their country at home, men who ought to be regarded as the sinews of the people, and cherished with every degree of political indulgence. And what are the commodities which this colony, when establish'd, are to produce in return? Raw silk, hemp, and tobacco. England, therefore, must make an exchange of her best and bravest subjects for raw silk, hemp, and tobacco; their hardy veterans and honest tradesmen must be truck'd for a box of snuff or a silk petticoat. Strange absurdity! Sure the politics of the Daures are not more strange, who sell their religion, their wives, and their liberty for a glass bead or a paltry looking-glass. Adieu.

LETTER EIGHTEEN

The story of the Chinese Matron.

From the same.

The English love their wives with much passion, the Hollanders with much prudence. The English when they give their hands, frequently give their hearts; the Dutch give the hand, but keep the heart wisely in their own possession. The English love with violence, and expect violent love in return; the Dutch are satisfied with the slightest acknowledgments, for they give little away. The English expend many of the matrimonial comforts in the first year; the Dutch frugally husband out their pleasures, and are always constant because they are always indifferent.

There seems very little difference between a Dutch bridegroom and a Dutch husband. Both are equally possessed of the same cool unexpecting serenity; they can see neither Elysium nor Paradise behind the curtain; and *Yiffrow*[20] is not more a goddess on the wedding night than after twenty years matrimonial acquaintance. On the other hand, many of the English marry in order to have one happy month in their lives; they seem incapable of looking beyond that period; they unite in hopes of finding rapture, and disappointed in that, disdain ever to accept of happiness. From hence we see open hatred ensue; or what is worse, concealed disgust under the appearance of fulsome endearment. Much formality, great civility, and studied compliments are exhibited in public; cross looks, sulky silence, or open recrimination, fill up their hours of private entertainment.

Hence I am taught, whenever I see a new married couple more than ordinarily fond before faces, to consider them as attempting to impose upon the company or themselves, either hating each other heartily, or consuming that stock of love in the beginning of their course, which should serve them through their whole journey. Possessions, caresses, and open endearments are very equivocal marks of passion; and neither side should expect those instances of kindness which are inconsistent with true freedom or happiness to bestow. Love, when founded in the heart, will shew itself in a thousand unpremeditated sallies of fondness; but every cool deliberate exhibition of the passion, only argues little understanding, or great insincerity.

Choang was the fondest husband and Hansi the most endearing wife in all the kingdom of Korea: they were a pattern of conjugal bliss; the inhabitants of the country around saw and envied their felicity; wherever Choang came, Hansi was sure to follow; and in all the pleasures of Hansi Choang was admitted a partner. They walked hand in hand wherever they appeared, kissing, embracing, and shewing every mark of mutual satisfaction.

Their love was so great that it was thought nothing could interrupt their mutual peace, when an accident happened which, in some measure, diminished the husband's assurance of his wife's fidelity; for love so refin'd as his was subject to a thousand little disquietudes.

Happening to go one day alone among the tombs that lay at some distance from his house, he there perceived a lady dressed in the deepest mourning, (being cloathed all over in white) fanning the wet clay that was raised over one of the graves with a large fan, which she held in her hand. Choang, who had early been taught wisdom in the school of Lao the law-giver, was unable to assign a cause for her present employment; and coming up, civilly demanded the reason. "Alas," replied the lady, her eyes bathed in tears; "how is it possible to survive the loss of my husband, who lies buried in this grave; he was the best of men, the tenderest of husbands; with his dying breath he bid me never marry again till the earth over his grave should be dry; and here you see me steadily resolving to obey his will and endeavouring to dry it with my fan. It is now almost dry. I have employed two whole days in fulfilling his commands and am determined not to marry till they are punctually obeyed, even though that should not happen these three days."

Choang, who was struck with the widow's beauty, could not, however, avoid smiling at her haste to be married; but, concealing the cause of his mirth, civilly invited her home; adding that he had a wife who might be capable of giving her some consolation. As soon as he and his guest were returned, he imparted to Hansi in private what he had seen and could not avoid expressing his uneasiness that such might be his own case if his dearest wife should one day happen to survive him.

It is impossible to describe Hansi's resentment at so unkind a suspicion, as her passion for him was not only great but extremely delicate. She employ'd tears, anger, frowns, and exclamations, to chide his ill nature; the widow herself was inveigh'd against; and Hansi declared she was resolved never to sleep under the same roof with a wretch who, like her, could be guilty of such barefac'd inconstancy. The night was cold and stormy; however, the stranger was obliged to seek another lodging, for Choang was not disposed to resist, and Hansi would have her way.

The widow had scarce been gone an hour when an old disciple of Choang's, whom he had not seen for many years before, came to pay him a visit. He was received with the utmost ceremony, placed in the most honourable seat at supper, and the wine began to circulate with great freedom. Choang and Hansi exhibited open marks of mutual tenderness and unfeigned reconciliation: nothing could equal their apparent happiness; so fond an husband, so obedient a wife were no where else to be seen. When, lo! their happiness was at once disturbed by a most fatal accident. Choang fell lifeless in an apoplectic fit upon the floor. Every method was used, but in vain, for his recovery. Hansi was at first inconsolable for his death: after some hours, however, she found spirits to read the will. The ensuing day she began to moralize and talk wisdom; the next day she was able to comfort the young disciple; and, on the third, to shorten a long story, they both agreed to be married.

There was now no longer mourning in the apartments; the body of Choang was now thrust into an old coffin and placed in one of the meanest rooms, there to lie unattended until the time prescribed by law for his interment. In the mean time Hansi and the young disciple were arrayed in the most magnificent habits; the bride wore in her nose a jewel of immense price, and her lover was dressed in all the finery of his former master, and had a pair of artificial whiskers that reached almost down to his toes. The hour of their nuptials was arrived; the whole family sympathized with their approaching happiness; the apartments were brightened up with lights that diffused the most exquisite perfume and a lustre more bright than noon day. The lady expected her youthful lover from an inner apartment with impatience, when his servant, approaching with terror in his countenance, informed her that his master was fallen into a fit which would certainly be mortal, unless the heart of a man newly killed could be obtained and applied to his forehead. Hansi with the utmost consternation demanded whether the heart of a man lately dead would not do. It was answered that it might possibly effect a cure, but that dispatch was absolutely requisite. She scarce waited to hear the end of his reply, when, tucking up her cloaths, and running with a mattock in her hand to the coffin where Choang lay, she struck the lid with the utmost violence. In a few blows the coffin flew open, when the body which to all appearance had been dead, began to move. Terrified at the sight, Hansi dropped the mattock, and Choang walked out, astonished at his own situation, at his wife's unusual magnificence, and her more amazing surprise. He went among the apartments, but could not conceive the cause of so much splendor. He was not long in suspense before his domestics informed him of every transaction since he first became insensible. He could scarce believe what they told him and went in pursuit of Hansi herself in order to receive more certain information or to reproach her infidelity. But she prevented his reproaches: he found her weltering in blood; for she had stabbed herself to the heart, being unable to survive her shame and disappointment.

Choang, being a philosopher, was too wise to make any loud lamentations; he thought it best to bear his loss with serenity; so, mending up the old coffin where he had lain himself, he placed his faithless spouse in his room; and, unwilling that so many nuptial preparations should be expended in vain, the same night married the widow with the large fan.

As they both were apprised of the foibles of each other before-hand, they knew how to excuse them after marriage. They lived together for many years in great tranquility, and not expecting rapture, found content.

LETTER NINETEEN

The English method of treating women caught in adultery. The Russian method.

To the same.

The gentleman dressed in black who was my companion thro' Westminster Abbey came yesterday to pay me a visit; and after drinking tea, we both resolved to take a walk together in order to enjoy the freshness of the country, which now begins to resume its verdure. Before we got out of the suburbs, however, we were stopped in one of the streets by a crowd of people who were gathered in a circle round a man and his wife, who seemed too loud and too angry to be understood. The people were highly pleased with the dispute, which upon enquiry we found to be between Dr. Carbuncle an apothecary, and his wife. The doctor, it seems, coming unexpectedly into his wife's apartment, found a gentleman there in circumstances even too strong for his suspicion.

The doctor, who was a person of nice honour, resolving to revenge the flagrant insult, immediately flew to the chimney-piece, and taking down a rusty blunderbuss, drew the trigger upon the defiler of his bed, and would have shot him through the head, but that the piece had not been charged for many years. The gallant made a shift to escape through the window, but the lady still remained; and as she well knew her husband's temper, undertook to manage the quarrel alone. He was furious, and she loud; their noise had gathered all the mob who were assembled on this occasion, not to prevent, but to enjoy the quarrel.

"Alas," said I to my companion, "what will become of this poor unhappy creature thus caught in adultery! Believe me, I pity her from my heart; her husband, I suppose, will shew no mercy. Will they burn her as in India, or behead her as in Persia; will they load her with stripes as in Turkey, or keep her in perpetual imprisonment, as with us in China! Prythee, what is the wife's punishment for such offences?" "When a lady is thus caught tripping, they never punish her, but the husband," replied my companion. "You surely jest," interrupted I; "you know me to be a foreigner, and abuse my ignorance." "I am really serious," returned he. "Dr. Carbuncle has caught his wife, I own, but as he had no witnesses, his testimony goes for nothing. The consequence, therefore, of his discovery will be that madam may be packed off to live among her relations, and the doctor must be obliged to allow her a separate maintenance." "Amazing," cried I! "is it not enough that she is permitted to live separate from the object she detests, but must he give her money to keep her in spirits too?" "That he must," says my guide; "and be called a cuckold by all his neighbours into the bargain. The men will laugh at him, the ladies will pity him; and all that his warmest friends can say in his favour, will be, that the *poor good soul has never had any harm in him.*" "I want patience," interrupted I; "what! are there no private chastisements for the wife; no schools of penitence to shew her her folly; no rods for such delinquents?" "Psha, man," replied he smiling; "if every delinquent among us were to be treated in your manner, one half of the kingdom would flog the other."

I must confess, my dear Fum Hoam, that if I were an English husband, of all things I would take care not to be jealous of my wife, nor busily pry into those secrets she was pleased to keep from me, for should I detect my wife's infidelity, what is the consequence? If I calmly pocket the abuse, I am laugh'd at by her and her gallant; if I talk my griefs aloud like a tragedy heroe, I am laugh'd at by the whole world, treated like a monster, and universally said to wear horns. The course then I'd take is thus: whenever I went out, I would tell my wife where I was going, least I should unexpectedly meet her abroad in company with some dear deceiver. Whenever I returned, I would use a peculiar rap at the door and give four loud hems as I walked deliberately up the stairs; and I would never inquisitively peep under her bed or look behind the curtains, even though I knew the captain was there. I would calmly take a dish of my wife's cool tea and talk of the army with reverence.

Of all nations I have seen, the Russians seem to me to behave most wisely in such circumstances. The wife promises her husband never to let him see her transgressions of this nature; and he as punctually promises, whenever she is so detected, to beat her without mercy: so they both know what each has to expect; the lady transgresses, is beaten, and all goes on as before.

Whenever a Russian young lady, therefore, is to be married, her father, with a cudgel in his hand, asks the bridegroom whether he chuses this virgin for his bride? to which the other replies in the affirmative. Upon this, the father turning the lady three times round, and giving her three strokes with his cudgel on the back, "My dear daughter," cries he, "these are the last blows you will ever receive from your tender father. I resign my authority and my cudgel to your husband, who knows better than me the use of either." The bridegroom knows decorums too well to accept of the cudgel abruptly; he assures the father that the lady will never want it. The father, who knows what the lady may want better than he, insists upon his acceptance. Upon this, there follows a scene of Russian politeness, while one refuses, and the other offers the cudgel. The whole, however, ends with the bridegroom's taking it, upon which the lady drops a curtesy in token of obedience, and the rest of the ceremony is performed as usual.

There is something excessively fair and open in this method of courtship. By this, both sides are prepared for all the matrimonial adventures that are to follow. Marriage has been compared to a game of skill for life; it is generous in both parties, therefore, to declare they are sharpers in the beginning. In England, I am told both sides use every art to conceal their defects from each other while they are lovers. When such a faulty couple are married, all the rest of their lives may be regarded as a penance for their former dissimulation. Adieu.

LETTER TWENTY-ONE

The Chinese goes to see a play.

To the same.

The English are equally fond of seeing plays acted with the Chinese; but there is a vast difference in the manner of conducting them. We play our pieces in the open air, the English theirs under cover; we act by day-light, they by the blaze of torches. One of our plays continues eight or ten days successively; an English piece seldom takes up above four hours in the representation.

My companion in black, with whom I am now beginning to contract an intimacy, introduced me a few nights ago to the play-house, where we placed ourselves conveniently at the foot of the stage. As the curtain was not drawn before my arrival, I had an opportunity of observing the behaviour of the spectators and indulging those reflections which novelty generally inspires.

The rich in general were placed in the lowest seats, and the poor rose above them in degrees proportioned to their poverty. The order of precedence seemed here inverted; those who were undermost all the day now enjoyed a temporary eminence and became masters of the ceremonies. They who called for the music, indulged every noisy freedom, and testified all the insolence of beggary in exaltation.

They who held the middle region seem'd not so riotous as those above them, nor yet so tame as those below; to judge by their looks, many of them seem'd strangers there as well as myself. They were chiefly employed during this period of expectation in eating oranges, reading the story of the play, or making assignations.

Those who sat in the lowest rows, which are called the pit, seemed to consider themselves as judges of the merit of the poet and the performers; they were assembled partly to be amused and partly to shew their taste, appearing to labour under that restraint which an affectation of superior discernment generally produces. My companion, however, informed me that not one in an hundred of them knew even the first principles of criticism; that they assumed the right of being censors because there was none to contradict their pretences; and that every man now who called himself a connoisseur found that alone sufficient to be regarded as such by all his acquaintance.

Those who sat in the boxes appeared to me in the most unhappy situation of all. The rest of the audience came merely for their own amusement; these rather to furnish out a part of the entertainment of others. I could not avoid considering them as acting parts in dumb shew, not a curtesy or nod that was not the result of art; not a look nor a smile that was not designed for murder. Gentlemen ogled their mistresses through spectacles; for my companion observed that blindness was of late come into fashion; while the ladies affected indifference and ease, their hearts at the same time burning for conquest. Upon the whole, the lights, the music, the ladies in their gayest dresses, the men with chearfulness and expectation in their looks, all conspired to make a most agreeable picture and to fill an heart that sympathises with human happiness like mine with inexpressible serenity.

The expected time for the play to begin at last arrived, the curtain was drawn, and the actors came on.[21] A woman who personated a queen first came in curtesying to the audience, who had clapped their hands upon her appearance. Clapping of hands is, it seems, the manner of applauding in England: the manner is absurd; but every country, you know, has its peculiar absurdities. I was equally surprised, however, at the submission of the actress, who should have considered herself as a queen, as at the little discernment of the audience who gave her such marks of applause before she attempted to deserve them. Preliminaries between her and the audience being thus adjusted, the dialogue was supported by her and a most hopeful youth, who acted the part of her confidant. They both appeared in extreme distress, for it seems the queen had lost a child some fifteen years before, and still kept its dear resemblance next her heart, and it was but kind in the companion to bear a part in her sorrows.

Her lamentations are loud. Comfort is offered, but she detests the very sound. She bids them preach comfort to the winds. Upon this her husband comes in, who, seeing the queen so much afflicted, can himself hardly avoid partaking in the soft distress. After they had thus grieved through three scenes, the curtain dropp'd for the first act.

"Truly," said I to my companion, "these kings and queens are very much disturbed at no very great misfortune; certain I am were people of humbler stations to act in this manner, they would be thought divested of common sense." I had scarce finish'd this observation when the curtain rose, and the king came on in a violent passion. His wife had, it seems, refused his proffered tenderness, had spurned his royal embrace; and he seemed resolved not to survive her fierce disdain. After he had thus fretted, and the queen herself had fretted through the second act, the curtain was let down once more.

"Now," says my companion, "you perceive the king to be a

man of spirit, he feels at every pore; one of your phlegmatic sons of clay would have given the queen her own way and let her come to herself by degrees; but the king is for immediate tenderness or instant death: death and tenderness are the leading passions of every modern buskin'd heroe; this moment they embrace, and the next stab the wayward object of their affections."

I was going to second his remarks when my attention was engrossed by a new object; a man came in balancing a straw upon his nose, and the audience were clapping their hands in all the raptures of applause. "To what purpose," cried I, "does this unmeaning figure make its appearance; is he a part of the plot?" "Unmeaning do you call him," replied my friend in black; "this is one of the most important characters of the whole play; nothing pleases the people more than the seeing a straw balanced; there is a great deal of meaning in the straw; there is something suited to every apprehension in the sight; and a fellow possessed of talents like these is sure of making his fortune."

The third act now began with an actor who came to inform us that he was the villain of the play and that he intended to shew strange things before all was over. He was joined by another, who seem'd as much disposed for mischief as he, and their intrigues continued through this whole division. "If that be a villain," said I, "he must be a very stupid one, to tell his secrets without being ask'd; such soliloquies of late are never admitted in China."

The noise of clapping interrupted me once more; a child of six years old was learning to dance on the stage, which gave the ladies and mandarines infinite satisfaction. "I am sorry," said I, "to see the pretty babby[22] so early learning so very bad a trade, dancing being, I presume, as contemptible here as it is in China." "Quite the reverse," interrupted my companion; "dancing is a very reputable and genteel employment here; here a man has a greater chance for encouragement from the merit of his heels than his head. One who jumps up and flourishes his toes three times before he comes to the ground may have three hundred a year among us; he who flourishes them four times gets four hundred; but he who arrives at five is inestimable and may demand what salary he thinks proper. The female dancers too are valued for this sort of jumping and crossing; and 'tis a cant word among them that she deserves most who shews highest. But the fourth act is begun, let us be attentive."

In the fourth act the queen finds her long lost child, now grown up into a youth of smart parts and great qualifications; wherefore she wisely considers that the crown will fit his head better than that of her husband, whom she knows to be a driveler. The king discovers her design, and here comes on the deep distress; he loves the queen, and he loves the kingdom; he resolves therefore, in order to possess both, that her son must die. The queen exclaims at his barbarity; is frantic with rage, and at length overcome with sorrow, falls into a fit; upon which the curtain drops, and the act is concluded.

"Observe the art of the poet," cries my companion; "when the queen can say no more, she falls into a fit. While with her eyes shut, she is supported in the arms of Abigail, what horrors do we not experience; we feel it in every nerve; take my word for it that fits are the true aposiopesis of modern tragedy."

The fifth act began, and a busy piece it was. Scenes shifting, trumpets sounding, mobs hallooing, carpets spreading, guards bustling from one door to another; gods, dæmons, daggers, racks and ratsbane. But whether the king was killed or the queen was drowned or the son was poisoned, I have absolutely forgotten.

When the play was over, I could not avoid observing that the persons of the drama appeared in as much distress in the first act as the last: "how is it possible," said I, "to sympathize with them through five long acts; pity is but a short-lived passion; I hate to hear an actor mouthing trifles, neither startings, strainings, nor attitudes affect me unless there be cause: after I have been once or twice deceived by those unmeaning alarms, my heart sleeps in peace, probably unaffected by the principal distress. There should be one great passion aimed at by the actor as well as the poet; all the rest should be subordinate, and only contribute to make that the greater; if the actor therefore exclaims upon every occasion in the tones of despair, he attempts to move us too soon; he anticipates the blow, he ceases to affect though he gains our applause."

I scarce perceived that the audience were almost all departed; wherefore, mixing with the crowd, my companion and I got into the street; where essaying an hundred obstacles from coach wheels and palanquin poles, like birds in their flight through the branches of a forest, after various turnings, we both at length got home in safety. Adieu.

LETTER TWENTY-FOUR

The venders of quack medicines and nostrums, ridiculed.

To the same.

Whatever may be the merits of the English in other sciences, they seem peculiarly excellent in the art of healing. There is scarcely a disorder incident to humanity against which they are not possessed with a most infallible antidote. The professors of other arts confess the inevitable intricacy of things, talk with doubt, and decide with hesitation; but doubting is entirely unknown in medicine. Be the disorder never so desperate or radical, you will find numbers in every street who, by leveling a pill at the part affected, promise a certain cure without loss of time, or hindrance of business.

When I consider the assiduity of the physicians here, their benevolence amazes me. They not only in general give their medicines for half value, but use the most persuasive remonstrances to induce the sick to come and be cured. Sure there must be something strangely obstinate in an English patient who refuses so much health upon such easy terms; does he take a pride in being swolen up with a dropsy? Does he find pleasure in the alternations of an intermittent fever? Or feel as much satisfaction in nursing up his gout as he found pleasure in acquiring it? He certainly must, or he would never reject such repeated assurances of instant relief. What can be more convincing than the manner in which the sick are invited to be well? The doctor first begs the most earnest attention of the public to what he is going to propose; he solemnly affirms the pill was never found to want success; he produces a list of those who have been rescued from the grave by taking it. Yet, notwithstanding all this, there are many here who now and then think proper to be sick; only sick did I say? There are some who even think proper to die! Yes, by the head of Confucius they die; though they might have purchas'd the health-restoring specific for half a crown at every corner.

I am amazed, my dear Fum Hoam, that these doctors who know what an obstinate set of people they have to deal with have never thought of attempting to revive the dead. As the living are sometimes found to reject their prescriptions, they could expect no such mortifying repulses from those I refer to; they would find in the dead the most complying patients imaginable; and what gratitude might they not expect from the patient's wife, now no longer a widow.

Think not, my friend, that there is any thing chimerical in such an attempt; they already perform cures equally strange: for what can be more truly astonishing than to see old age restored to youth, and vigour to the most feeble constitutions; yet this is performed here every day; a simple electuary effects these wonders, even without the bungling ceremonies of having the patient either boiled up in a kettle, or ground down in a mill.

Few physicians here go through the ordinary courses of education, but receive all their knowledge of medicine by immediate inspiration from heaven. Some are thus inspired even in the womb; and what is very remarkable, are found to understand their profession as well at three years old as at threescore. Others have spent a great part of their lives unconscious of any latent excellence, till a statute of bankruptcy or a residence in gaol have called their miraculous powers into exertion. And others still there are indebted to their superlative ignorance alone for success. The more ignorant the practitioner, the less capable is he thought of deceiving. The people here judge, as they do in several countries of the East, who hold it absolutely requisite that a man should be an ideot before he can pretend to be either a dervise or a doctor.

When a physician by inspiration is sent for, he never perplexes the patient by previous examination; he asks very few questions, and those only for form sake, as he knows every disorder by intuition. He administers the pill or drop for every distemper, being otherwise no more inquisitive than the farrier while he drenches an horse. If the patient lives, then has he one more to add to the surviving list; if he dies, then it may be justly said: because it was not cured, the disorder was incurable.

LETTER TWENTY-SIX

The character of the man in black; with some instances of his inconsistent conduct.

From the same.

Tho' I am fond of many acquaintances, I desire an intimacy only with a few. The man in black whom I have often mentioned is one whose friendship I cou'd wish to acquire, because he possesses my esteem. His manners it is true, are tinctured with some strange inconsistencies; and he may be justly termed an humourist in a nation of humourists. Tho' he is generous even to profusion, he affects to be thought a prodigy of parsimony and prudence; though his conversation be replete with the most sordid and selfish maxims, his heart is dilated with the most unbounded love to his fellow creatures. I have heard him profess himself a man-hater while his cheek was glowing with compassion; and while his looks were softened into pity I have heard him use the language of the most unbounded ill nature. Some may affect humanity and tenderness, others may boast that they have such dispositions from nature; but he is the only man I ever knew who seemed ashamed of his natural benevolence. He takes as much pains to hide his feelings as an hypocrite would to conceal his indifference; but on every unguarded moment the mask drops off and reveals him to the most superficial observer.

In one of our late excursions into the country, happening to discourse upon the provision that was made for the English poor, he seemed amazed how any of his countrymen could be so foolishly weak as to relieve occasional objects of charity when the laws had made such ample provision for their support. "In every parish house," says he, "the poor are supplied with food, cloaths, fire, and a bed to lie on; they want no more, I desire no more; yet still they seem discontented. I'm surprized at the inactivity of our magistrates, in not taking up such vagrants who are only a weight upon the industrious; I'm surprized that people are found to relieve them, when they must be at the same time sensible that it, in some measure, encourages idleness, extravagance, and imposture. Were I to advise any man for whom I had the least regard, I would caution him by all means not to be imposed upon by their false pretences: let me assure you, Sir, they are impostors, every one of them, and rather merit a prison than relief."

He was proceeding in this strain earnestly to dissuade me from an imprudence of which I am seldom guilty, when an old man who still had about him the remnants of tattered finery implored our compassion. He assured us that he was no common beggar, but forced into the shameful profession in order to support a dying wife and five hungry children. As I was prepossessed against such falshoods, his story had not the least influence upon me; but it was quite otherwise with the man in black; I could see it visibly operate upon his countenance, while it effectually interrupted his harangue. I could easily perceive that his heart burned to relieve the five starving children, but he seemed ashamed to discover his weakness to me. While he thus hesitated between compassion and pride, I pretended to look another way, and he seized this opportunity of giving the poor petitioner a piece of silver, bidding him at the same time, in order that I should hear, go work for his bread and not teize passengers with such impertinent falsehoods.

As he fancied himself quite unperceived, he continued as we proceeded to rail against beggars with as much animosity as before; he threw in some episodes on his own amazing prudence and œconomy, with his profound skill in discovering impostors; he explained the manner in which he would deal with beggars were he a magistrate, hinted at enlarging some of the prisons for their reception, and told two stories of ladies that were robbed by beggarmen. He was beginning a third to the same purpose when a sailor with a wooden leg once more crossed our walks, desiring our pity and blessing our limbs. I was for going on without taking any notice, but my friend looking wishfully upon the poor petitioner, bid me stop, and he would shew me with how much ease he could at any time detect an impostor.

He now therefore assumed a look of importance, and in an angry tone began to examine the sailor, demanding in what engagement he was thus disabled and rendered unfit for service. The sailor replied in a tone as angrily as he, that he had been an officer on board a private ship of war, and that he had lost his leg abroad in defence of those who staid at home. At this reply all my friend's importance vanished in a moment; he had not a single question more to ask; he now only studied what method he should take to relieve him unobserved. He had however no easy part to act, as he was obliged to preserve the appearance of ill nature before me and yet relieve himself by relieving the sailor. Casting therefore a furious look upon some bundles of chips which the fellow carried in a string at his back, my friend demanded how he sold his matches, but not waiting for a reply, desired in a surly tone to have a shilling's worth. The sailor seemed at first surprised at his demand, but soon recollecting himself and presenting his whole bundle, "Here, master," says he, "take all my cargo, and a blessing into the bargain."

It is impossible to describe with what an air of triumph my friend marched off with his new purchase; he assured me he was firmly of opinion that those fellows must have stolen their goods who could thus afford to sell them for half value; he informed me of several different uses to which those chips might be applied; he expatiated largely upon the savings that would result from lighting candles with a match instead of thrusting them into the fire. He averred that he would as soon have parted with a tooth as his money to those vagabonds, unless for some valuable consideration. I cannot tell how long this panegyric upon frugality and matches might have continued had not his attention been called off by another object more distressful than either of the former. A woman in rags, with one child in her arms and another on her back, was attempting to sing, but with such a voice that it was difficult to determine whether she was singing or crying. A wretch who in the deepest distress still aimed at good humour was an object my friend was by no means capable of withstanding: his vivacity and his discourse were instantly interrupted; upon this occasion his very dissimulation had forsaken him. Even in my presence he immediately applied his hands to his pockets in order to relieve her; but guess his confusion when he found he had already given away all the money he carried about him to former objects. The misery painted in the woman's visage was not half so strongly expressed as the agony in the countenance of my friend. He continued to search for some time but to no purpose, till at length recollecting himself, with a face of ineffable good-nature, as he had no money, he put into her hands his shilling's worth of matches. Adieu.

LETTER TWENTY-SEVEN

The history of the man in black.

To the same.

As there appeared something reluctantly good in the character of my companion, I must own I was surpriz'd at what could be the motives for his thus concealing virtues which others take such pains to display. I was unable to repress my desire of knowing the history of a man who thus seemed to act under continual restraint, and whose benevolence was rather the effect of nature than reason.

It was not till after repeated solicitations he thought proper to gratify my curiosity, and in the following account, as nearly as I can remember, you have The History of the Man in Black. "If you are fond of hearing of *hair breadth 'scapes,*" said he, "my history must certainly please; for I have been for twenty years upon the very verge of starving, without ever being starved.

"My father, the younger son of a good family, was possessed of a small living in the church. His education was above his fortune and his generosity greater than his education. Poor as he was, he had his flatterers still poorer who for every dinner he gave them, returned him an equivalent in praise. This was all he wanted; the same ambition for glory that actuates a monarch at the head of an army influenced my father at the head of his table: he told the story of the ivy-tree, and that was laugh'd at; he repeated the jest of the two scholars and one pair of breeches, and they laughed at that; but the story of Taffy in the sedan chair was sure to set the table in a roar; thus his pleasure encreased in proportion to that he gave; he loved all the world, and all the world pretended to love him.

"As his fortune was but small, he lived up to the very extent of it; he had no intentions of leaving his children money, for that was dross, but he was resolved they should have more than an equivalent in learning, for learning, he used to observe, was better than silver or gold. For this purpose he undertook to instruct his children himself, and took as much pains in forming our morals as improving our understanding. We were told that universal benevolence was the first law of nature; we were taught to consider all the wants of mankind as our own; to regard the *human face divine* with affection and esteem; he wound us up to be mere machines of pity, incapable of withstanding the slightest impulse made upon us either by real or fictitious distress; and we were perfectly versed in the art of *giving away* thousands, before we were taught the more necessary qualifications of *getting* sixpence.

"I can't avoid imagining, that, thus refined by his lessons out of all my suspicion and prudence, divested of even the little cunning which nature had given me, I resembled, upon my first entrance into the busy and insidious world, those gladiators who were exposed without armour in the amphitheatre to combat wild beasts. My father, however, who had only seen the world on one side, seemed to triumph in my superior discernment, my whole stock of wisdom consisting in being able to talk like himself upon subjects that once were useful, because they were the topics of the busy world, but that now were utterly unserviceable, because connected with the busy world no longer.

"The first opportunity he had of finding his expectations disappointed was at the very middling figure I made in the university: he had flattered himself that he should soon see me rising into the foremost rank in literary reputation, but was mortified to find me utterly unnoticed and unknown. His disappointment might have been partly ascribed to his having too highly rated my talents, and partly to my dislike of mathematical reasonings when my imagination and memory were yet unsatisfied. Curiosity after new objects was greater than my desire of reasoning upon those I knew. This did not, however, please my tutors, who observed, indeed, that I was a little dull; but at the same time allowed that I had no harm in me and seemed to be very good natured.

"After I had resided at college seven years, my father died and left me—his blessing. Thus shoved from shore without ill-nature to protect, or cunning to guide, or proper stores to subsist me in so dangerous a voyage, I was obliged to embark in the wide world at twenty-two. In order to settle me in life, my friends *advised* (for they always advise when they begin to despise us) they advised me, I say, to go into orders.

"To be obliged to wear a long wig, when I liked a short one, or a black coat, when I generally dressed in brown, I thought was such a restraint upon my liberty that I absolutely rejected the proposal. A priest in England, my friend, is not the same mortified creature with one of your bonzes in China; with us, not he that fasts best, but eats best, is called the best liver; yet I at once rejected a life of luxury, indolence, and ease, from no other consideration but that boyish one of dressing as I thought proper. My friends were now perfectly satisfied that I was undone; and yet they thought it a pity for one who had not the least harm in him, and was very good natured.

"Poverty naturally begets dependance, and I was admitted as flatterer to a great man. At first I was surprised that the situation of a flatterer at a great man's table could be thought disagreeable; there was no great trouble in listening attentively when his lordship spoke and laughing when he looked round for applause. This even good-manners might have obliged me to perform. I found, however, too soon that his lordship was a greater dunce than myself; and from that very moment I could flatter no longer. I rather aimed at setting him right than at receiving his absurdities with submission: to flatter those we don't know is an easy task; but to flatter our intimate acquaintances is drudgery insupportable. Every time I now opened my lips in praise, it went to my conscience; his lordship soon perceived me to be unfit for service; I was therefore discharged, my patron at the same time being graciously pleased to observe that he believed I was tolerably good-natured and had not the least harm in me.

"Disappointed in ambition I had recourse to love. A young lady, who lived with her aunt and was possessed of a pretty fortune in her own disposal, had given me, as I fancied, some reasons to expect success. The symptoms by which I was guided were these: she had always laughed with me at her aukward acquaintance, and her aunt among the number; she always observed that a man of sense would make a better

husband than a fool, and I applied the observation in my
own favour. She continually talked in my company of friendship and the beauties of the mind and spoke of Mr. Shrimp
my rival's high-heel'd shoes with detestation. These were circumstances which I thought strongly in my favour; so after
resolving, and re-resolving, I had courage enough to tell her
my mind. Miss heard my proposal with serenity, seeming
at the same time to study the figures of her fan. There was
but one small objection to complete our happiness, which was
no more, than——that she was married three months before to
Mr. Shrimp with high-heel'd shoes! By way of consolation,
however, she observed that tho' I was disappointed in her,
my addresses to her aunt would probably find her not insensible, as the old lady always allowed me to be very good
natured and not to have the least share of harm in me.

"Poverty now began to come fast upon me, yet instead of
growing more provident or cautious as I grew poor, I became
every day more indolent and simple. A friend was arrested for
fifty pounds; I was unable to extricate him except by becoming
his bail. When at liberty he fled from his creditors and left me
to take his place. In prison I expected greater satisfactions
than I had enjoyed at large. I hoped to converse with men in
this new world simple and believing like myself, but I found
them as cunning and as cautious as those in the world I had
left behind. They spunged up my money whilst it lasted, borrowed my coals and never paid them, and cheated me when I
play'd at cribbage. All this was done because they believed me
to be very good-natured and knew that I had no harm in me.

"Upon my first entrance into this mansion which is to some
the abode of despair, I felt no sensations different from those I
experienced abroad. I was now on one side the door, and those
who were unconfined were on the other; this was all the
difference between us. At first indeed I felt some uneasiness in
considering how I should be able to provide this week for the
wants of the week ensuing; but after some time if I found
myself sure of eating one day, I never troubled my head how
I was to be supplied another. I seized every precarious meal
with the utmost good humour, indulged no rants of spleen
at my situation, never called down heaven and all the stars to
behold me dining upon an halfpenny-worth of radishes; my

very companions were taught to believe that I liked the sallad better than mutton. I contented myself with thinking that all my life I should either eat white bread or brown; I considered that all that happened was best; I laughed when I was not in pain, took the world as it went, and read Tacitus often, for want of more books and better company.

"How long I might have continued in this torpid state of simplicity I cannot tell, had I not been rouzed by seeing an old acquaintance whom I knew to be a prudent blockhead preferred to a place in the government. I now found that I had pursued a wrong track, and that the true way of being able to relieve others was first to aim at independance myself. My immediate care, therefore, was to leave my present habitation and make an entire reformation in my conduct and behaviour. For a free, open, undesigning deportment, I put on that of closeness, prudence and œconomy. One of the most heroic actions I ever performed, and for which I shall praise myself as long as I live, was the refusing half a crown to an old acquaintance at the time when he wanted it and I had it to spare.

"I now pursued a course of uninterrupted frugality, seldom wanted a dinner, and was consequently invited to twenty. I soon began to get the character of a saving hunks that had money; and I insensibly grew into esteem. Neighbours have asked my advice in the disposal of their daughters, and I have always taken care not to give any. I have contracted a friendship with an alderman only by observing that if we take a farthing from a thousand pound it will be a thousand pound no longer. I have been invited to a pawnbroker's table by pretending to hate gravy; and am now actually upon treaty of marriage with a rich widow for only having observed that the bread was rising. If ever I am ask'd a question, whether I know it or not, instead of answering, I only smile and look wise. If a charity is proposed, I often go about with the hat but put nothing in myself. If a wretch solicits my pity, I take a certain method of not being deceived by impostors, for I never relieve any. In short, I now find that the truest way of finding esteem even from the indigent is by giving away nothing, to keep much in our power to give away."

LETTER TWENTY-NINE

A description of a club of authors.

From the same.

Were we to estimate the learning of the English by the number of books that are every day published among them, perhaps no country, not even China itself, could equal them in this particular. I have reckoned not less than twenty-three new books published in one day, which upon computation makes eight thousand three hundred and ninety-five in one year. Most of these are not confined to one single science, but embrace the whole circle. History, politics, poetry, mathematics, metaphysics, and the philosophy of nature are all comprized in a manual not larger than that in which our children are taught the letters. If then we suppose the learned of England to read but an eighth part of the works which daily come from the press (and sure none can pretend to learning upon less easy terms), at this rate every scholar will read a thousand books in one year. From such a calculation you may conjecture what an amazing fund of literature a man must be possessed of who thus reads three new books every day, not one of which but contains all the good things that ever were said or written.

And yet I know not how it happens, but the English are not in reality so learned as would seem from this calculation. We meet but few who know all arts and sciences to perfection; whether it is that the generality are incapable of such extensive knowledge or that the authors of those books are not adequate instructors. In China, the emperor himself takes cognisance of all the doctors in the kingdom who profess authorship. In England, every man may be an author that can write; for they have by law a liberty not only of saying what they please, but of being as dull as they think proper.

The man in black paid me a visit yesterday, when I testified my surprize, where writers could be found in sufficient numbers to throw off the books I daily saw crowding from the press. I at first imagined, that their learned seminaries might take this method of instructing the world. But to obviate this

objection, my companion assured me, that the doctors of colleges never wrote, and that some of them had actually forgot
their reading; "but if you desire," continued he, "to see a
collection of authors, I fancy I can introduce you this evening
to a club which assembles every Saturday at seven, at the
sign of the Broom near Islington, to talk over the business
of the last and the entertainment of the week ensuing." I
accepted his invitation, we walked together, and entered the
house at the usual hour, but the company were not yet
assembled.

My friend took this opportunity of letting me into the
characters of the principal members of the club, not even
the host excepted, who, it seems, was once an author himself,
but preferred by a bookseller to this situation as a reward of
his former services.

"The first person," said he, "of our society is doctor Nonen-
tity, a metaphysician. Most people think him a profound
scholar; but as he seldom speaks, I cannot be positive in that
particular; he generally spreads himself before the fire, sucks
his pipe, talks little, drinks much, and is reckoned very good
company. I'm told he writes indexes to perfection, makes
essays on the origin of evil, philosophical enquiries upon any
subject, and draws up an answer to any book upon twenty-
four hours warning. You may distinguish him from the rest
of the company by his long grey wig, and the blue handkerchief round his neck.

"The next to him in merit and esteem is Tim Syllabub, a
drole creature; he sometimes shines as a star of the first
magnitude among the choice spirits of the age; he is reckoned
equally excellent at a rebus, a riddle, a baudy song, and an
hymn for the tabernacle. You'll know him by his shabby
finery, his powdered wig, dirty shirt, and broken silk stockings.

"After him succeeds Mr. Tibs, a very *useful hand*; he writes
receipts for the bite of a mad dog, and throws off an eastern
tale to perfection; he understands the *business* of an author
as well as any man, for no bookseller alive can cheat him;
you may distinguish him by the peculiar clumsiness of his
figure and the coarseness of his coat: however, though it be
coarse, (as he frequently tells the company) he has paid for it.

"Lawyer Squint is the politician of the society; he makes

speeches for parliament, writes addresses to his fellow subjects and letters to noble commanders; he gives the history of every new play and finds *seasonable thoughts* upon every occasion."—My companion was proceeding in his description, when the host came running in with terror on his countenance to tell us that the door was beset by bailiffs. "If that be the case then," says my companion, "we had as good be going; for I am positive we shall not see one of the company this night." Wherefore disappointed we were both obliged to return home, he to enjoy the oddities which compose his character alone, and I to write as usual to my friend the occurrences of the day. Adieu.

LETTER THIRTY

The proceedings of the club of authors.

From the same.

By my last advices from Moscow, I find the caravan has not yet departed for China: I still continue to write, in expectation that you will receive a large number of my letters at once. In them you will find rather a minute detail of the English peculiarities than a general picture of their manners, genius, or disposition. Happy it were for mankind if all travellers would thus, instead of characterising a people at once, lead us into a detail of those minute circumstances which first influenced their opinion. By this means we should be led to have more precise and just notions of foreign countries, and detect travellers themselves when they happened to form wrong conclusions.

To a philosopher no circumstance, however trifling, is too minute. He finds instruction and entertainment in occurrences which are passed over by the rest of mankind as low, trite, and indifferent. It is from the number of these particulars, which to many appear insignificant, that he is at last enabled to form general conclusions; this, therefore, must be my excuse for sending so far as China accounts of manners and follies which, though minute in their own nature, serve more truly to characterise this people than histories of their public treaties, courts, ministers, negotiations, and ambassadors.

My friend and I lately repeated our visit to the club of

authors I mentioned some time ago, where, upon our entrance, we found the members all assembled and engaged in a loud debate.

A poet with a pale complexion, holding a manuscript in his hand, was earnestly endeavouring to persuade the company to hear him read the first book of an heroic poem which he had composed the day before. But against this all the members very warmly objected. They knew no reason why any member of the club should be indulged with a particular hearing, when many of them had published whole volumes without ever being looked into. They insisted that the law should be observed, where reading to the company was expresly noticed. It was in vain that the plaintiff pleaded the peculiar merit of his piece; he spoke to an assembly insensible of all his remonstrances; the book of laws was opened and read by the secretary, where it was expresly enacted, "That whatsoever poet, speech-maker, critic, or historian, should presume to engage the company by reading his own works, he was to lay down sixpence previous to his opening the manuscript and should be charged one shilling an hour while he continued reading, the said shilling to be equally distributed among the company as a recompence for their pain in listening."

Our poet seemed at first to shrink at the penalty, hesitating for some time whether he should deposit the fine or shut up the poem; but looking round and perceiving two strangers in the room, his love of fame out-weighed his prudence, and laying down the sum by law established, he insisted on his privilege of reading.

A profound silence ensuing, he began by explaining his design. "Gentlemen," says he, "the present piece is not one of your common epic poems, which come from the press like paper kites in summer[23]; there are none of your Turnuses or Dido's in it; it is an heroical description of nature. I only beg you'll endeavour to tune your soul's unison with mine while you listen, and hear with the same enthusiasm with which I shall read. The poem begins with the description of an author's bed-chamber: the picture was sketched in my own apartment, for you must know, gentlemen, that I am myself the heroe." Then putting himself into the attitude of an orator, with all the emphasis of voice and action, he proceeded.

"Where the Red Lion flaring o'er the way,
Invites each passing stranger that can pay;
Where Calvert's butt, and Parson's black champaign,
Regale the drabs and bloods of Drury lane;
There in a lonely room, from bailiffs snug,
The muse found Scroggen stretch'd beneath a rug.
A window patch'd with paper lent a ray
That dimly shew'd the state in which he lay;
The sanded floor that grits beneath the tread,
The humid wall with paltry pictures spread:
The royal game of goose was there in view,
And the twelve rules the royal martyr drew;
The seasons fram'd with listing found a place,
And brave prince William shew'd his lamp-black face.
The morn was cold, he views with keen desire
The rusty grate unconscious of a fire;
With beer and milk arrears the frieze was scor'd,
And five crack'd tea cups dress'd the chimney board;
A night cap deck'd his brows instead of bay,
A cap by night——a stocking all the day!" [24]

With this last line he seem'd so much elated that he was
unable to proceed: "There gentlemen," cries he, "there is a
description for you; Rablais's bed-chamber is but a fool to it:

A cap by night—a stocking all the day!

There is sound and sense, and truth, and nature in the trifling
compass of ten little syllables."

He was too much employed in self-admiration to observe
the company: who by nods, winks, shrugs, and stifled laughter, testified every mark of contempt. He turned severally
to each for their opinion and found all ready to applaud. One
swore it was inimitable; another said it was damn'd fine;
and a third cried out in rapture, "Carissimo." At last addressing himself to the president, "and pray, Mr. Squint," says he,
"let us have your opinion." "Mine," answered the president,
(taking the manuscript out of the author's hands) "may this
glass suffocate me, but I think it equal to any thing I have
seen; and I fancy, (continued he, doubling up the poem, and
thrusting it into the author's pocket) that you will get great

honour when it comes out, and so I shall beg leave to put it in. We will not impose upon your good-nature, in desiring to hear more on't at present; *ex ungue Herculem*[25]; we are satisfied, perfectly satisfied." The author made two or three attempts to pull it out a second time, and the president made as many to prevent him. Thus though with reluctance he was at last obliged to sit down, contented with the commendations which had been paid for.

When this tempest of poetry and praise was blown over, one of the company changed the subject by wondering how any man could be so dull as to write poetry at present, since prose itself would hardly pay. "Would you think it, gentlemen," continued he, "I have actually written last week sixteen prayers, twelve bawdy jests, and three sermons, all at the rate of sixpence a-piece; and what is still more extraordinary, the bookseller has lost by the bargain. Such sermons would once have gain'd me a prebend's stall; but now alas we have neither piety, taste, nor humour among us. Positively if this season does not turn out better than it has begun, unless the ministry commit some blunders to furnish us with a new topic of abuse, I shall resume my old business of working at the press, instead of finding it employment."

The whole club seem to join in condemning the season as one of the worst that had come for some time; a gentleman particularly observed that the nobility were never known to subscribe worse than at present. "I know not how it happens," said he, "though I follow them up as close as possible, yet I can hardly get one subscription in a week. [The houses of the great are as inaccessible as a frontier garrison at mid-night.] I never see a nobleman's door opened that some surly porter or footman does not stand in the breach. I was yesterday to wait with a proposal upon my lord Squash the creolian. I had posted myself at his door the whole morning, and just as he was getting into his coach, thrust my proposal into his hand folded up in a letter from myself. He just glanced at the superscription, and, not knowing the hand, consigned it to his valet de chambre; this respectable personage treated it just as his master had done, and put it into the hands of the porter. The porter took the proposal frowning; and, measuring my figure from top to toe, put it back into my hand unopened."

"To the devil I pitch all the nobility," cries a little man, in a peculiar accent, "I am sure they have of late used me most scurvily. You must know, gentlemen, some time ago upon the arrival of a certain noble duke from his travels I set myself down and vamp'd up a fine flaunting, poetical panegyric, which I had written in such a strain that I fancied it would have even wheedled milk from a mouse. In this I represented the whole kingdom, and in their name welcomed his grace to his native soil, not forgetting the loss France and Italy would sustain in their arts by his departure. I had expected to prevail, so folding up my verses in gilt paper, I gave my last half crown to a genteel servant to be the bearer. My letter was safely conveyed to his grace, and the servant after four hours absence, during which time I led the life of a fiend, returned with a letter in his hand four times as big as that I had sent. Guess my extasy at the prospect of so fine a return. I eagerly took the pacquet into my hands, that trembled to receive it. I kept it some time unopened before me, brooding over the expected treasure within; when opening it, as I hope to be saved, gentlemen, his grace had sent me in payment no Bank bills, but six long poems addressed to himself upon the same occasion."

"The nobility," cries a member who had hitherto been silent, "are certainly created for the confusion of authors. I'll tell you a story, gentlemen, which is as true as that this pipe is made of clay. When I was delivered of my first book, I owed my taylor for a suit of cloaths, but that is nothing new, you know, and may be any man's case as well as mine. Well, owing my taylor for a suit of cloaths, and he hearing that my book took very well, he sent for his money and insisted upon being paid immediately. Though I was at that time rich in fame, for my book run like wild-fire, yet I was very short in money, and being unable to satisfy his demand, prudently resolved to keep my chamber, preferring a prison of my own chusing at home, to one of my taylor's chusing abroad. In vain the bailiffs used all their arts to decoy me from my citadel, in vain they sent to let me know that a gentleman wanted to speak with me at the next tavern, in vain they came with an urgent message from my aunt in the country; [in vain I was told that a particular friend was at the point of death, and desired to take his last farewell;] I was deaf, insensible, rock, adamant, they could make no impression on my hard heart, for I effectually kept my liberty by never stirring out of the room.

"This was very well for a fortnight; when one morning I received a most splendid message from the earl of Doomsday, importing, that he had read my book and was in raptures with every line of it; he impatiently longed to see the author, and had some designs which might turn out greatly to his advantage. I paused upon the contents of this message and found there could be no deceit, for the card was gilt at the edges, and the bearer, I was told, had quite the looks of a gentleman. Witness ye powers, how my heart triumphed at my own importance; I saw a long perspective of felicity before me, I applauded the taste of the times, which never saw genius forsaken; I had prepared a set introductory speech for the occasion, five compliments for his lordship, and two for myself. The next morning, therefore, in order to be punctual to my appointment, I took coach and ordered the fellow to drive to the street and house mentioned in his lordship's address. I had the precaution to pull up the windows as I went along and, big with expectation, fancied I never went fast enough. At length, however, the wish'd for moment of the coach's stopping arrived; it is what for some time I had impatiently expected, and letting down the coach door in a transport, in order to take a previous view of his lordship's magnificent palace and situation, I found—poison to my sight! I found myself, not in an elegant street, but a paltry lane, not at a nobleman's door, but the door of a spunging-house; I found the coachman had all this while been driving me to jail, and I saw the bailiff with a devil's face, coming down to receive me." Adieu.

LETTER THIRTY-ONE

The perfection of the Chinese in the art of Gardening. The description of a Chinese garden.

From the same.

The English have not yet brought the art of gardening to the same perfection with the Chinese but have lately begun to imitate them; nature is now followed with greater assiduity than formerly; the trees are suffered to shoot out into the utmost luxuriance; the streams, no longer forced from their native beds, are permitted to wind along the vallies; spontaneous flowers take place of the finished parterre, and the enamelled meadow of the shaven green.

Yet still the English are far behind us in this charming art, since their designers have not yet attained a power of uniting instruction with beauty. An European will scarcely conceive my meaning when I say that there is scarce a garden in China which does not contain some fine moral couch'd under the general design, where one is not taught wisdom as he walks and feels the force of some noble truth or delicate precept resulting from the disposition of the groves, streams, or grotto's. Permit me to illustrate what I mean by a description of my gardens at Luamsi—mine, did I say—of those which were mine. My heart still hovers round those scenes of former happiness with pleasure; and I find satisfaction in enjoying them at this distance, tho' but in imagination.

You descended from the house between two groves of trees, planted in such a manner that they were impenetrable to the eye; while on each hand the way was adorned with all that was beautiful in porcelaine, statuary, and painting. This passage from the house opened into an area surrounded with rocks, flowers, trees and shrubs, but all so disposed as if each was the spontaneous production of nature. As you proceeded forward on this lawn, to your right and left-hand were two gates opposite each other, of very different architecture and design; and before you lay a temple built rather with minute elegance than ostentation.

The right-hand gate was planned with the utmost simplicity, or rather rudeness; ivy clasp'd round the pillars, the baleful cyprus hung over it; time seemed to have destroyed all the smoothness and regularity of the stone: two champions with lifted clubs appeared in the act of guarding its access; dragons and serpents were seen in the most hideous attitudes, to deter the spectator from approaching; and the perspective view that lay behind seemed dark and gloomy to the last degree; the stranger was tempted to enter only from the motto which I received from an English merchant there: PERVIA VIRTUTI (pervious to virtue).

The opposite gate was formed in a very different manner; the architecture was light, elegant, and inviting; flowers hung in wreaths round the pillars; all was finished in the most exact and masterly manner; the very stone of which it was built still preserved its polish; nymphs, wrought by the hand of a master, in the most alluring attitudes beckoned the stranger to approach; while all that lay behind, as far as the eye could reach, seemed gay, luxuriant, and capable of affording endless pleasure. The motto itself contributed to invite him; for over the gate was written these words: FACILIS DESCENSUS (the descent is easy).

By this time I fancy you begin to perceive that the gloomy gate was designed to represent the road to virtue; the opposite, the more agreeable passage to vice. It is but natural to suppose that the spectator was always tempted to enter by the gate which offered him so many allurements. I always in these cases left him to his choice, but generally found that he took to the left, which promised most entertainment.

Immediately upon his entering the gate of vice, the trees and flowers were disposed in such a manner as to make the most pleasing impression; but as he walked farther on he insensibly found the garden assume the air of a wilderness, the landskips began to darken, the paths grew more intricate, he appeared to go downwards, frightful rocks seemed to hang over his head, gloomy caverns, unexpected precipices, awful ruins, heaps of unburied bones, and terrifying sounds caused by unseen waters, began to take place of what at first appeared so lovely; it was in vain to attempt returning; the labyrinth was too much perplexed for any but myself to find the way back. In short, when sufficiently impressed with the horrors of what he saw and the imprudence of his choice, I brought him by an hidden door a shorter way back into the area from whence at first he had strayed.

The gloomy gate now presented itself before the stranger; and though there seemed little in its appearance to tempt his curiosity, yet encouraged by the motto, he generally proceeded. The darkness of the entrance, the frightful figures that seemed to obstruct his way, the trees of a mournful green, conspired at first to disgust him; as he went forward, however, all began to open and wear a more pleasing appearance, beautiful cascades, beds of flowers, trees loaded with fruit or blossoms, and unexpected brooks, improved the scene: he now found that he was ascending, and, as he proceeded, all nature grew more beautiful, the prospect widened as he went higher, even the air itself seemed to become more pure. Thus pleased, and happy from unexpected beauties, I at last led him to an arbour, from whence he could view the garden and the whole country around, and where he might own that the road to Virtue terminated in Happiness.

Though from this description you may imagine that a vast tract of ground was necessary to exhibit such a pleasing variety in, yet be assured that I have seen several gardens in England take up ten times the space which mine did, without half the beauty. A very small extent of ground is enough for an elegant taste; the greater room is required if magnificence is in view. There is no spot, tho' ever so little, which a skilful designer might not thus improve, so as to convey a delicate allegory and impress the mind with the most useful and necessary truths. Adieu.

LETTER THIRTY-FOUR

Of the present ridiculous passion of the nobility for painting.

To the same.

The polite arts are in this country subject to as many revolutions as its laws or politics; not only the objects of fancy and dress but even of delicacy and taste are directed by the capricious influence of fashion. I am told there has been a time when poetry was universally encouraged by the great, when men of the first rank not only patronized the poet but produced the finest models for his imitation; it was then that the English sent forth those glowing rhapsodies, which we have so often read over together with rapture; poems big with all the sublimity of Mentius, and supported by reasoning as strong as that of Zimpo.

The nobility are ever fond of wisdom, but they also are fond of having it without study; to read poetry required thought, and the English nobility were not fond of thinking;

they soon therefore placed their affections upon music, because in this they might indulge an happy vacancy and yet
still have pretensions to delicacy and taste as before. They
soon brought their numerous dependents into an approbation
of their pleasures; who in turn led their thousand imitators
to feel or feign a similitude of passion. Colonies of singers
were now imported from abroad at a vast expence, and it was
expected the English would soon be able to set examples to
Europe; all these expectations however were soon dissipated;
in spite of the zeal which fired the great, the ignorant vulgar
refused to be taught to sing, refused to undergo the ceremonies which were to initiate them in the singing fraternity;
thus the colony from abroad dwindled by degrees, for they
were of themselves unfortunately incapable of propagating
the breed.

Music having thus lost its former splendour, painting is
now become the sole object of fashionable care; the title of
connoisseur in that art is at present the safest passport into
every fashionable society; a well timed shrug, an admiring
attitude, and one or two exotic tones of exclamation are
sufficient qualifications for men of low circumstances to
curry favour; even some of the young nobility are themselves
early instructed in handling the pencil, while their happy parents, big with expectation, foresee the walls of every apartment covered with the manufactures of their posterity.

But many of the English are not content with giving all
their time to this art at home; some young men of distinction
are found to travel thro' Europe with no other intent than
that of understanding and collecting pictures, studying seals,
and describing statues; on they travel from this cabinet of
curiosities to that gallery of pictures, waste the prime of life
in wonder, skilful in pictures, ignorant in men, yet impossible
to be reclaimed, because their follies take shelter under the
names of delicacy and taste.

It is true painting should have due encouragement, as the
painter can undoubtedly fit up our apartments in a much
more elegant manner than the upholsterer can; but I should
think a man of fashion makes but an indifferent exchange
who lays out all that time in furnishing his house which he
should have employed in the furniture of his head; a person

who shews no other symptoms of taste than his cabinet or gallery might as well boast to me of his dexterity in carving.

I know of no other motive but vanity that induces the great to testify such an inordinate passion for pictures; after the piece is bought and gazed at eight or ten days successively, the purchaser's pleasure must surely be over; all the satisfaction he can then have is to shew it to others; he may be considered as the guardian of a treasure of which he makes no manner of use; his gallery is furnished not for himself, but the connoisseur, who is generally some humble flatterer, ready to feign a rapture he does not feel, and as necessary to the happiness of a picture-buyer as slaves are to the magnificence of an Asiatic procession.

I have procured for your amusement a letter from a youth of distinction on his travels to his father in England, in which he appears addicted to no vice, seems obedient to his governor[26], of a good natural disposition, and fond of improvement, but at the same time early taught to regard cabinets and galleries as the only proper schools of improvement and to consider a skill in pictures as the properest knowledge for a man of quality.

"My lord,

"We have been but two days at Antwerp; wherefore I have sat down as soon as possible to give you some account of what we have seen since our arrival, desirous of letting no opportunity pass without writing to so good a father. Immediately upon alighting from our Rotterdam machine, my governor, who is immoderately fond of paintings and at the same time an excellent judge, would let no time pass till we paid our respects to the church of the virgin-mother, which contains a treasure beyond estimation. I really believe my governor and I could have lived and died there. There is scarce a pillar in the whole church that is not adorned by a Reubens, a Vander Meulen, a Vandyke, or a Woverman. What attitudes, carnations, and draperies! I am almost induced to pity the English who have none of those exquisite pieces among them. As we were willing to let slip no opportunity of doing business, we immediately after went to wait on Mr. Hogendorp, whom you have so frequently commended for his judicious collection. His cameo's are indeed beyond price; his intaglio's not so good. He shewed us one of an officiating flamen, which he thought to be an antique; but my governor, who is not to be deceived in these particulars, soon found it to be an arrant *cinque cento*. I could not, however, sufficiently admire the genius of Mr. Hogendorp, who has been able to collect from all parts of the world a thousand things which no body knows the use of. Except your lordship and my governor, I do not know any body I admire so much. The next morning early, as we were resolved to take the whole day before us, we sent our compliments to Mr. Van Sprokcken, desiring to see his gallery, which request he very politely complied with. His gallery measures fifty feet by twenty and is well filled; but what surprized me most of all was to see an holy family just like your lordship's, which this ingenious gentleman assures me is the true original. I own this gave me inexpressible uneasiness, as I fear it will to your lordship, as I had flattered myself that the only original was in your lordship's possession; I would advise you, however, to take yours down till its merit can be ascertained, my governor assuring me that he intends to write a long dissertation to prove its originality. One might study in this city for ages and still find something new; we went from this to view the cardinal's statues, which are really very fine; there were three spintria that were executed in a very masterly manner, all arm and arm:[27] the torse which I heard you talk so much of is at last discovered to be an Hercules spinning and not a Cleopatra bathing, as your lordship had conjectured: there has been a treatise written to prove it.

"My lord * * * is certainly a Goth, a Vandal, has no taste for painting. I wonder how any call him a man of taste; passing through the streets of Antwerp a few days ago and observing the nakedness of the inhabitants, he was so barbarous as to observe that he thought the best method the Flemings could take was to sell their pictures and buy cloaths. Ah, Coglione! We shall go to-morrow to Mr. Carwarden's cabinet, and the next day we shall see the curiosities collected by Van Ran, and the day after we shall pay a visit to Mount Calvary, and after that—but I find my paper finished; so with the most sincere wishes to your lordship's happiness, and with hopes after having seen Italy, that centre of pleasure, to return home worthy the care and expence which has been generously laid out in my improvement, I remain, my Lord, Yours, &c."

LETTER FORTY

The English still have poets, tho' not versifiers.

From the same.

You have always testified the highest esteem for the English poets and thought them not inferior to the Greeks, Romans, or even the Chinese in their art. But it is now thought even by the English themselves that the race of their poets is extinct; every day produces some pathetic exclamation upon the decadence of taste and genius. Pegasus, say they, has slipped the bridle from his mouth, and our modern bards attempt to direct his flight by catching him by the tail.

Yet, my friend, it is only among the ignorant that such discourses prevail; men of true discernment can see several poets still among the English, some of whom equal if not surpass their predecessors. The ignorant term all that poetry which is couch'd in a certain number of syllables in every line, where a vapid thought is drawn out into a number of verses of equal length, and perhaps pointed with rhymes at the end. But my conception of poetry is very different. Glowing sentiment, striking imagery, concise expression, natural description, and modulated periods seem entirely to fill up my idea of this art, and make way to every passion of my soul.

If my idea of poetry be just, the English are not at present so destitute of poetical merit as they seem to imagine. I can see several poets in disguise among them; men furnished with that strength of soul, sublimity of sentiment, and grandeur of expression, which constitutes the character. Many of the writers of their modern odes, sonnets, tragedies or rebusses, it is true, deserve not the name, tho' they have done nothing but clink rhymes and measure syllables for years together; their Johnson's or Smollet's are truly poets; tho' for aught I know they never made a single verse in their whole lives.

In every incipient language the poet and the prose writer are very distinct in their qualifications; but when once the language is perfectly formed, they become one and the same. In the beginning the poet always proceeds forward, treading unbeaten paths, enriching his native funds, and employed in new adventures. The other follows with more cautious steps, and though slow in his motions, treasures up every useful or pleasing discovery. But when once all the extent and the force of the language is known, the poet then seems to rest from his labour and is at length overtaken by the assiduous pursuer. [Both characters are then blended into one, the historian and orator catch all the poet's fire and leave him no real mark of distinction except the iteration of numbers regularly returning.] Thus in the decline of ancient European learning Seneca, though he wrote in prose, is as much a poet as Lucan, and Longinus, tho' but a critic, more sublime than Apollonius.

From this then it appears that poetry is not discontinued, but altered among the English at present; the outward form seems different from what it was, but poetry still continues internally the same; the only question remains whether the metric feet used by the good writers of the last age or the prosaic numbers employed by the good writers of this be preferable. And here the practice of the last age appears to me superior; they submitted to the restraint of numbers and similar sounds; and this restraint, instead of diminishing, augmented the force of their sentiment and stile. Fancy restrained may be compared to a fountain which plays highest by diminishing the aperture. Of the truth of this maxim in every language, every fine writer is perfectly sensible from his own experience, and yet to explain the reason would be perhaps as difficult as to make a frigid genius profit by the discovery.

There is still another reason in favour of the practice of the last age, to be drawn from the variety of modulation. The musical period in prose is confined to a very few changes; the numbers in verse are capable of infinite variation. I speak not now from the practice of their modern verse writers, few of whom have any idea of musical variety but run on in the same monotonous flow through the whole poem, but rather from the example of their former poets, who were tolerable masters of this variety, and also from a capacity in the language of still admitting various unanticipated music.

Several rules have been drawn up for varying the poetic measure, and critics have elaborately talked of accents and syllables, but good sense and a fine ear which rules can never teach are what alone can in such a case determine. The rapturous flowings of joy or the interruptions of indignation require accents placed entirely different and a structure consonant to the emotions they would express. Changing passions and numbers changing with those passions make the whole secret of western as well as eastern poetry. In a word, the great faults of the modern professed English poets are that they seem to want numbers which should vary with the passion and are more employed in describing to the imagination than striking at the heart. Adieu.

LETTER FORTY-SEVEN

Misery best relieved by dissipation.

From Lien Chi Altangi to Hingpo, a slave in Persia.[28]

Your last letters betray a mind seemingly fond of wisdom, yet tempested up by a thousand various passions. You would fondly persuade me that my former lessons still influence your conduct, and yet your mind seems not less enslaved than your body. Knowledge, wisdom, erudition, arts and elegance, what are they but the mere trappings of the mind if they do not serve to encrease the happiness of the possessor? A mind rightly instituted in the school of philosophy acquires at once the stability of the oak and the flexibility of the osier. The truest manner of lessening our agonies is to shrink from their pressure; is to confess that we feel them.

The fortitude of European sages is but a dream, for where lies the merit in being insensible to the strokes of fortune or in dissembling our sensibility; if we are insensible, that arises only from an happy constitution; that is a blessing previously granted by heaven, and which no arts of our own can procure, no institutions improve. Being merely accidental, we can derive no merit from such a qualification, and as justly might boast of our birth, exaltation, or beauty.

If we dissemble our feelings, we only artificially endeavour to persuade others that we enjoy privyleges which we actually do not possess. Thus while we endeavour to appear happy we feel at once all the pangs of internal misery and all the self-reproaching consciousness of endeavouring to deceive.

I know but of two sects of philosophers in the world that have propagated this doctrine of fortitudes being an effectual support,—I mean the followers of Confucius and those who profess the doctrines of Christ. All other sects teach pride under misfortunes; they alone teach humility. Night, says our Chinese philosopher, not more surely follows day, than groans and tears grow out of pain; when misfortunes, therefore, oppress, when tyrants threaten, it is our interest, it is our duty, to seek redress from friendship, to seek redress from that best of friends who loved us into being.

Philosophers, my son, have long declaimed against the passions, as being the source of all our miseries; they are the source of all our misfortunes I own; but they are the source of our pleasures too; and every endeavour of our lives and all the institutions of philosophy should tend to this, not to dissemble an absence of passion, but to repel those which lead to vice by those which direct to virtue.

The soul may be compared to a field of battle where two armies are ready every moment to encounter; not a single vice but has a more powerful opponent; and not one virtue but may be overborne by a combination of vices. Reason guides the bands of either host, nor can it subdue one passion but by the assistance of another. Thus, as a bark on every side beset with storms enjoys a state of rest, so does the mind, when influenced by a just equipoize of the passions, enjoy tranquility.

I have used such means as my little fortune would admit to procure your freedom. I have lately written to the governor of Argun to pay your ransom, though at the expence of all the wealth I brought with me from China. If we become poor we shall at least have the pleasure of bearing poverty together; for what is fatigue or famine when weighed against friendship and freedom. Adieu.

LETTER FORTY-EIGHT

The absurdity of persons in high station pursuing employments beneath them, exemplified in a fairy tale.

*From Lien Chi Altangi to ***** merchant in Amsterdam.*

Happening a few days ago to call at a painter's to be amused in examining some pictures (I had no design to buy), it surprised me to see a young nobleman in the working room, dressed in a painter's apron, and assiduously learning the trade. We instantly remembered to have seen each other; and after the usual compliments I stood by while he continued to paint on as before. As every thing done by the rich is praised, as lords here as well as in China are never without followers, three or four persons, who had the appearance of gentlemen, were placed behind to comfort and applaud him at every stroke.

Need I tell that it struck me with very disagreeable sensations to see a youth, who by his station in life had it in his power to be useful to thousands, thus letting his mind run to waste upon canvas, though at the same time fancying himself improving in taste and filling his rank with proper decorum.

As seeing an error and attempting to redress it are one and the same with me, I took the opportunity, upon his lordship's desiring my opinion of a Chinese scroll intended for the frame of a picture, to assure him that a mandarine of China thought a minute acquaintance with such mechanical trifles beneath his dignity.

My reply raised the indignation of some and the contempt of others. I could hear the names of Vandal, Goth, taste, polite arts, delicacy, and fire, repeated in tones of ridicule or resentment. As it was vain to argue against people who had so much to say for themselves, without contradicting them I begged leave to repeat a Chinese fairy tale. This request redoubled their laughter; but not easily abashed at the rallery of boys, I persisted, adding that it was hoped the moral would recompence for its stupidity. "For heaven's sake," cried his lordship, washing his brush in water, "let us have no morality at present; if we must have a story, let it be in the modern taste, without any moral." I pretended not to hear; and while his lordship handled the brush, I proceeded as follows with *The History of Prince Bonbenin and his White Mouse.*

In the kingdom of Bonbobbin, which, by the Chinese annal, appears to have flourished twenty thousand years ago, there reigned a prince, endowed with every accomplishment which generally distinguishes the sons of kings. His beauty was brighter than the sun. The sun itself, to which he was nearly related, would sometimes stop its course in order to look down and admire him.

His mind was not less perfect than his body; he knew almost all things without having ever learned anything; philosophers, poets, and historians, submitted their works to his decision; and so penetrating was he, that he could tell the merit of a book merely by looking on the cover. He made epic poems, trage- dies, and pastorals with surprising facility; song, epigram, or rebus, was all one to him [tho' it is observed he could never finish an acrostic]. In short, the fairy who presided at his birth had endowed him with almost every perfection, or what was just the same, his subjects were ready to acknowledge he possessed them all; and, for his own part, he knew nothing to the contrary. A prince so accomplished received a name suit- able to his merit; and he was called Bonbenin bonbobbin bon- bobbinet, which in the language of the country signifies *En- lightener of the Sun.*

As he was very powerful, and yet unmarried, all the neigh- bouring kings earnestly sought his alliance. Each sent his daughter, dressed out in the most magnificent manner and with the most sumptuous retinue imaginable to the court of Bonbob- bin in order to allure the prince; so that at one time were seen at court not less than seven hundred foreign princesses of ex- quisite sentiment and beauty, each alone sufficient to make seven hundred ordinary men happy.

Distracted in such a variety, the generous Bonbenin, had he not been obliged by the laws of the empire to make choice of one, would very willingly have married them all, for none understood gallantry better than he. He spent numberless hours of solicitude in endeavouring to determine whom he should chuse; one lady was possessed of every perfection but he dis-

liked her father; another was brighter than the morning star
but he disapproved her fong whang[29]; a third did not lay
white enough on her cheek; and a fourth did not sufficiently
blacken her nails. At last after numberless disappointments on
the one side and the other he made choice of the incomparable
Nanhoa, queen of the scarlet dragons.

The preparations for the royal nuptials or the envy of the
disappointed ladies needs no description; both the one and
the other were as great as they could be; the beautiful princess
was conducted amidst admiring multitudes to the royal couch,
where after being divested of every encumbering ornament,
she was placed expecting the youthful bridegroom, who did
not keep her long in expectation. He came more chearful than
the morning, and printing on her lips a burning kiss, the attendants took this as a proper signal to withdraw.

Perhaps I ought to have mentioned before that, among
several other qualifications, the prince was fond of collecting
and breeding mice, which being an harmless pastime, none of
his counsellors thought proper to dissuade him against; a great
variety of these pretty little animals were kept in the most
beautiful cages enriched with diamonds, rubies, emeralds, and
other precious stones; thus he *innocently* spent four hours each
day in contemplating their innocent amusements.

But to proceed, the Prince and Princess were now in bed;
the one with all the love and expectation, the other with all
the modesty and fear, which so much become each sex; both
seemed willing, yet afraid to begin; when the Prince happening to look towards the outside of the bed, perceived a white
mouse with green eyes, one of the most beautiful animals in
the world, playing about the floor and performing an hundred
pretty tricks. He was already master of blue mice, red mice,
and even white mice with yellow eyes; but a white mouse
with green eyes was what he long endeavoured to be possessed
of; wherefore leaping from bed with the utmost impatience
and agility, the youthful Prince attempted to seize the little
trifler, but it was fled in a moment; for alas! the mouse was
a fairy.

It is impossible to describe the agony of the Prince upon this
occasion. He sought round and round every part of the room,
even the bed where the Princess lay was not exempt from the

enquiry; he turned the Princess on one side and t'other, [stripped her quite naked,] but no mouse was to be found; the Princess herself was kind enough to assist, but still to no purpose.

"Alas," cryed the young Prince in an agony, "how unhappy am I to be thus disappointed; never sure was so beautiful an animal seen. I would give half my kingdom and my princess to him that should find it." The Princess, though not much pleased with the latter part of his offer, endeavoured to comfort him as well as she could; she let him know that he had an hundred mice already, which ought to be at least sufficient to satisfy any philosopher like him. Tho' none of them had green eyes, yet he should learn to thank heaven that they had any eyes at all. She told him (for she was a profound moralist) that incurable evils must be borne, and that useless lamentations were vain, and that man was born to misfortunes; she even entreated him to return to bed, and she would endeavour to lull him on her bosom to repose; still however the Prince continued inconsolable; and regarding her with a stern air, for which his family was remarkable, he vow'd never to sleep in the royal palace or indulge himself in the innocent pleasures of matrimony till he had found the white mouse with green eyes.

"Prithee, Col. Leech," cried his Lordship, interrupting me, "how do you like that nose; don't you think there is something of the manner of Rembrandt in it? A prince in all this agony for a white mouse, O ridiculous! Don't you think, Major Vampyre, that eye-brow stippled very prettily? but pray what are the green eyes to the purpose, except to amuse children? I would give a thousand guineas to lay on the colouring of this cheek more smoothly. But I ask pardon, pray Sir, proceed."

LETTER FORTY-NINE

The fairy tale continued.

From the same.

Kings, continued I, at that time were different from what they are now; for they then never engaged their word for any thing which they did not rigorously intend to perform. This was the case of Bonbenin, who continued all night to lament his misfortunes to the Princess, who ecchoed groan for groan; and when morning came, he published an edict, offering half his kingdom, and also his Princess, to the person who should catch and bring him the white mouse with green eyes.

The edict was scarce published when all the traps in the kingdom were baited with cheese; numberless mice were taken and destroyed; but still the much desired mouse was not among the number. The privy council were assembled more than once to give their advice, but all their deliberations came to nothing, even though there were two professed rat-catchers of the number. Frequent addresses, as is usual on extraordinary occasions, were sent from all parts of the empire; but tho' these promised well, tho' in them he received an assurance that his faithful subjects would assist in his search with their lives and fortunes, yet, with all their loyalty, they failed when the mouse was to be caught.

The Prince therefore was resolved to go himself in search, determined never to lie two nights in one place till he had found what he sought for. Thus quitting his palace without attendants, he set out upon his journey and travelled through many a desert and crossed many a river, high over hills and down along the vales, still restless, still enquiring wherever he came; but no white mouse was to be found.

As one day, fatigued with his journey, he was shading himself from the heat of the mid-day sun under the arching branches of a banana tree, meditating on the object of his pursuit, he perceived an old woman, hideously deformed, approaching him; by her stoop and the wrinkles of her visage she seemed at least five hundred years old; and the spotted toad was not more freckled than was her skin. "Ah! prince Bonbenin-bonbobbin-bonbobbinet," cried the feature,[30] "what has led you so many thousand miles from your own kingdom; what is it you look for, and what brings you so far away into the Kingdom of Emmets?" The prince, who was excessively complaisant every where but at home, told her the whole story three times over, because she was hard of hearing. "Well then," says the old fairy, for such she was, "I'll promise to put you in possession of the white mouse with green eyes, and that immediately too, upon one condition." "One condition," cried the prince in a rapture, "name a thousand, and I shall undergo them all with pleasure." "Nay," interrupted the old fairy, "I ask but one, and that not very mortifying neither; it is only that you instantly marry me."

It is impossible to express the prince's confusion at this demand; he loved the mouse, but he detested the bride; he hesitated, desired time to think upon the proposal, adding that he would have been glad to consult his friends on such an occasion. "Nay, nay," cried the odious fairy, "if you demur, I retract my promise; I don't desire to force my favours on any man. Here, you my attendants," cried she, stamping with her foot, "let my machine be driven up. Barbacela, Queen of the Emmets, is not used to contemptuous treatment." She had no sooner spoken than her fiery chariot appeared in the air, drawn by two snails; and she was just going to step in, when the prince reflected that now or never was the time to be possessed of the white mouse; and quite forgetting his lawful princess Nanhoa, falling on his knees, implored forgiveness for his having rashly rejected so much beauty. This well-timed compliment instantly appeased the angry fairy. She affected an hideous leer of approbation, and taking the young prince by the hand, conducted him to a neighbouring church, where they were married together in a moment. As soon as the ceremony was performed, the prince, who was to the last degree desirous of seeing his little favourite, reminded the bride of her promise. "To confess a truth, my prince," cried she, "I myself am that very white mouse you saw on your wedding night in the royal apartment. I now therefore give you the choice, whether you would have me a mouse by day and a woman by night, or a mouse by night and a woman by day." Tho' the prince was an excellent casuist, he was quite at a loss how to determine, but at last thought it most prudent to have recourse to a blue cat that had followed him from his own dominions, and frequently amused him with its conversation and assisted him with its advice; in fact this cat was no other than the faithful Princess Nanhoa herself, who had shared with him all his hardships in this disguise.

By her instructions he was determined in his choice, and returning to the old fairy, prudently observed that as she must have been sensible he had married her *only for the sake of what she had* and not for her personal qualifications, he thought it would for several reasons be most convenient if she continued a woman by day and appeared a mouse by night.

The old fairy was a good deal mortified at the want of gallantry in her husband's choice, though she was reluctantly obliged to comply; the day was spent in the most polite amusements, the gentlemen talked smut and the ladies laughed and were angry. At last the happy night drew near; the blue cat still stuck by the side of its master and even followed him to the bridal apartment. Barbacela entered the chamber wearing a train fifteen yards long, supported by porcupines, and all over beset with jewels, which only served to render her more detestable. She was just stepping into bed to the Prince, forgetting her promise, when he insisted upon seeing her in the shape of a mouse, at the same time regarding her with a look of infinite tenderness. She had promised, and no fairy can break her word; wherefore assuming the figure of the most beautiful mouse in the world, she skipped and play'd about with an infinity of amusement. The Prince in an agony of rapture was desirous of seeing his pretty playfellow move a slow dance about the floor to his own singing; the mouse immediately began to perform with the most perfect knowledge of time and the finest grace and greatest gravity imaginable; it only began, for Nanhoa, who had long waited for the opportunity in the shape of a cat, flew upon it instantly without remorse, and eating it up in the hundredth part of a moment, broke the charm and resumed her natural figure.

The Prince now found that he had all along been under the power of enchantment, that his passion for the white mouse was entirely fictitious and not the genuine complexion of his soul; he now saw that his earnestness after mice was an illiberal amusement and much more becoming a ratcatcher than a Prince. All his meannesses now stared him in the face; he begged the discreet Princess's pardon an hundred times. The Princess very readily forgave him, and both returning to their palace in Bonbobbin, lived very happily together, and reigned many years with all that wisdom which, by the story, they appear to have been possessed of, perfectly convinced that they who place their affections on trifles at first for amusement, will find those trifles at length become their most serious concern. Adieu.

LETTER FIFTY-ONE

A Bookseller's visit to the Chinese.

From Lien Chi Altangi, to Fum Hoam, first president of the Ceremonial Academy at Pekin, in China.

As I was yesterday seated at breakfast over a pensive dish of tea, my meditations were interrupted by my old friend and companion, who introduced a stranger, dressed pretty much like himself. The gentleman made several apologies for his visit, begged of me to impute his intrusion to the sincerity of his respect and the warmth of his curiosity.

As I am very suspicious of my company when I find them very civil without an apparent reason, I answered the stranger's caresses at first with reserve; which my friend perceiving, instantly let me into my visitant's trade and character, asking Mr. Fudge whether he had lately published any thing new? I now conjectured that my guest was no other than a bookseller, and his answer confirmed my suspicions.

"Excuse me, Sir," says he, "it is not the season; books have their time as well as cucumbers. I would no more bring out a new work in summer than I would sell pork in the dog-days. Nothing in my way goes off in summer except very light goods indeed. A review, a magazine, or a sessions paper, may amuse a summer reader; but all our stock of value we reserve for a spring and winter trade." "I must confess, Sir," says I, "a curiosity to know what you call a valuable stock, which can only bear a winter perusal." "Sir," reply'd the bookseller, "it is not my way to cry up my own goods, but without exaggeration I will venture to shew with any of the trade; my books at least have the peculiar advantage of being always new; and it is my way to clear off my old to the trunkmakers every season. I have ten new title pages now about me which only want books to be added to make them the finest things in nature. Others may pretend to direct the vulgar, but that is not my way. I always let the vulgar direct me; wherever popular clamour arises, I always eccho the million. For instance, should the people in general say that such a man is a rogue, I instantly give orders to set him down in print a villain; thus every man buys the book, not to learn new sentiments, but to have the pleasure of seeing his own reflected." "But Sir," interrupted I, "you speak as if you yourself wrote the books you publish; may I be so bold as to ask a sight of some of those intended publications which are shortly to surprize the world?" "As to that, Sir," reply'd the talkative bookseller, "I only draw out the plans myself; and though I am very cautious of communicating them to any, yet as in the end I have a favour to ask, you shall see a few of them. Here, Sir, here they are, diamonds of the first water, I assure you. Imprimis, a translation of several medical precepts for the use of such physicians as do not understand Latin. Item, the young clergyman's art of placing patches regularly, with a dissertation on the different manners of smiling without distorting the face. Item, the whole art of love made perfectly easy by a broker of 'Change Alley. Item, the proper manner of cutting black-lead pencils and making crayons, by the Right Hon. the Earl of * * * . Item, the muster master general, or the review of reviews. Item—" "Sir," cried I, interrupting him, "my curiosity with regard to title pages is satisfied. I should be glad to see some longer manuscript, an history or an epic poem."—"Bless me," cries the man of industry, "now you speak of an epic poem, you shall see an excellent farce. Here it is; dip into it where you will, it will be found replete with true modern humour. Strokes, Sir; it is filled with strokes of wit and satire in every line." "Do you call these dashes of the pen strokes," reply'd I, "for I must confess I can see no other?" "And pray Sir," returned he, "what do you call them? Do you see any thing good now a-days that is not filled with strokes—and dashes?—Sir, a well placed dash makes half the wit of our writers of modern humour. I bought last season a piece that had no other merit upon earth than nine hundred and ninety-five breaks, seventy-two ha ha's, three good things, and a caster.[31] And yet it played off, and bounced, and cracked, and made more sport than a fire work." "I fancy then, Sir, you were a considerable gainer?" "It must be owned the piece did pay; but upon the whole I cannot much boast of last winter's success. I gain'd by two murders, but then I lost by an ill timed charity sermon. I was a considerable sufferer by my *Direct road to an estate,* but the

Infernal Guide brought me up again. Ah, Sir, that was a piece touch'd off by the hands of a master, filled with good things from one end to the other. The author had nothing but the jest in view, no dull moral lurking beneath nor ill-natured satyr to sour the reader's good humour; he wisely considered that moral and humour at the same time were quite over-doing the business." "To what purpose was the book then published?" cried I. "Sir, the book was published in order to be sold; and no book sold better except the criticisms upon it, which came out soon after. Of all kinds of writing that goes off best at present; and I generally fasten a criticism upon every silly book that is published.

"I once had an author who never left the least opening for the critics; close was the word, always very right, and very dull, ever on the safe side of an argument, yet with all his qualifications, incapable of coming into favour. I soon perceived that his bent was for criticism; and as he was good for nothing else, supplied him with pens and paper and planted him at the beginning of every month as a censor on the works of others. In short, I found him a treasure; no merit could escape him; but what is most remarkable of all, he ever wrote best and bitterest when drunk." "But are there not some works," interrupted I, "that from the very manner of their composition must be exempt from criticism, particularly such as profess to disregard its laws." "There is no work whatsoever but he can criticise," replied the bookseller; "even though you wrote in Chinese he would have a pluck at you. Suppose you should take it into your head to publish a book, let it be a volume of Chinese letters for instance; write how you will, he shall shew the world you could have written better. Should you, with the most local exactness, stick to the manners and customs of the country from whence you come; should you confine yourself to the narrow limits of eastern knowledge, and be perfectly simple and perfectly natural, he has then the strongest reason to exclaim. He may with a sneer send you back to China for readers. He may observe that after the first or second letter the iteration of the same simplicity is insupportably tedious; but the worst of all is, the public in such a case will anticipate his censures and leave you with all your uninstructive simplicity to be mauled at discretion."

"Yes, but," cried I, "in order to avoid his indignation, and what I should fear more, that of the public, I would in such a case write with all the knowledge I was master of. As I am not possessed of much learning, at least I would not suppress what little I had; nor would I appear more stupid than nature made me." "Here then," cries the bookseller, "we should have you entirely in our power; unnatural, uneastern, quite out of character, erroneously sensible would be the whole cry. Sir, we should then hunt you down like a rat." "Head of my father!" said I, "sure there are but the two ways; the door must either be shut, or it must be open. I must either be natural or unnatural." "Be what you will, we shall criticise you," returned the bookseller, "and prove you a dunce in spite of your teeth. But, Sir, it is time that I should come to business. I have just now in the press an history of China; and if you will but put your name to it as the author, I shall repay the obligation with gratitude." "What, Sir," replied I, "put my name to a work which I have not written! Never while I retain a proper respect for the public and myself." The bluntness of my reply quite abated the ardour of the bookseller's conversation, and after about half an hour's disagreeable reserve he with some ceremony took his leave and withdrew. Adieu.

LETTER FIFTY-THREE

The absurd taste for obscene and pert novels, such as *Tristram Shandy,* ridiculed.

From the same.

How often, my friend, have we admired the eloquence of Europe! That strength of thinking, that delicacy of imagination, even beyond the efforts of the Chinese themselves. How were we enraptured with those bold figures which sent every sentiment with force to the soul! How have we spent whole days together in learning those arts by which European writers got within the passions and led the reader as if by enchantment!

But though we have learned most of the rhetorical figures of the last age, tho' we are no strangers to the catachresis, the epianadiplosis, the aposiopesis, and the rest of them, yet there seems to be one or two of great use here which have not yet travelled to China. What may perhaps be still more amazing is that no figures are more fashionable; none so sure of admirers; they are of such a nature that the merest blockhead, by a proper use of them, shall have the reputation of a wit; they lye level to the meanest capacities and address those passions which all have, or would be ashamed to disown. The figures I mean are called baudy and pertness.

It has been often observed, and I believe with some truth, that it is very difficult for a dunce to obtain the reputation of a wit; yet by the assistance of the figure baudy this may be easily effected, [and a bawdy blockhead often passes for a fellow of smart parts and pretensions]. Every object in nature helps the joke forward without scarce any effort of the imagination. If a lady happens to stand or fall, with the help of a little fashionable pruriency something good may be said on the occasion. If a gentleman should leap or run, still the figure may be easily applied. By the use of this in common conversation, I never knew a dunce that could not make the company laugh whenever he thought proper, but it has always been found to give most pleasure to a few very old gentlemen, who being in some measure dead to other sensations, feel the force of the jest with double violence on the organs of risibility.

An author who writes in this manner is generally sure therefore of having the very old and the impotent among his admirers; for these he may properly be said to write, and from these he ought to expect his reward, his works being often a very proper succedaneum to cantharides or an assafœtida pill. His pen should be considered in the same useful light as the squirt of an apothecary, both being directed at the same generous end.

Though this manner of writing be perfectly adapted to the taste of gentlemen and ladies of fashion here, yet still it deserves greater praise in being equally suited to the most vulgar apprehensions. The very ladies and gentlemen of Benin or Cafraria are in this respect tolerably polite and can relish a prurient joke of this kind with critical propriety; and probably, too, with higher gust, as they wear neither breeches nor petticoats to intercept the application.

It is certain I could never have expected the ladies here, biassed as they are by education, capable at once of bravely throwing off their prejudices, and not only applauding books in which this figure makes the only merit but even adopting it in their own conversation. Yet so it is; the pretty innocents now carry those books openly in their hands which formerly were hid under the cushion; they now lisp their double meanings with so much grace, and talk over the raptures they bestow with such little reserve, that I am sometimes reminded of a custom among some entertainers in China, who think it a piece of necessary breeding to whet the appetites of their guests by letting them smell dinner in the kitchen, long before it is served up to table.

The veneration we have for many things entirely proceeds from their being carefully concealed. Were the idolatrous Tartar permitted to lift up the veil which keeps his idol from view, it might be a certain method to cure his future super-stition; with what a noble spirit of freedom therefore must that writer be possessed who bravely paints things as they are, who displays the most hidden recesses of the temple, and shews the erring people that what they offer incense to is either perhaps a mouse or a monkey.

Though this figure be at present so much in fashion, though the professors of it are so much caressed by the great, those perfect judges of literary excellence, yet it is confessed to be only a revival of what was once fashionable here before. There was a time when by this very manner of writing the gentle Tom. Durfey, as I read in English authors, acquired his great reputation and became the favourite of a king.[32]

The works of this original genius, tho' they never travelled abroad to China, and scarce reach'd posterity at home, were once found upon every fashionable toilet and made the subject of polite, I mean very polite conversation. "Has Your Grace seen Mr. Durfey's last new thing, the Oylet Hole. A most facetious piece?" "Sure, my Lord, all the world must have seen it; Durfey is certainly the most comical creature alive. It is impossible to read his things and live. Was there ever anything so natural and pretty, as when the Squire and Bridget meet in the cellar. And then the difficulties they both find in broaching the wine cask are so arch and so ingenious! We have certainly nothing of the kind in the language." In this manner they spoke then, and in this manner they speak now; for though the successors of Durfey do not excel him in wit, the world must confess they out-do him in obscenity.

There are several very dull fellows who, by a few mechanical helps, sometimes learn to become extremely brilliant and pleasing; with a little dexterity in the management of the eye brows, fingers, and nose, many a wag has extended his reputation over half a street. By imitating a cat, a sow and pigs, by a loud laugh and a slap on the shoulder, the most ignorant are furnished out for conversation. In a companion there are thus many helps to festivity, but the writer is unfortunately destitute of them all. He finds it impossible to throw his winks, his shrugs, or his attitudes upon paper; he may borrow some assistance indeed by printing his face at the title page; but still without wit to pass for a man of ingenuity, several other mechanical helps are absolutely necessary. Nothing in this case can be so useful as the figure in question. By speaking to some peculiar sensations we are always sure of exciting laughter, for the jest does not lie in the writer, but in the subject he has chosen.

But this manner is defective unless helped on by another figure, called pertness; and few indeed are found to excell in one that are not possessed of the other.

As in common conversation the best way to make the audience laugh is by first laughing yourself; so in writing the properest manner is to shew an aim at humour, which will pass upon most for humour in reality. To effect this, readers must be treated with the most perfect familiarity: in one page the author is to make them a low bow and in the next to pull them by the nose: he must talk in riddles and then send them to bed in order to dream for the solution. He must speak of himself and his chapters and his manner and what he would be at, with the most unpitying prolixity, and now and then testify his contempt for all the world beside. Ever smiling without a jest, and without wit possessed of vivacity, he may use what freedoms he thinks proper, provided he now and then throws out a hint of being too contemptible for resentment. Adieu.

LETTER FIFTY-FOUR

The character of an important trifler.

From the same.

Tho' naturally pensive, yet I am fond of gay company, and take every opportunity of thus dismissing the mind from duty. From this motive I am often found in the centre of a crowd, and wherever pleasure is to be sold am always a purchaser. In those places without being remarked by any I join in whatever goes forward, work my passions into a similitude of frivolous earnestness, shout as they shout, and condemn as they happen to disapprove. A mind thus sunk for a while below its natural standard is qualified for stronger flights, as those first retire who would spring forward with greater vigour.

Attracted by the serenity of the evening, my friend and I lately went to gaze upon the company in one of the public walks near the city. Here we sauntred together for some time, either praising the beauty of such as were handsome or the dresses of such as had nothing else to recommend them. We had gone thus deliberately forward for some time, when stopping on a sudden, my friend caught me by the elbow and led me out of the public walk. I could perceive by his accelerated pace and by his frequently looking behind that he was attempting to avoid somebody who followed; we now turned to the right, then to the left; as we went forward he still went faster, but in vain; the person whom he attempted to escape hunted us through every doubling and gained upon us each moment, so that at last we fairly stood still, resolving to face what we could not avoid.

Our pursuer soon came up and joined us with all the familiarity of an old acquaintance. "My dear Drybone," cries he, shaking my friend's hand, "where have you been hiding this half a century? Positively I had fancied you were gone down to cultivate matrimony and your estate in the country." During the reply I had an opportunity of surveying the appearance of our new companion; his hat was pinch'd up with peculiar smartness; his looks were pale, thin, and sharp; round his neck he wore a broad black ribbon and in his bosom a buckle studded with glass; his coat was trimmed with tarnish'd twist;

he wore by his side a sword with a black hilt, and his stockings of silk, though newly wash'd, were grown yellow by long service. I was so much engaged with the peculiarity of his dress that I attended only to the latter part of my friend's reply, in which he complimented Mr. Tibbs on the taste of his cloaths and the bloom in his countenance. "Psha, psha, Will," cried the figure, "no more of that if you love me; you know I hate flattery, on my soul I do; and yet to be sure an intimacy with the great will improve one's appearance, and a course of venison will fatten; and yet faith I despise the great as much as you do; but there are a great many damn'd honest fellows among them; and we must not quarrel with one half because the other wants weeding. If they were all such as my lord Mudler, one of the most good-natured creatures that ever squeez'd a lemon, I should myself be among the number of their admirers. I was yesterday to dine at the Dutchess of Piccadilly's. My lord was there. 'Ned,' says he to me, 'Ned,' says he, 'I'll hold gold to silver I can tell where you were poaching last night.' 'Poaching my lord,' says I; 'faith you have missed it already; for I staid at home and let the girls poach for me. That's my way; I take a fine woman as some animals do their prey; stand still, and swoop, she falls into my mouth.' "

"Ah, Tibbs, thou art an happy fellow," cried my companion with looks of infinite pity, "I hope your fortune is as much improved as your understanding in such company?" "Improved," reply'd the other; "You shall know,—but let it go no further,—a great secret——five hundred a year to begin with.——My Lord's word of honour for it—His Lordship took me down in his own Chariot yesterday, and we had a tete-a-tete dinner in the country; where we talked of nothing else." "I fancy you forget, sir," cried I, "you told us but this moment of your dining yesterday in town!" "Did I say so," replied he, cooly, "to be sure if I said so, it was so—Dined in town: egad now I do remember, I did dine in town; but I dined in the country too; for you must know, my boys, I eat two dinners. By the bye, I am grown as nice as the Devil in my eating. I'll tell you a pleasant affair about that, we were a select party of us to dine at Lady Grogram's, an affected piece, but let it go no farther; a secret: well, there happened to be no Assafœtida in the sauce to a turkey, upon which, says I, 'I'll hold a thousand guineas, and say done first, that'—But dear Drybone, you are an honest creature, lend me half-a-crown for a minute or two, or so, just till—But hearkee, ask me for it the next time we meet, or it may be twenty to one but I forget."

When he left us our conversation naturally turned upon so extraordinary a character. "His very dress," cries my friend, "is not less extraordinary than his conduct. If you meet him this day you find him in rags, if the next in embroidery. With those persons of distinction of whom he talks so familiarly, he has scarce a coffee-house acquaintance. Both for the interests of society, and perhaps for his own, heaven has made him poor, and while all the world perceive his wants, he fancies them concealed from every eye. An agreeable companion because he understands flattery, and all must be pleased with the first part of his conversation, though all are sure of its ending with a demand on their purse. While his youth countenances the levity of his conduct, he may thus earn a precarious subsistance, but when age comes on, the gravity of which is incompatible with buffoonery, then will he find himself forsaken by all. Condemned in the decline of life to hang upon some rich family whom he once despised, there will he undergo all the ingenuity of studied contempt, be employed only as a spy upon the servants, or a bug-bear to fright the children into good humour." Adieu.

LETTER FIFTY-FIVE

His character continued: With that of his wife, his house, and furniture.

To the same.

I am apt to fancy I have contracted a new acquaintance whom it will be no easy matter to shake off. The little shabby beau I described in one of my former letters again overtook me alone in one of the publick walks, and slapping me on the shoulder, saluted me with an air of the most perfect familiarity. His dress was the same as usual, except that he had more powder in his hair, wore dirtier linen, a pair of temple spectacles, and his hat under his arm.

As I knew him to be an harmless amusing little thing, I could not return his smiles with any degree of severity; so we walked forward on terms of the utmost intimacy and in a few minutes discussed all the usual topics preliminary to particular conversation.

The oddities that marked his character, however, soon began to appear; he bowed to several well dressed persons who, by their manner of returning the compliment, appeared perfect strangers, and at intervals drew out a pocket book, seeming to take memorandums before all the company, with much importance and assiduity. In this manner he led me through the length of the whole walk, fretting at his absurdities and fancying myself laughed at by every spectator.

When we were got to the end of our procession, "Blast me," cries he, with an air of vivacity, "I never saw the people so thin in my life before; there's no company at all to day. Not a single face to be seen." "No company," interrupted I peevishly; "why man, there's too much. What is the thousand that has been laughing at us but company!" "Lord, my dear," returned he with the utmost good humour, "you seem immensely chagrined; when the world laughs at me, why, I laugh at the world, and so we are even. My Lord Trip, Bill Squash the Creolian, and I sometimes make a party at being ridiculous; and so we say and do a thousand things for the joke sake, all which is nothing. But I see you are grave, and if you are for a fine sentimental companion, you shall dine with me to day, I must insist on 't; I'll introduce you to my spouse, Mrs. Tibbs, a Lady of as elegant qualifications as any in nature; she was bred, but that's between ourselves, under the inspection of the Countess of All-night. A charming body of voice, but no more of that, she shall give us a song. You shall see my little girl too, Carolina Wilhelma Amelia Tibbs, a sweet pretty creature; I design her for my Lord Drumstick's eldest son, but that's in friendship, let it go no farther; she's but six years old, and yet she dances a minuet, and plays on the guittar immensely already. I intend she shall be as perfect as possible in every accomplishment. In the first place I'll make her a scholar; I'll teach her Greek myself, and learn that language purposely to instruct her; but let that be a secret."

Thus saying, without waiting for a reply, he took me by the arm and haul'd me along. We passed through many dark alleys and winding ways; for, from some motives to me unknown, he seemed to have a particular aversion to every frequented street; at last, however, we got to the door of a dismal looking house in the outlets of the town, where he informed me he chose to reside for the benefit of the air.

We entered the lower door, which ever seemed to lie most hospitably open; and began to ascend an old and creaking stair-case, when, as he mounted to shew me the way, he demanded whether I delighted in prospects, to which answering in the affirmative, "Then," says he, "I shall shew you one of the most charming in the world out of my windows; we shall see the ships sailing and the whole country for twenty miles round, tip top, quite high. My Lord Swamp would give ten thousand guineas for such a one; but as I sometimes pleasantly tell him, I always love to keep my prospects at home, that my friends may see me the oftener."

By this time we were arrived as high as the stairs would permit us to ascend, till we came to what he was facetiously pleased to call the first floor down the chimney; and knocking at the door, a voice from within demanded, "who's there?" My conductor answered that it was him. But this not satisfying the querist, the voice again repeated the demand: to which he answered louder than before; and now the door was opened by an old woman with cautious reluctance.

When we were got in, he welcomed me home with great ceremony, and turning to the old woman, asked where was her lady? "Gud troth," replied she, in a provincial dialect, "she's washing your twa shirts at the next door, because they have taken an oath against lending out the tub any longer." "My two shirts," cries he in a tone that faultered with confusion, "what does the ideot mean?" "I ken what I mean well enough," replied the other, "she's washing your twa shirts at the next door, because——" "Well, no more of thy stupid explanations, ideot," cried he.——"Go and inform her we have got company. Were that Scotch hag," continued he when she was gone, "to be forever in my family, she would never be polite, or forget that absurd poisonous accent of hers, or testify the smallest specimen of high life; and yet it is very surprizing too, as I had her from a parliament man, a friend of mine, from the highlands, one of the politest men in the world; but that's a secret."

We waited some time for the lady's arrival, during which

interval I had a full opportunity of surveying the chamber and all its furniture. This consisted of four chairs with old wrought bottoms which he assured me were his wife's embroidery, a square table that had been once japanned, a cradle in one corner, a lumbering cabinet in the other, a broken shepherdess and a mandarine without an head were stuck over the chimney; and round the walls several paltry, unframed pictures which he observed were all his own drawing: "What do you think, Sir, of that head in the corner, done in the manner of Grisoni? there's the true keeping in it; its my own face, and though there happens to be no likeness, a countess offered me an hundred for its fellow; I refused her, for, hang it, that would be mechanical, you know."

The wife at last made her appearance, at once a slattern and a coquet, much emaciated, but still carrying the remains of beauty. She made twenty apologies for being seen in such an odious dishabille, but hoped to be excused, as she had staid out all night at the gardens with the countess, who was excessively fond of the *horns.* "And, indeed, my dear," added she, turning to her husband, "his lordship drank your health in a bumper." "Poor Jack," cries he, "a dear good-natured creature, I know he loves me; but I hope, my dear, you have given orders for dinner; though you need make no great preparations neither, there are but three of us, something elegant, and little will do; a bechamele, a turbot, an ortolan, or a ——." "Or what do you think, my dear," interrupts the wife, "of a nice pretty bit of ox cheek, piping hot, and dressed with a little of my own sauce.— "The very thing," replies he, "it will eat best with some porter; but be sure to let's have that sauce his Grace was so fond of. I hate your immense loads of meat, it is extreme disgusting to those who are in the least acquainted with high life."

By this time my curiosity began to abate, and my appetite to encrease; the company of fools may at first make us smile, but at last never fails of rendering us melancholy. I therefore pretended to recollect a prior engagement, and after having shewn my respect to the house, according to the fashion of the English, by giving the old servant a piece of money at the door, I took my leave. Adieu.

LETTER FIFTY-SEVEN

The difficulty of rising in literary reputation without intrigue or riches.

From the same.

I have frequently admired the manner of criticising in China, where the learned are assembled in a body to judge of every new publication, to examine the merits of the work without knowing the circumstances of the author, and then to usher it into the world with the proper marks of respect or reprobation.

In England there are no such tribunals erected; but if a man thinks proper to be a judge of genius, there are none found who will be at the pains to contradict his pretensions. If any chuse to be critics, it is but saying they are critics; and from that time forward they are invested with full power and authority over every caitiff who aims at their instruction or entertainment.

As almost every subject has by this means a vote in literary transactions, it is no way surprizing to find the rich leading the way here as in other common concerns of life, to see them either bribing the numerous herd of voters by their interest or brow-beating them by their authority.

A great man says at his table that such a book *is no bad thing*. Immediately the praise is carried off by five led captains to be dispersed at twelve different coffee-houses, from whence it circulates, still improving as it proceeds, through forty-five houses where cheaper liquors are sold; from thence it is carried away by the honest tradesman to his own fire-side, where the applause is eagerly caught up by his wife and children who have been long taught to regard his judgment as the standard of perfection. Thus when we have traced a wide extended literary reputation up to its original source, we shall find it derived from some great man who has perhaps received all his education and English from a tutor of Berne and a dancing-master of Picardie.

The English are a people of good sense; and I am the more surprized to find them sway'd in their opinions by men who often from their very education are incompetent judges. Men who being always bred in affluence see the world only on one side are surely improper judges of human nature; they may indeed describe a ceremony, a pageant or a ball; but how can they pretend to dive into the secrets of the human heart, who have been nursed up only in forms and daily behold nothing but the same insipid adulation smiling upon every face. Few of them have been bred in that best of schools, the school of adversity; and by what I can learn fewer still have been bred in any school at all.

From such a description one would think that a droning Duke or a Dowager Duchess was not possessed of more just pretensions to taste than persons of less quality; and yet whatever either may write or praise shall pass for perfection, without farther examination. A nobleman has but to take pen, ink, and paper, and write away through three large volumes and then sign his name to the title page, tho' the whole might have been before more disgusting than his own rent-roll, yet signing his name and title gives value to the deed, title being alone equivalent to taste, imagination, and genius.

As soon as a piece is published here, the first questions are, Who is the author? Does he keep a coach? Where lies his estate? What sort of a table does he keep? If he happens to be unqualified for such a scrutiny, he and his works sink into irremediable obscurity; and too late he finds that having fed upon Turtle is a more ready way to fame than having digested Tully.

The poor devil against whom fashion has set its face vainly alledges that he has been bred in every part of Europe where knowledge was to be sold, that he has grown pale in the study of nature and himself; his works may please upon the perusal, but his pretensions to fame are intirely disregarded; he is treated like a fidler whose music, though liked, is not much praised because he lives by it, while a gentleman performer, though the most wretched scraper alive, throws the audience into raptures. It is true the fidler may in such a case console himself by thinking that while the other goes off with all the praise he runs away with all the money; but here the parallel drops, for while the nobleman triumphs in unmerited applause, the author by profession steals off with—*Nothing*.

The poor therefore here, who draw their pens auxiliary to the laws of their country, must think themselves very happy if they find not fame but forgiveness; and yet they are hardly treated; for as every country grows more polite, the press becomes more useful; and writers become more necessary as readers are supposed to increase. In a polished society that man, though in rags, who has the power of enforcing virtue from the press is of more real use than forty stupid brachmans or bonzes or guebres, though they preached never so often, never so loud, or never so long. That man, though in rags, who is capable of deceiving even indolence into wisdom and who professes amusement while he aims at reformation, is more useful in refined society than twenty cardinals with all their scarlet and tricked out in the fopperies of scholastic finery. Adieu.

LETTER FIFTY-EIGHT

A Visitation dinner described.

To the same.

As the man in black takes every opportunity of introducing me to such company as may serve to indulge my speculative temper or gratify my curiosity, I was by his influence lately invited to a *visitation* dinner. To understand this term you must know that it was formerly the custom here for the principal priests to go about the country once a year and examine upon the spot whether the inferior priests did their duty, or were qualified for the task; whether their temples were kept in proper repair, or the laity pleased with their administration.

Though a visitation of this nature was very useful, yet it was found to be extremely troublesome, and for many reasons utterly inconvenient; for as the principal priests were obliged to attend at court, in order to solicit preferment, it was impossible they could at the same time attend in the country, which was quite out of the road to promotion; if we add to this the gout, which has ever stuck by the clergy and which is a disorder averse to travelling, together with the bad wine and ill dressed provisions that must infallibly be met by the way, it was not strange that the custom has been long discontinued. At present, therefore, every head of the church, instead of going about to visit his priests, is satisfied if his priests come in a body once a year to visit him; by this means the duty of half a year is dispatched in a day. Here he asks each in his turn how they have behaved, and how they are liked; upon which, those who have neglected their duty, or are disagreeable to their congregation, accuse themselves and tell him all their faults, for which no doubt he reprimands them most severely.

The thoughts of being introduced into a company of philosophers and learned men, (for as such I conceived them) gave me no small pleasure; I expected our entertainment would resemble those sentimental banquets so finely described by Xenophon and Plato; I was hoping some Socrates would be brought in from the door in order to harangue upon divine love; but as for eating and drinking I had prepared myself to be disappointed in that particular. I was apprized that fasting and temperance were tenets strongly recommended to the professors of Christianity, and I had seen the frugality and mortification of the priests of the east, so that I expected an entertainment where we should have much reasoning and little food.

Upon being introduced I confess I found no great signs of mortification in the faces or persons of the company. However, their florid looks I imputed to temperance, and their corpulence to a sedentary way of living. I saw several preparations indeed for dinner, but none for philosophy. The company seemed to gaze upon the table with silent expectation, but this I easily excused. Men of wisdom, thought I, are ever slow of speech; they deliver nothing unadvisedly. *Silence,* says Confucius, *is a friend that will never betray*. They are now probably inventing maxims or hard sayings for their mutual instruction, when some one shall think proper to begin.

My curiosity was now wrought up to the highest pitch; I impatiently looked round to see if any were going to interrupt the mighty pause; when, at last, one of the company declared that there was a sow in his neighbourhood that farrowed fifteen pigs at a litter; just as another was going to second the remark, dinner was served, which interrupted the conversation that had begun so auspiciously.

The appearance of dinner, which consisted of a variety of dishes, seemed to diffuse new chearfulness upon every face; so that I now expected the philosophical conversation to begin as they improved in good humour. The principal priest, however, opened his mouth with only observing that the venison had not been kept enough, though he had given strict orders for having it killed ten days before. "I fear," continues he, "it will be found to want the true heathy flavour; you will find nothing of the original wildness in it." A priest who sate next him, having smelt it and wiped his nose: "Ah, my good lord," cries he, "you are too modest; it is perfectly fine; every body knows that no body understands keeping venison with your Lordship." "Ay, and partridges too," interrupted another; "I never find them right any where else." His Lordship was going to reply, when a third took off the attention of the company by recommending the pig as inimitable. "I fancy, my Lord," continues he, "it has been smothered in its own blood." "If it has been smothered in its blood," cried a facetious member, helping himself, "we'll now smother it in egg sauce." This poignant piece of humour produced a long loud laugh, which the facetious brother observing, and now that he was in luck, willing to second his blow, assured the company he would tell them a good story about that: "As good a story," cries he, bursting into a violent fit of laughter himself, "as ever you heard in your lives; there was a farmer of my parish, who used to sup upon wild ducks and flummery; so this farmer—" "Doctor Marrowfat," cries his Lordship, interrupting him, "give me leave to drink your health—" "so being fond of wild ducks and flummery—" "Doctor," adds a gentleman who sate next him, "let me advise you to a wing of this turkey;—" "so this farmer being fond—" "Hob nob, Doctor, which do you chuse, white or red?—" "So being fond of wild ducks and flummery;—" "take care of your band, Sir, it may dip in the gravy." The Doctor, now looking round, found not a single *eye* disposed to hearken; wherefore calling for a glass of wine, he gulped down the disappointment and the tale in a bumper.

The conversation now began to be little more than a rhapsody of exclamations; as each had pretty well satisfied his own appetite, he now found sufficient time to press others. *Excellent, the very thing; let me recommend the pig, do but taste the bacon; never eat a better thing in my life; exquisite, delicious.* This edifying discourse continued thro' three courses, which lasted as many hours, till every one of the company were unable to swallow or utter any thing more.

It is very natural for men who are abridged in one excess, to break into some other. The clergy here, particularly those who are advanced in years, think if they are abstemious with regard to women and wine, they may indulge their other appetites without censure. Thus some are found to rise in the morning only to a consultation with their cook about dinner, and when that has been swallowed, make no other use of their faculties (if they have any) but to ruminate on the succeeding meal.

A debauch in wine is even more pardonable than this, since one glass insensibly leads on to another, and instead of sateing whets the appetite. The progressive steps to it are chearful and seducing; the grave are animated, the melancholy relieved, and there is even classic authority to countenance the excess. But in eating after nature is once satisfied every additional morsel brings stupidity and distempers with it, and as one of their own poets expresses it,

> The soul subsides, and wickedly inclines,
> To seem but mortal, even in sound divines.[33]

Let me suppose, after such a meal as this I have been describing, while all the company are sitting in lethargic silence round the table grunting under a load of soup, pig, pork, and bacon; let me suppose, I say, some hungry beggar, with looks of want, peeping thro' one of the windows and thus addressing the assembly, *Prithee, pluck those napkins from each chin; after nature is satisfied all that you eat extraordinary is my property, and I claim it as my due. It was given you in order to relieve me, and not to oppress yourselves. How can they comfort or instruct others who can scarce feel their own existence, except from the unsavoury returns of an ill digested meal? But tho' neither you nor the cushions you sit upon will hear me, yet the world regards the excesses of its teachers with a prying eye and notes their conduct with double severity.* I know no other answer any one of the company could make to such an expostulation but this: "Friend, you talk of our losing a character, and being disliked by the world; well, and supposing all this to be true, what then! who cares for the world? We'll preach for the world, and the world shall pay us for preaching, whether we like each other or not." Adieu.

LETTER FIFTY-NINE

The Chinese philosopher's son escapes with the beautiful captive from slavery.

From Hingpo to Lien Chi Altangi, by the way of Moscow.

You will probably be pleased to see my letter dated from Terki, a city which lies beyond the bounds of the Persian empire: here, blessed with security, with all that is dear, I double my raptures by communicating them to you; the mind sympathizing with the freedom of the body, my whole soul is dilated in gratitude, love, and praise.

Yet were my own happiness all that inspired my present joy, my raptures might justly merit the imputation of self-interest; but when I think that the beautiful Zelis is also free, forgive my triumph when I boast of having rescued from captivity the most deserving object upon earth.

You remember the reluctance she testified at being obliged to marry the tyrant she hated. Her compliance at last was only feigned, in order to gain time to try some future means of escape. During the interval between her promise and the intended performance of it, she came undiscovered one evening to the place where I generally retired after the fatigues of the day; her appearance was like that of an aerial genius when it descends to minister comfort to undeserved distress; the mild lustre of her eye served to banish my timidity; her accents were sweeter than the eccho of some distant symphony. "Unhappy stranger," said she, in the Persian language, "you here perceive one more wretched than thyself; all this solemnity of preparation, this elegance of dress, and the number of my attendants, serve but to encrease my miseries; if you have courage to rescue an unhappy woman from approaching ruin and our detested tyrant, you may depend upon my future gratitude." I bowed to the ground, and she left me filled with rapture and astonishment. Night brought no rest, nor could the ensuing morning calm the anxieties of my mind. I projected a thousand methods for her delivery; but each, when strictly examined, appeared impracticable; in this uncertainty the evening again arrived, and I placed myself on my former station in hopes of a repeated visit. After some short expectation, the bright perfection again appeared; I bowed, as before, to the ground; when raising me up she observed that the time was not to be spent in useless ceremony; she observed that the day following was appointed for the celebration of her nuptials, and that something was to be done that very night for our mutual deliverance. I offered with the utmost humility to pursue whatever scheme she should direct; upon which she proposed that instant to scale the garden wall, adding that she had prevailed upon a female slave, who was now waiting at the appointed place, to assist her with a ladder of ropes.

Pursuant to this information I led her trembling to the place appointed; but instead of the slave we expected to see, Mostadad himself was there awaiting our arrival; the wretch in whom we confided, it seems, had betrayed our design to her master, and he now saw the most convincing proofs of her information. He was just going to draw his sabre, when a principle of avarice repressing his fury, he resolved, after a severe chastisement, to dispose of me to another master, in the mean time ordering me to be confined in the strictest manner, and the next day to receive an hundred blows on the soles of the feet.

When the morning came I was led out in order to receive the punishment, which, from the severity in which it is generally inflicted upon slaves, is worse even than death.

The sounding a trumpet was to be a signal for the solemnization of the nuptials of Zelis and for the infliction of my punishment. Each ceremony to me equally dreadful were just going to begin when we were informed that a large party of Circassian Tartars had invaded the town and were laying all in ruin. Every person now thought only of saving himself; I instantly unloosed the cords with which I was bound, and seizing a scymetar from one of the slaves who had not courage to resist me, flew to the women's apartment where Zelis was confined, dressed out for the intended nuptials. I bade her follow me without delay; and going forward, cut my way through eunuchs, who made but a faint resistance. The whole city was now a scene of conflagration and terror; every person was willing to save himself, unmindful of others. In this confusion seizing upon two of the fleetest coursers in the stables of Mostadad, we fled northward towards the kingdom of Circassia. As there were several others flying in the same manner, we passed without notice, and in three days arrived at Terki, a city that lies in a valley within the bosom of the frowning mountains of Caucasus.

Here, free from every apprehension of danger, we enjoy all those satisfactions which are consistent with virtue; though I find my heart at intervals give way to unusual passions, yet such is my admiration for my fair companion that I lose even tenderness in distant respect. Though her person demands particular regard even among the beauties of Circassia, yet is her mind far more lovely. How very different is a woman who thus has cultivated her understanding and been refined into delicacy of sentiment from the daughters of the east, whose education is only formed to improve the person, and make them more tempting objects of prostitution! Adieu.

LETTER SIXTY

The history of the beautiful captive.

From Hingpo to Lien Chi Altangi, by the way of Moscow.

When sufficiently refreshed after the fatigues of our precipitate flight, my curiosity, which had been restrained by the appearance of immediate danger, now began to revive: I longed to know by what distressful accidents my fair fugitive became a captive, and could not avoid testifying a surprize how so much beauty could be involved in the calamities from whence she had been so lately rescued.

"Talk not of personal charms," cried she with emotion, "since to them I owe every misfortune: look round on the numberless beauties of the country where we are. See how nature has poured its charms upon every face, and yet by this profusion heaven would seem to shew how little it regards such a blessing, since the gift is lavished upon a nation of prostitutes.

"I perceive you desire to know my story, and your curiosity is not so great as my impatience to gratify it. I find a pleasure in telling past misfortunes to any, but when my deliverer is pleased with the relation, my pleasure is prompted by duty.

"I [34] was born in a country far to the west, where the men are braver, and the women more fair than those of Circassia;

where the valour of the hero is guided by wisdom, and where delicacy of sentiment points the shafts of female beauty. I was the only daughter of an officer in the army, the child of his age, and as he used fondly to express it, the only chain that bound him to the world or made his life pleasing. His station procured him an acquaintance with men of greater rank or fortune than himself, and his regard for me induced him to bring me into every family where he was acquainted. Thus I was early taught all the elegancies and fashionable foibles of such as the world calls polite, and though without fortune myself, was taught to despise those who lived as if they were poor.

"My intercourse with the great and my affectation of grandeur procured me many lovers, but want of fortune deterred them all from any other views than those of passing the present moment agreeably or of meditating my future ruin. In every company I found myself addressed in a warmer strain of passion than other ladies who were superior in point of rank and beauty; and this I imputed to an excess of respect, which in reality proceeded from very different motives.

"Among the number of such as paid me their addresses was a gentleman, a friend of my father, rather in the decline of life, with nothing remarkable either in his person or address to recommend him. His age which was about forty, his fortune which was moderate and barely sufficient to support him, served to throw me off my guard, so that I considered him as the only sincere admirer I had.

"A designing lover in the decline of life is ever most dangerous. Skilled in all the weaknesses of the sex, they seize each favourable opportunity and by having less passion than a youthful admirer, have less real respect, and therefore less timidity. This insidious wretch used a thousand arts to succeed in his base designs, all which I saw, but imputed to different views, because I thought it absurd to believe the real motives.

"As he continued to frequent my father's, the friendship between them became every day greater; and at last from the intimacy with which he was received I was taught to look upon him as a guardian and a friend. Though I never loved, yet I esteemed him; and this was enough to make me wish for an union for which he seemed desirous but to which he feigned several delays; while in the mean time, from a false report of our being married, every other admirer forsook me.

"I was at last however awakened from the delusion by an account of his being just married to another young lady with a considerable fortune. This was no great mortification to me, as I had always regarded him merely from prudential motives; but it had a very different effect upon my father, who, rash and passionate by nature, and besides stimulated by a mistaken notion of military honour, upbraided his friend in such terms that a challenge was soon given and accepted.

"It was about midnight when I was awakened by a message from my father, who desired to see me that moment. I rose with some surprize, and following the messenger, attended only by another servant, came to a field not far from the house, where I found him, the assertor of my honour, my only friend and supporter, the tutor and companion of my youth, lying on one side covered over with blood, and just expiring. No tears streamed from my cheeks, nor sigh from my breast, at an object of such terror. I sate down, and supporting his aged head in my lap, gazed upon the gastly visage with an agony more poignant even than despairing madness. The servants were gone for more assistance. In this gloomy stillness of the night no sounds were heard but his agonizing respirations; no object was presented but his wounds, which still continued to stream. With silent anguish I hung over his dear face, and with my hands strove to stop the blood as it flowed from his wounds; he seemed at first insensible, but at last turning his dying eyes upon me, 'My dear, dear child,' cried he, 'dear, though you have forgotten your own honour and stained mine, I will yet forgive you; by abandoning your virtue you have undone me and yourself, yet take my forgiveness with the same compassion I wish heaven may pity me.' He expired. All my succeeding happiness fled with him. Reflecting that I was the cause of his death whom I only loved upon earth, accused of betraying the honour of his family with his latest breath, conscious of my own innocence, yet without even a possibility of vindicating it, without fortune or friends to relieve or pity me, abandoned to infamy and the wide censuring world, I called out upon the dead body that lay stretched before me, and in the agony of my heart asked why he could have left me thus? 'Why, my dear, my only pappa, why could you ruin me thus and yourself for ever! O pity, and return, since there is none but you to comfort me.'

"I soon found that I had real cause for sorrow, that I was to expect no compassion from my own sex, nor assistance from the other, and that reputation was much more useful in our commerce with mankind than really to deserve it. Wherever I came I perceived myself received either with contempt or detestation; or whenever I was civilly treated, it was from the most base and ungenerous motives.

"Thus driven from the society of the virtuous, I was at last, in order to dispell the anxieties of insupportable solitude, obliged to take up with the company of those whose characters were blasted like my own, but who perhaps deserved their infamy. Among this number was a lady of the first distinction, whose character the public thought proper to use in the freest manner. A similitude of distress soon united us; I knew that general reproach had made her miserable; and I had learned to regard misery as an excuse for guilt. Though this lady had not virtue enough to avoid reproach, yet she had too much delicate sensibility not to feel it. She therefore proposed our leaving the country where we were born, and going to live in Italy, where our characters and misfortunes would be un-known. With this I eagerly complied, and we soon found ourselves in one of the most charming retreats in the most beautiful province of that inchanting country.

"Had my companion chosen this as a retreat for injured virtue, an harbour where we might look with tranquility on the distant angry world, I should have been happy; but very different was her design; she had pitch'd upon this situation only to enjoy those pleasures in private which she had not sufficient effrontery to satisfy in a more open manner. A nearer acquaintance soon shewed me the vicious part of her character; her mind as well as her body seemed formed only for pleasure; she was sentimental only as it served to protract the immediate enjoyment. Formed for society alone, she spoke infinitely better than she wrote, and wrote infinitely better than she lived. A person devoted to pleasure often leads the most miserable life imaginable; such was her case; she con-sidered the natural moments of languor as insupportable, passed all her hours between rapture and anxiety, ever in an extreme of agony or of bliss. She felt a pain as sincere for want of appetite as the wretch who has not means to gratify the wants of nature. In those intervals she usually kept her bed, and rose only when in expectation of some new enjoyment. The luxuriant air of the country, the romantic situation of her palace, and the genius of a people whose only happiness lies in sensual refinement, all contributed to banish the remembrance of her native country.

"But tho' such a life gave her pleasure, it had a very different effect upon me. I grew every day more pensive, and my melancholy was regarded as an insult upon her good humour. I now perceived myself entirely unfit for all society; discarded from the good and detesting the infamous, I seemed in a state of war with every rank of people; that virtue which should have been my protection in the world was here my crime; in short, detesting life, I was determined to become a recluse, to leave a world where I found no pleasure that could allure me to stay. Thus determined, I embarked in order to go by sea to Rome, where I intended to take the veil; but even in so short a passage my hard fortune still attended me; our ship was taken by a Barbary corsair, the whole crew, and I among the number, being made slaves. It carries too much the air of romance to inform you of my distresses or obstinacy in this miserable state; it is enough to observe that I have been bought by several masters, each of whom perceiving my reluctance, rather than use violence, sold me to another, till it was my happiness to be at last rescued by you."

Thus ended her relation, which I have abridg'd, but as soon as we are arrived at Moscow, for which we intend to set out shortly, you shall be informed of all more particularly. In the mean time, the greatest addition to my happiness will be to hear of yours. Adieu.

LETTER SIXTY-ONE

Proper lessons to a youth entring the world, with fables suited to
the occasion.

From Lien Chi Altangi to Hingpo.

The news of your freedom lifts the load of anxiety from my
mind. I can now think of my son without regret, applaud his
resignation under calamity and his conduct in extricating
himself from it.

*You are now free, just let loose from the bondage of an hard
master:* this, this is the crisis of your fate; and as you now
manage your fortune, succeeding life is likely to be marked
with happiness or misery; a few years perseverance in prudence, which at your age is but another name for virtue, will
insure comfort, pleasure, tranquility, esteem; but too eager an
enjoyment now of every good that offers will reverse the medal
and present you with poverty, anxiety, remorse, contempt.

As it has been observed that none are better qualified to
give others advice than those who have taken the least of it
themselves, so in this respect I find myself perfectly authorized
to offer mine, even though I should wave my paternal authority upon this occasion.

The most usual way among young men who have no resolution of their own is first to ask one friend's advice and follow
it for some time, then to ask advice of another and turn to
that, so of a third, still unsteady, always changing. However,
be assured that every change of this nature is for the worse;
people may tell you of your being unfit for this or that employment, but heed them not; whatever employment you follow
with perseverance and assiduity will be found fit for you; it
will be your support in youth and comfort in age. In learning
the useful part of every profession very moderate abilities will
suffice; nor do I jest when I observe that if the mind be a little
balanced with stupidity it may in this case be useful. Great
abilities have always been more unserviceable to the possessors
than moderate ones. Life has been compar'd to a race, but
the allusion still improves by observing that the most swift are
ever the least manageable.

To know one profession only is enough for one man; and

this (whatever the professors may tell you to the contrary) is soon learned. Be contented therefore with one good employment, for if you understand two at a time, people will give you business in neither.

A conjurer and a taylor once happened to converse together. "Alas," cries the taylor, "what an unhappy poor creature am I; if people should ever take it in their heads to live without cloaths I am undone; I have no other trade to have recourse to." "Indeed, friend, I pity you sincerely," replies the conjurer; "but thank heaven, things are not quite so bad with me; for if one trick should fail, I have an hundred tricks more for them yet. However, if at any time you are reduced to beggary, apply to me, and I will relieve you." A famine overspread the land; the taylor made a shift to live because his customers could not be without cloaths; but the poor conjurer, with all his hundred tricks, could find none that had money to throw away; it was in vain that he promised to eat fire or vomit pins; no single creature would relieve him, till he was at last obliged to beg from the very taylor whose calling he had formerly villified.

There are no surer obstructions to fortune than pride and resentment. If you must resent injuries, at least suppress your indignation until you become rich; the resentment of a poor man is like the efforts of an harmless insect to sting; it may get him crushed, but cannot defend him. Who values that anger which is consumed only in empty menaces?

Once upon a time a goose fed its young by a pond side; and a goose in such circumstances is always extremely proud and excessive punctilious. If any other animal without the least design to offend happened to pass that way, the goose was immediately at him. The pond, she said, was hers, and she would maintain a right in it and support her honour while she had a bill to hiss or a wing to flutter. In this manner she drove away ducks, pigs, and chickens; nay, even the insidious cat was seen to scamper. A lounging mastiff, however, happened to pass by, and thinking it no harm if he lapped a little of the water, as he was thirsty, made up to the pond. The guardian goose flew at him like a fury, pecked at him with her beak, and slapped him with her feathers. The dog grew angry, had twenty times a good mind to give her a sly snap, but suppressing his indignation because his master was nigh, "A pox take thee," cries he, "for a fool; sure those who have neither strength nor weapons to fight at least should be civil; that fluttering and hissing of thine may one day get thine head snapt off, but it can neither injure thy enemies or ever protect thee." So saying, he went forward to the pond, quenched his thirst, and followed his master.

Another obstruction to the fortune of youth is that while they are willing to take offence from none, they are also equally desirous of giving none offence. From hence they endeavour to please all, comply with every request, attempt to suit themselves to every company, have no will of their own, but like wax catch every contiguous impression. By thus attempting to give universal satisfaction, they at last find themselves miserably disappointed; to bring the generality of admirers on our side it is sufficient to attempt pleasing a very few.

A painter of eminence was once resolved to finish a piece which should please the whole world. When, therefore, he had drawn a picture in which his utmost skill was exhausted, it was exposed in the public market-place, with directions at the bottom for every spectator to mark with a brush which lay by, every limb and feature which seemed erroneous. The spectators came and in general applauded; but each, willing to shew his talent at criticism, marked whatever he thought proper. At evening, when the painter came, he was mortified to find the whole picture one universal blot, not a single stroke that was not stigmatized with marks of disapprobation; not satisfied with this trial, the next day he was resolved to try them in a different manner, and [exposing his picture as before,] desired that every spectator would mark those beauties he approved or admired. The people complied, and the artist returning now found his picture replete with the marks of beauty; every stroke that had been yesterday condemned had now received the character of approbation. "Well," cries the painter, "I now find that the best way to please one half of the world is not to mind what the other half says, since what are faults in the eyes of those, by these are regarded as beauties." Adieu.

LETTER SIXTY-SEVEN

The folly of attempting to learn wisdom by being recluse.

From the same.

Books, my son, while they teach us to respect the interests of others, often make us unmindful of our own; the youthful reader, while he grasps at social happiness, grows miserable in detail, and, attentive to universal harmony, often forgets that he himself has a part in the contest to sustain. I dislike therefore the philosopher who describes the inconveniencies of life in such pleasing colours that the pupil grows enamoured of distress, longs to try the charms of poverty, meets it without dread, nor fears its inconveniencies till he severely feels them.

A youth who has thus spent his life among books, new to the world and unacquainted with man but by philosophic information, may be considered as a being whose mind is filled with the vulgar errors of the wise; utterly unqualified for a journey through life, yet confident of his own skill in the direction, he sets out with confidence, blunders on with vanity, and finds himself at last undone.

He first lays it down as a maxim that all mankind are virtuous or vicious, and he has been long taught to detest the one and love the other; warm therefore in attachments and stedfast in enmity, he treats every creature as a friend or foe, expects from those he loves unerring integrity, and consigns his enemies to the reproach of wanting every virtue. Here then begin his disappointments; upon a closer inspection of human nature he perceives that he should have moderated his friendship and softened his severity; for the excellencies of one part of mankind he often finds clouded with vice, and the faults of the other brightened with virtue; he finds no character so sanctified that has not its failings, none so infamous but has somewhat to attract our esteem; he sees impiety in lawn and fidelity in fetters.

He now therefore perceives that his regards should have been more cool and his hatred less violent, that the truly wise seldom court romantic friendships with the good, and avoid, if possible, the resentment even of the wicked; every moment gives him fresh instances that the bonds of friendship are

broken if drawn too closely, and that those whom he has
treated with disrespect more than retaliate the injury; at length
therefore too late he deplores that he has declared war upon
one half of mankind, without being able to form an alliance
among the rest to espouse his quarrel.

Our book-taught philosopher, however, is now too far advanced to recede; and tho' poverty be the just consequence of
his conduct, yet he is resolved to meet it without shrinking;
philosophers have described it in most charming colours, and
even his vanity is touched in thinking that he shall shew the
world, in himself, one more example of patience, fortitude,
and resignation. *Come then, O Poverty! for what is there in
thee dreadful to the* WISE; *temperance, health, and frugality
walk in thy train; chearfulness and liberty are ever thy companions. Shall any be ashamed of thee of whom Cincinatus
was not ashamed? the running brook, the herbs of the field can
amply satisfy nature; man wants but little, nor that little long;
come then, O Poverty, while kings stand by and gaze with
admiration at the true philosopher's contentment, and the
philosopher is ready to receive thee.*

The goddess appears, for Poverty ever comes when called
for; but alas! he finds her by no means the charming figure
books and his warm imagination had painted. Like an eastern
bride whom her friends and relations had long described as a
model of perfection, the longing bridegroom lifts the veil to
see a face he had never seen before, but instead of a countenance blazing with beauty like the sun, he beholds deformity
shooting icicles to his heart, such appears Poverty to her new
entertainer; all the fabric of enthusiasm is at once demolished,
and a thousand miseries rise upon its ruins, while Contempt,
with pointing finger, is foremost in the hideous procession.

The poor man now finds that he can get no kings to look
at him while he is eating; he finds that in proportion as he
grows poor, the world turns its back upon him and gives him
leave to act the philosopher in all the majesty of solitude; it
is agreeable enough to be philosophers while we are conscious
that mankind are spectators; but what signifies wearing the
mask of contentment, and mounting the stage, when not one
creature will assist at the exhibition! Thus is he forsaken of
men, while his fortitude wants the satisfaction even of self-

applause; for either he does not feel his present calamities, and that is natural *insensibility,* or he disguises his feelings, and that is *dissimulation.*

Spleen now begins to take up the man; not distinguishing in his resentments, he regards all mankind with detestation, commences man-hater, and seeks solitude to be at liberty to rail. It has been said that he who retires to solitude is either a brute or an angel; the censure is too severe, and the praise unmerited; the discontented being who retires from society is generally some good-natured unexperienced man such as has been represented, who has begun life upon wrong principles; his intercourse with mankind was too weak or too vain to correct the mistake.

LETTER SEVENTY-ONE

The shabby beau, the man in black, the Chinese philosopher, &c. at Vaux-hall.

From Lien Chi Altangi, to Fum Hoam, first president of the Ceremonial Academy at Pekin, in China.

The People of London are as fond of walking as our friends at Pekin of riding; one of the principal entertainments of the citizens here in summer is to repair about nightfall to a garden [35] not far from town, where they walk about, shew their best cloaths and best faces, and listen to a concert provided for the occasion.

I accepted of an invitation a few evenings ago from my old friend, the man in black, to be one of a party that was to sup there, and at the appointed hour waited upon him at his lodgings, where I found the company met and expecting my arrival. Our party consisted of my friend in superlative finery, his stockings rolled; his black velvet waistcoat appeared not much worse for wearing, and his grey wig was combed down in imitation of hair. Besides him, a pawn-broker's widow, of whom, by the bye, he was a professed admirer, dressed out in a green damask gown, with three gold rings on every finger. Mr. Tibbs the second-rate beau I have formerly described, together with his lady in a flimsy silk, dirty gauze instead of linnen, and an hat as big as an umbrello.

Our first difficulty was in settling how we should set out.

Mrs. Tibbs had a natural aversion to the water, and the widow being a little in flesh, as warmly protested against walking; a coach was therefore agreed upon, which being too small to carry five, Mr. Tibbs contented himself with sitting in his wife's lap.

In this manner therefore we set forward, being entertained by the way with the bodings of Mr. Tibbs, who assured us he did not expect to see a single creature for the evening above the degree of a cheesemonger; that this was the last night of the gardens, and that consequently we should be pestered with the nobility and gentry from Thames-street and Crooked-lane, with several other melancholy bodings probably inspired by the uneasiness of his situation.

The illuminations began before we arrived, and I must confess that upon entring the gardens I found every sense overpaid with more than expected pleasure; the lights every where glimmering through the scarcely moving trees, the full-bodied consort bursting on the stillness of the night, [the natural consort of the birds in the more retired part of the grove vying with that which was formed by art,] the company gayly dressed and looking satisfaction, the tables spread with various delacacies, all conspired to fill my imagination with the visionary happiness of the Arabian lawgiver [and lifted me into an extasy of admiration.] "Head of Confucius," cried I to my friend, "but this is fine! this unites rural beauty with courtly magnificence; if we except the virgins of immortality that hang on every tree and may be plucked at every desire, I don't see how it falls short of Mahomet's Paradise!" "As for virgins," cries my friend, "it is true they are a fruit that don't much abound in our gardens about London, but if ladies as plenty as apples in autumn and as complying as any *hoüry* of them all can content you, I fancy you have no need to go to heaven for Paradise."

I was going to second his remarks, when we were called to a consultation by Mr. Tibbs and the rest of the company to know in what manner we were to lay out the evening to the greatest advantage. Mrs. Tibbs was for keeping the genteel walk of the garden, where she observed there was always the very best company; the widow, on the contrary, who came but once a season, was for securing a good standing place to see the water-works,[36] which she assured us would begin in less than an hour at farthest; a dispute now began, and as it was managed between two of very opposite characters, it threatned to grow more bitter at every reply. Mrs. Tibbs wondered how people could pretend to know the polite world who had received all their rudiments of breeding behind a compter; to which the other replied that tho' some people sat behind compters, yet they could sit at the head of their own tables too, and carve three good dishes of hot meat whenever they thought proper, which was more than some people could say for themselves, that hardly knew a rabbet and onions from a green goose and gooseberries.

It is hard to say where this might have ended, had not the husband, who probably knew the impetuosity of his wife's disposition, proposed to end the dispute by adjourning to a box, and try if there was any thing to be had for supper that was supportable. To this we all consented, but here a new distress arose, Mr. and Mrs. Tibbs would sit in none but a genteel box, a box where they might see and be seen, one, as they expressed it, in the very focus of public view; but such a box was not easy to be obtained, for tho' we were perfectly convinced of our own gentility and the gentility of our appearance, yet we found it a difficult matter to persuade the keepers of the boxes, who are a kind of masters here, to be of our opinion; they chose to reserve genteel boxes for what they judged to be more genteel company.

At last however we were fixed, tho' somewhat obscurely, and supplied with the usual entertainment of the place. The widow found the supper excellent, but Mrs. Tibbs thought every thing detestable; "come, come, my dear," cries the husband, by way of consolation, "to be sure we can't find such dressing here as we have at lord Crump's or lady Crimp's; but for Vauxhall dressing it is pretty good; it is not their victuals indeed I find fault with, but their wine; their wine," cries he, drinking off a glass, "is most abominable indeed."

By this last stroke the widow was fairly conquered in point of politeness. She perceived now that she had no pretensions in the world to taste; her very senses were vulgar, since she had praised detestable custard and smacked at wretched wine;

she was therefore content to yield the victory and for the rest of the night to listen and improve. It is true she would now and then forget herself and confess she was pleased, but they soon brought her back again to miserable refinement. She once praised the painting of the box in which we were sitting, but was soon convinced that such paltry pieces ought rather to excite horror than satisfaction; she ventured again to commend one of the singers, but Mrs. Tibbs soon let her know, in the style of a connoisseur, that the singer in question had neither ear, voice, nor judgment.

Mr. Tibbs was now willing to prove that his wife's pretensions to music were just, and entreated her to favour the company with a song; but to this she gave a positive denial, "for you know very well, my dear," says she, "that I am not in voice to day, and when one's voice is not equal to one's judgment, what signifies singing; besides as there is no accompanyment, it would be but spoiling music." All these excuses however were over-ruled by the rest of the company, who joined in the intreaty. But particularly the widow, now willing to convince the company of her breeding, pressed so warmly that she seem'd determined to take no refusal. At last then the lady complied, and [after humming for some minutes] began with such a voice and such affectation as I could perceive gave but little satisfaction to any except her husband, who sate with rapture in his eye and beating time with his hand on the table.

You must observe, my friend, that it is the custom of this country, when a lady or gentleman happens to sing in company, to sit as mute and motionless as statues. Every feature, every limb must seem to correspond in fixed attention, and while the song continues, the whole audience are to remain in a state of universal petrefaction. In this mortifying situation we had continued for some time, when the master of the box came to inform us that the water-works were going to begin. I could instantly perceive the widow bounce from her seat, but instantly correct herself and sit down again, repressed by motives of good breeding. Mrs. Tibbs, who had seen the water-works an hundred times, was resolved not to be interrupted, continued her song without the smallest share of mercy, and kept us all prisoners of complaisance. The widow's face, I own, gave me high entertainment; in it I could plainly read the struggle she felt between good breeding and curiosity; she had talked of the water-works the whole evening before and seemed to have come merely in order to see them; but then she could not bounce out in the very middle of a song, for that would be forfeiting all pretensions to high life or high-lived company ever after. At last, therefore, when the song was just concluded, the waiter came to inform us that the water-works were over!

"The water-works over," cried the widow! "that's impossible, they can't be over so soon!" "It is not my business," replied the fellow, "to contradict your ladyship, but I'll run again and see." He went and soon returned with a confirmation of the dismal tidings. No ceremony could now bind my friend's disappointed mistress; she testified her displeasure in the openest manner; in short, she now began to find fault in turn, and at last insisted upon going home, just at the time that Mr. and Mrs. Tibbs were growing into spirits and beginning to shew away. Adieu.

LETTER SEVENTY-SEVEN
The behaviour of a shop keeper and his journeyman.

To the same.

The Shops of London are as well furnished as those of Pekin. Those of London have a picture hung at their door, informing the passengers what they have to sell, as those at Pekin have a board to assure the buyer that they have no intentions to cheat him.

I was this morning to buy silk for a night-cap; immediately upon entering the mercer's shop, the master and his two men, with wigs plaistered with powder, appeared to ask my commands. They were certainly the civillest people alive; if I but looked, they flew to the place where I cast my eye; every motion of mine sent them running round the whole shop for my satisfaction. I informed them that I wanted what was good, and they shewed me not less than forty pieces, each of which was said to be the prettiest pattern in nature, and the fittest in the world for night-caps. "My very good friend," said I to the mercer, "you must not pretend to instruct me in silks.

I know them in particular to be no better than one of your mere flimsy Bungees." "That may be," cried the mercer, who I afterwards found had never contradicted a man in his life, "I can't pretend to say but they may; but I can assure you, my Lady Trail has had a sacque from it this very morning." "But friend," said I, "though my Lady has chosen a sacque from it, I see no necessity that I should wear it for a night-cap." "That may be," returned he again, "yet what becomes a pretty Lady, will at any time look well on a handsome Gentleman." This short compliment was thrown in so very seasonably upon my ugly face that even tho' I disliked the silk, I desired him to cut me off the pattern of a night-cap.

While this business was consigned to his journeyman, the master himself took down some pieces of silk still finer than any I had yet seen, and spreading them before me, "There," cries he, "there's beauty; my Lord Snakeskin has bespoke the fellow to this for the birth-night[37] this very morning; it would look charmingly in waistcoats." "But I don't want a waistcoat," replied I: "Not want a waistcoat," returned the mercer; "then I would advise you to buy one; when waistcoats are wanted, you may depend upon it they will come dear. Always buy before you want, and you are sure to be well used, as the saying is." There was so much justice in his advice that I could not refuse taking it; besides, the silk, which was really a good one, encreased the temptation, so I gave orders for that too.

As I was waiting to have my bargains measured and cut, which, I know not how, they executed but slowly, during the interval the mercer entertained me with the modern manner of some of the nobility receiving company in their morning gowns; "Perhaps, Sir," adds he, "you have a mind to see what kind of silk is universally worn." Without waiting for my reply he spreads a piece before me which might be reckoned beautiful even in China. "If the nobility," continues he, "were to know I sold this to any, under a Right Honourable, I should certainly lose their custom; you see, my Lord, it is at once rich, tastey, and quite the thing." "I am no Lord," interrupted I.—"I beg pardon," cried he, "but be pleased to remember when you intend buying a morning gown, that you had an offer from me of something worth money. Conscience, Sir, conscience is my way of dealing; you may buy a morning gown now, or you may stay till they become dearer and less fashionable, but it is not my business to advise." In short, most reverend Fum, he persuaded me to buy a morning gown also, and would probably have persuaded me to have bought half the goods in his shop if I had stayed long enough, or was furnished with sufficient money.

Upon returning home, I could not help reflecting with some astonishment how this very man with such a confined education and capacity was yet capable of turning me as he thought proper and molding me to his inclinations! I knew he was only answering his own purposes, even while he attempted to appear solicitous about mine; yet by a voluntary infatuation, a sort of passion compounded of vanity and good nature, I walked into the snare with my eyes open and put myself to future pain in order to give him immediate pleasure. The wisdom of the ignorant somewhat resembles the instinct of animals; it is diffused in but a very narrow sphere, but within the circle it acts with vigour, uniformity, and success. Adieu.

LETTER SEVENTY-NINE

The preparations of both theatres for a winter campaign.

From the same.

The two theatres[38] which serve to amuse the citizens here are again opened for the winter. The troops of the stage, different from those of the state, begin their campaign when all others quit the field; and at a time when the Europeans cease to destroy each other in reality, they are entertained with mock battles upon the theatre.

The dancing master once more shakes his quivering feet; the carpenter prepares his paradise of pasteboard; the hero resolves to cover his forehead with brass, and the heroine begins to scour up her copper tail, preparative to future operations; in short, all are in motion, from the theatrical letter-carrier in yellow cloaths to Alexander the Great who stands on a stool.

Both houses have already commenced hostilities. War, open war! and no quarter received or given! Two singing women,[39] like heralds, have begun the contest; the whole town is divided on this solemn occasion; one has the finest pipe, the other the finest manner; one curtesies to the ground, the other salutes the audience with a smile; one comes on with modesty which asks, the other with boldness which extorts applause; one wears powder, the other has none; one has the longest waist, but the other appears most easy; all, all is important and serious; the town as yet perseveres in its neutrality, and they continue to exhibit the most mature deliberation; and it is very possible this contest may be carried on to the end of the season.

But the Generals of either army have, as I am told, several reinforcements to lend occasional assistance. If they produce a pair of diamond buckles at one house, we have a pair of eye-brows that can match them at t'other. If we outdo them in our attitude, they can overcome us by a shrug; if we can bring more children on the stage, they can bring more guards in red cloaths, who strut and shoulder their swords to the astonishment of every spectator.

They tell me here that people frequent the theatre in order to be instructed as well as amused. I smile to hear the assertion. If I ever go to one of their play-houses, what with drums, trumpets, hallowing behind the stage, and bawling upon it, I am quite dizzy before the performance is over. If I enter the house with any sentiments in my head, I am sure to have none going away, and the whole mind is only filled with a dead march, a funeral procession, a cat-call, and a jigg or a tempest.

There is perhaps nothing more difficult than to write properly for the English theatre; one must be bound 'prentice to it. The author must be well acquainted with the value of every pound of thunder and lightning in the house; he must be versed in all the mystery of scene-shifting and trap-doors; he must know the proper periods to introduce a wire-walker or a water-fall; he must understand every actor's peculiar talent and adapt his speeches to the supposed excellence. One player shines in an exclamation, another in a groan, a third in an horror, a fourth in a start, a fifth in a smile, a sixth faints away with grace, and a seventh figets round the stage with peculiar vivacity; that piece therefore will succeed best where each has a proper opportunity of shining; the actor's business is not so much to adapt himself to the poet, as the poet's to write for the actor.

The great secret therefore of tragedy-writing here at present is a perfect acquaintance with theatrical *ah*'s and *oh*'s; a certain number of these interspersed with *gods! tortures, racks,* and *damnation,* shall distort every actor almost into convulsions, and draw tears from every spectator; a proper use of these has filled the whole house with applause.

All modern plays that would keep the audience alive must be conceived in this manner. This is the merit that lifts the heart, like opium, into a rapturous insensibility, and can dismiss the mind from all the fatigue of thinking; this the merit that shines in many a long forgotten play, which has been reckoned excessive fine upon acting; this the lightening that flashes no less in the Hyperbolical tyrant, *who breakfasts on the wind,* than in little Norval, *as harmless as the babe unborn.* Adieu.

LETTER EIGHTY-THREE

Some cautions on life, taken from a modern philosopher of China.

From Lien Chi Altangi to Hingpo, by the way of Moscow.

You are now arrived at an age, my son, when pleasure dissuades from application, but rob not by present gratification all the succeeding period of life of its happiness. Sacrifice a little pleasure at first to the expectance of greater. The study of a very few years will make the rest of life compleatly easy.

But instead of continuing the subject myself, take the following instructions borrowed from a modern philosopher of China. "He who has begun his fortune by study will certainly confirm it by perseverance. The love of books damps the passion for pleasure, and when this passion is once extinguished, life is then cheaply supported; thus a man being possessed of more than he wants can never be subject to great disappointments, and avoids all those meannesses which indigence sometimes unavoidably produces.

"There is unspeakable pleasure attending the life of a voluntary student. The first time I read an excellent book, it is to me just as if I had gained a new friend. When I read over a book I have perused before, it resembles the meeting with on old one. We ought to lay hold of every incident in life for improvement, the trifling as well as the important. It is not one diamond alone which gives lustre to another, a common coarse stone is also employed for that purpose. Thus I ought to draw advantage from the insults and contempt I meet with from a worthless fellow. His brutality ought to induce me to self-examination, and correct every blemish that may have given rise to his calumny.

"Yet with all the pleasures and profits which are generally produced by learning, parents often find it difficult to induce their children to study. They often seem dragged to what wears the appearance of application. Thus being dilatory in the beginning, all future hopes of eminence are entirely cut off. If they find themselves obliged to write two lines more polite than ordinary, their pencil then seems as heavy as a mill-stone, and they spend ten years in turning two or three periods with propriety.

"These persons are most at a loss when a banquet is almost over; the plate and the dice go round, that the number of little verses which each is obliged to repeat may be determined by chance. The booby, when it comes to his turn, appears quite stupid and insensible. The company divert themselves with his confusion, and sneers, winks, and whispers are circulated at his expence. As for him, he opens a pair of large heavy eyes, stares at all about him, and even offers to join in the laugh, without ever considering himself as the burthen of all their good humour.

"But it is of no importance to read much, except you be regular in your reading. If it be interrupted for any considerable time, it can never be attended with proper improvement. There are some who study for one day with intense application and repose themselves for ten days after. But wisdom is a coquet and must be courted with unabating assiduity.

"It was a saying of the ancients that a man never opens a book without reaping some advantage by it. I say with them that every book can serve to make us more expert except romances, and these are no better than instruments of debauchery. They are dangerous fictions where love is the ruling passion.

"The most indecent strokes there pass for turns of wit, intrigue and criminal liberties for gallantry and politeness. Assignations and even villainy are put in such strong lights as may inspire even grown men with the strongest passion; how much more therefore ought the youth of either sex to dread them, whose reason is so weak and whose hearts are so susceptible of passion?

"To slip in by a back-door or leap a wall are accomplishments that when handsomely set off enchant a young heart. It is true the plot is commonly wound up by a marriage, concluded with the consent of parents, and adjusted by every ceremony prescribed by law. But as in the body of the work there are many passages that offend good morals, overthrow laudable customs, violate the laws, and destroy the duties most essential to society, virtue is thereby exposed to the most dangerous attacks.

"But, say some, the authors of these romances have nothing in view but to represent vice punished and virtue rewarded. Granted. But will the greater number of readers take notice of these punishments and rewards? Are not their minds carried to something else? Can it be imagined that the art with which the author inspires the love of virtue can overcome that crowd of thoughts which sway them to licentiousness? To be able to inculcate virtue by so leaky a vehicle, the author must be a philosopher of the first rank. But in our age we can find but few first rate philosophers.

"Avoid such performances where vice assumes the face of virtue; seek wisdom and knowledge without ever thinking you have found them. A man is wise while he continues in the pursuit of wisdom; but when he once fancies that he has found the object of his enquiry, he then becomes a fool. Learn to pursue virtue from the man that is blind, who never makes a step without first examining the ground with his staff.

"The world is like a vast sea, mankind like a vessel sailing on its tempestuous bosom. Our prudence are its sails, the sciences serve us for oars, good or bad fortune are the favourable or contrary winds, and judgment is the rudder; without this last the vessel is tossed by every billow and will find shipwreck in every breeze. In a word, obscurity and indigence are the parents of vigilance and œconomy, vigilance and œconomy of riches and honour, riches and honour of pride and luxury, pride and luxury of impurity and idleness, and impurity and idleness again produce indigence and obscurity. Such are the revolutions of life." Adieu.

LETTER EIGHTY-SIX

The races of Newmarket ridiculed. The description of a cart race.

From Lien Chi Altangi, to Fum Hoam, first president of the
Ceremonial Academy at Pekin, in China.

Of all the places of amusement where gentlemen and ladies are entertained, I have not been yet to visit Newmarket. This, I am told, is a large field, on which upon certain occasions three or four horses are brought together, then set a running, and that horse which runs fastest wins the wager.

This is reckoned a very polite and fashionable amusement here, much more followed by the nobility than partridge fighting at Java or paper kites in Madagascar; several of the great here, I am told, understand as much of farriery as their grooms; and a horse with any share of merit can never want a patron among the nobility.

We have a description of this entertainment almost every day in some gazette, as for instance: "On such a day the Give and Take Plate was run for between his Grace's Crab, his Lordship's Periwinkle, and 'Squire Smackem's Slamerkin. All rode their own horses. There was the greatest concourse of nobility that has been known there for several seasons. The odds were in favour of Crab in the beginning, but Slamerkin, after the first heat, seemed to have the match hollow; however it was seen that Periwinkle improved in wind, which at last turned out accordingly; [Crab was run to a stand still, Slamerkin was knocked up,] and Periwinkle was brought in with universal applause." Thus you see Periwinkle received universal applause, and no doubt his Lordship came in for some share of that praise which was so liberally bestowed upon his horse. Sun of China! how glorious must the Senator appear in his cap and leather breeches, his whip crossed in his mouth, and thus coming to the goal amongst the shouts of grooms, jockeys, pimps, stable-bred Dukes, and degraded Generals!

From the description of this princely amusement, now transcribed, and from the great veneration I have for the characters of its principal promoters, I make no doubt but I shall look upon an horse-race with becoming reverence, particularly as my mind has been predisposed by a similar amusement of which I have lately been a spectator, just now having had an opportunity of being present at a Cart-race.

Whether this contention between three carts of different parishes was promoted by a subscription among the nobility or whether the grand jury, in council assembled, had gloriously combined to encourage plaustral [40] merit, I cannot take upon me to determine; but certain it is, the whole was conducted with the utmost regularity and decorum, and the company, which made a brilliant appearance, were universally of opinion that the sport was high and without any take in.

It was run on the road from London to a village called Brentford, between a turnip cart, a dust cart, and a dung cart, each of the owners condescending to mount and be his own driver. The odds at starting were *dust* against *dung* five to four; but after half a miles going the knowing ones found themselves all on the wrong side, and it was *turnip* against the field, pence to half-pence.

Soon however the contest became more doubtful; Turnip indeed kept the way, but it was perceived that Dung had better bottom. The road re-ecchoed with the shouts of the spectators; "Dung against Turnip," "Turnip against Dung," was now the universal cry; neck and neck; one rode lighter, but the other had more judgment. I could not but particularly observe the ardour with which the fair sex espoused the cause of the different riders on this occasion; one was charmed with the unwashed beauties of Dung; another was captivated with the patibulary [41] aspect of Turnip: while in the mean time unfortunate gloomy Dust, who came whipping behind, was cheared by the encouragements of some, and pity of all.

The contention now continued for some time without a possibility of determining to whom victory designed the prize. The winning post appeared in view, and he who drove the turnip cart assured himself of success; and successful he might have been, had his horse been as ambitious as he; but upon approaching a turn from the road, which led homewards,

the horse fairly stood still and refused to move a foot farther.
The dung cart had scarce time to enjoy this temporary triumph, when it was pitched headlong into a ditch by the way
side, and the rider left to wallow in congenial mud. Dust
in the mean time soon came up and not being far from the
post came in amidst the shouts and acclamations of the spectators, and was greatly caressed by all the quality of Brentford. Fortune was kind only to one, who ought to have been
favourable to all; each had peculiar merit, each laboured
hard to earn the prize, and each richly deserved the cart he
drove.

I do not know whether this description may not have
anticipated that which I intended giving of Newmarket. I am
told there is little else to be seen even there. There may be
some minute differences in the dress of the spectators, but none
at all in their understandings; the quality of Brentford are
as remarkable for politeness and delicacy as the breeders of
Newmarket. The quality of Brentford drive their own carts,
and the honourable fraternity of Newmarket ride their own
horses. In short, the matches in one place are as rational as
those in the other; and it is more than probable that turnips,
dust, and dung are all that can be found to furnish out
description in either.

Forgive me, my friend, but a person like me, bred up in a
philosophic seclusion, is apt to regard, perhaps with too much
asperity, those occurrences which sink man below his station
in nature and thus diminish the intrinsic value of humanity.

LETTER EIGHTY-SEVEN

The folly of the Western parts of Europe, in employing the
Russians to fight their battles.

From Fum Hoam to Lien Chi Altangi.

You tell me the people of Europe are wise; but where lies
their wisdom? You say they are valiant too; yet I have some
reasons to doubt of their valour. They are engaged in war
among each other, yet apply to the Russians, their neighbours
and ours, for assistance. Cultivating such an alliance argues
at once imprudence and timidity. All subsidies paid for aid
from them is strengthening the Russians, already too power-

ful, and weakening themselves, already exhausted by intestine commotions.

I cannot avoid beholding the Russian empire as the natural enemy of the more western parts of Europe, as an enemy already possessed of great strength, and, from the nature of the government, every day threatening to become more powerful. This extensive empire, which both in Europe and Asia occupies almost a third of the old world, was about two centuries ago divided into separate kingdoms and dukedoms and from such a division consequently feeble. Since the times however of Johan Basilides it has encreased in strength and extent; and those untrodden forests, those innumerable savage animals which formerly covered the face of the country, are now removed, and colonies of mankind planted in their room. A kingdom thus enjoying peace internally, possessed of an unbounded extent of dominion, and learning the military art at the expence of others abroad, must every day grow more powerful; and it is probable we shall hear Russia, in future times, as formerly, called the Officina Gentium.[42]

It was long the wish of Peter, their great monarch, to have a fort in some of the western parts of Europe; many of his schemes and treaties were directed to this end, but happily for Europe he failed in them all. A fort in the power of this people would be like the possession of a flood-gate; and whenever ambition, interest, or necessity prompted, they would then be able to deluge the whole western world with a barbarous inundation.

Believe me, my friend, I can't sufficiently contemn the politics of Europe, who thus make this powerful people arbitrators in their quarrel. The Russians are now at that period between refinement and barbarity, which seems most adapted to military atchievement; and if once they happen to get footing in the western parts of Europe, it is not the feeble efforts of the sons of effeminacy and dissention that can serve to remove them. The fertile valley and soft climate will ever be sufficient inducements to draw whole myriads from their native desarts, the trackless wild, or snowy mountain.

History, experience, reason, nature, expand the book of wisdom before the eyes of mankind, but they will not read. We have seen with terror a winged phalanx of famished locusts each singly contemptible, but from multitude become hideous, cover like clouds the face of day and threaten the whole world with ruin. We have seen them, settling on the fertile plains of India and Egypt, destroy in an instant the labours and the hopes of nations, sparing neither the fruit of the earth nor the verdure of the fields, and changing into a frightful desert landscapes of once luxuriant beauty. We have seen myriads of ants issuing together from the southern desert, like a torrent whose source was inexhaustible, succeeding each other without end and renewing their destroyed forces with unwearied perseverance, bringing desolation wherever they came, banishing men and animals, and, when destitute of all subsistence, in heaps infecting the desert air! Like these have been the migrations of men. When as yet savage, and almost resembling their brute partners in the forest, subject like them only to the laws and even to the excesses of nature, and directed by hunger alone in the choice of an abode, how have we seen whole armies starting wild at once from their forests and their dens, Goths, Huns, Vandals, Saracens, Turks, Tartars, myriads of men—or rather, animals in human form,—without country, without name, or without laws, out-powering by numbers all opposition, ravaging cities, overturning empires; and, after having destroyed whole nations and spreading extensive desolation, how have we seen them sink oppressed by some new enemy, more barbarous and even more unknown than they! Adieu.

LETTER EIGHTY-EIGHT

The ladies advised to get husbands. A story to this purpose.

From Lien Chi Altangi, to Fum Hoam, first president of the Ceremonial Academy at Pekin, in China.

As the instruction of the fair sex in this country is entirely committed to the care of foreigners, as their language-masters, music-masters, hair-frizzers, and governesses, are all from abroad, I had some intentions of opening a female academy myself, and made no doubt, as I was quite a foreigner, of meeting a favourable reception.

In this I intended to instruct the ladies in all the conjugal mysteries; wives should be taught the art of managing husbands, and maids the skill of properly chusing them. I would teach a wife how far she might venture to be sick without giving disgust; she should be acquainted with the great benefits of the cholic in the stomach, and all the rules for chusing a confident; maids should learn the secret of nicely distinguishing every competitor; they should be able to know the difference between a pedant and a scholar, a citizen and a prig, a squire and his horse, a beau and his monkey; but chiefly they should be taught the art of managing their smiles, from the contemptuous simper to the long laborious laugh.

But I have discontinued the project; for what would signify teaching ladies the manner of governing or chusing husbands when marriage is at present so much out of fashion that a lady is very well off who can get any husband at all. Celibacy now prevails in every rank of life; the streets are crouded with old bachelors and the houses with ladies who have refused good offers and are never likely to receive any for the future.

The only advice, therefore, I could give the fair sex, as things stand at present, is to get husbands [as fast as they can]. There is certainly nothing in the whole creation, not even Babylon in ruins excepted, more truly deplorable than a lady in the virgin bloom of sixty-three, or a battered unmarried beau who squibs about from place to place, shewing his pig-tail wig and his ears. The one appears to my imagination in the form of a double night-cap or a roll of pomatum, the other in the shape of an electuary or a box of pills.

I would once more therefore advise the ladies to get husbands. I would desire them not to discard an old lover without very sufficient reasons, and treat the new with ill-nature; let not prudes tell me of the falseness of the sex, coquets of the pleasures of long courtship, or parents of the necessary preliminaries of penny for penny. I have reasons that would silence even a casuist in this particular. In the first place, therefore, I divide the subject into fifteen heads, and then *sic argumentor*—but not to give you and myself the spleen, I'll be content at present with telling you an improbable Indian tale.

In a winding of the river Amidar, just before it falls into the Caspian sea, there lies an island unfrequented by the inhabitants of the Continent. In this seclusion, blest with all that wild uncultivated nature could bestow, lived a princess and her two daughters. She had been wrecked upon the coast while her children as yet were infants, and they consequently were entirely unacquainted with man. Yet, unexperienced as the young ladies were in the opposite sex, both early discovered symptoms, the one of prudery, the other of being a coquet. The eldest was ever learning maxims of wisdom and discretion from her mamma, while the youngest employed all her hours in gazing at her own face in a muddy brook, which always reflects better than the glassy stream.

Their usual amusement in this solitude was fishing. Their mother had taught them all the secrets of the art; she shewed them which were the most likely places to throw out the line, what baits were most proper for the various seasons and different fish, and the best manner to draw up the finny prey when they had hooked it. In this manner they spent their time, easy and innocent, till upon a certain day the Princess, being indisposed, desired the young princesses to go and catch her a sturgeon or a shark for supper, which she fancied might sit easy on her stomach. The daughters obeyed, and clapping on a gold fish, the usual bait on those occasions, went and sate upon one of the rocks, letting the gilded hook glide down with the stream.

On the opposite shore, further down at the mouth of the river, lived a diver for pearls, grown by long habit in his trade almost amphibious; so that he could remain whole hours at the bottom of the water, without ever fetching breath. He happened to be at that very instant diving when the ladies were fishing with the gilded hook. Seeing therefore the bait, which to him had the appearance of gold, he was resolved to seize the prize, but both his hands being already filled with pearl oysters, he found himself obliged to snap at it with his mouth. The consequence is easily imagined; the hook, before unperceived, was instantly fastened in his jaw, nor could he, with all his efforts, or his floundering, get free.

"Sister," cries the youngest Princess, "I have certainly caught a monstrous fish. I never perceived any thing struggle so at the end of my line before; come, and help me to draw it in." They both now therefore assisted in fishing up the diver on shore; but nothing could equal their surprize upon seeing him. "Bless my eyes," cries the prude, "what have we got here; this is a very odd fish to be sure. I never saw any thing in my life look so hideous; what eyes, what terrible claws, what a monstrous snout. I have read of this monster somewhere before; it certainly must be a *Tanlang* that eats women; quickly let us throw it back into the sea where we found it."

The diver in the mean time stood upon the beach at the end of the line, with the hook in his mouth, using every art that he thought could best excite pity, and looking extremely tender. The coquet therefore, in some measure influenced by the innocence of his looks, ventured to contradict her companion's advice. "Upon my word, sister," says she, "I see nothing in the animal so very terrible as you are pleased to apprehend. I think it may serve well enough for a change. Always sharks, and sturgeons, and lobsters, and crawfish, make me quite sick. I fancy a slice of this, barbacued and dressed up with shrimp sauce, would be very pretty eating. [I fancy mamma would like a bit with pickles above all things in the world; and if it should not sit easy on her stomach, it will be time enough to discontinue it when found disagreeable, you know."] "Horrid," cries the prude, "would the girl be poisoned? I tell you it's a *Tanlang*. I have read of it in twenty places, and it is every where described as the most pernicious animal that ever infested the ocean. [I am certain it is the most insidious, ravenous creature in the world, and is certain destruction if taken internally."] The younger sister was now therefore obliged to submit; both assisted in drawing the hook with some violence from the diver's jaw; and he finding himself at liberty, bent his breast against the broad wave and disappeared in an instant.

Just at this juncture the mother came down to the beach to know the cause of her daughters' delay; they told her every circumstance and described the monster they had caught. The old lady was one of the most discreet women in the world; she was called the black-eyed Princess, from two black eyes she had received in her youth, being a little addicted to boxing in her drink. "Alas, my children," cries she, "what have you done? The fish you caught was a man-fish, one of the most tame domestic animals in the world. We could have let him run and play about the garden, and he would have been twenty times more entertaining than your squirrel or your monkey." "If that be all," says the young coquet, "we'll fish for him again. [If that be all, I'll hold three tooth-picks to one pound of snuff I catch him whenever I please.]" Accordingly they threw in their line once more, but with all their gilding and assiduity, they could never after catch a diver. In this state of solitude and disappointment they continued for many years, still fishing without success, till at last the genius of the place, in pity to their distress, changed the prude into a shrimp and the coquet into an oyster. Adieu.

LETTER NINETY-SEVEN

Almost every subject of literature has been already exhausted.

To the same.

It is usual for the booksellers here, when a book has given universal pleasure upon one subject, to bring out several more upon the same plan, which are sure to have purchasers and readers from that desire which all men have to view a pleasing object on every side. The first performance serves rather to awake than satisfy attention; and when that is once moved, the slightest effort serves to continue its progression; the merit of the first diffuses a light sufficient to illuminate the succeeding efforts, and no other subject can be relished, till that is exhausted. A stupid work coming thus immediately in the train of an applauded performance, prepares the mind to be pleased upon different topics and resembles the sponge thrust into the mouth of a discharged culverin in order to adapt it for a new explosion.

This manner, however, of drawing off a subject or a peculiar mode of writing to the dregs, effectually precludes a revival of that subject or manner for some time for the future; the sated reader turns from it with a kind of literary nausea; and though the titles of books are the part of them most read, yet he has scarce perseverance enough to wade through the title page.

Of this number I own myself one. I am now grown callous to several subjects, and different kinds of composition; whether such originally pleased I will not take upon me to determine; but at present I spurn a new book merely upon seeing its name in an advertisement, nor have the smallest curiosity to look beyond the first leaf, even though in the second the author promises his own face neatly engraved on copper.

I am become a perfect epicure in reading; plain beef or solid mutton will never do. I'm for a true Chinese dish of bear's claws and bird's nests. I am for sauce strong with assafœtida or fuming with garlic. For this reason there are an hundred very wise, learned, virtuous, well-intended productions that have no charms for me. Thus, for the soul of me, I could never find courage nor grace enough to wade above two pages deep into *Thoughts upon God and Nature,* or *Thoughts upon Providence,* or *Thoughts upon Free Grace,* or indeed into Thoughts upon any thing at all. I can no longer meditate with Meditations upon every day in the year. Essays upon divers subjects can't allure me, though never so interesting; and as for Funeral Sermons, or even Thanksgiving Sermons, the very sound gives me the spleen.

But it is chiefly in gentle poetry where I seldom look farther than the title. The truth is, I take up books to be told something new; but here, as it is now managed, the reader is told nothing. He opens the book and there finds very good words, truly, and much exactness of rhyme, but no information. A parcel of gaudy images pass on before his imagination like the figures in a dream; but curiosity, induction, reason, and the whole train of affections are fast asleep. The *jocunda et idonea vitæ,*[43] those sallies which mend the heart while they amuse the fancy, are quite forgotten; so that a reader who would take up some modern applauded performances of this kind must, in order to be pleased, first leave his good sense behind him, take for his recompence and guide bloated and compound epithet, and dwell on paintings, just indeed, because laboured with minute exactness.

If we examine, however, our internal sensations, we shall find ourselves but little pleased with such laboured vanities; we shall find that our applause rather proceeds from a kind of contagion caught up from others, and which we contribute to diffuse, than from what we privately feel. There are some subjects of which almost all the world perceive the futility, yet all combine in imposing upon each other, as worthy of praise. But chiefly this imposition obtains in literature, where men publicly contemn what they relish with rapture in private, and approve abroad what has given them disgust at home. The truth is, we deliver those criticisms in public which are supposed to be best calculated not to do justice to the author, but to impress others with an opinion of our superior discernment.

But let the works of this kind, which have already come off with such applause, enjoy it all. It is neither my wish to diminish, as I was never considerable enough to add to their fame. But for the future I fear there are many poems of which I shall find spirits to read but the title. In the first place, all odes upon winter or summer or autumn, in short all odes, epodes, and monodies whatsoever, shall hereafter be deemed too polite, classical, obscure, and refined, to be read, and entirely above the human comprehension. Pastorals are pretty enough—for those that like them—but to me Thyrsis is one of the most insipid fellows I ever conversed with; and as for Corydon, I don't chuse to part company. Elegies and epistles are very fine to those to whom they are addressed; and as for epic poems, I am generally able to discover the whole plan in reading the two first pages.

Tragedies, however, as they are now made, are good instructive moral *sermons* enough; and it would be a fault not to be pleased with *good things*. There I learn several great truths, as: that it is impossible to see into the ways of futurity, that punishment always attends the villain, that love is the fond soother of the human breast, that we should not resist heaven's will, with several other sentiments equally new, delicate and striking. Every new tragedy therefore I shall go to see; for reflections of this nature make up a tolerable harmony when mixed up with a proper quantity of drum, trumpet, thunder, lightening, or the scene shifter's whistle. Adieu.

LETTER NINETY-EIGHT

A description of the courts of justice in Westminster Hall.

From the same.

I had some intentions lately of going to visit Bedlam, the place where those who go mad are confined. I went to wait upon the Man in Black to be my conductor, but I found him preparing to go to Westminster-hall, where the English hold their courts of justice. It gave me some surprize to find my friend engaged in a law-suit, but more so when he informed me that it had been depending for several years. "How is it possible," cried I, "for a man who knows the world to go to law. I am well acquainted with the courts of justice in China; they resemble rat traps every one of them, nothing more easy to get in, but to get out again is attended with some difficulty, and more cunning than rats are generally found to possess!"

"Faith," replied my friend, "I should not have gone to law, but that I was assured of success before I began; things were represented to me in so alluring a light that I thought by barely declaring myself a candidate for the prize, I had nothing more to do but to enjoy the fruits of the Victory. Thus have I been upon the eve of an imaginary triumph every term these ten years, have travelled forward with victory ever in my view, but ever out of reach; however at present I fancy we have hampered our antagonist in such a manner that without some unforeseen demur, we shall this very day lay him fairly upon his back."

"If things be so situated," said I, "I don't care if I attend you to the courts and partake in the pleasure of your success. But prithee," continued I as we set forward, "what reasons have you to think an affair at last concluded which has given you so many former disappointments?" "My lawyer tells me," returned he, "that I have Salkeld and Ventris strong in my favour, and that there are no less than fifteen cases in point." "I understand," said I; "those are two of your judges who have already declared their opinions." "Pardon me," replied my friend; "Salkeld and Ventris are lawyers who some hundred years ago gave their opinion on cases similar to mine; these opinions which make for me my lawyer is to cite, and those opinions which look another way are cited by the lawyer employed by my antagonist; as I observed I have Salkeld and Ventris for me; he has Coke and Hales for him; and he that has most opinions is most likely to carry his cause." "But where is the necessity," cried I, "of prolonging a suit by citing the opinions and reports of others, since the same good sense which determined lawyers in former ages may serve to guide your judges at this day. They at that time gave their opinions only from the light of reason; your judges have the same light at present to direct them, let me even add a greater, as in former ages there were many prejudices from which the present is happily free. If arguing from authorities be exploded from every other branch of learning, why should it be particularly adhered to in this? I plainly foresee how such a method of investigation must embarrass every suit, and even perplex the student; ceremonies will be multiplied, formalities must encrease, and more time will thus be spent in learning the arts of litigation than in the discovery of right."

"I see," cries my friend, "that you are for a speedy administration of justice, but all the world will grant that the more time is taken up in considering any subject, the better it will be understood. Besides, it is the boast of an Englishman that his property is secure, and all the world will grant that a deliberate administration of justice is the best way to *secure his property*. Why have we so many lawyers *but to secure our property*, why so many formalities but *to secure our property*? Not less than one hundred thousand families live in oppulence, elegance and ease, merely by *securing our property*."

"To embarrass justice," returned I, "by a multiplicity of laws, or to hazard it by a confidence in our judges, are, I grant, the opposite rocks on which legislative wisdom has ever split; in one case the client resembles that emperor who is said to have been suffocated with the bedcloaths which were only designed to keep him warm; in the other, to that town which let the enemy take possession of its walls, in order to shew the world how little they depended on aught but courage for safety.—But bless me, what numbers do I see here—all in black.—How is it possible that half this multitude find employment?" "Nothing so easily conceived," returned my companion, "they live by watching each other. For instance, the catchpole watches the man in debt, the attorney watches the catchpole, the counsellor watches the attorney, the solicitor the counsellor, and all find sufficient employment." "I conceive you," interrupted I, "they watch each other, but it is the client that pays them all for watching; it puts me in mind of a Chinese fable, which is entituled, *Five animals at a meal*. The fable is this:

A grasshopper filled with dew was merrily singing under the shade; a whangam that eats grasshoppers had marked it for its prey, and was just stretching forward to devour it; a serpent that had for a long time fed only on whangams was coiled up to fasten on the whangam; a yellow bird was just upon the wing to dart upon the serpent; an hawk had just stooped from above to seize the yellow bird; all were intent on their prey and unmindful of their danger. So the whangam eat the grasshopper, the serpent eat the whangam, the yellow bird the serpent, the hawk the yellow bird, when sousing from on high, a vulture gobbled up the hawk, grasshopper, whangam, and all in a moment."

I had scarce finished my fable, when the lawyer came to inform my friend that his cause was put off to another term, that money was wanted to retain, and that all the world was of opinion that the very next hearing would bring him off victorious. "If so," then cries my friend, "I believe it will be my wisest way to continue the cause for another term, and in the mean time my friend here and I will go and see Bedlam." Adieu.

LETTER ONE HUNDRED AND THREE [44]

The Chinese Philosopher begins to think of quitting England.

From Lien Chi Altangi to ***, Merchant in Amsterdam.

I have just received a letter from my son in which he informs me of the fruitlessness of his endeavours to recover the lady with whom he fled from Persia.[45] He strives to cover under the appearance of fortitude a heart torn with anxiety and disappointment. I have offered little consolation, since that but too frequently feeds the sorrow which it pretends to deplore, and strengthens the impression which nothing but the external rubs of time and accident can thoroughly efface.

He informs me of his intentions of quitting Moscow the first opportunity, and travelling by land to Amsterdam. I must therefore, upon his arrival, entreat the continuance of your friendship and beg of you to provide him with proper directions for finding me in London. You can scarcely be sensible of the joy I expect upon seeing him once more; the ties between the father and the son among us of China are much more closely drawn than with you of Europe.

The remittances sent me from Argun to Moscow came in safety. I cannot sufficiently admire that spirit of honesty which prevails through the whole country of Siberia; perhaps the savages of that desolate region are the only untutored people of the globe that cultivate the moral virtues, even without knowing that their actions merit praise. I have been told surprising things of their goodness, benevolence, and generosity; and the uninterrupted commerce between China and Russia serves as a collateral confirmation.

Let us, says the Chinese law-giver, *admire the rude virtues of the ignorant, but rather imitate the delicate morals of the polite.* In the country where I reside, though honesty and benevolence be not so congenial, yet art supplies the place of nature. Though here every vice is carried to excess, yet every virtue is practised also with unexampled superiority. A city like this is the soil for great virtues and great vices; the villain can soon improve here in the deepest mysteries of deceiving, and the practical philosopher can every day meet new incitements to mend his honest intentions. There are no pleasures, sensual or sentimental, which this city does not produce; yet, I know not how, I could not be content to reside here for life. There is something so seducing in that spot in which we first had existence that nothing but it can please; whatever vicissitudes we experience in life, however we toil, or wheresoever we wander, our fatigued wishes still recur to home for tranquillity; we long to die in that spot which gave us birth, and in that pleasing expectation opiate every calamity.

You now therefore perceive that I have some intentions of leaving this country; and yet my designed departure fills me with reluctance and regret. Though the friendships of travellers are generally more transient than vernal snows, still I feel an uneasiness at breaking the connections I have formed since my arrival; particularly I shall have no small pain in leaving my usual companion, guide, and instructor.

I shall wait for the arrival of my son before I set out. He shall be my companion in every intended journey for the future; in his company I can support the fatigues of the way with redoubled ardour, pleased at once with conveying instruction, and exacting obedience. Adieu.

LETTER ONE HUNDRED AND SIX

Funeral elegies written upon the great, ridiculed. A specimen of one.

From Lien Chi Altangi, to Fum Hoam, first president of the Ceremonial Academy at Pekin, in China.

It was formerly the custom here, when men of distinction died, for their surviving acquaintance to throw each a slight present into the grave. Several things of little value were made use of for that purpose: perfumes, reliques, spices, bitter herbs, camomile, wormwood, and verses. This custom however is almost discontinued; and nothing but verses alone are now lavished on such occasions. When a Tartar dies, his bow, his horse, and all his worldly possessions are buried with him; the wiser English, however, throw nothing but poetry into the grave, an oblation which they suppose may be interred with the dead, without any injury to the living.

Upon the death of the great therefore, the poets and undertakers are sure of employment. While one provides the long cloak, black staff, and mourning coach, the other produces the pastoral or elegy, the monody or apotheosis. The nobility need be under no apprehensions; they may die as fast as they think proper, the poet and undertaker are ready to supply them; these can find metaphorical tears and family escutcheons at half an hour's warning; and when the one has soberly laid the body in the grave, the other is ready to fix it figuratively among the constellations.

There are several ways of being poetically sorrowful on such occasions. The bard is now some pensive youth of science, who sits deploring among the tombs; again he is Thyrsis, complaining in a circle of harmless sheep. Now Britannia sits upon her own shore and gives a loose to maternal tenderness; at another time, Parnassus, even the mountain Parnassus, gives way to sorrow and is bathed in tears of distress.

But the most usual manner is Damon's meeting Menalcas, who has got a most gloomy countenance. The shepherd asks his friend, whence that look of distress? to which the other replies that Pollio is no more. "If that be the case then," cries Damon, "let us retire to yonder bower at some distance off, where the cypress and the jessamine add fragrance to the breeze; and let us weep alternately for Pollio, the friend of shepherds, and the patron of every muse." "Ah," returns his fellow shepherd, "what think you rather of that grotto by the fountain side; the murmuring stream will help to assist our complaints, and a nightingale on a neighbouring tree will join her voice to the concert." When the place is settled, they begin; the brook stands still to hear their lamentations; the cows forget to graze; and the very tygers start from the forest with sympathetic concern. By the tombs of our ancestors, my dear Fum, I am quite unaffected in all this distress; the whole is liquid laudanum to my spirits; and a tyger of common sensibility has twenty times more tenderness than I.

But though I could never weep with the complaining shepherd, yet I am sometimes induced to pity the poet whose trade is thus to make Demigods and Heroes for a dinner. There is not in nature a more dismal figure than a man who sits down to premeditated flattery; every stanza he writes tacitly reproaches the meanness of his occupation, till at last his stupidity becomes more stupid, and his dullness more diminutive.

I am amazed therefore that none have yet found out the secret of flattering the worthless, and yet of preserving a safe conscience. I have often wished for some method by which a man might do himself and his deceased patron justice, without being under the hateful reproach of self-conviction. After long lucubration, I have hit upon such an expedient, and send you the specimen of a poem upon the decease of a great man in which the flattery is perfectly fine, and yet the poet perfectly innocent.

On the Death of the Right Honourable ***

Ye muses, pour the pitying tear
For Pollio snatch'd away:
For had he liv'd another year!
——*He had not dy'd to-day.*

O, were he born to bless mankind,
In virtuous times of yore,
Heroes themselves had fall'n behind!
——*Whene'er he went before.*

How sad the groves and plains appear,
And sympathetic sheep;
Even pitying hills would drop a tear!
——*If hills could learn to weep.*

His bounty in exalted strain
Each bard might well display:
Since none implor'd relief in vain!
——*That went reliev'd away.*

And hark! I hear the tuneful throng;
His obsequies forbid.
He still shall live, shall live as long
——*As ever dead man did.*

LETTER ONE HUNDRED AND EIGHT

The utility and entertainment which might result from a journey
into the East.

To the same.

I have frequently been amazed at the ignorance of almost all
the European travellers who have penetrated any considerable
way eastward into Asia. They have all been influenced either
by motives of commerce or piety, and their accounts are such
as might reasonably be expected from men of a very narrow or
very prejudiced education, the dictates of superstition or the
result of ignorance. Is it not surprizing that of such a variety

of adventurers not one single philosopher should be found among the number; for as to the travels of Gemelli, the learned are long agreed that the whole is but an imposture.[46]

There is scarce any country how rude or incultivated soever, where the inhabitants are not possessed of some peculiar secrets, either in nature or art, which might be transplanted with success; in Siberian Tartary the natives extract a strong spirit from milk, which is a secret probably unknown to the chymists of Europe. In the most savage parts of India they are possessed of the secret of dying vegetable substances scarlet and of refining lead into a metal which, for hardness and colour, is little inferior to silver, not one of which secrets but would in Europe make a man's fortune. The power of the Asiatics in producing winds or bringing down rain the Europeans are apt to treat as fabulous, because they have no instances of the like nature among themselves; but they would have treated the secrets of gunpowder and the mariner's compass in the same manner, had they been told the Chinese used such arts before the invention was common with themselves at home.

Of all the English philosophers I most reverence Bacon, that great and hardy genius; he it is who [allows of secrets yet unknown, who,] undaunted by the seeming difficulties that oppose, prompts human curiosity to examine every part of nature and even exhorts man to try whether he cannot subject the tempest, the thunder, and even earthquakes to human controll. O had a man of his daring spirit, of his genius, penetration, and learning travelled to those countries which have been visited only by the superstitious or mercenary, what might not mankind expect; how would he enlighten the regions to which he travelled! And what a variety of knowledge and useful improvement would he not bring back in exchange!

There is probably no country so barbarous that would not disclose all it knew, if it received equivalent information; and I am apt to think that a person who was ready to give more knowledge than he received, would be welcome wherever he came. All his care in travelling should only be to suit his intellectual banquet to the people with whom he conversed; he should not attempt to teach the unlettered Tartar astronomy, nor yet instruct the polite Chinese in the arts of subsistence;

he should endeavour to improve the barbarian in the secrets of living comfortably, and the inhabitant of a more refined country in the speculative pleasures of science. How much more nobly would a philosopher thus employed spend his time than by sitting at home earnestly intent upon adding one star more to his catalogue, or one monster more to his collection, or still, if possible, more triflingly sedulous in the incatenation of fleas or the sculpture of cherry-stones.

I never consider this subject without being surprized how none of those societies so laudably established in England for the promotion of arts and learning have never thought of sending one of their members into the most eastern parts of Asia to make what discoveries he was able. To be convinced of the utility of such an undertaking, let them but read the relations of their own travellers. It will there be found that they are as often deceived themselves as they attempt to deceive others. The merchants tell us perhaps the price of different commodities, the methods of baling them up, and the properest manner for an European to preserve his health in the country. The missioner, on the other hand, informs us with what pleasure the country to which he was sent embraced Christianity, and the numbers he converted, what methods he took to keep Lent in a region where there was no fish, or the shifts he made to celebrate the rites of his religion in places where there was neither bread nor wine; such accounts, with the usual appendage of marriages and funerals, inscriptions, rivers, and mountains, make up the whole of an European traveller's diary; but as to all the secrets of which the inhabitants are possessed, those are universally attributed to magic; and when the traveller can give no other account of the wonders he sees performed, he very contentedly ascribes them to the devil.

It was an usual observation of Boyle, the English chymist, that if every artist would but discover what new observations occurred to him in the exercise of his trade, philosophy would thence gain innumerable improvements. It may be observed with still greater justice, that if the useful knowledge of every country, howsoever barbarous, was gleaned by a judicious observer, the advantages would be inestimable. Are there not even in Europe many useful inventions known or practised, but in one place? The instrument, as an example, for cutting down corn in Germany is much more handy and expeditious, in my opinion, than the sickle used in England. The cheap and expeditious manner of making vinegar without previous fermentation is known only in a part of France. If such discoveries therefore remain still to be known at home, what funds of knowledge might not be collected in countries yet unexplored or only passed through by ignorant travellers in hasty caravans.

The caution with which foreigners are received in Asia may be alledged as an objection to such a design. But how readily have several European merchants found admission into regions the most suspicious, under the character of *Sanjapins*, or northern pilgrims; to such not even China itself denies access.

To send out a traveller, properly qualified for these purposes, might be an object of national concern; it would in some measure repair the breaches made by ambition, and might shew that there were still some who boasted a greater name than that of patriots, who professed themselves lovers of men. The only difficulty would remain in chusing a proper person for so arduous an enterprize. He should be a man of a philosophical turn, one apt to deduce consequences of general utility from particular occurrences, neither swolen with pride nor hardened by prejudice, neither wedded to one particular system nor instructed only in one particular science, neither wholly a botanist nor quite an antiquarian; his mind should be tinctured with miscellaneous knowledge, and his manners humanized by an intercourse with men. He should be, in some measure, an enthusiast to the design, fond of travelling from a rapid imagination and an innate love of change, furnished with a body capable of sustaining every fatigue and an heart not easily terrified at danger. Adieu.

LETTER ONE HUNDRED AND NINE

The Chinese philosopher attempts to find out famous men.

From the same.

One of the principal tasks I had proposed to myself on my arrival here was to become acquainted with the names and characters of those now living who as scholars or wits had acquired the greatest share of reputation. In order to succeed in this design I fancied the surest method would be to begin my enquiry among the ignorant, judging that his fame would be greatest which was loud enough to be heard by the vulgar. Thus predisposed I began the search, but only went in quest of disappointment and perplexity. I found every district had a peculiar famous man of its own. Here the story-telling shoe-maker had engrossed the admiration on one side of the street, while the bellman, who excelled at a catch, was in quiet possession of the other. At one end of a lane the Parson of the parish was regarded as the greatest man alive, but I had not travelled half its length till I found an enthusiast teacher had divided his reputation. My landlady perceiving my design was kind enough to offer me her little advice in this affair. It was true, she observed, that she was no critic, yet she knew what pleased herself, and if I would rest upon her judgment, I should set down Tom Collins as the most ingenious man in the world, for Tom was able to take off all mankind and imitate besides a sow and pigs to perfection.

I now perceived that taking my standard of reputation among the vulgar would swell my catalogue of great names above the size of a Court Calendar. I therefore discontinued this method of pursuit, and resolved to prosecute my enquiry in that usual residence of fame, a bookseller's shop. In consequence of this I entreated the bookseller to let me know who were they who now made the greatest figure either in morals, wit, or learning. Without giving me a direct answer, he pulled a pamphlet from the shelf, *The Young Attorney's Guide;* "there, Sir," cries he, "there's a touch for you, fifteen hundred of these moved off in one day. I take the author of this pamphlet either for title, preface, plan, body, or index to be the completest hand in England." I found it was vain to prosecute my enquiry where my informer appeared so incompetent a judge of merit, so paying for the *Young Attorney's Guide,* which good manners obliged me to buy, I walked off.

My pursuit after famous men now brought me into a print shop. Here, thought I, the painter only reflects the public voice. As every man who deserved it had formerly his statue placed up in the Roman forum, so here probably the pictures of none but such as merit a place in our affections are held up for public sale. But guess my surprize when I came to examine this depositary of noted faces; all distinctions seemed to be levelled here as in the grave, and I could not but regard it as the catacomb of real merit. The brick dust man took up as much room as the truncheoned hero, and the judge was elbowed by the thieftaker; quacks, pimps, and buffoons encreased the groupe, and noted stallions only made room for more noted whores. I had read the works of some of the moderns previous to my coming to England with delight and approbation, but I found their faces had no place here; the walls were covered with the names of authors I had never known, or had endeavoured to forget, with the little self-advertising things of a day who had forced themselves into fashion, but not into fame. I could read at the bottom of some pictures the names of * *, and * * *, and * * * *, all equally candidates for the vulgar shout and foremost to propagate their unblushing faces upon brass. My uneasiness therefore at not finding my few favourite names among the number was now changed into congratulation. I could not avoid reflecting on the fine observation of Tacitus on a similar occasion. "In this cavalcade of flattery," cries the historian, "neither the pictures of Brutus, Cassius, nor Cato, were to be seen, *eo clariores quia imagines eorum non deferebantur,* their absence being the strongest proof of their merit."

"It is in vain," cried I, "to seek for true greatness among these monuments of the unburied dead; let me go among the tombs of those who are confessedly famous, and see if any have been lately deposited there who deserve the attention of posterity, and whose names may be transmitted to my distant friend as an honour to the present age. Determined in my pursuit, I paid a second visit to Westminster Abbey. There I found several new monuments erected to the memory of several great men; the names of the great men I absolutely forget, but I well remember that Roubillac was the statuary who cut them. I could not however help smiling at two modern epitaphs in particular, one of which praised the deceased for being *ortus ex antiqua stirpe;* the other commended the dead because *hanc ædem suis sumptibus reædificavit;* the greatest merit of one consisted in his being descended from an illustrious house; the chief distinction of the other, that he had propped up an old house that was falling. "Alas, alas," cried I, "such monuments as these confer honour, not upon the great men, but upon little Roubillac."

Hitherto disappointed in my enquiry after the famous men of the present age, I was resolved to mix in company, and try what I could learn among critics in coffee-houses; and here it was that I heard my favourite names talked of indeed, but mentioned with inverted fame. A gentleman of acknowledged merit as a writer was branded in general terms as a bad man; another of exquisite delicacy as a poet was reproached for wanting good nature; a third was accused of free-thinking, and a fourth for having once been a player. "Strange," cried I, "how unjust are mankind in the distribution of fame; the ignorant among whom I sought at first were willing to grant, but incapable of distinguishing the virtues of those which deserved it; among those I now converse with, they know the proper objects of admiration, but mix envy with applause."

Disappointed so often, I was now resolved to examine those characters in person of whom the world talked so freely; just what I expected was the result of my search. I found the truly great, possessed of numerous small faults and a few shining virtues. We have often observed, my friend, that there is a sublime in morals as in writing, and that they who have attained an excellence in either, commit numberless transgressions, observable to the meanest understanding. The ignorant critic and dull remarker can readily spy a blemish in eloquence or morals, whose sentiments are not sufficiently elevated to observe a beauty. Such are judges neither of books nor of life; they can diminish no solid reputation by their censure, nor bestow a lasting character by their applause. In short, I found by my search that such only can confer real fame upon others, who have merit themselves to deserve it. Adieu.

LETTER ONE HUNDRED AND TWELVE

An election described.

To the same.

The English are at present employed in celebrating a feast which becomes general every seventh year; the old parliament being then dissolved and another appointed to be chosen. This solemnity falls infinitely short of our feast of the lanthorns in

magnificence and splendour; it is also surpassed by others of
the East in unanimity and pure devotion, but no festival in the
world can compare with it for eating. Their eating indeed
amazes me. Had I five hundred heads, and were each head
furnished with brains, yet would they all be insufficient to
compute the number of cows, sheep, pigs, geese and turkies,
which upon this occasion die for the good of their country!

To say the truth, eating seems to make a grand ingredient
in all English parties of zeal, business or amusement. When a
Church is to be built, or Hospital endowed, the Directors
assemble, and instead of consulting upon it, they eat upon it,
by which means the business goes forward with success. When
the Poor are to be relieved, the officers appointed to dole out
public charity, assemble and eat upon it. Nor has it ever been
known that they filled the bellies of the poor till they had
previously satisfied their own. But in the election of magistrates the people seem to exceed all bounds; the merits of a
candidate are often measured by the number of his treats; his
constituents assemble, eat upon him, and lend their applause
not to his integrity or sense, but the quantities of his beef and
brandy.

And yet I could forgive this people their plentiful meals on
this occasion, as it is extremely natural for every man to eat a
great deal when he gets it for nothing; but what amazes me is
that all this good living no way contributes to improve their
good humour. On the contrary, they seem to lose their temper
as they lose their appetites; every morsel they swallow and
every glass they pour down serves to encrease their animosity.
Many an honest man, before as harmless as a tame rabbit,
when loaded with a single election dinner has become more
dangerous than a charged culverin. Upon one of these occasions I have actually seen a bloody minded Man Milliner sally
forth at the head of a mob, determined to face a desperate
Pastry Cook who was General of the opposite party.

But you must not suppose they are without a pretext for
thus beating each other. On the contrary, no man here is so
uncivilized as to beat his neighbour without producing very
sufficient reasons. One part of the village, for instance, drinks
gin, a spirit of their own manufacture; another always drinks
brandy imported from abroad. Brandy is a wholesome liquor;

gin a liquor wholly their own. This then furnishes an obvious cause of quarrel, Whether it be most reasonable to get drunk with gin or to get drunk with brandy? They meet upon the debate, fight themselves sober, and then draw off to get drunk again, and charge for another encounter. So that the English may now properly be said to be engaged in war, since while they are subduing their enemies abroad, they are breaking each other's heads at home.

I lately made an excursion to a neighbouring village, in order to be a spectator of the ceremonies practised upon this occasion. I left town in company with three fidlers, nine dozen of hams, and a corporation poet, which were designed as reinforcements to the gin drinking party. We entered the town with a very good face; the fidlers, no way intimidated by the enemy, kept handling their arms up the principal street. By prudent manœuvre they took peaceable possession of their head-quarters, amidst the shouts of multitudes who seemed perfectly rejoiced at hearing their music, but above all at seeing their bacon.

I must own I could not avoid being pleased to see all ranks of people on this occasion levelled into an equality, and the poor, in some measure, enjoying the primitive privileges of nature. If there was any distinction shewn, the lowest of the people seemed to receive it from the rich. I could perceive a cobler with a levee at his door, and an haberdasher giving audience from behind his counter. But my reflections were soon interrupted by a mob who demanded whether I was for the Distillery or the Brewery? As these were terms with which I was totally unacquainted, I chose at first to be silent; however, I know not what might have been the consequence of my reserve, had not the attention of the mob been called off to a skirmish between a brandy-drinker's cow and a gin-drinker's mastiff, which turned out greatly to the advantage of the latter.

This spectacle, which afforded high satisfaction, was at last ended by the appearance of one of the candidates, who came to harangue the mob; he made a very pathetic speech upon the late excessive importation of foreign drams and the downfall of the distillery. I could see some of the audience shed tears. He was accompanied in his procession by Mrs. Deputy and

Mrs. Mayoress. Mrs. Deputy was not the least bit in liquor; and for Mrs. Mayoress, one of the spectators assured me in my ear that,—she was a very fine woman before she had the small-pox.

Mixing with the croud, I was now conducted to the hall where the magistrates are chosen; but what tongue can describe this scene of confusion; the whole crowd seemed equally inspired with anger, jealousy, politics, patriotism and punch. I remarked one figure that was carried up by two men upon this occasion. I at first began to pity his infirmities as natural, but soon found the fellow so drunk that he could not stand; another made his appearance to give his vote, but though he could stand, he had actually lost the use of his tongue, and remained silent; a third, who though excessively drunk could both stand and speak, being asked the Candidate's name for whom he voted, could be prevailed upon to return no other answer but "Tobacco and Brandy for ever!" In short, an election-hall seems to be a theatre where every passion is seen without disguise, a school where fools may readily become worse and where philosophers may gather wisdom. Adieu.

LETTER ONE HUNDRED AND SIXTEEN

Whether love be a natural or a fictitious passion.

To the same.

There is something irresistibly pleasing in the conversation of a fine woman; even though her tongue be silent, the eloquence of her eyes gives lectures of wisdom. The mind sympathizes with the regularity of the object in view, and struck with external beauty, vibrates into respondent harmony. In this agreeable disposition, I lately found myself in company with my friend and his niece.[47] Our conversation turned upon love, which she seemed equally capable of defending and inspiring. We were each of different opinions upon this subject; the lady insisted that it was a natural and universal passion, and procured the happiness of those who cultivated it with proper precaution. My friend denied it to be the work of nature, but allowed it a real existence and affirmed that it was of infinite service in refining society; while I, to keep up the dispute, affirmed it to be merely a name, first used by the cunning part of the fair sex and admitted by the silly part of ours, therefore no way more natural than taking snuff or chewing opium.

"How is it possible," cried I, "that such a passion can be natural, when our opinions even of beauty, which inspires it, are entirely the result of fashion and caprice? The ancients, who pretended to be connoisseurs in the art, have praised narrow foreheads, red hair, and eyebrows that joined each other over the nose. Such were the charms that once captivated Catullus, Ovid, and Anacreon. Ladies would at present be out of humour, if their lovers praised them for such graces; and should an antique beauty now revive, her face would certainly be put under the discipline of the tweezer, forehead-cloth and lead comb, before it could be seen in public company.

"But the difference between the antients and moderns is not so great as between the different countries of the present world. A lover of Gongora, for instance, sighs for thick lips; a Chinese lover is poetical in praise of thin. In Circassia a streight nose is thought most consistent with beauty; cross but a mountain which separates it from the Tartars, and there flat noses, tawny skins, and eyes three inches asunder, are all the fashion. In Persia and some other countries, a man when he marries chuses to have his bride a maid; in the Phillipine Islands, if a bridegroom happens to perceive on the first night that he is fobbed off with a virgin, the marriage is (by Act of Parliament, I suppose) declared null and void to all intents and purposes, and the bride sent back with disgrace. In some parts of the East a woman of beauty, properly fed up for sale, often amounts to an hundred crowns; in the kingdom of Loango, ladies of the very best fashion are sold for a pig, queens however sell better, and are seldom bought under a cow. In short, turn even to England, don't I there see the beautiful part of the sex neglected; and none now marrying or making love but old men and old women that have saved money? Don't I see beauty from fifteen to twenty one rendered null and void to all intents and purposes, and those six precious years of womanhood put under a statute of virginity? What! shall I call that rancid passion love which passes between an old batchelor of fifty-six and a widow lady of forty-nine? What advantage is society to reap from an intercourse where the big belly is oftnest on the man's side? Would any persuade me that such a passion was natural, unless the human race were more fit for love as they approach'd the decline, and, like silk-worms, became breeders just before they expired?"

"Whether love be natural or no," replied my friend gravely, "it contributes to the happiness of every society into which it is introduced. All our pleasures are short and can only charm at intervals; love is a method of protracting our greatest pleasure; and surely that gamester who plays the greatest stake to the best advantage will at the end of life rise victorious. This was the opinion of Vanini, who affirmed that *every hour was lost which was not spent in love*. His accusers were unable to comprehend his meaning, and the poor advocate for love was burned in flames, alas, no way metaphorical. But whatever advantages the individual may reap from this passion, society will certainly be refined and improved by its introduction. All laws calculated to discourage it tend to embrute the species and weaken the state. Tho' it cannot plant morals in the human breast, it cultivates them when there; pity, generosity, and honour, receive a brighter polish from its assistance; and a single amour is sufficient entirely to brush off the clown.

"But it is an exotic of the most delicate constitution; it requires the greatest art to introduce it into a state, and the smallest discouragement is sufficient to repress it again. Let us only consider with what ease it was formerly extinguished in Rome, and with what difficulty it was lately revived in Europe; it seemed to sleep for ages and at last fought its way among us through tilts, tournaments, dragons, and enchanted castles. The rest of the world, China only excepted, are and have ever been utter strangers to its delights and advantages. In other countries, as men find themselves stronger than women, they lay a claim to a rigorous superiority; this is natural, and love which gives up this natural advantage must certainly be the effect of art, an art calculated to lengthen out our happier moments and add new graces to society."

"I entirely acquiesce in your sentiments," says the lady, "with regard to the advantages of this passion, but cannot avoid giving it a nobler origin than you have been pleased to assign. I must think that those countries where it is rejected are obliged to have recourse to art to stifle so natural a production, and those nations where it is cultivated only make nearer advances to nature. The same efforts that are used in some places to suppress pity and other natural passions may have been employed to extinguish love. No nation, however unpolished, is remarkable for innocence that is not famous for this passion; it has flourished in the coldest, as well as the warmest regions. Even in the sultry wilds of southern America the lover is not satisfied with possessing his mistress's person without having her mind.

> *In all my Enna's beauties blest*
> *Amidst profusion still I pine;*
> *For tho' she gives me up her breast*
> *Its panting tenant is not mine.*[48]

But its effects are too violent to be the result of an artificial passion. Nor is it in the power of fashion to force the constitution into those changes which we every day observe. Several have died of it. Few lovers are unacquainted with the fate of the two Italian lovers, Da Corsin and Julia Bellamano, who after a long separation expired with pleasure in each others arms. Such instances are too strong confirmations of the reality of the passion, and serve to shew that suppressing it is but opposing the natural dictates of the heart."

"Upon the whole," cries my friend, interrupting her, "this topic is too metaphysical for conversation, and rather more adapted to the closet than the tea-table. The best way of treating a subject like this is to endeavour to get at the bottom of it, in private." Adieu.

LETTER ONE HUNDRED AND TWENTY-TWO

The Conclusion.

To the same.

After a variety of disapointments, my wishes are at length fully satisfied. My son so long expected is arrived, at once by his presence banishing my anxiety, and opening a new scene of unexpected pleasure. His improvements in mind and person have far surpass'd even the sanguine expectations of a father. I left him a boy, but he is returned a man, pleasing in person, hardened by travel, and polished by adversity. His disappointment in love, however, had infused an air of melancholy into his conversation, which seemed at intervals to interrupt our mutual satisfaction. I expected that this could find a cure only from time; but fortune, as if willing to load us with her favours, has in a moment repaid every uneasiness with rapture.

Two days after his arrival, the Man in Black with his beautiful niece came to congratulate us upon this pleasing occasion; but guess our pleasure and surprize when my friend's lovely kinswoman was found to be the very captive that my son had rescued from Persia, and who was carried by the Russian peasants to the port of Archangel. Were I to hold the pen of a novelist, I might be prolix in describing their feelings at so unexpected an interview; but you may conceive their joy, without my assistance; words were unable to express their transports, then how can words describe it?

When two young persons are sincerely enamoured of each other, nothing can give me such pleasure as seeing them married; whether I know the parties or not, I am happy at thus binding one link more in the universal chain. Nature has, in some measure, formed me for a match-maker and given me a soul to sympathize with every mode of human felicity. I instantly therefore consulted the Man in Black, whether we might not crown their mutual wishes by marriage; his soul seems formed of similar materials with mine; he instantly gave his consent, and the next day was appointed for the solemnization of their nuptials.

All the acquaintances which I had made since my arrival were present at this gay solemnity. The little beau was constituted master of the ceremonies, and his wife Mrs. Tibbs conducted the entertainment with proper decorum. The Man in Black and the pawn-broker's widow were very sprightly and sweet upon this occasion. The widow was dressed up under the inspection of Mrs. Tibbs; and as for the Man in Black, his face was set off by the assistance of a pig-tail wig, which was lent by the little beau, to fit him for making love with proper formality. The whole company easily perceived that it would be a double wedding before all was over, and indeed my friend and the widow seemed to make no secret of their passion; [he even called me aside, in order to know my candid opinion, whether I did not think him a little too old to be married. "As for my own part," continued he, "I know I am going to play the fool, but all my friends will praise my wisdom, and produce me as the very pattern of discretion to others."]

At dinner, every thing seemed to run on with good humour and satisfaction. Every creature in company thought themselves pretty, and every jest was laught at: the Man in Black sat next his mistress, helped her plate, chimed her glass, and jogged [her knees and] her elbow; he whispered something arch in her ear, and she patted his cheek; never was antiquated passion so playful, harmless, and amusing.

[The second course was now called for, and among a variety of other dishes, a fine turkey was placed before the widow. The Europeans, you know, carve as they eat; my friend therefore begged his mistress to help him to a part of the turkey. The widow, pleased with an opportunity of shewing her skill in carving, an art upon which it seems she picqued herself, began to cut it up by first taking off the leg. "Madam," cries my friend, "if I might be permitted to advise, I would begin by cutting off the wing, and then the leg will come off more easily." "Sir," replies the widow, "give me leave to understand cutting up a fowl. I always begin with the leg." "Yes Madam," replies the lover, "but if the wing be the most convenient manner, I would begin with the wing." "Sir," interrupts the lady, "when you have fowls of your own, begin with the wing if you please; but give me leave to take off the leg. I hope I am not to be taught at this time of day." "Madam," interrupts he, "we are never too old to be instructed." "Old, Sir!" interrupts the other, "who is old, Sir? When I die of age, I know of some that will quake for fear; if the leg does not come off, take the turkey to yourself." "Madam," replied the Man in Black, "I don't care a farthing whether the leg or the wing comes off; if you are for the leg first, why you shall have the argument, even though it be as I say." "As for the matter of that," cries the widow, "I don't care a fig, whether you are for the leg off, or on; and friend, for the future keep your distance." "O," replied the other, "that is easily done; it is only removing to the other end of the table, and so, madam, your most obedient humble servant."

Thus was this courtship of an age destroyed in one moment; for this dialogue] [49] effectually broke off the match between this respectable couple that had been but just concluded. The smallest accidents disappoint the most important treaties. However, though this quarrel in some measure interrupted the general satisfaction, it no way lessened the happiness of the youthful couple; and by the young lady's looks I could perceive she was not entirely displeased with the interruption.

In a few hours the whole transaction seemed entirely forgotten, and we have all since enjoyed those satisfactions which result from a consciousness of making each other happy. My son and his fair partner are fixed here for life; the Man in Black has given them up a small estate in the country, which added to what I was able to bestow will be capable of supplying all the real, but not the fictitious demands of happiness. As for myself, the world being but one city to me, I don't much care in which of the streets I happen to reside. I shall therefore spend the remainder of my days in examining the manners of different countries, and have prevailed upon the Man in Black to be my companion. *They must often change,* says Confucius, *who would be constant in happiness or wisdom.* Adieu.

The Life of Nash

[*The Life of Richard Nash, Esq., Late Master of the Ceremonies at Bath* was first published in 1762, twenty months after Nash's death. On the title-page appeared the opening words of a sentence from Horace's *Art of Poetry* (lines 351-2) which can be translated: "I will not take offence at a few blemishes against which human nature has failed to be on its guard."]

History owes its excellence more to the writer's manner than the materials of which it is composed. The intrigues of courts or the devastation of armies are regarded by the remote spectator with as little attention as the squabbles of a village or the fate of a malefactor that fall under his own observation. The great and the little, as they have the same senses and the same affections, generally present the same picture to the hand of the draughtsman; and whether the hero or the clown be the subject of the memoir, it is only man that appears with all his native minuteness about him; for nothing very great was ever yet formed from the little materials of humanity.

Thus none can properly be said to write history but he who understands the human heart, and its whole train of affections and follies. Those affections and follies are properly the materials he has to work upon. The relations of great events may surprize indeed; they may be calculated to instruct those very few who govern the million beneath, but the generality of mankind find the most real improvement from relations which are levelled to the general surface of life, which tell, not how men learned to conquer, but how they endeavoured to live, not how they gained the shout of the admiring croud, but how they acquired the esteem of their friends and acquaintance.

Every man's own life would perhaps furnish the most pleasing materials for history, if he only had candour enough to be sincere and skill enough to select such parts as once making him more prudent, might serve to render his readers

233

more cautious. There are few who do not prefer a page of Montaigne or Colley Cibber, who candidly tell us what they thought of the world and the world thought of them, to the more stately memoirs and transactions of Europe, where we see kings pretending to immortality that are now almost forgotten, and statesmen planning frivolous negociations that scarce outlive the signing.

It were to be wished that ministers and kings were left to write their own histories; they are truly useful to few but themselves; but for men who are contented with more humble stations I fancy such truths only are serviceable as may conduct them safely through life. That knowledge which we can turn to our real benefit should be most eagerly pursued. Treasures which we cannot use but little encrease the happiness or even the pride of the possessor.

I profess to write the history of a man placed in the middle ranks of life, of one whose vices and virtues were open to the eye of the most undiscerning spectator, who was placed in public view without power to repress censure or command adulation, who had too much merit not to become remarkable yet too much folly to arrive at greatness. I attempt the character of one who was just such a man as probably you or I may be, but with this difference, that he never performed an action which the world did not know, or ever formed a wish which he did not take pains to divulge. In short, I have chosen to write the life of the noted Mr. Nash, as it will be the delineation of a mind without disguise, of a man ever assiduous without industry and pleasing to his superiors, without any superiority of genius or understanding.

Yet if there be any who think the subject of too little importance to command attention, and had rather gaze at the actions of the great than be directed in guiding their own, I have one undeniable claim to their attention. Mr. Nash was himself a king. In this particular, perhaps no biographer has been so happy as I. They who are for a delineation of men and manners may find some satisfaction that way, and those who delight in adventures of kings and queens may perhaps find their hopes satisfied in another.

It is a matter of very little importance who were the parents, or what was the education of a man who owed so little of his advancement to either. He seldom boasted of family or learning, and his father's name and circumstances were so little known that Doctor Cheyne used frequently to affirm that Nash had no father. The Dutchess of Marlborough one day rallying him in public company upon the obscurity of his birth, compared him to Gil Blas, who was ashamed of his father. "No, Madam," replied Nash, "I seldom mention my father in company, not because I have any reason to be ashamed of him, but because he has some reason to be ashamed of me."

However, though such anecdotes be immaterial, to go on in the usual course of history it may be proper to observe that Richard Nash, Esq., the subject of this memoir, was born in the town of Swansea, in Glamorganshire, on the 18th of October in the year 1674. His father was a gentleman whose principal income arose from a partnership in a glass-house; his mother was niece to Colonel Poyer, who was killed by Oliver Cromwell for defending Pembroke castle against the rebels. He was educated under Mr. Maddocks at Carmarthan school, and from thence sent to Jesus college in Oxford, in order to prepare him for the study of the law. His father had strained his little income to give his son such an education, but from the boy's natural vivacity he hoped a recompence from his future preferment. In college, however, he soon shewed that though much might be expected from his genius, nothing could be hoped from his industry. A mind strongly turned to pleasure always is first seen at the university; there the youth first finds himself freed from the restraint of tutors, and being treated by his friends in some measure as a man, assumes the passions and desires of riper age, and discovers in the boy what are likely to be the affections of his maturity.

The first method Mr. Nash took to distinguish himself at college was not by application to study, but by his assiduity in intrigue. In the neighbourhood of every university there are girls who with some beauty, some coquettry, and little fortune, lie upon the watch for every raw amorous youth more inclined to make love than to study. Our heroe was quickly caught, and went through all the mazes and adventures of a college intrigue before he was seventeen; he offered marriage, the offer was accepted, but the whole affair coming to the knowledge of his tutors, his happiness, or perhaps his future misery, was prevented, and he was sent home from college with necessary advice to him and proper instructions to his father.

When a man knows his power over the fair sex, he generally commences their admirer for the rest of life. That triumph which he obtains over one, only makes him the slave of another; and thus he proceeds, conquering and conquered, to the closing of the scene. The army seemed the most likely profession in which to display this inclination for gallantry; he therefore purchased a pair of colours, commenced a professed admirer of the sex, and dressed to the very edge of his finances. But the life of a soldier is more pleasing to the spectator at a distance than to the person who makes the experiment. Mr. Nash soon found that a red coat alone would never succeed, that the company of the fair sex is not to be procured without expence, and that his scanty commission could never procure him the proper reimbursements. He found too that the profession of arms required attendance and duty, and often encroached upon those hours he could have wished to dedicate to softer purposes. In short, he soon became disgusted with the life of a soldier, quitted the army, entered his name as a student in the temple books, and here went to the very summit of second-rate luxury. Though very poor he was very fine; he spread the little gold he had in the most ostentatious manner, and though the gilding was but thin, he laid it on as far as it would go. They who know the town cannot be unacquainted with such a character as I describe; one who, though he may have dined in private upon a banquet served cold from a cook's shop, shall dress at six for the side box; one of those whose wants are only known to their laundress and tradesmen and their fine cloaths to half the nobility; who spend more in chair hire than housekeeping, and prefer a bow from a Lord to a dinner from a Commoner.

In this manner Mr. Nash spent some years about town, till at last his genteel appearance, his constant civility, and still more, his assiduity, gained him the acquaintance of several persons qualified to lead the fashion both by birth and fortune. To gain the friendship of the young nobility little more is requisite than much submission and very fine cloaths; dress has a mechanical influence upon the mind, and we naturally are awed into respect and esteem at the elegance of those whom even our reason would teach us to contemn. He seemed early sensible of human weakness in this respect, he brought a person genteelly dressed to every assembly, he always made one of those who are called very good company, and assurance gave him an air of elegance and ease.

When King William was upon the throne, Mr. Nash was a member of the Middle Temple.[50] It had been long customary for the Inns of court to entertain our monarchs upon their accession to the crown, or some such remarkable occasion, with a revel and pageant. In the earlier periods of our history poets were the conductors of these entertainments; plays were exhibited, and complimentary verses were then written; but by degrees the pageant alone was continued, Sir John Davis being the last poet that wrote verses upon such an occasion in the reign of James I.

This ceremony, which has been at length totally discontinued, was last exhibited in honour of King William, and Mr. Nash was chosen to conduct the whole with proper decorum. He was then but a very young man, but we see at how early an age he was thought proper to guide the amusements of his country, and be the *Arbiter Elegantiarum* of his time; we see how early he gave proofs of that spirit of regularity for which he afterwards became famous, and shewed an attention to those little circumstances of which, tho' the observance be trifling, the neglect has often interrupted men of the greatest abilities in the progress of their fortunes.

In conducting this entertainment, Nash had an opportunity of exhibiting all his abilities, and King William was so well satisfied with his performance that he made him an offer of knighthood. This, however, he thought proper to refuse, which in a person of his disposition seems strange. "Please your Majesty," replied he, when the offer was made him, "if you intend to make me a knight, I wish it may be one of your poor Knights of Windsor, and then I shall have a fortune at least able to support my title." Yet we do not find that the king took the hint of encreasing his fortune; perhaps he could not: he had at that time numbers to oblige, and he never cared to give money without important services.

But though Nash acquired no riches by his late office, yet he gained many friends, or what is more easily obtained, many acquaintance, who often answer the end as well. In the populous city where he resided, to be known was almost synonimous with being in the road to fortune. How many little things do we see, without merit or without friends, push themselves forward into public notice, and by self-advertizing attract the attention of the day. The wise despise them, but the public are not all wise. Thus they succeed, rise upon the wing of folly or of fashion, and by their success give a new sanction to effrontery.

But beside his assurance, Mr. Nash had in reality some merit and some virtues. He was, if not a brilliant, at least an easy companion. He never forgot good manners, even in the highest warmth of familiarity, and, as I hinted before, never went in a dirty shirt to disgrace the table of his patron or his friend. These qualifications might make the furniture of his head; but for his heart, that seemed an assemblage of the virtues which display an honest benevolent mind with the vices which spring from too much good nature. He had pity for every creature's distress, but wanted prudence in the application of his benefits. He had generosity for the wretched in the highest degree, at a time when his creditors complained of his justice. He often spoke falshoods, but never had any of his harmless tales tinctured with malice.

An instance of his humanity is told us in the Spectator, though his name is not mentioned. When he was to give in his accompts to the masters of the temple, among other articles he charged *For making one man happy* 10*l*. Being questioned about the meaning of so strange an item, he frankly declared that happening to over-hear a poor man declare to his wife and a large family of children that 10*l*. would make him happy, he could not avoid trying the experiment. He added that if they did not chuse to acquiesce in his charge, he was ready to refund the money. The masters, struck with such an uncommon instance of good nature, publicly thanked him for his benevolence, and desired that the sum might be doubled as a proof of their satisfaction.

Another instance of his unaccountable generosity, and I shall proceed. In some transactions with one of his friends, Mr. Nash was brought in debtor twenty pounds. His friend frequently asked for the money, and was as often denied. He found at last that assiduity was likely to have no effect, and therefore contrived an honourable method of getting back his money without dissolving the friendship that subsisted between them. One day, returning from Nash's chamber with the usual assurance of being paid to morrow, he went to one of their mutual acquaintance and related the frequent disappointments he had received and the little hopes he had of being ever paid. "My design," continues he, "is that you should go, and try to borrow twenty pounds from Nash, and bring me the money. I am apt to think he will lend to you, tho' he will not pay me. Perhaps we may extort from his generosity what I have failed to receive from his justice." His friend obeys, and going to Mr. Nash, assured him that unless relieved by his friendship, he should certainly be undone; he wanted to borrow twenty pounds, and had tried all his acquaintance without success. Mr. Nash, who had but some minutes before refused to pay a just debt, was in raptures at thus giving an instance of his friendship, and instantly lent what was required. Immediately upon the receipt, the pretended borrower goes to the real creditor and gives him the money, who met Mr. Nash the day after; our heroe upon seeing him, immediately began his usual excuses, that the billiard room had stript him, that he was never so damnably out of cash, but that in a few days— "My dear Sir, be under no uneasiness," replied the other, "I would not interrupt your tranquillity for the world; you lent twenty pounds yesterday to our friend of the back stairs, and he lent it to me; give him your receipt, and you shall have mine." "Perdition seize thee," cried Nash, "thou hast been too many for me. You demanded a debt, he asked a favour; to pay thee would not encrease our friendship, but to lend him was procuring a new friend, by conferring a new obligation."

Whether men, at the time I am now talking of, had more wit than at present, I will not take upon me to determine; but certain it is, they took more pains to shew what they had. In that age a fellow of high humour would drink no wine but what was strained through his mistress's smock. He would eat a pair of her shoes tossed up in a fricasee. He would swallow tallow-candles instead of toasted cheese, and even run naked about town, as it was then said, to divert the ladies. In short, that was the age of such kind of wit as is the most distant of all others from wisdom.

Mr. Nash, as he sometimes played tricks with others, upon certain occasions received very severe retaliations. Being at York, and having lost all his money, some of his companions agreed to equip him with fifty guineas upon this proviso, that he would stand at the great door of the Minster, in a blanket, as the people were coming out of church. To this proposal he readily agreed, but the Dean passing by unfortunately knew him. "What," cried the Divine, "Mr. Nash, in masquerade?" "Only a Yorkshire penance, Mr. Dean, for keeping bad company," says Nash, pointing to his companions.

Some time after this, he won a wager of still greater consequence by riding naked through a village upon a cow. This was then thought an harmless frolic; at present it would be looked upon with detestation.

He was once invited by some gentlemen of the navy, on board a man of war that had sailing orders for the Mediterranean. This was soon after the affair of the revels, and being ignorant of any design against him, he took his bottle with freedom. But he soon found, to use the expression then in fashion, that he was absolutely *bitten*.[51] The ship sailed away before he was aware of his situation, and he was obliged to make the voyage in the company where he had spent the night.

Many lives are often passed without a single adventure, and I do not know of any in the life of our hero that can be called such, except what we are now relating. During this voyage he was in an engagement in which his particular friend was killed by his side and he himself wounded in the leg. For the anecdote of his being wounded we are solely to trust to his own veracity; but most of his acquaintance were not much inclined to believe him when he boasted on those occasions. Telling one day of the wound he had received for his country in one of the public rooms at Bath, (Wiltshire's if I don't forget) a lady of distinction, that sat by, said it was all false. "I protest, Madam," replied he, "it is true; and if I cannot be believed, your Ladyship may, if you please, receive farther information, and feel the ball in my leg."

Mr. Nash was now fairly for life entered into a new course of gaiety and dissipation, and steady in nothing but in pursuit of variety. He was thirty years old, without fortune, or useful talents to acquire one. He had hitherto only led a life of expedients, he thanked chance alone for his support, and having been long precariously supported, he became at length totally a stranger to prudence or precaution. Not to disguise any part of his character, he was now, by profession, a gamester, and went on from day to day, feeling the vicissitudes of rapture and anguish, in proportion to the fluctuations of fortune.

At this time, London was the only theatre in England for pleasure or intrigue. A spirit of gaming had been introduced in the licentious age of Charles II. and had by this time thriven surprizingly. Yet all its devastations were confined to London alone. To this great mart of every folly sharpers from every country daily arrived for the winter, but were obliged to leave the kingdom at the approach of summer, in order to open a new campaign at Aix, Spaw, or the Hague. Bath, Tunbridge, Scarborough, and other places of the same kind here, were then frequented only by such as really went for relief; the pleasures they afforded were merely rural, the company splenetic, rustic, and vulgar. In this situation of things, people of fashion had no agreeable summer retreat from the town, and usually spent that season amidst a solitude of country squires, parsons wives, and visiting tenants or farmers; they wanted some place where they might have each others company, and win each others money, as they had done during the winter in town.

To a person who does not thus calmly trace things to their source, nothing will appear more strange than how the healthy could ever consent to follow the sick to those places of spleen, and live with those whose disorders are ever apt to excite a gloom in the spectator. The truth is, the gaming table was properly the salutary font, to which such numbers flocked. Gaming will ever be the pleasure of the rich, while men continue to be men, while they fancy more happiness in being possessed of what they want, than they experience pleasure in the fruition of what they have. The wealthy only stake those riches, which give no real content, for an expectation of riches in which they hope for satisfaction. By this calculation they cannot lose happiness, as they begin with none; and they hope to gain it by being possessed of something they have not had already.

Probably upon this principle and by the arrival of Queen Anne there for her health, about the year 1703 the city of Bath became in some measure frequented by people of distinction. The company was numerous enough to form a country dance upon the bowling green; they were amused with a fiddle and hautboy, and diverted with the romantic walks round the city. They usually sauntered in fine weather in the grove, between two rows of sycamore trees. Several learned physicians, Doctor Jordan and others, had even then praised the salubrity of the wells, and the amusements were put under the direction of a master of the ceremonies.

Captain Webster was the predecessor of Mr. Nash. This I take to be the same gentleman whom Mr. Lucas describes in his history of the lives of the gamesters, by which it appears that Bath, even before the arrival of Mr. Nash, was found a proper retreat for men of that profession. This gentleman in the year 1704 carried the balls to the town hall, each man paying half a guinea each ball.

Still, however, the amusements of this place were neither elegant nor conducted with delicacy. General society among people of rank or fortune was by no means established. The nobility still preserved a tincture of Gothic haughtiness, and refused to keep company with the gentry at any of the public entertainments of the place. Smoking in the rooms was permitted; gentlemen and ladies appeared in a disrespectful manner at public entertainments in aprons and boots. With an eagerness common to those whose pleasures come but seldom, they generally continued them too long; and thus they were rendered disgusting by too free an enjoyment. If the company liked each other, they danced till morning; if any person lost at cards, he insisted on continuing the game till luck should turn. The lodgings for visitants were paltry, though expensive, the dining rooms and other chambers were floored with boards, coloured brown with soot and small beer, to hide the dirt; the walls were covered with unpainted wainscot, the furniture corresponded with the meanness of the architecture; a few oak chairs, a small looking glass, with a fender and tongs, composed the magnificence of these temporary habitations. The city was in itself mean and contemptible, no elegant buildings, no open streets, nor uniform squares. The pump-house was without any director; the chairmen permitted no gentlemen or ladies to walk home by night without insulting them; and to add to all this, one of the greatest physicians of his age conceived a design of ruining the city, by writing against the efficacy of the waters. It was from a resentment of some affronts he had received there that he took this resolution; and accordingly published a pamphlet, by which he said, *he would cast a toad into the spring.*

In this situation of things it was, that Mr. Nash first came into that city, and hearing the threat of this physician, he humorously assured the people that if they would give him leave, he would charm away the poison of the Doctor's toad, as they usually charmed the venom of the tarantula, by music. He therefore was immediately empowered to set up the force of a band of music, against the poison of the Doctor's reptile; the company very sensibly encreased, Nash triumphed, and the sovereignty of the city was decreed to him by every rank of people.

We are now to behold this gentleman as arrived at a new dignity for which nature seemed to have formed him; we are to see him directing pleasures which none had better learned to share, placed over rebellious and refractory subjects that were to be ruled only by the force of his address, and governing such as had been long accustomed to govern others. We see a kingdom beginning with him, and sending off Tunbridge as one of its colonies.

But to talk more simply, when we talk at best of trifles. None could possibly conceive a person more fit to fill this employment than Nash. He had some wit, as I have said once or twice before, but it was of that sort which is rather happy than permanent. Once a week he might say a good thing; this the little ones about him took care to divulge; or if they happened to forget the joke, he usually remembered to repeat it himself. In a long intercourse with the world he had acquired an impenetrable assurance; and the freedom with which he was received by the Great, furnished him with vivacity, which could be commanded at any time, and which some mistook for wit. His former intercourse among people of fashion in town had let him into most of the characters of the nobility; and he was acquainted with many of their private intrigues. He understood rank and precedence with the utmost exactness, was fond of shew and finery himself, and generally set a pattern of it to others. These were his favourite talents, and he was the favourite of such as had no other.

But to balance these, which some may consider as foibles, he was charitable himself, and generally shamed his betters into a similitude of sentiment, if they were not naturally so before. He was fond of advising those young men, who, by youth and too much money, are taught to look upon extravagance as a virtue. He was an enemy to rudeness in others, though in the latter part of his life he did not much seem to encourage a dislike of it by his own example. None talked with more humanity of the foibles of others, when absent, than he, nor kept those secrets with which he was entrusted more inviolably. But above all (if moralists will allow it among the number of his virtues) tho' he gamed high, he always played very fairly. These were his qualifications. Some of the nobility regarded him as an inoffensive, useful companion, the size of whose understanding was, in general, level with their own; but their little imitators admired him as a person of fine sense and great good breeding. Thus people became fond of ranking him in the number of their acquaintance, told over his jests, and Beau Nash at length became the fashionable companion.

His first care, when made master of the ceremonies, or king of Bath, as it is called, was to promote a music subscription of one guinea each for a band which was to consist of six performers, who were to receive a guinea a week each for their trouble. He allowed also two guineas a week for lighting and sweeping the rooms, for which he accounted to the subscribers by receipt.

The pump-house was immediately put under the care of an officer by the name of the *Pumper*, for which he paid the corporation an annual rent. A row of new houses was begun on the south side of the gravel walks, before which a handsome pavement was then made for the company to walk on. Not less than seventeen or eighteen hundred pounds was raised this year and in the beginning of 1706, by subscription, and laid out in repairing the roads near the city. The streets began to be better paved, cleaned and lighted, the licences of the chairmen were repressed, and, by an act of parliament procured on this occasion, the invalids who came to drink or bathe were exempted from all manner of toll, as often as they should go out of the city for recreation.

The houses and streets now began to improve, and ornaments were lavished upon them even to profusion. But in the midst of this splendor the company still were obliged to assemble in a booth to drink tea and chocolate, or to game. Mr. Nash undertook to remedy this inconvenience. By his direction, one Thomas Harrison erected a handsome Assembly-house for these purposes. A better band of music was also procured, and the former subscription of one guinea was raised to two. Harrison had three guineas a week for the room and candles, and the music two guineas a man. The money Mr. Nash received and accounted for with the utmost exactness and punctuality. To this house were also added gardens for people of rank and fashion to walk in; and the beauty of the suburbs continued to encrease, notwithstanding the opposition that was made by the corporation, who, at that time, looked upon every useful improvement, particularly without the walls, as dangerous to the inhabitants within.

His dominion was now extensive and secure, and he determined to support it with the strictest attention. But, in order to proceed in every thing like a king, he was resolved to give his subjects a law, and the following rules were accordingly put up in the pump-room.

RULES TO BE OBSERVED AT BATH

1. That a visit of ceremony at first coming and another at going away are all that are expected or desired by ladies of quality and fashion,—except impertinents.

2. That ladies coming to the ball appoint a time for their footmen coming to wait on them home, to prevent disturbance and inconveniencies to themselves and others.

3. That gentlemen of fashion never appearing in a morning before the ladies in gowns and caps shew breeding and respect.

4. That no person take it ill that any one goes to another's play, or breakfast, and not theirs;—except captious by nature.

5. That no gentleman give his ticket for the balls to any but gentlewomen.—N.B. Unless he has none of his acquaintance.

6. That gentlemen crowding before the ladies at the ball shew ill manners; and that none do so for the future,—except such as respect nobody but themselves.

7. That no gentleman or lady takes it ill that another dances before them;—except such as have no pretence to dance at all.

8. That the elder ladies and children be content with a second bench at the ball, as being past or not come to perfection.

9. That the younger ladies take notice how many eyes observe them. N.B. This does not extend to the *Have-at-alls*.[52]

10. That all whisperers of lies and scandal be taken for their authors.

11. That all repeaters of such lies and scandal be shun'd by all company;—except such as have been guilty of the same crime.

N.B. Several men of no character, old women and young ones of question'd reputation, are great authors of lies in these places, being of the sect of levellers.

These laws were written by Mr. Nash himself, and, by the manner in which they are drawn up, he undoubtedly designed them for wit. The reader, however, it is feared, will think them dull. Poor Nash was not born a writer; for whatever humour he might have in conversation, he used to call a pen his torpedo; whenever he grasped it, it numbed all his faculties.

But were we to give laws to a nursery, we should make them childish laws; his statutes, tho' stupid, were addressed to fine gentlemen and ladies, and were probably received with sympathetic approbation. It is certain they were in general religiously observed by his subjects and executed by him with impartiality; neither rank nor fortune shielded the refractory from his resentment.

The balls, by his directions, were to begin at six, and to end at eleven. Nor would he suffer them to continue a moment longer, lest invalids might commit irregularities, to counteract the benefit of the waters. Every thing was to be performed in proper order. Each ball was to open with a minuet, danced by two persons of the highest distinction present. When the minuet concluded, the lady was to return to her seat, and Mr. Nash was to bring the gentleman a new partner. This ceremony was to be observed by every succeeding couple, every gentleman being obliged to dance with two ladies till the minuets were over, which generally continued two hours. At eight, the country dances were to begin, ladies of quality, according to their rank, standing up first. About nine o'clock a short interval was allowed for rest, and for the gentlemen to help their partners to tea. That over, the company were to pursue their amusements till the clock struck eleven. Then the master of the ceremonies entering the ball-room, ordered the music to desist, by lifting up his finger. The dances discontinued, and some time allowed for becoming cool, the ladies were handed to their chairs.

Even the royal family themselves had not influence enough to make him deviate from any of these rules. The princess Amelia once applying to him for one dance more, after he had given the signal to withdraw, he assured her royal highness, that the established rules of Bath resembled the laws of Lycurgus, which would admit of no alteration, without an utter subversion of all his authority.

He was not less strict with regard to the dresses in which ladies and gentlemen were to appear. He had the strongest aversion to a white apron, and absolutely excluded all who ventured to come to the assembly dressed in that manner. I have known him on a ball night strip even the dutchess of Q, and throw her apron at one of the hinder benches among the ladies women, observing that none but *Abigails* appeared in white aprons. This from another would be insult; in him it was considered as a just reprimand; and the good-natured dutchess acquiesced in his censure, [and with great good sense, and good humour, begged his *Majesty's* pardon.]

But he found more difficulty in attacking the gentlemen's irregularities; and for some time strove, but in vain, to prohibit the use of swords. Disputes arising from love or play were sometimes attended with fatal effects. To use his own expression, he was resolved to hinder people from doing *what they had no mind to;* but for some time without effect. However, there happened about that time a duel between two gamesters whose names were Taylor and Clarke, which helped to promote his peaceable intentions. They fought by torchlight in the grove; Taylor was run through the body, but lived seven years after, at which time his wound breaking out afresh, it caused his death. Clarke from that time pretended to be a Quaker, but the orthodox brethren never cordially received him among their number; and he died at London, about eighteen years after, in poverty and contrition. From that time it was thought necessary to forbid the wearing of swords at Bath, as they often tore the ladies' cloaths, and frighted them by sometimes appearing upon trifling occasions. Whenever therefore Nash heard of a challenge given or accepted, he instantly had both parties arrested. The gentlemen's boots also made a very desperate stand against him; the country 'squires were by no means submissive to his usurpations, and probably his authority alone would never have carried him thro', had he not reinforced it with ridicule. He wrote a song upon the occasion, which, for the honour of his poetical talents, the world shall see.

Frontinella's invitation to the Assembly

Come, one and all, to Hoyden Hall,
    For there's the assembly this night;
        None but prude fools,
        Mind manners and rules;
We *Hoydens* do decency slight.

Come, Trollops and Slatterns,
    Cockt hats and white aprons,
This best our modesty suits;
        For why should not we
        In dress be as free
As Hogs-Norton 'squires in boots?

The keenness, severity, and particularly the good rhymes of this little *morçeau,* which was at that time highly relished by many of the nobility at Bath, gained him a temporary triumph. But to push his victories, he got up a puppet-shew, in which Punch came in booted and spurred, in the character of a country 'squire. He was introduced as courting his mistress, and having obtained her consent to comply with his wishes, upon going to bed, he is desired to pull off his boots. "My boots," replies Punch, "why, madam, you may as well bid me pull off my legs. I never go without boots, I never ride, I never dance without them; and this piece of politeness is quite the thing at Bath. We always dance at our town in boots, and the ladies often move minuets in riding-hoods." Thus he goes on, till his mistress, grown impatient, kicks him off the stage.

From that time few ventured to appear at the assemblies in Bath in a riding-dress; and whenever any gentleman, thro' ignorance, or haste, appeared in the rooms in boots, Nash would make up to him, and, bowing in an arch manner, would tell him, that he had forgot his horse. Thus he was at last completely victorious.

> *Dolisque coacti*
> *Quos neque Tydides nec Larissaeus Achilles*
> *Non anni domuere decem.*[53]

He began therefore to reign without a rival, and like other kings had his mistresses, flatterers, enemies and calumniators. The amusements of the place however wore a very different aspect from what they did formerly. Regularity repressed pride, and that lessened, people of fortune became fit for society. Let the morose and grave censure an attention to forms and ceremonies, and rail at those whose only business it is to regulate them; but tho' ceremony is very different from politeness, no country was ever yet polite, that was not first ceremonious. The natural gradation of breeding begins in savage disgust, proceeds to indifference, improves into attention, by degrees refines into ceremonious observance, and the trouble of being ceremonious at length produces politeness, elegance and ease. There is therefore some merit in mending society, even in one of the inferior steps of this gradation; and no man was more happy in this respect than Mr. Nash. In every nation there are enough who have no other business or care, but that of buying pleasure; and he taught them, who bid at such an auction, the art of procuring what they sought without diminishing the pleasure of others.

The city of Bath, by such assiduity, soon became the theatre of summer amusements for all people of fashion; and the manner of spending the day there must amuse any but such as disease or spleen had made uneasy to themselves. The following is a faint picture of the pleasures that scene affords. Upon a stranger's arrival at Bath, he is welcomed by a peal of the Abbey bells, and in the next place, by the voice and music of the city waits. For these civilities the ringers have generally a present made them of half a guinea; and the waits of half a crown, or more, in proportion to the person's fortune, generosity, or ostentation. These customs, tho' disagreeable, are however generally liked, or they would not continue. The greatest incommodity attending them is the disturbance the bells must give the sick. But the pleasure of knowing the name of every family that comes to town recompences the inconvenience. Invalids are fond of news, and upon the first sound of the bells, every body sends out to enquire for whom they ring.

After the family is thus welcomed to Bath, it is the custom for the master of it to go to the public places and subscribe two guineas at the assembly-houses towards the balls and music in the pump-house, for which he is entitled to three tickets every ball night. His next subscription is a crown, half a guinea, or a guinea, according to his rank and quality, for the liberty of walking in the private walks belonging to Simpson's assembly-house; a crown or half a guinea is also given to the booksellers, for which the gentleman is to have what books he pleases to read at his lodgings. And at the coffee-house another subscription is taken for pen, ink and paper, for such letters as the subscriber shall write at it during his stay. The ladies too may subscribe to the booksellers, and to a house by the pump-room, for the advantage of reading the news, and for enjoying each other's conversation.

Things being thus adjusted, the amusements of the day are generally begun by bathing, which is no unpleasing method of passing away an hour or so.

The baths are five in number. On the south-west side of

the abbey church is the King's Bath; which is an oblong square; the walls are full of niches, and at every corner are steps to descend into it; this bath is said to contain 427 tons and 50 gallons of water; and on its rising out of the ground over the springs, it is sometimes too hot to be endured by those who bathe therein. Adjoining to the King's Bath there is another, called the Queen's Bath; this is of a more temperate warmth, as borrowing its water from the other.

In the south-west part of the city are three other baths, viz. The Hot Bath, which is not much inferior in heat to the King's Bath, and contains 53 tons 2 hogsheads, and 11 gallons of water, the Cross Bath, which contains 52 tons 3 hogsheads, and 11 gallons, and the Leper's Bath, which is not so much frequented as the rest.

The King's Bath (according to the best observations) will fill in about nine hours and a half, the Hot Bath in about eleven hours and a half and the Cross Bath in about the same time.

The hours for bathing are commonly between six and nine in the morning; and the Baths are every morning supplied with fresh water, for when the people have done bathing, the sluices in each Bath are pulled up, and the water is carried off by drains into the river Avon.

In the morning the lady is brought in a close chair, dressed in her bathing cloaths, to the Bath; and, being in the water, the woman who attends presents her with a little floating dish like a bason, into which the lady puts an handkerchief, a snuff-box, and a nosegay. She then traverses the Bath, if a novice with a guide, if otherwise by herself; and having amused herself thus while she thinks proper, calls for her chair, and returns to her lodgings.

The amusement of bathing is immediately succeeded by a general assembly of people at the pump-house, some for pleasure, and some to drink the hot waters. Three glasses at three different times is the usual portion for every drinker; and the intervals between every glass are enlivened by the harmony of a small band of music, as well as by the conversation of the gay, the witty, or the forward.

From the pump-house the ladies, from time to time, withdraw to a female coffee-house, and from thence return to their lodgings to breakfast. The gentlemen withdraw to their coffee-houses, to read the papers or converse on the news of the day, with a freedom and ease not to be found in the metropolis.

People of fashion make public breakfasts at the assembly-houses, to which they invite their acquaintances, and they sometimes order private concerts, or when so disposed, attend lectures upon the arts and sciences, which are frequently taught there in a pretty superficial manner, so as not to teize the understanding, while they afford the imagination some amusement. The private concerts are performed in the ball-rooms, the tickets a crown each.

Concert breakfasts at the assembly-house sometimes make also a part of the morning's amusement here, the expences of which are defrayed by a subscription among the men. Persons of rank and fortune who can perform are admitted into the orchestra, and find a pleasure in joining with the performers.

Thus we have the tedious morning fairly over. When noon approaches, and church (if any please to go there) is done, some of the company appear upon the parade and other public walks, where they continue to chat and amuse each other, 'till they have formed parties for the play, cards, or dancing for the evening. Another part of the company divert themselves with reading in the booksellers shops, or are generally seen taking the air and exercise, some on horse-back, some in coaches. Some walk in the meadows round the town, winding along the side of the river Avon and the neighbouring canal; while others are seen scaling some of those romantic precipices that overhang the city.

When the hour of dinner draws nigh and the company is returned from their different recreations, the provisions are generally served with the utmost elegance and plenty. Their mutton, butter, fish, and fowl, are all allowed to be excellent, and their cookery still exceeds their meat.

After dinner is over and evening prayers ended, the company meet a second time at the pump-house. From this they retire to the walks, and from thence go to drink tea at the assembly-houses, and the rest of the evenings are concluded either with balls, plays or visits. A theatre was erected in the year 1705 by subscription, by people of the highest rank, who permitted their arms to be engraven on the inside of the house, as a public testimony of their liberality towards it. Every tuesday and friday evening is concluded with a public ball, the contributions to which are so numerous that the price of each ticket is trifling. Thus Bath yields a continued rotation of diversions, and people of all ways of thinking, even from the libertine to the methodist, have it in their power to complete the day with employments suited to their inclinations.

In this manner every amusement soon improved under Mr. Nash's administration. The magistrates of the city found that he was necessary and useful, and took every opportunity of paying the same respect to his fictitious royalty, that is generally extorted by real power. The same satisfaction a young lady finds upon being singled out at her first appearance, or an applauded poet on the success of his first tragedy, influenced him. All admired him as an extraordinary character, and some who knew no better, as a very fine gentleman; he was perfectly happy in their little applause, and affected at length something particular in his dress, behaviour and conversation.

His equipage was sumptuous, and he usually travelled to Tunbridge in a post chariot and six greys, with out-riders, foot-men, French horns, and every other appendage of expensive parade. He always wore a white hat, and, to apologize for this singularity, said he did it purely to secure it from being stolen; his dress was tawdry, tho' not perfectly genteel; he might be considered as a beau of several generations, and in his appearance he, in some measure, mixed the fashions of the last age with those of the present. He perfectly understood elegant expence and generally passed his time in the very best company, if persons of the first distinction deserve that title.

But I hear the reader now demand, what finances were to support all this finery, or where the treasures that gave him such frequent opportunities of displaying his benevolence, or his vanity? To answer this, we must now enter upon another part of his character, his talents as a gamester; for by gaming alone at that period of which I speak, he kept up so very genteel an appearance. When he first figured at Bath, there were few laws against this destructive amusement. The gaming-table was the constant resource of despair and indigence, and the frequent ruin of opulent fortunes. Wherever people of fashion came, needy adventurers were generally found in waiting. With such Bath swarmed, and among this class Mr. Nash was certainly to be numbered in the beginning, only with this difference, that he wanted the corrupt heart, too commonly attending a life of expedients; for he was generous, humane and honourable, even tho' by profession a gamester.

A thousand instances might be given of his integrity, even in this infamous profession; where his generosity often impelled him to act in contradiction to his interest. Wherever he found a novice in the hands of a sharper, he generally forewarned him of the danger; whenever he found any inclined to play, yet ignorant of the game, he would offer his services, and play for them. I remember an instance to this effect, tho' too nearly concerned in the affair to publish the gentleman's name of whom it is related. In the year 1725 there came to Bath a giddy youth, who had just resigned his fellowship at Oxford. He brought his whole fortune with him there; it was but a trifle; however, he was resolved to venture it all. Good fortune seemed kinder than could be expected. Without the smallest skill in play he won a sum sufficient to make any unambitious man happy. His desire of gain encreasing with his gains, in the October following he was *at all,* and added four thousand pounds to his former capital. Mr. Nash one night, after losing a considerable sum to this undeserving son of fortune, invited him to supper. "Sir," cried this honest, tho' veteran gamester, "perhaps you may imagine I have invited you in order to have my revenge at home; but, Sir! I scorn so inhospitable an action. I desired the favour of your company to give you some advice, which you will pardon me, Sir, you seem to stand in need of. You are now high in spirits, and drawn away by a torrent of success. But there will come a time when you will repent having left the calm of a college life for the turbulent profession of a gamester. Ill runs will come, as sure as day and night succeed each other. Be therefore advised, remain content with your present gains; for be persuaded that had you the bank of England, with your present ignorance of gaming it would vanish like a fairy dream. You are a stranger to me, but to convince you of the part I take in your welfare, I'll give you fifty guineas, to forfeit twenty, every time you lose two hundred at one sitting." The young gentleman refused his offer, and was at last undone!

The late duke of B. being chagrined at losing a considerable sum, pressed Mr. Nash to tie him up for the future from playing deep. Accordingly the beau gave his grace an hundred guineas to forfeit ten thousand, whenever he lost a sum to the same amount at play, in one sitting. The duke loved play to distraction, and soon after at hazard lost eight thousand guineas, and was going to throw for three thousand more, when Nash, catching hold of the dice-box, entreated his Grace to reflect upon the penalty if he lost; the Duke for that time desisted, but so strong was the furor of play upon him that soon after, losing a considerable sum at New-market, he was contented to pay the penalty.

When the late earl of T——d was a youth, he was passionately fond of play, and never better pleased than with having Mr. Nash for his antagonist. Nash saw with concern his lordship's foible, and undertook to cure him, tho' by a very disagreeable remedy. Conscious of his own superior skill, he determined to engage him in single play for a very considerable sum. His lordship, in proportion as he lost his game, lost his temper too; and as he approached the gulph, seemed still more eager for ruin. He lost his estate; some writings were put into the winner's possession; his very equipage was deposited as a last stake, and he lost that also. But, when our generous gamester had found his lordship sufficiently punished for his temerity, he returned all; only stipulating that he should be paid five thousand pounds whenever he should think proper to make the demand. However, he never made any such demand during his lordship's life; but some time after his decease, Mr. Nash's affairs being in the wane, he demanded the money of his lordship's heirs, who honourably paid it without any hesitation.

But whatever skill Nash might have acquired by long practice in play, he was never formed by nature for a successful gamester. He was constitutionally passionate and generous. To acquire a perfection in that art, a man must be naturally phlegmatic, reserved and cool; every passion must learn to obey controul; but he frequently was unable to restrain the violence of his, and was often betrayed by this means into unbecoming rudeness or childish impertinence, was sometimes a minion of fortune and as often deprest by adversity. While others made considerable fortunes at the gaming-table, he was ever in the power of chance; nor did even the intimacy with which he was received by the great, place him in a state of independance.

The considerable inconveniences that were found to result from a permission of gaming at length attracted the attention of the legislature, and in the twelfth year of his late majesty, the most prevalent games at that time were declared fraudulent and unlawful. Every age has had its peculiar modes of gaming. The games of Gleek, Primero, In and In, and several others now exploded, employed our sharping ancestors; to these succeeded the Ace of hearts, Pharaoh, Basset, and Hazard, all games of chance like the former. But tho' in these the chances seemed equal to the novice, in general those who kept the bank were considerable winners. The act therefore, passed upon this occasion, declared all such games and lotteries illicit, and directed that all who should set up such games should forfeit two hundred pounds, to be levied by distress on the offender's goods, one third to go to the informer, the residue to the poor.

The act further declared that every person who played in any place, except in the royal palace where his majesty resided, should forfeit fifty pounds, and should be condemned to pay treble costs in case of an appeal.

This law was scarcely made before it was eluded by the invention of divers fraudulent and deceitful games; and a particular game called Passage was daily practised and contributed to the ruin of thousands. To prevent this, the ensuing year it was enacted that this and every other game invented or to be invented, with one die or more, or any other instrument of the same nature with numbers thereon, should be subject to a similar penalty; and at the same time, the persons playing with such instruments should be punished as above.

This amendment of the law soon gave birth to new evasions; the game of Rolly Polly, Marlborough's Battles, but particularly the E O, were set up; and strange to observe! several of those very noblemen who had given their voices to suppress gaming were the most ready to encourage it. This game was at first set up at Tunbridge. It was invented by one C———k and carried on between him and one Mr. A———e, proprietor of the assembly-room at that place, and was reckoned extremely profitable to the bank, as it gained two and an half per cent on all that was lost or won.

As all gaming was suppressed but this, Mr. Nash was now utterly destitute of any resource that he could expect from his superior skill and long experience in the art. The money to be gained in private gaming is at best but trifling, and the opportunity precarious. The minds of the generality of mankind shrink with their circumstances; and Nash, upon the immediate prospect of poverty, was now mean enough (I will call it no worse) to enter into a base confederacy with those low creatures to evade the law and to share the plunder. The occasion was as follows. The profits of the table were, as I observed, divided between C———k the inventor and A———e the room-keeper. The first year's profits were extraordinary, and A———e the room-keeper now began to wish himself sole proprietor. The combinations of the worthless are ever of short duration. The next year therefore A———e turned C———k out of his room and set up the game for himself. The gentlemen and ladies who frequented the wells, unmindful of the immense profit gained by these reptiles, still continued to game as before; and A———e was triumphing in the success of his politics, when he was informed that C———k and his friends hired the crier to cry the game down. The consequences of this would have been fatal to A———e's interest, for by this means frauds might have been discovered which would deter even the most ardent lovers of play. Immediately, therefore, while the crier was yet upon the walks, he applied to Mr. Nash to stop these proceedings, and at the same time offered him a fourth share of the bank, which Mr. Nash was mean enough to accept. This is the greatest blot in his life, and this it is hoped will find pardon.

The day after, the inventor offered an half of the bank; but this Mr. Nash thought proper to refuse, being pre-engaged to A———e. Upon which, being disappointed, he applied to one Mr. J———e, and under his protection another table was

set up, and the company seemed to be divided equally between them. I cannot reflect without surprize at the wisdom
of the gentlemen and ladies, to suffer themselves to be thus
parcelled out between a pack of sharpers, and permit themselves to be defrauded, without even the shew of opposition.
The company thus divided, Mr. Nash once more availed himself of their parties, and prevailed upon them to unite their
banks and to divide the gains into three shares, of which he
reserved one to himself.

Nash had hitherto enjoyed a fluctuating fortune; and had
he taken the advantage of the present opportunity, he might
have been for the future not only above want, but even in
circumstances of opulence. Had he cautiously employed himself in computing the benefits of the table and exacting his
stipulated share, he might have soon grown rich, but he
entirely left the management of it to the people of the
rooms; he took them (as he says in one of his memorials
upon this occasion) to be honest, and never enquired what
was won or lost; and, it is probable, they were seldom
assiduous in informing him. I find a secret pleasure in thus
displaying the insecurity of friendships among the base. They
pretended to pay him regularly at first, but he soon discovered, as he says, that at Tunbridge he had suffered to
the amount of two thousand guineas.

In the mean time, as the E O table thus succeeded at Tunbridge, Mr. Nash was resolved to introduce it at Bath, and
previously asked the opinion of several lawyers, who declared
it no way illegal. In consequence of this, he wrote to Mrs.
A——, who kept one of the great rooms at Bath, acquainting
her with the profits attending such a scheme and proposing
to have a fourth share with her, and Mr. W——, the proprietor of the other room, for his authority and protection.
To this Mr. W—— and she returned him for answer that
they would grant him a fifth share, which he consented to
accept. Accordingly he made a journey to London and bespoke
two tables, one for each room, at the rate of fifteen pounds
each table.

The tables were no sooner set up at Bath than they were
frequented with a greater concourse of gamesters than those
at Tunbridge. Men of that infamous profession from every

part of the kingdom and even other parts of Europe flocked here to feed on the ruins of each other's fortune. This afforded another opportunity for Mr. Nash to become rich; but, as at Tunbridge, he thought the people here also would take care of him, and therefore he employed none to look after his interest. The first year they paid him what he thought just; the next, the woman of the room dying, her son paid him and shewed his books. Sometime after the people of the rooms offered him one hundred pounds a year each for his share, which he refused; every succeeding year they continued to pay him less and less, 'till at length he found, as he pretends, that he had thus lost not less than twenty thousand pounds.

Thus they proceeded, deceiving the public and each other, 'till the legislature thought proper to suppress these seminaries of vice. It was enacted that after the 24th of June, 1745, none should be permitted to keep an house, room or place, for playing, upon pain of such forfeitures as were declared in former acts instituted for that purpose.

The legislature likewise amended a law, made in the reign of Queen Anne, for recovering money lost at play, on the oath of the winner. By this act no person was rendered incapable of being a witness; and every person present at a gaming-table might be summoned by the magistrate who took cognizance of the affair. No privilege of parliament was allowed to those convicted of having gaming-tables in their houses. Those who lost ten pounds at one time were liable to be indicted within six months after the offence was committed, and being convicted, were to be fined five times the value of the sum won or lost, for the use of the poor. Any offender before conviction, discovering another so as to be convicted, was to be discharged from the penalties incurred by his own offences.

By this wise and just act, all Nash's future hopes of succeeding by the tables were blown up. He had now only the justice and generosity of his confederates to trust to; but that he soon found to be a vain expectation; for, if we can depend on his own memorials, what at one time they confessed, they would at another deny; and tho' upon some occasions they seemed at variance with each other, yet when they were to oppose him, whom they considered as a common enemy, they generally united with confidence and success. He now therefore had nothing but a law-suit to confide in for redress; and this is ever the last expedient to retrieve a desperate fortune. He accordingly threw his suit into Chancery, and by this means the public became acquainted with what he had long endeavoured to conceal. They now found that he was himself concerned in the gaming-tables of which he only seemed the conductor; and that he had shared part of the spoil, tho' he complained of having been defrauded of a just share.

The success of his suit was what might have been naturally expected; he had but at best a bad cause, and as the oaths of the defendants were alone sufficient to cast him in Chancery, it was not surprizing that he was nonsuited. But the consequence of this affair was much more fatal than he had imagined; it lessened him in the esteem of the public, it drew several enemies against him, and in some measure diminished the authority of any defence he could make. From that time (about the year 1745) I find this poor, good-natured, but misguided man involved in continual disputes, every day calumniated with some new slander, and continually endeavouring to obviate its effects.

Upon these occasions his usual method was, by printed bills handed about among his acquaintance, to inform the public of his most private transactions with some of those creatures with whom he had formerly associated; but these apologies served rather to blacken his antagonists than to vindicate him. They were in general extremely ill written, confused, obscure, and sometimes unintelligible. By these however it appeared, that W—— was originally obliged to him for the resort of company to his room, that lady H——, who had all the company before W——'s room was built, offered Mr. Nash an hundred pound for his protection, which he refused, having previously promised to support Mrs. W——. It appears by these apologies that the persons concerned in the rooms made large fortunes, while he still continued in pristine indigence, and that his nephew, for whom he had at first secured one of the rooms, was left in as great distress as he.

His enemies were not upon this occasion contented with aspersing him, as a confederate with sharpers; they even as-

serted that he spent and embezzled the subscriptions of gentlemen and ladies which were given for useful or charitable
purposes. But to such aspersions he answered by declaring,
to use his own expression, before God and man, that he never
diverted one shilling of the said subscriptions to his own use;
nor was he ever thought to have done it, till new enemies
started up against him. . . .

But now that we have viewed his conduct as a gamester
and seen him on that side of his character which is by far the
most unfavourable, seen him declining from his former favour
and esteem, the just consequence of his quitting, tho' but ever
so little, the paths of honour, let me turn to those brighter
parts of his life and character, which gained the affection of
his friends, the esteem of the corporation which he assisted,
and may possibly attract the attention of posterity. By his
successes we shall find that figuring in life proceeds less from
the possession of great talents than from the proper application
of moderate ones. Some great minds are only fitted to put
forth their powers in the storm, and the occasion is often
wanting during a whole life for a great exertion; but trifling
opportunities of shining are almost every hour offered to the
little sedulous mind, and a person thus employed is not only
more pleasing but more useful in a state of tranquil society.

Tho' gaming first introduced him into polite company, this
alone could hardly have carried him forward without the
assistance of a genteel address, much vivacity, some humour,
and some wit. But once admitted into the circle of the Beau
Monde, he then laid claim to all the privileges by which it is
distinguished. Among others, in the early part of his life, he
entered himself professedly into the service of the fair sex; he
set up for a man of gallantry and intrigue; and if we can
credit the boasts of his old age, he often succeeded. In fact,
the business of love somewhat resembles the business of
physic; no matter for qualifications, he that makes vigorous
pretensions to either is surest of success. Nature had by no
means formed Mr. Nash for a Beau Garçon; his person was
clumsey, too large and aukward, and his features harsh, strong,
and peculiarly irregular; yet even with those disadvantages
he made love, became an universal admirer of the sex, and
was universally admired. He was possessed, at least, of some

requisites of a lover. He had assiduity, flattery, fine cloaths, and as much wit as the ladies he addressed. Wit, flattery, and fine cloaths, he used to say, were enough to debauch a nunnery. But my fair readers of the present day are exempt from this scandal; and it is no matter now what he said of their grand-mothers.

As Nestor was a man of three ages, so Nash sometimes humorously called himself a beau of three generations. He had seen flaxen bobs succeeded by majors, which in their turn gave way to negligents, which were at last totally routed by bags and ramilees.[54] The manner in which gentlemen managed their amours in these different ages of fashion were not more different than their perriwigs. The lover in the reign of King Charles was solemn, majestic, and formal. He visited his mistress in state, languished for the favour, kneeled when he toasted his goddess, walked with solemnity, performed the most trifling things with decorum, and even took snuff with a flourish. The beau of the latter part of Queen Ann's reign was disgusted with so much formality; he was pert, smart and lively; his billet-doux were written in a quite different stile from that of his antiquated predecessor; he was ever laughing at his own ridiculous situation, till at last he persuaded the lady to become as ridiculous as himself. The beau of the third age, in which Mr. Nash died, was still more extraordinary than either; his whole secret in intrigue consisted in perfect indifference. The only way to make love now, I have heard Mr. Nash say, was to take no manner of notice of the lady, which method was found the surest way to secure her affections.

However these things be, this gentleman's successes in amour were in reality very much confined in the second and third age of intrigue; his character was too public for a lady to consign her reputation to his keeping. But in the beginning of life, it is said, he knew the secret history of the times and contributed himself to swell the page of scandal. Were I upon the present occasion to hold the pen of a novelist I could recount some amours in which he was successful. I could fill a volume with little anecdotes which contain neither pleasure nor instruction, with histories of professing lovers and poor believing girls deceived by such professions. But such adventures are easily written, and as easily atchieved. The plan even of fictitious novel is quite exhausted; but truth, which I have followed here and ever design to follow, presents in the affair of love scarce any variety. The manner in which one reputation is lost exactly resembles that by which another is taken away. The gentleman begins at timid distance, grows more bold, becomes rude, till the lady is married or undone; such is the substance of every modern novel; nor will I gratify the pruriency of folly at the expence of every other pleasure my narration may afford.

Mr. Nash did not long continue an universal gallant; but in the earlier years of his reign entirely gave up his endeavours to deceive the sex in order to become the honest protector of their innocence, the guardian of their reputation, and a friend to their virtue.

This was a character he bore for many years and supported it with integrity, assiduity and success. It was his constant practice to do every thing in his power to prevent the fatal consequences of rash and inconsiderate love; and there are many persons now alive who owe their present happiness to his having interrupted the progress of an amour that threatened to become unhappy, or even criminal, by privately making their guardians or parents acquainted with what he could discover. [And his manner of disconcerting these schemes was such as generally secured him from the rage and resentment of the disappointed. One night, when I was in Wiltshire's room, Nash came up to a lady and her daughter who were people of no inconsiderable fortune and bluntly told the mother, *she had better be at home;* this was at that time thought an audacious piece of impertinence, and the lady turned away piqued and disconcerted. Nash, however, pursued her and repeated the words again; when the old lady, wisely conceiving there might be some hidden meaning couched under this seeming insolence, retired and coming to her lodgings, found a coach and six at the door which a sharper had provided to carry off her eldest daughter.]

I shall beg leave to give some instances of Mr. Nash's good-nature on these occasions, as I have had the accounts from himself. At the conclusion of the treaty of peace at Utrecht, colonel M—— was one of the thoughtless, agreeable, gay creatures that drew the attention of the company at Bath. He danced and talked with great vivacity; and when he gamed among the ladies, he shewed that his attention was employed rather upon their hearts than their fortunes. His own fortune however was a trifle when compared to the elegance of his expence; and his imprudence at last was so great that it obliged him to sell an annuity, arising from his commission, to keep up his splendor a little longer.

However thoughtless he might be, he had the happiness of gaining the affections of Miss L——, whose father designed her a very large fortune. This lady was courted by a nobleman of distinction, but she refused his addresses, resolved upon gratifying rather her inclinations than her avarice. The intrigue went on successfully between her and the colonel, and they both would certainly have been married, and been undone, had not Mr. Nash apprized her father of their intentions. The old gentleman recalled his daughter from Bath and offered Mr. Nash a very considerable present for the care he had taken, which he refused.

In the mean time colonel M—— had an intimation how his intrigue came to be discovered; and by taxing Mr. Nash, found that his suspicions were not without foundation. A challenge was the immediate consequence, which the King of Bath, conscious of having only done his duty, thought proper to decline. As none are permitted to wear swords at Bath, the colonel found no opportunity of gratifying his resentment, and waited with impatience to find Mr. Nash in town, to require proper satisfaction.

During this interval, however, he found his creditors became too importunate for him to remain longer at Bath; and his finances and credit being quite exhausted, he took the desperate resolution of going over to the Dutch army in Flanders, where he enlisted himself a volunteer. Here he underwent all the fatigues of a private centinel, with the additional misery of receiving no pay, and his friends in England gave out that he was shot at the battle of ——.

In the mean time the nobleman pressed his passion with ardour, but during the progress of his amour, the young lady's father died and left her heiress to a fortune of fifteen hundred a year. She thought herself now disengaged from her former passion. An absence of two years had in some measure abated her love for the colonel; and the assiduity, the merit, and real regard of the gentleman who still continued to solicit her were almost too powerful for her constancy. Mr. Nash, in the mean time, took every opportunity of enquiring after colonel M——, and found that he had for some time been returned to England, but changed his name in order to avoid the fury of his creditors and that he was entered into a company of strolling players who were at that time exhibiting at Peterborough.

He now therefore thought he owed the colonel, in justice, an opportunity of promoting his fortune, as he had once deprived him of an occasion of satisfying his love. Our Beau therefore invited the lady to be of a party to Peterborough, and offered his own equipage, which was then one of the most elegant in England, to conduct her there. The proposal being accepted, the lady, the nobleman, and Mr. Nash, arrived in town just as the players were going to begin.

Colonel M——, who used every means of remaining incognito and who was too proud to make his distresses known to any of his former acquaintance, was now degraded into the character of Tom in the *Conscious Lovers*.[55] Miss L—— was placed in the foremost row of the spectators, her lord on one side, and the impatient Nash on the other, when the unhappy youth appeared in that despicable situation upon the stage. The moment he came on, his former mistress struck his view, but his amazement was encreased when he saw her fainting away in the arms of those who sate behind her. He was incapable of proceeding and scarce knowing what he did, he flew and caught her in his arms.

"Colonel," cried Nash, when they were in some measure recovered, "you once thought me your enemy because I endeavoured to prevent you both from ruining each other; you were then wrong, and you have long had my forgiveness. If you love well enough now for matrimony, you fairly have my consent, and d——n him, say I, that attempts to part you." Their nuptials were solemnized soon after, and affluence added a zest to all their future enjoyments. Mr. Nash had the thanks of each, and he afterwards spent several agreeable days in that society which he had contributed to render happy.

I shall beg the reader's patience while I give another instance, in which he ineffectually offered his assistance and advice. This story is not from himself, but told us partly by Mr. Wood, the architect of Bath, as it fell particularly within his own knowledge and partly from another memoir to which he refers.

Miss Sylvia S—— was descended from one of the best families in the kingdom, and was left a large fortune upon her sister's decease. She had early in life been introduced into the best company, and contracted a passion for elegance and expence. It is usual to make the heroine of a story very witty and very beautiful, and such circumstances are so surely expected that they are scarce attended to. But whatever the finest poet could conceive of wit or the most celebrated painter imagine of beauty were excelled in the perfections of this young lady. Her superiority in both was allowed by all who either heard or had seen her. She was naturally gay, generous to a fault, good-natured to the highest degree, affable in conversation, and some of her letters and other writings, as well in verse as prose, would have shone amongst those of the most celebrated wits of this or any other age, had they been published.

But these great qualifications were marked by another, which lessened the value of them all. She was imprudent! But let it not be imagined that her reputation or honour suffered by her imprudence; I only mean she had no knowledge of the use of money; she relieved distress, by putting herself into the circumstances of the object whose wants she supplied.

She was arrived at the age of nineteen when the croud of her lovers and the continual repetition of new flattery had taught her to think she could never be forsaken, and never poor. Young ladies are apt to expect a certainty of success from a number of lovers; and yet I have seldom seen a girl courted by an hundred lovers that found a husband in any. Before the choice is fixed, she has either lost her reputation or her good sense; and the loss of either is sufficient to consign her to perpetual virginity.

Among the number of this young lady's lovers was the celebrated S——, who, at that time, went by the name of *the good-natured man.* This gentleman, with talents that might have done honour to humanity, suffered himself to fall at length into the lowest state of debasement. He followed the dictates of every newest passion; his love, his pity, his generosity, and even his friendships were all in excess; he was unable to make head against any of his sensations or desires, but they were in general worthy wishes and desires, for he was constitutionally virtuous. This gentleman, who at last died in a gaol, was at that time this lady's envied favourite.

It is probable that he, thoughtless creature, had no other prospect from this amour but that of passing the present moments agreeably. He only courted dissipation, but the lady's thoughts were fixed on happiness. At length, however, his debts amounting to a considerable sum, he was arrested and thrown into prison. He endeavoured at first to conceal his situation from his beautiful mistress; but she soon came to a knowledge of his distress and took a fatal resolution of freeing him from confinement by discharging all the demands of his creditors.

Mr. Nash was at that time in London, and represented to the thoughtless young lady that such a measure would effectually ruin both, that so warm a concern for the interests of Mr. S—— would in the first place quite impair her fortune in the eyes of our sex, and what was worse, lessen her reputation in those of her own. He added that thus bringing Mr. S—— from prison would be only a temporary relief; that a mind so generous as his would become bankrupt under the load of gratitude, and instead of improving in friendship or affection, he would only study to avoid a creditor he could never repay; that tho' small favours produce good-will, great ones destroy friendship. These admonitions however were disregarded, and she too late found the prudence and truth of her adviser. In short, her fortune was by this means exhausted, and with all her attractions she found her acquaintance began to dis-esteem her, in proportion as she became poor.

In this situation she accepted Mr. Nash's invitation of returning to Bath; he promised to introduce her to the best company there, and he was assured that her merit would do the rest; upon her very first appearance, ladies of the highest distinction courted her friendship and esteem; but a settled melancholy had taken possession of her mind, and no amusements that they could propose were sufficient to divert it. Yet still, as if from habit, she followed the crowd in its levities and frequented those places where all persons endeavour to forget themselves in the bustle of ceremony and shew.

Her beauty, her simplicity, and her unguarded situation soon drew the attention of a designing wretch who at that time kept one of the rooms at Bath, and who thought that this lady's merit, properly managed, might turn to good account. This woman's name was dame Lindsey, a creature who, though vicious, was in appearance sanctified; and though designing, had some wit and humour. She began by the humblest assiduity to ingratiate herself with miss S——, shewed that she could be amusing as a companion and by frequent offers of money proved that she could be useful as a friend. Thus, by degrees, she gained an entire ascendant over this poor, thoughtless, deserted girl; and, in less than one year, namely about 1727, miss S, without ever transgressing the laws of virtue, had entirely lost her reputation. Whenever a person was wanting to make up a party for play at dame Lindsey's, Sylvia, as she was then familiarly called, was sent for and was obliged to suffer all those slights which the rich but too often let fall upon their inferiors in point of fortune.

In most, even the greatest, minds, the heart at last becomes level with the meanness of its condition; but in this charming girl it struggled hard with adversity and yielded to every encroachment of contempt with sullen reluctance.

But tho' in the course of three years she was in the very eye of public inspection, yet Mr. Wood the architect avers, that he could never, by the strictest observations, perceive her to be tainted with any other vice than that of suffering herself to be decoyed to the gaming-table, and, at her own hazard, playing for the amusement and advantage of others. Her friend, Mr. Nash, therefore, thought proper to induce her to break off all connections with dame Lindsey and to rent part of Mr. Wood's house, in Queen square, where she behaved with the utmost complaisance, regularity, and virtue.

In this situation her detestation of life still continued; she found that time would infallibly deprive her of part of her attractions and that continual solicitude would impair the rest. With these reflections she would frequently entertain herself and an old faithful maid in the vales of Bath, whenever the weather would permit them to walk out. She would even sometimes start questions in company with seeming unconcern, in order to know what act of suicide was easiest and which was attended with the smallest pain. When tired with exercise, she generally retired to meditation, and she became habituated to early hours of sleep and rest. But when the weather prevented her usual exercise and her sleep was thus more difficult, she made it a rule to rise from her bed and walk about her chamber till she began to find an inclination for repose.

This custom made it necessary for her to order a burning candle to be kept all night in her room. And the maid usually, when she withdrew, locked the chamber door, and pushing the key under it beyond reach, her mistress by that constant method lay undisturbed till seven o'clock in the morning; then she arose, unlocked the door, and rang the bell, as a signal for the maid to return.

This state of seeming piety, regularity, and prudence, continued for some time, till the gay, celebrated, toasted Miss Sylvia was sunk into an housekeeper to the gentleman at whose house she lived. She was unable to keep company for want of the elegancies of dress that are the usual passport among the polite, and she was too haughty to seem to want them. The fashionable, the amusing, and the polite in society now seldom visited her, and from being once the object of every eye, she was now deserted by all and preyed upon by the bitter reflections of her own imprudence.

Mr. Wood and part of his family were gone to London. Miss Sylvia was left with the rest as a governess at Bath. She sometimes saw Mr. Nash, and acknowledged the friendship of his admonitions, tho' she refused to accept any other marks of his generosity than that of advice. Upon the close of the day in which Mr. Wood was expected to return from London, she expressed some uneasiness at the disappointment of not seeing him, took particular care to settle the affairs of his family, and then as usual sate down to meditation. She now cast a retrospect over her past misconduct and her approaching misery; she saw that even affluence gave her no

real happiness, and from indigence she thought nothing could
be hoped but lingering calamity. She at length conceived the
fatal resolution of leaving a life in which she could see no
corner for comfort, and terminating a scene of imprudence in
suicide.

Thus resolved, she sate down at her dining-room window,
and with cool intrepidity wrote the following elegant lines on
one of the panes of the window.

> O death, thou pleasing end of human woe!
> Thou cure for life! Thou greatest good below!
> Still may'st thou fly the coward, and the slave,
> And thy soft slumbers only bless the brave.

She then went into company with the most chearful
serenity, talked of indifferent subjects till supper, which she
ordered to be got ready in a little library belonging to the
family. There she spent the remaining hours preceding bed-
time in dandling two of Mr. Wood's children on her knees.
In retiring from thence to her chamber, she went into the
nursery to take her leave of another child as it lay sleeping in
the cradle. Struck with the innocence of the little babe's
looks and the consciousness of her meditated guilt, she could
not avoid bursting into tears and hugging it in her arms; she
then bid her old servant a good night, for the first time she
had ever done so, and went to bed as usual.

It is probable she soon quitted her bed, and was seized with
an alternation of passions before she yielded to the impulse
of despair. She dressed herself in clean linen and white gar-
ments of every kind, like a bride-maid. Her gown was pinned
over her breast, just as a nurse pins the swaddling cloaths of an
infant. A pink silk girdle was the instrument with which she
resolved to terminate her misery, and this was lengthened by
another made of gold thread. The end of the former was tied
with a noose, and the latter with three knots, at a small distance from one another.

Thus prepared, she sate down again and read; for she left
the book open at that place in the story of Olympia in the
Orlando Furioso of Ariosto, where, by the perfidy and ingratitude of her bosom friend, she was ruined and left to the mercy

of an unpitying world. This tragical event gave her fresh spirits to go through her fatal purpose; so standing upon a stool and flinging the girdle, which was tied round her neck, over a closet-door that opened into her chamber, she remained suspended. Her weight however broke the girdle, and the poor despairer fell upon the floor with such violence that her fall awakened a workman that lay in the house about half an hour after two o'clock.

Recovering herself, she began to walk about the room, as her usual custom was when she wanted sleep; and the workman imagining it to be only some ordinary accident, again went to sleep. She once more, therefore, had recourse to a stronger girdle made of silver thread; and this kept her suspended till she died.

Her old maid continued in the morning to wait as usual for the ringing of the bell, and protracted her patience, hour after hour, till two o'clock in the afternoon, when the workmen at length entering the room through the window, found their unfortunate mistress still hanging and quite cold. The coroner's jury being impanelled, brought in their verdict lunacy; and her corpse was next night decently buried in her father's grave, at the charge of a female companion with whom she had for many years an inseparable intimacy.

Thus ended a female wit, a toast, and a gamester; loved, admired, and forsaken. Formed for the delight of society, fallen by imprudence into an object of pity. Hundreds in high life lamented her fate and wished, when too late, to redress her injuries. They who once had helped to impair her fortune now regretted that they had assisted in so mean a pursuit. The little effects she had left behind were bought up with the greatest avidity by those who desired to preserve some token of a companion that once had given them such delight. The remembrance of every virtue she was possessed of was now improved by pity. Her former follies were few, but the last swelled them to a large amount. As she remains the strongest instance to posterity that want of prudence alone almost cancels every other virtue.

In all this unfortunate lady's affairs Mr. Nash took a peculiar concern; he directed her when they played, advised her when she deviated from the rules of caution, and performed the last offices of friendship after her decease by raising the auction of her little effects.

But he was not only the assistant and the friend of the fair sex, but also their defender. He secured their persons from insult and their reputations from scandal. Nothing offended him more than a young fellow's pretending to receive favours from ladies he probably never saw; nothing pleased him so much as seeing such a piece of deliberate mischief punished. Mr. Nash and one of his friends, being newly arrived at Tunbridge from Bath, were one day on the walks, and seeing a young fellow of fortune with whom they had some slight acquaintance, joined him. After the usual chat and news of the day was over, Mr. Nash asked him how long he had been at the wells, and what company was there? The other replied he had been at Tunbridge a month, but as for company, he could find as good at a Tyburn ball. Not a soul was to be seen, except a parcel of gamesters and whores who would grant the last favour for a single stake at the Pharaoh bank. "Look you there," continued he, "that Goddess of midnight, so fine, at t'other end of the walks, by Jove, she was mine this morning for half a guinea. And she there, who brings up the rear with powdered hair and dirty ruffles, she's pretty enough, but cheap, perfectly cheap; why, my boys, to my own knowledge, you may have her for a crown, and a dish of chocolate into the bargain. Last Wednesday night we were happy." "Hold there, sir," cried the gentleman; "as for your having the first lady, it is possible it may be true, and I intend to ask her about it, for she is my sister; but as to your lying with the other last Wednesday, I am sure you are a lying rascal—she is my wife, and we came here but last night." The Buck vainly asked pardon; the gentleman was going to give him proper chastisement, when Mr. Nash interposed in his behalf, and obtained his pardon upon condition that he quitted Tunbridge immediately.

But Mr. Nash not only took care, during his administration, to protect the ladies from the insults of our sex, but to guard them from the slanders of each other. He in the first place prevented any animosities that might arise from place and precedence by being previously acquainted with the rank and quality of almost every family in the British dominions. He endeavoured to render scandal odious by marking it as the result of envy and folly united. Not even Solon could have enacted a wiser law in such a society as Bath. The gay, the heedless, and the idle, which mostly compose the groupe of water-drinkers, seldom are at the pains of talking upon universal topics, which require comprehensive thought or abstract reasoning. The adventures of the little circle of their own acquaintance or of some names of quality and fashion make up their whole conversation. But it is too likely that when we mention those, we wish to depress them, in order to render ourselves more conspicuous; scandal must therefore have fixed her throne at Bath, preferable to any other part of the kingdom. However, tho' these endeavours could not totally suppress this custom among the fair, yet they gained him the friendship of several ladies of distinction, who had smarted pretty severely under the lash of censure. . . .

Whatever might have been Mr. Nash's other excellencies, there was one in which few exceeded him; I mean his extensive humanity. None felt pity more strongly, and none made greater efforts to relieve distress. If I were to name any reigning and fashionable virtue in the present age, I think it should be charity. The numberless benefactions privately given, the various public solicitations for charity, and the success they meet with, serve to prove that tho' we may fall short of our ancestors in other respects, yet in this instance we greatly excel them. I know not whether it may not be spreading the influence of Mr. Nash too widely to say that he was one of the principal causes of introducing this noble emulation among the rich; but certain it is, no private man ever relieved the distresses of so many as he.

Before gaming was suppressed, and in the meridian of his life and fortune, his benefactions were generally found to equal his other expences. The money he got without pain, he gave away without reluctance; and whenever unable to relieve a wretch who sued for assistance, he has been often seen to shed tears. A gentleman of broken fortune, one day standing behind his chair as he was playing a game of picquet for two hundred pounds and observing with what indifference he won the money, could not avoid whispering these words to another who stood by; "Heavens! how happy would all that money make me!" Nash, overhearing him, clapp'd the money into his hand and cried, "Go and be happy."

About six and thirty years ago, a clergyman brought his family to Bath for the benefit of the waters. His wife laboured under a lingering disorder which it was thought nothing but the Hot Wells could remove. The expences of living there soon lessened the poor man's finances; his cloaths were sold, piece by piece, to provide a temporary relief for his little family; and his appearance was at last so shabby that, from the number of holes in his coat and stockings, Nash gave him the name of doctor Cullender. Our beau, it seems, was rude enough to make a jest of poverty, tho' he had sensibility enough to relieve it. The poor clergyman combated his distresses with fortitude; and, instead of attempting to solicit relief, endeavoured to conceal them. Upon a living of thirty pounds a year he endeavoured to maintain his wife and six children; but all his resources at last failed him, and nothing but famine was seen in the wretched family. The poor man's circumstances were at last communicated to Nash, who with his usual chearfulness undertook to relieve him. On a Sunday evening, at a public tea-drinking at Harrison's, he went about to collect a subscription and began it himself by giving five guineas. By this means, two hundred guineas were collected in less than two hours, and the poor family raised from the lowest despondence into affluence and felicity. A bounty so unexpected had a better influence even upon the woman's constitution than all that either the physicians or the waters of Bath could produce, and she recovered. But his good offices did not rest here. He prevailed upon a nobleman of his acquaintance to present the Doctor with a living of an hundred and sixty pounds a year, which made that happiness he had before produced, in some measure permanent.

In the severe winter which happened in the year 1739, his charity was great, useful, and extensive. He frequently, at that season of calamity, entered the houses of the poor, whom he thought too proud to beg, and generously relieved them. The colliers were at this time peculiarly distressed; and, in order to excite compassion, a number of them yoaked themselves to a waggon loaded with coals, and drew it into Bath, and presented it to Mr. Nash. Their scheme had the proper effect.

Mr. Nash procured them a subscription, and gave ten guineas towards it himself. The weavers also shared his bounty at that season. They came begging in a body into Bath, and he provided a plentiful dinner for their entertainment and gave each a week's subsistence at going away.

There are few public charities to which he was not a subscriber, and many he principally contributed to support. Among others, Mr. Annesly, that strange example of the mutability of fortune and the inefficacy of our laws, shared his interest and bounty. I have now before me a well written letter, addressed to Mr. Nash, in order to obtain his interest for that unhappy gentleman; it comes from Mr. Henderson, a Quaker, who was Mr. Annesly's father's agent. This gentleman warmly espoused the young adventurer's interest and, I am told, fell with him.

London, October 23, 1756.

My Good Friend,

When I had the honour of conversing with thee at Tunbridge, in September last, concerning that most singular striking case of Mr. Annesley, whom I have known since he was about six years old, I being then employed by the late Lord Baron of Altham, his father, as his agent. From what I know of the affairs of that family, I am well assured that Mr. Annesly is the legitimate son of the late Lord Baron of Altham, and in consequence thereof, is intitled to the honours and estates of Anglesey. Were I not well assured of his right to those honours and estates, I would not give countenance to his claim.— I well remember that thou then madest me a promise to assist him in soliciting a subscription that was then begun at Tunbridge; but as that place was not within the limits of thy province, thou couldest not promise to do much there. But thou saidst that in case he would go to Bath in the season thou wouldest then and there shew how much thou wouldest be his friend.

And now, my good friend, as the season is come on and Mr. Annesley now at Bath, I beg leave to remind thee of that promise, and that thou wilt keep in full view the honour, the everlasting honour, that will naturally redound to thee from thy benevolence and crown all the good actions of thy life.—

I say, now in the vale of life, to relieve a distressed young nobleman, to extricate so immense an estate from the hands of oppression, to do this will fix such a ray of glory on thy memory as will speak forth thy praise to future ages.— This with great respect is the needful,

from thy assured Friend,

William Henderson.

Be pleased to give my respects to Mr. Annesley and his spouse.

Mr. Nash punctually kept his word with this gentleman; he began the subscription himself with the utmost liberality, and procured such a list of encouragers as at once did honour to Mr. Annesly's cause and their own generosity. What a pity it was that this money, which was given for the relief of indigence only, went to feed a set of reptiles who batten upon our weakness, miseries and vice.

It may not be known to the generality of my readers that the last act of the comedy called *Esop*, which was added to the French plot of Boursault by Mr. Vanbrugh, was taken from a story told of Mr. Nash, upon a similar occasion. He had in the early part of life made proposals of marriage to Miss V——, of D——; his affluence at that time, and the favour which he was in with the nobility, readily induced the young lady's father to favour his addresses. However, upon opening the affair to herself, she candidly told him her affections were placed upon another, and that she could not possibly comply. Tho' this answer satisfied Mr. Nash, it was by no means sufficient to appease the father, and he peremptorily insisted upon her obedience. Things were carried to the last extremity, when Mr. Nash undertook to settle the affair; and desiring his favoured rival to be sent for, with his own hand presented his mistress to him, together with a fortune equal to what her father intended to give her. Such an uncommon instance of generosity had an instant effect upon the severe parent; he considered such disinterestedness as a just reproach to his own mercenary disposition, and took his daughter once more into favour. I wish, for the dignity of history, that the sequel could be concealed, but the young lady ran away with her footman, before half a year was expired, and her husband died of grief.

In general, the benefactions of a generous man are but ill

bestowed. His heart seldom gives him leave to examine the real distress of the object which sues for pity; his good-nature takes the alarm too soon, and he bestows his fortune on only apparent wretchedness. The man naturally frugal, on the other hand, seldom relieves, but when he does, his reason and not his sensations generally find out the object. Every instance of his bounty is therefore permanent, and bears witness to his benevolence.

Of all the immense sums which Nash lavished upon real or apparent wretchedness, the effects, after a few years, seemed to disappear. His money was generally given to support immediate want, or to relieve improvident indolence, and therefore it vanished in an hour. Perhaps towards the close of life, were he to look round on the thousands he had relieved, he would find but few made happy, or fixed by his bounty in a state of thriving industry; it was enough for him that he gave to those that wanted; he never considered that charity to some might impoverish himself without relieving them; he seldom considered the merit or the industry of the petitioner; or he rather fancied that misery was an excuse for indolence and guilt. It was an usual saying of his, when he went to beg for any person in distress, that they who could stoop to the meanness of solicitation must certainly *want* the favour for which they petitioned.

In this manner therefore he gave away immense sums of his own, and still greater, which he procured from others. His way was, when any person was proposed to him as an object of charity, to go round with his hat, first among the nobility, according to their rank, and so on, till he left scarce a single person unsolicited. They who go thus about to beg for others, generally find a pleasure in the task. They consider, in some measure, every benefaction they procure as given by themselves, and have at once the pleasure of being liberal without the self reproach of being profuse.

But of all the instances of Mr. Nash's bounty, none does him more real honour than the pains he took in establishing an hospital at Bath, in which benefaction, however, Doctor Oliver had a great share. This was one of those well guided charities, dictated by reason and supported by prudence. By this institution the diseased poor might recover health when incapable of receiving it in any other part of the kingdom. As the disorders of the poor, who could expect to find relief at Bath, were mostly chronical, the expence of maintaining them there was found more than their parishes thought proper to afford. They therefore chose to support them in a continual state of infirmity by a small allowance at home, rather than be at the charge of an expensive cure. An hospital therefore at Bath it was thought would be an assylum and a place of relief to those disabled creatures, and would, at the same time, give the physician more thorough insight into the efficacy of the waters, from the regularity with which such patients would be obliged to take them. These inducements therefore influenced Doctor Oliver and Mr. Nash to promote a subscription towards such a benefaction. The design was set on foot so early as the year 1711, but not completed till the year 1742. This delay, which seems surprizing, was in fact owing to the want of a proper fund for carrying the work into execution. What I said above of charity being the characteristic virtue of the present age, will be more fully evinced by comparing the old and new subscriptions for this hospital. These will shew the difference between ancient and modern benevolence. When I run my eye over the list of those who subscribed in the year 1723, I find the subscription in general seldom rise above a guinea each person; so that, at that time, with all their efforts they were unable to raise four hundred pounds; but in about twenty years after, each particular subscription was greatly encreased, ten, twenty, thirty pounds, being the most ordinary sums then subscribed, and they soon raised above two thousand pounds for the purpose.

Thus chiefly by the means of Doctor Oliver and Mr. Nash, but not without the assistance of the good Mr. Allen, who gave them the stone for building and other benefactions, this hospital was erected, and it is at present fitted up for the reception of one hundred and ten patients, the cases mostly paralytic or leprous. . . .

I am unwilling to leave this subject of his benevolence, because it is a virtue in his character which must stand almost single against an hundred follies; and it deserves the more to be insisted on because it was large enough to outweigh them all. A man may be an hypocrite safely in every other instance but in charity; there are few who will buy the character of benevolence at the rate for which it must be acquired. In short, the sums he gave away were immense; and, in old age, when at last grown too poor to give relief, *he gave,* as the poet has it, *all he had, a tear;* when incapable of relieving the agonies of the wretched, he attempted to relieve his own by a flood of sorrow.

[The sums he gave and collected for the hospital were great, and his manner of doing it was no less admirable. I am told that he was once collecting money in Wiltshire's room for that purpose, when a lady entered who is more remarkable for her wit than her charity, and not being able to pass by him unobserved, she gave him a pat with her fan, and said, "You must put down a trifle for me, Nash, for I have no money in my pocket." "Yes, Madam," says he, "that I will with pleasure, if your grace will tell me when to stop"; then taking a handful of guineas out of his pocket, he began to tell them into his white hat, one, two, three, four, five. "Hold, hold," says the dutchess, "consider what you are about." "Consider your rank and fortune, Madam," says Nash, and continued telling, six, seven, eight, nine, ten. Here the dutchess called again, and seemed angry. "Pray compose yourself, Madam," cried Nash, "and don't interrupt the work of charity; eleven, twelve, thirteen, fourteen, fifteen." Here the dutchess stormed, and caught hold of his hand. "Peace, Madam," says Nash; "you shall have your name written in letters of gold, Madam, and upon the front of the building, Madam. Sixteen, seventeen, eighteen, nineteen, twenty." "I won't pay a farthing more," says the dutchess. "Charity hides a multitude of sins," replies Nash. "Twenty-one, twenty-two, twenty-three, twenty-four, twenty-five." "Nash," says she, "I protest you frighten me out of my wits. L——d, I shall die!" "Madam, you will never die with doing good; and if you do, it will be the better for you," answered Nash, and was about to proceed; but perceiving her grace had lost all patience, a parley ensued, when he, after much altercation, agreed to stop his hand and compound with her grace for thirty guineas. The dutchess, however, seemed displeased the whole evening, and when he came to the table where she was playing, bid him *stand farther, an ugly devil, for she hated the sight of him.* But her grace afterwards, having a run of good luck, called Nash to her. "Come," says she, "I will be friends with you, though you are a fool; and to let you see I am not angry, there is ten guineas more for your charity. But this I insist on, that neither my name, nor the sum, shall be mentioned."]

From the hospital erected for the benefit of the poor it is an easy transition to the monuments erected by him in honour of the great. Upon the recovery of the Prince of Orange, by drinking the Bath waters, Mr. Nash caused a small obelisk, thirty feet high, to be erected in a grove near the Abbey church, since called *Orange Grove*. This Prince's arms adorn the west side of the body of the pedestal. The inscription is on the opposite side, in the following words:

> *In memoriam*
> *Sanitatis*
> *Principi Auriaco*
> *Aquarum thermalium potu.*
> *Favente Deo,*
> *Ovante Britannia,*
> *Feliciter restituæ,*
> M. DCC. XXXIV.

In English thus:

> In memory
> Of the happy restoration
> Of the health of the
> Prince of Orange,
> Through the favour of God,
> And to the great joy of Britain,
> By drinking the *Bath* waters.
> 1734.

I find it a general custom, at all Baths and Spaws, to erect monuments of this kind to the memory of every Prince who has received benefit from the waters. Aix, Spau and Pisa abound with inscriptions of this nature, apparently doing honour to the Prince, but in reality celebrating the efficacy of their springs. It is wrong, therefore, to call such monuments instances of gratitude, tho' they may wear that appearance.

In the year 1738 the Prince of Wales came to Bath, who presented Mr. Nash with a large gold enamelled snuff-box; and upon his departure, Nash, as King of Bath, erected an obelisk in honour of this Prince, as he had before done for the Prince of Orange. This handsome memorial in honour of that good-natured Prince is erected in Queen square. It is enclosed with a stone balustrade, and in the middle of every side there are large iron gates. In the center is the obelisk, seventy feet high, and terminating in a point. The expences of this were eighty pounds; and Mr. Nash was determined that the inscription should answer the magnificence of the pile. With this view he wrote to Mr. Pope, at London, requesting an inscription. I should have been glad to have given Mr. Nash's letter upon this occasion; the reader, however, must be satisfied with Pope's reply; which is as follows.

Sir

I have received yours, and thank your partiality in my favour. You say words cannot express the gratitude you feel for the favour of his R. H. and yet you would have me express what you feel, and in a few words. I own myself unequal to the task; for even granting it possible to express an inexpressible idea, I am the worst person you could have pitched upon for this purpose, who have received so few favours from the great myself that I am utterly unacquainted with what kind of thanks they like best. Whether the P—— most loves poetry or prose, I protest I do not know; but this I dare venture to affirm, that you can give him as much satisfaction in either as I can.

> I am,
>   SIR,
>   *Your affectionate Servant,*
>   *A. Pope*

What Mr. Nash's answer to this billet was, I cannot take upon me to ascertain, but it was probably a perseverance in his former request. The following is the copy of Mr. Pope's reply to his second letter.

Sir

I had sooner answered yours but in the hope of procuring a properer hand than mine; and then in consulting with some, whose office about the P—— might make them the best judges, what sort of inscription to set up. Nothing can be plainer than the inclosed; it is nearly the common sense of the thing, and I do not know how to flourish upon it. But this you would do as well, or better yourself, and I dare say may mend the expression. I am truly,

Dear SIR,

Your affectionate Servant,

A. Pope

I think I need not tell you my name should not be mentioned.

Such a letter as this was what might naturally be expected from Mr. Pope. Notwithstanding the seeming modesty towards the conclusion, the vanity of an applauded writer bursts through every line of it. The difficulty of concealing his hand from the clerks at the Post-office, and the solicitude to have his name concealed, were marks of the consciousness of his own importance. It is probable his hand was not so very well known nor his letters so eagerly opened by the clerks of the Office as he seems always to think. But in all his letters, as well as those of Swift, there runs a strain of pride, as if the world talked of nothing but themselves. "Alass," says he, in one of them, "the day after I am dead, the sun will shine as bright as the day before, and the world will be as merry as usual!" Very strange, that neither an eclipse nor an earthquake should follow the loss of a Poet!

The inscription referred to in this letter was the same which was afterwards engraved on the obelisk, and is as follows:

In memory of honours bestow'd,
And in gratitude for benefits conferred in this city,
By his Royal Highness
Frederick, Prince of Wales,
And his Royal Consort,
In the Year 1738,
This obelisk is erected by
Richard Nash, Esq.

I dare venture to say there was scarce a common-council-man in the corporation of Bath but could have done this as well. Nothing can be more frigid, though the subject was worthy of the utmost exertions of Genius.

About this period every season brought some new accession of honour to Mr. Nash; and the corporation now universally found that he was absolutely necessary for promoting the welfare of the city; so that this year seems to have been the meridian of his glory. About this time he arrived at such a pitch of authority, that I really believe Alexander was not greater at Persepolis. The countenance he received from the Prince of Orange, the favour he was in with the Prince of Wales, and the caresses of the nobility, all conspired to lift him to the utmost pitch of vanity. The exultation of a little mind upon being admitted to the familiarity of the Great is inexpressible. The prince of Orange had made him a present of a very fine snuff-box. Upon this some of the nobility thought it would be proper to give snuff-boxes too; they were quickly imitated by the middling gentry, and it soon became the fashion to give Mr. Nash snuff-boxes, [who had in a little time a number sufficient to have furnished a good toy-shop.]

To add to his honours, the corporation of Bath placed a full length statue of him in Wiltshire's Ball-room, between the busts of Newton and Pope. It was upon this occasion that the Earl of Chesterfield wrote that severe but witty epigram, the last lines of which were so deservedly admired, and ran thus:

> The statue placed the busts between,
>   Adds to the satire strength;
> Wisdom and Wit are little seen,
>   But Folly at full length.

The example of the corporation was followed by all his acquaintances of inferior rank. He was treated in every respect like a great man; he had his levee, his flatterers, his buffoons, his good-natured creatures, and even his dedicators. A trifling ill supported vanity was his foible, and while he received the homage of the vulgar and enjoyed the familiarity of the great, he felt no pain for the unpromising view of poverty that lay before him; he enjoyed the world as it went, and drew upon content for the deficiencies of fortune. If a cringing wretch called him his Honour, he was pleased; internally conscious that he had the justest pretensions to the title. If a beggar called him my Lord, he was happy, and generally sent the flatterer off happy too. I have known him, in London, wait a whole day at a window in the Smyrna coffee-house, in order to receive a bow from the Prince, or the Dutchess of Marlborough, as they passed by where he was standing; and he would then look round upon the company for admiration and respect.

But perhaps the reader desires to know who could be low enough to flatter a man who himself lived in some measure by dependance. Hundreds are ready upon those occasions. The very needy are almost ever flatterers. A man in wretched circumstances forgets his own value, and feels no pain in giving up superiority to every claimant. The very vain are ever flatterers, as they find it necessary to make use of all their arts to keep company with such as are superior to themselves. But particularly the prodigal are prone to adulation, in order to open new supplies for their extravagance. The poor, the vain, and extravagant, are chiefly addicted to this vice; and such hung upon his good nature. When these three characters are found united in one person, the composition generally becomes a great man's favourite. It was not difficult to collect such a groupe in a city that was the center of pleasure. Nash had them of all sizes, from the half pay captain in laced cloaths to the humble boot-catcher at the Bear.

I have before me a bundle of letters, all addressed from a pack of flattering reptiles to his *Honour,* and even some printed dedications in the same servile strain. In these *his Honour* is complimented as the great encourager of the polite arts, as a gentleman of the most accomplished taste, of the most extensive learning, and in short of every thing in the world. But perhaps it will be thought wrong in me to unveil the blushing muse, to brand learning with the meanness of its professors, or to expose scholars in a state of contempt.— For the honour of letters, the dedications to Mr. Nash are not written by scholars or poets, but by people of a different stamp.

Among this number was the highwayman who was taken after attempting to rob and murder Doctor Handcock. He was called Poulter, alias Baxter, and published a book exposing the tricks of gamblers, thieves and pick-pockets. This he intended to have dedicated to Mr. Nash, but the generous patron, tho' no man loved praise more, was too modest to have it printed. However, he took care to preserve the manuscript, among the rest of his papers. The book was entitled, *The discoveries of John Poulter, alias Baxter, who was apprehended for robbing Doctor Handcock, of Salisbury, on Clarken Down near Bath; and who has since been admitted king's evidence, and discovered a most numerous gang of villains. Being a full account of all the robberies he committed, and the surprizing tricks and frauds he has practised for the space of five years last past, in different parts of England, particularly in the West. Written wholly by himself.* The dedication intended to be prefixed is as follows, and will give a specimen of the stile of an highwayman and a gambler:

To the Honourable Richard Nash, *Esq.*

May it please your Honour,
With humblest submission, I make bold to present the following sheets to your Honour's consideration and well known humanity. As I am industriously careful, in respect to his Majesty and good subjects, to put an end to the unfortunate misconducts of all I know, by bringing them to the gallows. To be sure some may censure, as if from self-preservation I made this ample discovery; but I communicate this to your Honour and gentry, whether the life of one person being taken away would answer the end, as to let escape such a number of villains, who has been the ruining of many a poor family, for whom my soul is now much concerned. If my inclinations was ever so roguish enclined, what is it to so great a number of villains when they consult together. As your Honour's wisdom, humanity and interest are the friend of the virtuous, I make bold to lay at your Honour's feet the following lines, which will put every honest man upon his defence against the snares of the mischievous; and am, with greatest gratitude, honoured Sir, your Honour's most truly devoted and obedient Servant,

John Poulter *alias* Baxter.

Taunton Gaol, June 2d.

Flattery from such a wretch as this, one would think but little pleasing; however, certain it is that Nash was pleased with it; he loved to be called your Honour and Honourable, and the highwayman more than once experienced his generosity. . . .

By this fellow's discoveries Mr. Nash was enabled to serve many of the nobility and gentry of his acquaintance; he received a list of all those houses of ill fame which harboured or assisted rogues, and took care to furnish travellers with proper precautions to avoid them. It was odd enough to see a gamester thus employed, in detecting the frauds of gamblers. . . .

The man who is constantly served up with adulation must be a first-rate philosopher if he can listen without contracting new affectations. The opinion we form of ourselves is generally measured by what we hear from others; and when they conspire to deceive, we too readily concur in the delusion. Among the number of much applauded men in the circle of our own friends we can recollect but few that have heads quite strong enough to bear a loud acclamation of public praise in their favour; among the whole list we shall scarce find one that has not thus been made, on some side of his character, a coxcomb.

When the best head turns and grows giddy with praise, is it to be wondered that poor Nash should be driven by it almost into a phrenzy of affectation? Towards the close of life he became affected. He chiefly laboured to be thought a sayer of good things; and by frequent attempts was now and then successful, for he ever lay upon the lurch.

There never perhaps was a more silly passion than this desire of having a man's jests recorded. For this purpose it is necessary to keep ignorant or ill-bred company, who are only fond of repeating such stories; in the next place, a person must tell his own jokes in order to make them more universal; but what is worst of all, scarce a joke of this kind succeeds but at the expence of a man's good nature; and he who exchanges the character of being thought agreeable for that of being thought witty, makes but a very bad bargain.

The success Nash sometimes met with led him on, when late in life, to mistake his true character. He was really agreeable, but he chose to be thought a wit. He therefore indulged his inclination, and never mattered how rude he was, provided he was thought comical. He thus got the applause he sought for, but too often found enemies where he least expected to find them. Of all the jests recorded of him I scarce find one that is not marked with petulance; he said whatever came uppermost, and in the number of his remarks it might naturally be expected that some were worth repeating; he threw often, and sometimes had a lucky cast.

In a life of almost ninety years, spent in the very point of public view, it is not strange that five or six sprightly things of his have been collected, particularly as he took every opportunity of repeating them himself. His usual way, when he thought he said any thing clever, was to strengthen it with an oath, and to make up its want of sentiment by asseveration and grimace. For many years he thus entertained the company at the coffee-house with old stories, in which he always made himself the principal character. Strangers liked this well enough; but they who were used to his conversation found it insupportable. One story brought on another, and each came in the same order that it had the day preceding. But this custom may be rather ascribed to the peculiarity of age than a peculiarity of character; it seldom happens that old men allure, at least by novelty; age that shrivels the body contracts the understanding; instead of exploring new regions, they rest satisfied in the old and walk round the circle of their former discoveries. His manner of telling a story, however, was not displeasing, but few of those he told are worth transcribing. Indeed it is the manner which places the whole difference between the wit of the vulgar and of those who assume the name of the polite; one has in general as much good sense as the other; a story transcribed from the one will be as entertaining as that copied from the other, but in conversation the manner will give charms even to stupidity. The following is the story which he most frequently told, and pretty much in these words. Suppose the company to be talking of a German war or Elizabeth Canning,[56] he would begin thus: "I'll tell you something to that purpose that I fancy will make you laugh. A covetous old parson, as rich as the Devil, scraped a fresh acquaintance with me several years ago at Bath. I knew him when he and I were students at Oxford, where we both studied damnationly hard, but that's neither here nor there. Well.

Very well. I entertained him at my house in John's Court. (No, my house in John's Court was not built then;) but I entertained him with all that the city could afford, the rooms, the music, and every thing in the world. Upon his leaving Bath, he pressed me very hard to return the visit, and desired me to let him have the pleasure of seeing me at his house in Devonshire. About six months after, I happened to be in that neighbourhood and was resolved to see my old friend, from whom I expected a very warm reception. Well: I knocks at his door, when an old queer creature of a maid came to the door and denied him. I suspected, however, that he was at home; and going into the parlour, what should I see but the Parson's legs up the chimney, where he had thrust himself to avoid entertaining me. This was very well. 'My dear,' says I to the maid, 'it is very cold, extreme cold indeed, and I am afraid I have got a touch of my ague; light me the fire, if you please.' 'La, Sir,' says the maid, who was a modest creature to be sure, 'the chimney smokes monstrously; you could not bear the room for three minutes together.' By the greatest good luck there was a bundle of straw in the hearth, and I called for a candle. The candle came. 'Well, good woman,' says I, 'since you won't light me a fire, I'll light one for myself,' and in a moment the straw was all in a blaze. This quickly unkennelled the old fox; there he stood in an old rusty night gown, blessing himself, and looking like—a—hem—egad."

He used to tell surprizing stories of his activity when young. "Here I stand, gentlemen, that could once leap forty two feet upon level ground, at three standing jumps, backward or forward. One, two, three, dart like an arrow out of a bow. But I am old now. I remember I once leaped for three hundred guineas with Count Klopstock, the great leaper, leaping-master to the Prince of Passau; you must all have heard of him. First he began with the running jump, and a most damnable bounce it was, that's certain. Every body concluded that he had the match hollow, when only taking off my hat, stripping off neither coat, shoes, nor stockings, mind me, I fetches a run, and went beyond him one foot, three inches and three quarters, measured, upon my soul, by Captain Pately's own standard."

But in this torrent of insipidity there sometimes were found very severe satire, strokes of true wit, and lines of humour, *cum fluerent lutulentus, &c.*[57] He rallied very successfully, for he never felt another's joke, and drove home his own without pity. With his superiors he was familiar and blunt; the inferiority of his station secured him from their resentment; but the same bluntness which they laughed at, was by his equals regarded as insolence. Something like a familiar bootcatcher at an inn, a gentleman would bear that joke from him, for which a brother boot-catcher would knock him down.

Among other stories of Nash's telling, I remember one, which I the more chearfully repeat, as it tends to correct a piece of impertinence that reigns in almost every country assembly. The principal inhabitants of a market-town at a great distance from the capital, in order to encourage that harmony which ought to subsist in society, and to promote a mutual intercourse between the sexes so desirable to both and so necessary for all, had established a monthly assembly in the Town Hall, which was conducted with such decency, decorum, and politeness, that it drew the attention of the gentlemen and ladies in the neighbourhood; and a nobleman and his family continually honoured them with their presence. This naturally drew others, and in time the room was crouded with what the world calls good company, and the assembly prospered, till some of the new admitted ladies took it into their heads that the tradesmen's daughters were unworthy of their notice, and therefore refus'd to join hands with them in the dance. This was complained of by the town ladies, and that complaint was resented by the country gentlemen, who, more pert than wise, publickly advertised that they would not dance with tradesmen's daughters. This the most eminent tradesmen considered as an insult on themselves, and being men of worth and able to live independently, they in return advertised that they would give no credit out of their town, and desired all others to discharge their accounts. A general uneasiness ensued; some writs were actually issued out, and much distress would have happened, had not my Lord, who sided with no party, kindly interfered and composed the difference. The assembly however was ruined, and the families, I am told, are not friends yet, though this affair happened thirty years ago.

Nothing debases human nature so much as pride. This Nash knew, and endeavoured to stifle every emotion of it at Bath. When he observed any ladies so extremely delicate and proud of a pedigree as to only touch the back of an inferior's hand in the dance, he always called to order and desired them to leave the room or behave with common decency; and when any Ladies and Gentlemen drew off, after they had gone down a dance, without standing up till the dance was finished, he made up to them, and after asking whether they had done dancing, told them they should dance no more unless they stood up for the rest; and on these occasions he always was as good as his word.

Nash, tho' no great wit, had the art of sometimes saying rude things with decency and rendering them pleasing by an uncommon turn. But most of the good things attributed to him which have found their way into the jest books are no better than puns; the smartest things I have seen are against him. One day in the grove he joined some ladies, and asking one of them, who was crooked, whence she came? she replied, strait from London. "Confound me, Madam," said he, "then you must have been damnably warpt by the way."

She soon, however, had ample revenge. Sitting the following evening in one of the rooms, he once more joined her company, and with a sneer and a bow asked her if she knew her Catechism, and could tell the name of Tobit's dog? "His name, Sir, was Nash," replied the lady, "and an impudent dog he was." This story is told in a celebrated romance.[58] I only repeat it here to have an opportunity of observing that it actually happened.

Queen Anne once asked him why he would not accept of knighthood? To· which he replied, lest Sir William Read, the mountebank who had been just knighted, should call him brother.

An house in Bath was said to be haunted by the Devil, and a great noise was made about it, when Nash, going to the minister of St. Michael's, intreated him to drive the Devil out of Bath for ever, if it were only to oblige the ladies.

Nash used sometimes to visit the great Doctor Clarke. The Doctor was one day conversing with Locke and two or three more of his learned and intimate companions, with that free-

dom, gaiety and chearfulness, which is ever the result of innocence. In the midst of their mirth and laughter, the Doctor,
looking from the window, saw Nash's chariot stop at the door.
"Boys, boys," cried the philosopher to his friends, "let us now
be wise, for here is a fool coming."

Nash was one day complaining in the following manner to
the Earl of Chesterfield of his bad luck at play. "Would you
think it, my Lord, that damned bitch fortune, no later than last
night, tricked me out of 500. Is it not surprizing," continued
he, "that my luck should never turn, that I should thus eternally be mauled?" "I don't wonder at your losing money,
Nash," says his lordship, "but all the world is surprized where
you get it to lose."

Doctor Cheney once, when Nash was ill, drew up a prescription for him, which was sent in accordingly. The next day
the Doctor, coming to see his patient, found him up and well,
upon which he asked if he had followed his prescription?
"Followed your prescription," cried Nash, "No.—Egad, if I
had, I should have broke my neck, for I flung it out of the
two pair of stairs window."

It would have been well had he confined himself to such
sallies; but as he grew old he grew insolent, and seemed in
some measure insensible of the pain his attempts to be a wit
gave others. Upon asking a lady to dance a minuet, if she refused, he would often demand if she had got bandy legs. He
would attempt to ridicule natural defects; he forgot the deference due to birth and quality, and mistook the manner of
settling rank and precedence upon many occasions. He now
seemed no longer fashionable among the present race of gentry; he grew peevish and fretful, and they who only saw the
remnant of a man, severely returned that laughter upon him
which he had once lavished upon others.

Poor Nash was no longer the gay, thoughtless, idly industrious creature he once was; he now forgot how to supply new
modes of entertainment, and became too rigid to wind with
ease through the vicissitudes of fashion. The evening of his
life began to grow cloudy. His fortune was gone, and nothing
but poverty lay in prospect. To embitter his hopes, he found
himself abandoned by the great, whom he had long endeavoured to serve, and was obliged to fly to those of humbler

stations for protection, whom he once affected to despise. He now began to want that charity which he had never refused to any, and to find that a life of dissipation and gaiety is ever terminated by misery and regret.

Even his place of master of the ceremonies (if I can trust the papers he has left behind him) was sought after. I would willingly be tender of any living reputation, but these papers accuse Mr. Quin of endeavouring to supplant him. He has even left us a letter which he supposed was written by that gentleman, soliciting a Lord for his interest upon the occasion. As I chuse to give Mr. Quin an opportunity of disproving this, I will insert the letter and, to shew the improbability of its being his, with all its faults, both of style and spelling. I am the less apt to believe it written by Mr. Quin, as a gentleman who has mended Shakespear's plays so often would surely be capable of something more correct than the following. It was sent, as it should seem, from Mr. Quin to a nobleman, but left open for the perusal of an intermediate friend. It was this friend who sent a copy of it to Mr. Nash, who caused it to be instantly printed and left among his other papers. The letter from the intermediate friend to Nash is as follows;

London, October 8, 1760.

Dear Nash,

Two posts ago I received a letter from Quin, the old player, covering one to my Lord which he left open for my perusal, which after reading he desired I might seal up and deliver. The request he makes is so extraordinary that it has induced me to send you the copy of his letter to my Lord, which is as follows:

Bath, October 3, 1760.

My dear Lord,

Old beaux Knash has mead himselfe so dissagreeable to all the companey that comes here to Bath that the corperatian of this city have it now under thier consideration to remove him from beeing master of the cereymoines, should he be continuead the inhabitants of thiss city will be rueind, as the best companey declines to come to Bath on his acctt.

Give me leave to show to your Lords'hip how he beheaved

at the firs't ball he had here thiss' season which was Tus'day las't. A younge Lady was as'ked to dance a minueat she begg the gentm would be pleased to exquise here, as' she did not chuse to dance; upon thiss' old Nash called out so as to be head by all the companey in the room G— dam yo Madam what buisness have yo here if yo do not dance, upon which the Lady was so afrighted, she rose and danced, the ress'et of the companey was so much offended at the rudness of Nash that not one Lady more, would dance a minueat that night. In the country dances' no person of note danced except two boys' Lords S—— and T——, the res't of the companey that danced waire only the families of all the habberdas'hers' machinukes[59] and inkeepers in the three kingdoms' brushed up and colexted togither.

I have known upon such an occaison as' thiss' seventeen Dutchess' and Contiss' to be at the opening of the ball at Bath now not one. This man by his' pride and extravigancis has out lived his' reasein it would be happy for thiss' city that he was ded; and is, now only fitt to reed Shirlock upon death by which he may seave his soul and gaine more than all the proffits he can make, by his white hatt, suppose it was to be died red;

The favr I have now to reques't by what I now have wrote yo; is' that your Lordship will be so kind as to speke to Mr. Pitt, for to recommend me to the corperatian of this city to succede this old sinner as master of the cerremonies and yo will much oblige,

My Lord your Lords. and Hue. Obt. Sert.

N.B. There were some other private matters and offers in Quin's letter to my Lord, which do not relate to you.

Here Nash, if I may be permitted the use of a polite and fashionable phrase, was humm'd; but he experienced such rubs as these and a thousand other mortifications every day. He found poverty now denied him the indulgence not only of his favourite follies, but of his favourite virtues. The poor now solicited him in vain; he was himself a more pitiable object than they. The child of the public seldom has a friend, and he who once exercised his wit at the expence of others must naturally have enemies. Exasperated at last to the highest degree, an unaccountable whim struck him; poor Nash was resolved to become an author; he who, in the vigour of manhood, was incapable of the task, now at the impotent age of eighty-six was determined to write his own history! From the many specimens already given of his style, the reader will not much regret that the historian was interrupted in his design. Yet as Montaigne observes, as the adventures of an infant, if an infant could inform us of them, would be pleasing, so the life of a Beau, if a beau could write, would certainly serve to regale curiosity.

Whether he really intended to put this design in execution or did it only to alarm the nobility, I will not take upon me to determine; but certain it is that his friends went about collecting subscriptions for the work, and he received several encouragements from such as were willing to be politely charitable. It was thought by many that this history would reveal the intrigues of a whole age, that he had numberless secrets to disclose; but they never considered that persons of public character, like him, were the most unlikely in the world to be made partakers of those secrets which people desired the public should not know. In fact, he had few secrets to discover, and those he had are now buried with him in the grave.

He was now past the power of giving or receiving pleasure, for he was poor, old and peevish; yet still he was incapable of turning from his former manner of life to pursue his happiness. The old man endeavoured to practise the follies of the boy; he spurred on his jaded passions after every trifle of the day; tottering with age he would be ever an unwelcome guest in the assemblies of the youthful and gay, and he seemed willing to find lost appetite among those scenes where he was once young.

An old man thus striving after pleasure is indeed an object of pity; but a man at once old and poor, running on in this pursuit, might excite astonishment. To see a Being both by fortune and constitution rendered incapable of enjoyment, still haunting those pleasures he was no longer to share in, to see one of almost ninety settling the fashion of a lady's cap or assigning her place in a country dance, to see him unmindful of his own reverend figure or the respect he should have for himself, toasting demireps or attempting to entertain the lewd and idle, a sight like this might well serve as a satire on humanity, might shew that man is the only preposterous creature alive, who pursues the shadow of pleasure without temptation.

But he was not permitted to run on thus without severe and repeated reproof. The clergy sent him frequent calls to reformation, but the asperity of their advice in general abated its intended effects; they threatened him with fire and brimstone for what he had long been taught to consider as foibles, and not vices; so, like a desperated debtor, he did not care to settle an account that, upon the first inspection, he found himself utterly unable to pay. Thus begins one of his monitors:

"This admonition comes from your friend, and one that has your interest deeply at heart. It comes on a design altogether important, and of no less consequence than your everlasting happiness, so that it may justly challenge your careful regard. It is not to upbraid or reproach, much less to triumph and insult over your misconduct or misery; no, 'tis pure benevolence, it is disinterested good-will prompts me to write. I hope therefore I shall not raise your resentment. Yet be the consequence what it will, I cannot bear to see you walk in the paths that lead to death without warning you of the danger, without sounding in your ear the lawful admonition, 'Return and live! Why do you such things? I hear of your evil dealings by all this people.' I have long observed and pitied you, and must tell you plainly, Sir, that your present behaviour is not the way to reconcile yourself to God. You are so far from making atonement to offended justice that each moment you are aggravating the future account and heaping up an increase of his anger. As long as you roll on in a continued circle of sensual delights and vain entertainments, you are dead to all the purposes of piety and virtue. You are as odious to God as a corrupt carcase that lies putrefying in the church-yard. You are as far from doing your duty, or endeavouring after salvation, or restoring yourself to the divine favour, as a heap of dry bones nailed up in a coffin is from vigour and activity.— Think, Sir, I conjure you, think upon this, if you have any inclination to escape the fire that will never be quenched. Would you be rescued from the fury and fierce anger of God? Would you be delivered from weeping and wailing and incessant gnashing of teeth? Sure you would! But be certain that this will never be done by amusements which at best are trifling and impertinent, and for that, if for no other reason, foolish and sinful. 'Tis by seriousness, 'tis by retirement and mourning, you must accomplish this great and desirable deliverance. You must not appear at the head of every silly diversion; you must enter into your closet and shut the door; commune with your own heart and search out its defects. The pride of life and all its superfluity of follies must be put away. You must make haste, and delay not to keep every injunction of heaven. You must always remember that mighty sinners must be mightily penitent or else mightily tormented. Your example and your projects have been extremely *prejudicial*, I wish I could not say, *fatal* and *destructive* to many. For this there is no amends but an alteration of your conduct, as signal and remarkable as your *person* and *name*.

"If you do not by this method remedy in some degree the evils that you have sent abroad, and prevent the mischievous consequences that may ensue—wretched will you be, wretched above all men, to eternity. The blood of souls will be laid to your charge. God's jealousy, like a consuming flame, will smoke against you, as you yourself will see in that day when the mountains shall quake, and the hills melt, and the earth be burnt up at his presence.

"Once more then I exhort you as a friend; I beseech you as a brother; I charge you as a messenger from God, in his own most solemn words; 'Cast away from you your transgressions; make you a new heart, and a new spirit; so iniquity shall not be your ruin.'

"Perhaps you may be disposed to contemn this and its serious purport, or to recommend it to your companions as a subject for raillery. Yet let me tell you before-hand that for this, as well as for other things, God will bring you to judgment. He sees me now I write; He will observe you while you read. He notes down my words; He will also note down your consequent procedure. Not then upon me, not upon me, but upon your own soul, will the neglecting or despising my sayings turn. 'If thou be wise, thou shalt be wise for thyself; if thou scornest, thou alone shalt bear it.' "

Such repeated admonitions as these served to sting without

reforming him; they made him morose, but not pious. The dose was too strong for the patient to bear. He should have been met with smiles and allured into reformation, if indeed he was criminal. But in the name of piety, what was there criminal in his conduct; he had long been taught to consider his trifling profession as a very serious and important business. He went through his office with great gravity, solemnity, and care; why then denounce peculiar torments against a poor harmless creature who did a thousand good things, and whose greatest vice was vanity? He deserved ridicule, indeed, and he found it, but scarce a single action of his life, except one, deserves the asperity of reproach.

Thus we see a variety of causes concurred to embitter his departing life. The weakness and infirmities of exhausted nature, the admonitions of the grave, who aggravated his follies into vices, the ingratitude of his dependants, who formerly flattered his fortunes, but particularly the contempt of the great, many of whom quite forgot him in his wants, all these hung upon his spirits and soured his temper, and the poor man of pleasure might have terminated his life very tragically, had not the corporation of Bath charitably resolved to grant him ten guineas the first Monday of every month. This bounty served to keep him from actual necessity, tho' far too trifling to enable him to support the character of a gentleman. Habit, and not nature, makes almost all our wants; and he who had been accustomed in the early parts of life to affluence and prodigality, when reduced to an hundred and twenty-six pounds a year, must pine in actual indigence.

In this variety of uneasiness his health began to fail. He had received from nature a robust and happy constitution that was scarce even to be impaired by intemperance. He even pretended, among his friends, that he never followed a single prescription in his life; however, in this he was one day detected on the parade; for boasting there of his contempt and utter disuse of medicine, unluckily the water of two blisters, which Dr. Oliver had prescribed, and which he then had upon each leg, ouzed through his stockings and betrayed him. His aversion to physic, however, was frequently a topic of raillery between him and Doctor Cheney, who was a man of some wit and breeding. When Cheney recommended his veg-

etable diet, Nash would swear, that his design was to send half
the world grazing like Nebuchadnezzar. "Ay," Cheney would
reply, "Nebuchadnezzar was never such an infidel as thou art.
It was but last week, gentlemen, that I attended this fellow in
a fit of sickness; there I found him rolling up his eyes to
heaven, and crying for mercy; he would then swallow my
drugs like breast-milk; yet you now hear him, how the old
dog blasphemes the faculty." What Cheney said in jest was
true, he feared the approaches of death more than the generality of mankind, and was generally very devout while it
threatened him. Tho' he was somewhat the libertine in action,
none believed or trembled more than he, for a mind neither
schooled by philosophy nor encouraged by conscious innocence is ever timid at the appearance of danger.

For some time before his decease nature gave warning of
his approaching dissolution. The worn machine had run itself
down to an utter impossibility of repair; he saw that he must
die, and shuddered at the thought. His virtues were not of the
great but the amiable kind, so that fortitude was not among
the number. Anxious, timid, his thoughts still hanging on a
receding world, he desired to enjoy a little longer that life, the
miseries of which he had experienced so long. The poor unsuccessful gamester husbanded the wasting moments, with an
encreased desire to continue the game, and to the last eagerly
wished for one yet more happy throw. He died at his house in
St. John's Court, Bath, on the 12th of February, 1761, aged
eighty-seven years, three months, and some days.

His death was sincerely regretted by the city to which he
had been so long and so great a benefactor. The day after he
died, the Mayor of Bath called the corporation together,
where they granted fifty pounds towards burying their sovereign with proper respect. After the corpse had lain for days,
it was conveyed to the abbey church in that city, with a solemnity somewhat peculiar to his character. About five the procession moved from his house; the charity girls two and two
preceded, next the boys of the charity school singing a solemn occasional hymn. Next marched the city music and his
own band sounding at proper intervals a dirge. Three clergymen immediately preceded the coffin, which was adorned with
sable plumes, and the pall supported by the six senior alder-

men. The masters of the assembly-rooms followed as chief mourners; the beadles of that hospital which he had contributed so largely to endow went next; and last of all, the poor patients themselves, the lame, the emaciated, and the feeble, followed their old benefactor to his grave, shedding unfeigned tears and lamenting themselves in him.

The crowd was so great that not only the streets were filled, but, as one of the journals in a *rant* expresses it, "even the tops of the houses were covered with spectators; each thought the occasion affected themselves most; as when a real king dies, they asked each other, *where shall we find such another;* sorrow sate upon every face, and even children lisped that their Sovereign was no more. The awfulness of the solemnity made the deepest impression on the minds of the distressed inhabitants. The peasant discontinued his toil, the ox rested from the plough, all nature seemed to sympathize with their loss, and the muffled bells rung a peal of Bob Major."

Our deepest solemnities have something truly ridiculous in them; there is somewhat ludicrous in the folly of historians who thus declaim upon the death of kings and princes, as if there was any thing dismal or any thing unusual in it. "For my part," says Poggi, the Florentine, "I can no more grieve for another's death than I could for my own. I have ever regarded death as a very trifling affair; nor can black staves, long cloaks, or mourning coaches, in the least influence my spirits. Let us live here as long and as merrily as we can, and when we must die, why, let us die merrily too, but die so as to be happy."

The few things he was possessed of were left to his relations. A small library of well chosen books, some trinkets and pictures, were his only inheritance. Among the latter were a gold box, given by the late countess of Burlington, with lady Euston's picture in the lid; an agate etui with a diamond on the top, by the princess dowager of Wales, and some other things of no great value. The rings, watches, and pictures, which he formerly received from others, would have come to a considerable amount; but these his necessities had obliged him to dispose of. Some family pictures, however, remained, which were sold by advertisement for five guineas each, after Mr. Nash's decease.

It was natural to expect that the death of a person so long

in the eye of the public must have produced a desire in several to delineate his character or deplore his loss. He was scarce dead, when the public papers were filled with elegies, groans and characters; and before he was buried, there were epitaphs ready made to inscribe on his stone. I remember one of those character writers, and a very grave one too, after observing, alas! that Richard Nash, Esq. was no more, went on to assure us that he was *sagacious, debonair, and comode;* and concluded with gravely declaring, *that impotent posterity would in vain fumble to produce his fellow.* Another, equally sorrowful, gave us to know, *that he was indeed a man,* an assertion which I fancy none will be so hardy as to contradict. But the merriest of all the lamentations made upon this occasion was that where he is called *A constellation of the heavenly sphere.*

One thing, however, is common almost with each of them, and that is that Venus, Cupid, and the Graces, are commanded to weep, and that Bath shall never find such another. . . .

But a cool biographer, unbiased by resentment or regard, will probably find nothing in the man either truly great or strongly vicious. His virtues were all amiable, and more adapted to procure friends than admirers; they were more capable of raising love than esteem. He was naturally endued with good sense; but by having been long accustomed to pursue trifles, his mind shrunk to the size of the little objects on which it was employed. His generosity was boundless, because his tenderness and his vanity were in equal proportion, the one impelling him to relieve misery, and the other to make his benefactions known. In all his actions, however virtuous, he was guided by sensation and not by reason, so that the uppermost passion was ever sure to prevail. His being constantly in company had made him an easy tho' not a polite companion. He chose to be thought rather an odd fellow than a well-bred man; perhaps that mixture of respect and ridicule with which his mock royalty was treated first inspired him with this resolution. The foundations of his empire were laid in vicious compliance, the continuance of his reign was supported by a virtuous impartiality. In the beginning of his authority he in reality obeyed those whom he pretended to govern; towards the end he attempted to extort a real obedience from his subjects, and supported his right by prescription. Like a monarch Tacitus talks of, they complied with him at first because they loved, they obeyed at last because they feared him. He often led the rich into new follies, in order to promote the happiness of the poor, and served the one at the expence of the other. Whatever his vices were, they were of use to society; and this neither Petronius, nor Apicius, nor Tigellius, nor any other professed voluptuary, could say. To set him up, as some do, for a pattern of imitation is wrong, since all his virtues received a tincture from the neighbouring folly; to denounce peculiar judgments against him is equally unjust, as his faults raise rather our mirth than our detestation. He was fitted for the station in which fortune placed him. It required no great abilities to fill it, and few of great abilities but would have disdained the employment. He led a life of vanity and long mistook it for happiness. Unfortunately he was taught at last to know that a man of pleasure leads the most unpleasant life in the world. . . .

As the heart of a man is better known by his private than public actions, let us take a view of Nash in domestick life among his servants and dependants, where no gloss was required to colour his sentiments and disposition nor any mask necessary to conceal his foibles. Here we shall find him the same open-hearted, generous, good-natured man we have already described, one who was ever fond of promoting the interests of his friends, his servants, and dependants, and making them happy. In his own house no man perhaps was more regular, chearful, and beneficent than Mr. Nash. His table was always free to those who sought his friendship or wanted a dinner; and after grace was said, he usually accosted the company in the following extraordinary manner, to take off all restraint and ceremony. "Come, gentlemen, eat and welcome; spare, and the Devil choak you." I mention this circumstance for no other reason but because it is well known and is consistent with the singularity of his character and behaviour.

As Mr. Nash's thoughts were entirely employed in the affairs of his government, he was seldom at home but at the time of eating or of rest. His table was well served, but his entertainment consisted principally of plain dishes. Boiled chicken and roast mutton were his favourite meats, and he was so fond of the small sort of potatoes that he called them English pine-apples, and generally eat them as others do fruit, after dinner. In drinking he was altogether as regular and abstemious. Both in this, and in eating, he seemed to consult nature and obey only her dictates. Good small beer, with or without a glass of wine in it, and sometimes wine and water, was his drink at meals, and after dinner he generally drank one glass of wine. He seemed fond of hot suppers, usually supped about nine or ten o'clock upon roast breast of mutton and his potatoes, and soon after supper went to bed, which induced Dr. Cheney to tell him jestingly that he behaved like other brutes, and lay down as soon as he had filled his belly. "Very true," replied Nash, "and this prescription I had from my neighbour's Cow, who is a better physician than you, and a superior judge of plants, notwithstanding you have written so learnedly on the vegetable diet."

Nash generally arose early in the morning, being seldom in bed after five; and to avoid disturbing the family and depriving his servants of their rest, he had the fire laid after he was in bed, and in the morning lighted it himself and sat down to read some of his few, but well chosen books. After reading some time, he usually went to the pump-room and drank the waters, then took a walk on the parade and went to the coffee-house to breakfast, after which, till two o'clock (his usual time of dinner) his hours were spent in arbitrating differences amongst his neighbours, or the company resorting to the wells, directing the diversions of the day, in visiting the new comers or receiving friends at his own house, of which there were a great concourse till within six or eight years before his death.

His generosity and charity in private life, though not so conspicuous, was as great as that in publick, and indeed far more considerable than his little income would admit of. He could not stifle the natural impulse which he had to do good, but frequently borrowed money to relieve the distressed; and when he knew not conveniently where to borrow, he has been often observed to shed tears as he passed through the wretched supplicants who attended his gate.

This sensibility, this power of feeling the misfortunes of the miserable, and his address and earnestness in relieving their wants, exalts the character of Mr. Nash, and draws an impenetrable veil over his foibles. His singularities are forgotten when we behold his virtues, and he who laughed at the whimsical character and behaviour of this Monarch of Bath, now laments that he is no more.

The Vicar of Wakefield

A TALE SUPPOSED TO BE
WRITTEN BY HIMSELF

[Johnson told Boswell that he received a message from Goldsmith one morning "that he was in great distress, and as it was not in his power to come to me, begging that I would come to him as soon as possible. I sent him a guinea and promised to come to him directly. I accordingly went as soon as I was drest, and found that his landlady had arrested him for his rent, at which he was in a violent passion. I perceived that he had already changed my guinea and had got a bottle of Madeira and a glass before him. I put the cork into the bottle, desired he would be calm, and began to talk to him of the means by which he might be extricated. He then told me that he had a novel ready for the press, which he produced to me. I looked into it and saw its merit, told the landlady I should soon return, and having gone to a bookseller, sold it for sixty pounds. I brought Goldsmith the money, and he discharged his rent, not without rating his landlady in a high tone for having used him so ill." On 28 October 1762 a Salisbury bookseller named Collins paid twenty guineas for a third share of the book, which gives an approximate date for Johnson's intervention. But the novel was not published until March 1766, the delay being caused, Johnson thought, by the booksellers' "faint hopes of profit." On the title-page was the epigraph: *Sperate miseri, cavete felices* ("Take hope, you who are wretched; you who are happy, take care"). The early editions were in two volumes; the first contained Chapters I-XIX, and the chapters in the second volume were renumbered, beginning with I. But this division, which was made by the printers, distorts the structure of the book. In the present edition, therefore, the chapters have been numbered according to modern conventions.]

ADVERTISEMENT

There are an hundred faults in this Thing, and an hundred *critical theory* things might be said to prove them beauties. But it is needless. A book may be amusing with numerous errors, or it may be very dull without a single absurdity. The hero of this piece unites in himself the three greatest characters upon earth; he is a priest, an husbandman, and the father of a family. He is drawn as ready to teach, and ready to obey, as simple in affluence, and majestic in adversity. In this age of opulence and refinement whom can such a character please? Such as are fond of high life will turn with disdain from the simplicity of his country fire-side. Such as mistake ribaldry for humour will find no wit in his harmless conversation; and such as have been taught to deride religion will laugh at one whose chief stores of comfort are drawn from futurity.

Oliver Goldsmith

CHAPTER ONE

The description of the family of Wakefield; in which a kindred likeness prevails as well of minds as of persons.

I was ever of opinion that the honest man who married and brought up a large family did more service than he who continued single and only talked of population. From this motive I had scarce taken orders a year before I began to think seriously of matrimony, and chose my wife as she did her wedding gown, not for a fine glossy surface but such qualities as would wear well. To do her justice, she was a good-natured notable woman; and as for breeding, there were few country ladies who at that time could shew more. She could read any English book without much spelling; and for pickling, preserving, and cookery, none could excel her. She prided herself much also upon being an excellent contriver in house-keeping; yet I could never find that we grew richer with all her contrivances.

However, we loved each other tenderly, and our fondness encreased with age. There was in fact nothing that could make us angry with the world or each other. We had an elegant house, situated in a fine country, and a good neighbourhood. The year was spent in moral or rural amusements, in visiting our rich neighbours, and relieving such as were poor. We had no revolutions to fear, nor fatigues to undergo; all our adventures were by the fire-side, and all our migrations from the blue bed to the brown.

As we lived near the road, we often had the traveller or stranger come to taste our gooseberry wine, for which we had great reputation; and I profess with the veracity of an historian that I never knew one of them find fault with it. Our cousins too, even to the fortieth remove, all remembered their affinity without any help from the herald's office and came very frequently to see us. Some of them did us no great honour by these claims of kindred; for literally speaking we had the blind, the maimed, and the halt amongst the number. However, my wife always insisted that as they were the same *flesh and blood* with us, they should sit with us at the same table. So that if we had not very rich, we generally had very happy friends about us; for this remark will hold good thro' life, that the poorer the guest, the better pleased he ever is with being treated; and as some men gaze with admiration at the colours of a tulip and others are smitten with the wing of a butterfly, so I was by nature an admirer of happy human faces. However, when any one of our relations was found to be a person of very bad character, a troublesome guest, or one we desired to get rid of, upon his leaving my house for the first time I ever took care to lend him a riding coat, or a pair of boots, or sometimes an horse of small value, and I always had the satisfaction of finding he never came back to return them. By this the house was cleared of such as we did not like; but never was the family of Wakefield known to turn the traveller or the poor dependant out of doors.

Thus we lived several years in a state of much happiness, not but that we sometimes had those little rubs which Providence sends to enhance the value of its favours. My orchard was often robbed by school-boys, and my wife's custards plundered by the cats or the children. The 'Squire would sometimes fall asleep in the most pathetic parts of my sermon, or his lady return my wife's civilities at church with a mutilated curtesy. But we soon got over the uneasiness caused by such accidents, and usually in three or four days we began to wonder how they vext us.

My children, the offspring of temperance, as they were educated without softness, so they were at once well formed and healthy; my sons hardy and active, my daughters dutiful and blooming. When I stood in the midst of the little circle, which promised to be the supports of my declining age, I could not avoid repeating the famous story of Count Abensberg, who, in Henry II's progress through Germany, when other courtiers came with their treasures, brought his thirty-two children and presented them to his sovereign as the most valuable offering he had to bestow. In this manner, though I had but six, I considered them as a very valuable present made to my country, and consequently looked upon it as my debtor. Our eldest son was named George, after his uncle who left us ten thousand pounds. Our second child, a girl, I intended to call after her aunt Grissel; but my wife, who during her pregnancy had been reading romances, insisted upon her being called Olivia. In less than another year we had a daughter again, and now I was determined that Grissel should be her name; but a rich relation taking a fancy to stand godmother, the girl was, by her directions, called Sophia; so that we had two romantic names in the family; but I solemnly protest I had no hand in it. Moses was our next, and after an interval of twelve years, we had two sons more.

It would be fruitless to deny my exultation when I saw my little ones about me; but the vanity and the satisfaction of my wife were even greater than mine. When our visitors would usually say, "Well, upon my word, Mrs. Primrose, you have the finest children in the whole country."—"Ay, neighbour," she would answer, "they are as heaven made them, handsome enough, if they be good enough, for handsome is that handsome does." And then she would bid the girls hold up their heads; who, to conceal nothing, were certainly very handsome. Mere outside is so very trifling a circumstance with me that I should scarce have remembered to mention it, had it not been a general topic of conversation in the country. Olivia, now about eighteen, had that luxuriancy of beauty with which painters generally draw Hebe; open, sprightly, and commanding. Sophia's features were not so striking at first, but often did more certain execution; for they were soft, modest, and alluring. The one vanquished by a single blow, the other by efforts successfully repeated.

The temper of a woman is generally formed from the turn of her features, at least it was so with my daughters. Olivia wished for many lovers, Sophia to secure one. Olivia was often affected from too great a desire to please. Sophia even represt excellence from her fears to offend. The one entertained me with her vivacity when I was gay, the other with her sense when I was serious. But these qualities were never carried to excess in either, and I have often seen them exchange characters for a whole day together. A suit of mourning has transformed my coquet into a prude, and a new set of ribbands given her younger sister more than natural vivacity. My eldest son George was bred at Oxford, as I intended him for one of the learned professions. My second boy Moses, whom I designed for business, received a sort of a miscellaneous education at home. But it would be needless to attempt describing the particular characters of young people that had seen but very little of the world. In short, a family likeness prevailed through all, and properly speaking they had but one character, that of being all equally generous, credulous, simple, and inoffensive.

CHAPTER TWO

Family misfortunes. The loss of fortune only serves to encrease the pride of the worthy.

The temporal concerns of our family were chiefly committed to my wife's management; as to the spiritual I took them entirely under my own direction. The profits of my living, which amounted to but thirty-five pounds a year, I gave to the orphans and widows of the clergy of our diocese, for having a sufficient fortune of my own, I was careless of temporalities and felt a secret pleasure in doing my duty without reward. I also set a resolution of keeping no curate, and of being acquainted with every man in the parish, exhorting the married men to temperance and the bachelors to matrimony, so that in a few years it was a common saying that there were three strange wants at Wakefield, a parson wanting pride, young men wanting wives, and ale-houses wanting customers.

Matrimony was always one of my favourite topics, and I wrote several sermons to prove its utility and happiness; but there was a peculiar tenet which I made a point of supporting; for I maintained with Whiston that it was unlawful for a priest of the church of England, after the death of his first wife, to take a second, or to express it in one word, I valued myself upon being a strict monogamist.

I was early initiated into this important dispute on which so many laborious volumes have been written. I published some tracts upon the subject myself, which, as they never sold, I have the consolation of thinking are read only by the happy *Few*. Some of my friends called this my weak side; but alas! they had not like me made it the subject of long contemplation. The more I reflected upon it, the more important it appeared. I even went a step beyond Whiston in displaying my principles: as he had engraven upon his wife's tomb that she was the *only* wife of William Whiston, so I wrote a similar epitaph for my wife, though still living, in which I extolled her prudence, œconomy, and obedience till death; and having got it copied fair, with an elegant frame, it was placed over the chimney-piece, where it answered several very useful purposes. It admonished my wife of her duty to me, and my fidelity to her; it inspired her with a passion for fame, and constantly put her in mind of her end.

It was thus, perhaps, from hearing marriage so often recommended, that my eldest son, just upon leaving college, fixed his affections upon the daughter of a neighbouring clergyman, who was a dignitary in the church, and in circumstances to give her a large fortune; but fortune was her smallest accomplishment. Miss Arabella Wilmot was allowed by all (except my two daughters) to be completely pretty. Her youth, health, and innocence, were still heightened by a complexion so transparent and such an happy sensibility of look that even age could not gaze on with indifference. As Mr. Wilmot knew that I could make a very handsome settlement on my son, he was not averse to the match; so both families lived together in all that harmony which generally precedes an expected alliance. Being convinced by experience that the days of courtship are the most happy of our lives, I was willing enough to lengthen the period; and the various amusements which the young couple every day shared in each other's company seemed to encrease their passion. We were generally awaked in the morning by music, and on fine days rode a hunting. The hours between breakfast and dinner the ladies devoted to dress and study: they usually read a page, and then gazed at themselves in the glass, which even philosophers might own often presented the page of greatest beauty. At dinner my wife took the lead; for as she always insisted upon carving every thing herself, it being her mother's way, she gave us upon these occasions the history of every dish. When we had dined, to prevent the ladies leaving us, I generally ordered the table to be removed; and sometimes, with the music master's assistance, the girls would give us a very agreeable concert. Walking out, drinking tea, country dances, and forfeits, shortened the rest of the day, without the assistance of cards, as I hated all manner of gaming, except backgammon, at which my old friend and I sometimes took a two-penny hit. Nor can I here pass over an ominous circumstance that happened the last time we played together; I only wanted to fling a quatre, and yet I threw deuce ace five times running.

Some months were elapsed in this manner, till at last it was thought convenient to fix a day for the nuptials of the young couple, who seemed earnestly to desire it. During the preparations for the wedding, I need not describe the busy importance of my wife, nor the sly looks of my daughters; in fact, my attention was fixed on another object, the completing a tract which I intended shortly to publish in defence of monogamy. As I looked upon this as a master-piece both for argument and style, I could not in the pride of my heart avoid shewing it to my old friend Mr. Wilmot, as I made no doubt of receiving his approbation; but too late I discovered that he was most violently attached to the contrary opinion, and with good reason; for he was at that time actually courting a fourth wife. This, as may be expected, produced a dispute attended with some acrimony which threatened to interrupt our intended alliance; but on the day before that appointed for the ceremony, we agreed to discuss the subject at large.

It was managed with proper spirit on both sides: he asserted that I was heterodox, I retorted the charge: he replied, and I rejoined. In the mean time, while the controversy was hottest, I was called out by one of my relations, who, with a face of concern, advised me to give up the dispute and allow the old gentleman to be a husband if he could, at least till my son's wedding was over. "How," cried I, "relinquish the cause of truth, and let him be an husband, already driven to the very verge of absurdity. You might as well advise me to give up my fortune as my argument." "That fortune," returned my friend, "I am now sorry to inform you, is almost nothing. Your merchant in town, in whose hands your money was lodged, has gone off, to avoid a statute of bankruptcy, and it is thought has not left a shilling in the pound. I was unwilling to shock you or the family with the account till after the wedding, but now it may serve to moderate your warmth in the argument; for, I suppose, your own prudence will enforce the necessity of dissembling at least till your son has the young lady's fortune secure."—"Well," returned I, "if what you tell me be true, and if I am to be a beggar, it shall never make me a rascal, or induce me to disavow my principles. I'll go this moment and inform the company of my circumstances; and as for the argument, I even here retract my former concessions in the old gentleman's favour, nor will I allow him now to be an husband de jure, de facto, or in any sense of the expression."

It would be endless to describe the different sensations of both families when I divulged the news of our misfortunes, but what others felt was slight to what the young lovers appeared to endure. Mr. Wilmot, who seemed before sufficiently inclined to break off the match, was by this blow soon determined; one virtue he had in perfection, which was prudence, too often the only virtue that is left us unimpaired at seventy-two.

CHAPTER THREE

A migration. The fortunate circumstances of our lives are generally
found at last to be of our own procuring.

The only hope of our family now was that the report of our
misfortunes might be malicious or premature, but a letter
from my agent in town soon came with a confirmation of every particular. The loss of fortune to myself alone would have
been trifling; the only uneasiness I felt was for my family,
who were to be humble without such an education as could
render them callous to contempt.

Near a fortnight passed away before I attempted to restrain
their affliction, for premature consolation is but the remem-
brancer of sorrow. During this interval, my thoughts were employed on some future means of supporting them; and at last
a small Cure of fifteen pounds a year was offered me in a distant neighbourhood, where I could still enjoy my principles
without molestation. With this proposal I joyfully closed, having determined to encrease my salary by managing a little
farm.

Having taken this resolution, my next care was to get together the wrecks of my fortune; and all debts collected and
paid, out of fourteen thousand pounds we had now but four
hundred remaining. My chief attention therefore was next to
bring down the pride of my family to their circumstances; for
I well knew that aspiring beggary is wretchedness itself. "You
can't be ignorant, my children," cried I, "that no prudence of
ours could have prevented our late misfortune; but prudence
may do much in disappointing its effects. We are now poor,
my fondlings, and wisdom bids us conform to our humble situation. Let us then, without repining, give up those splendours with which numbers are wretched, and seek in humbler
circumstances that peace with which all may be happy. The
poor live pleasantly without our help, and we are not so im-
perfectly formed as to be incapable of living without theirs.
No, my children, let us from this moment give up all pretensions to gentility; we have still enough left for happiness if
we are wise, and let us draw upon content for the deficiencies
of fortune."

As my eldest son was bred a scholar, I determined to send him to town, where his abilities might contribute to our support and his own. The separation of friends and families is, perhaps, one of the most distressful circumstances attendant on penury. The day soon arrived on which we were to disperse for the first time. My son, after taking leave of his mother and the rest, who mingled their tears with their kisses, came to ask a blessing from me. This I gave him from my heart, and which, added to five guineas, was all the patrimony I had now to bestow. "You are going, my boy," cried I, "to London on foot in the manner Hooker, your great ancestor, travelled there before you. Take from me the same horse that was given him by the good bishop Jewel, this staff, and take this book too, it will be your comfort on the way; these two lines in it are worth a million: *I have been young, and now am old; yet never saw I the righteous man forsaken, or his seed begging their bread.*[60] Let this be your consolation as you travel on. Go, my boy, whatever be thy fortune let me see thee once a year; still keep a good heart, and farewell." As he was possest of integrity and honour, I was under no apprehensions from throwing him naked into the amphitheatre of life; for I knew he would act a good part whether he rose or fell.

His departure only prepared the way for our own, which arrived a few days afterwards. The leaving a neighbourhood in which we had enjoyed so many hours of tranquility was not without a tear, which scarce fortitude itself could suppress. Besides, a journey of seventy miles to a family that had hitherto never been above ten from home filled us with apprehension, and the cries of the poor, who followed us for some miles, contributed to encrease it. The first day's journey brought us in safety within thirty miles of our future retreat, and we put up for the night at an obscure inn in a village by the way. When we were shewn a room, I desired the landlord, in my usual way, to let us have his company, with which he complied, as what he drank would encrease the bill next morning. He knew, however, the whole neighbourhood to which I was removing, particularly 'Squire Thornhill, who was to be my landlord, and who lived within a few miles of the place. This gentleman he described as one who desired to know little more of the world than the pleasures it afforded, being particularly remarkable for his attachment to the fair sex. He observed that no virtue was able to resist his arts and assiduity, and that scarce a farmer's daughter within ten miles round but what had found him successful and faithless. Though this account gave me some pain, it had a very different effect upon my daughters, whose features seemed to brighten with the expectation of an approaching triumph, nor was my wife less pleased and confident of their allurements and virtue. While our thoughts were thus employed, the hostess entered the room to inform her husband that the strange gentleman who had been two days in the house wanted money and could not satisfy them for his reckoning. "Want money!" replied the host, "that must be impossible; for it was no later than yesterday he paid three guineas to our beadle to spare an old broken soldier that was to be whipped through the town for dog-stealing." The hostess, however, still persisting in her first assertion, he was preparing to leave the room, swearing that he would be satisfied one way or another, when I begged the landlord would introduce me to a stranger of so much charity as he described. With this he complied, shewing in a gentleman who seemed to be about thirty, drest in cloaths that once were laced. His person was well formed, though his face was marked with the lines of thinking. He had something short and dry in his address, and seemed not to understand ceremony, or to despise it. Upon the landlord's leaving the room, I could not avoid expressing my concern to the stranger at seeing a gentleman in such circumstances, and offered him my purse to satisfy the present demand. "I take it with all my heart, Sir," replied he, "and am glad that a late oversight in giving what money I had about me, has shewn me that there is still some benevolence left among us. I must, however, previously entreat being informed of the name and residence of my benefactor, in order to remit it as soon as possible." In this I satisfied him fully, not only mentioning my name and late misfortunes, but the place to which I was going to remove. "This," cried he, "happens still more luckily than I hoped for, as I am going the same way myself, having been detained here two days by the floods, which I hope by to-morrow will be found passable." I testified the pleasure I should have in his company, and my wife and daughters joining in entreaty, he was prevailed upon to stay supper. The stranger's conversation, which was at once pleasing and instructive, induced me to wish for a continuance of it; but it was now high time to retire and take refreshment against the fatigues of the following day.

The next morning we all set forward together: my family on horseback, while Mr. Burchell, our new companion, walked along the foot-path by the road-side, observing with a smile that as we were ill mounted, he would be too generous to attempt leaving us behind. As the floods were not yet subsided we were obliged to hire a guide, who trotted on before, Mr. Burchell and I bringing up the rear. We lightened the fatigues of the road with philosophical disputes, which he seemed to perfectly understand. But what surprised me most was that though he was a money borrower, he defended his opinions with as much obstinacy as if he had been my patron. He now and then also informed me to whom the different seats belonged that lay in our view as we travelled the road. "That," cried he, pointing to a very magnificent house which stood at some distance, "belongs to Mr. Thornhill, a young gentleman who enjoys a large fortune, though entirely dependant on the will of his uncle, Sir William Thornhill, a gentleman who content with a little himself, permits his nephew to enjoy the rest, and chiefly resides in town." "What!" cried I, "is my young landlord then the nephew of a man whose virtues, generosity, and singularities are so universally known? I have heard Sir William Thornhill represented as one of the most generous, yet whimsical, men in the kingdom; a man of consummate benevolence."—"Something, perhaps, too much so," replied Mr. Burchell, "at least he carried benevolence to an excess when young; for his passions were then strong, and as they all were upon the side of virtue, they led it up to a romantic extreme. He early began to aim at the qualifications of the soldier and scholar, was soon distinguished in the army, and had some reputation among men of learning. Adulation ever follows the ambitious; for such alone receive most pleasure from flattery. He was surrounded with crowds who showed him only one side of their character, so that he began to lose a regard for private interest in universal sympathy. He loved all mankind; for fortune prevented him from knowing that there were rascals. Physicians tell us of a disorder in which the whole body is so exquisitely sensible that the slightest touch gives pain; what some have thus suffered in their persons this gentleman felt in his mind. The slightest distress, whether real or fictitious, touched him to the quick, and his soul laboured under a sickly sensibility of the miseries of others. Thus disposed to relieve, it will be easily conjectured, he found numbers disposed to solicit; his profusions began to impair his fortune, but not his good-nature; that, indeed, was seen to encrease as the other seemed to decay; he grew improvident as he grew poor, and though he talked like a man of sense, his actions were those of a fool. Still, however, being surrounded with importunity, and no longer able to satisfy every request that was made him, instead of *money* he gave *promises*. They were all he had to bestow, and he had not resolution enough to give any man pain by a denial. By this means he drew round him crowds of dependants whom he was sure to disappoint, yet wished to relieve. These hung upon him for a time and left him with merited reproaches and contempt. But in proportion as he became contemptible to others, he became despicable to himself. His mind had leaned upon their adulation, and that support taken away, he could find no pleasure in the applause of his heart, which he had never learnt to reverence itself. The world now began to wear a different aspect; the flattery of his friends began to dwindle into simple approbation, that soon took the more friendly form of advice, and advice when rejected ever begets reproaches. He now found that such friends as benefits had gathered round him were by no means the most estimable; it was now found that a man's own heart must be ever given to gain that of another. I now found, that—but I forget what I was going to observe; in short, sir, he resolved to respect himself, and laid down a plan of restoring his shattered fortune. For this purpose, in his own whimsical manner, he travelled through Europe on foot, and before he attained the age of thirty, his circumstances were more affluent than ever. At present therefore, his bounties are more rational and moderate than before; but still he preserves the character of an humourist, and finds most pleasure in eccentric virtues."

My attention was so much taken up by Mr. Burchell's account that I scarce looked forward as we went along, till we were alarmed by the cries of my family, when turning, I perceived my youngest daughter in the midst of a rapid stream, thrown from her horse, and struggling with the torrent. She had sunk twice, nor was it in my power to disengage myself in time to bring her relief. My sensations were even too violent to permit my attempting her rescue; she would have certainly perished had not my companion, perceiving her danger, instantly plunged in to her relief, and, with some difficulty, brought her in safety to the opposite shore. By taking the current a little farther up, the rest of the family got safely over, where we had an opportunity of joining our acknowledgments to her's. Her gratitude may be more readily imagined than described; she thanked her deliverer more with looks than words and continued to lean upon his arm, as if still willing to receive assistance. My wife also hoped one day to have the pleasure of returning his kindness at her own house. Thus, after we were all refreshed at the next inn and had dined together, as he was going to a different part of the country, he took leave; and we pursued our journey. My wife observing as we went, that she liked Mr. Burchell extremely, and protesting that if he had birth and fortune to entitle him to match into such a family as our's, she knew no man she would sooner fix upon. I could not but smile to hear her talk in this strain; one almost at the verge of beggary thus to assume language of the most insulting affluence might excite the ridicule of ill-nature; but I was never much displeased with those innocent delusions that tend to make us more happy.

CHAPTER FOUR

A proof that even the humblest fortune may grant happiness and delight, which depend not on circumstance, but constitution.

The place of our new retreat was in a little neighbourhood, consisting of farmers who tilled their own grounds and were equal strangers to opulence and poverty. As they had almost all the conveniencies of life within themselves, they seldom visited towns or cities in search of superfluity. Remote from the polite, they still retained a primæval simplicity of manners; and frugal by long habit, scarce knew that temperance was a virtue. They wrought with chearfulness on days of labour, but observed festivals as intervals of idleness and pleasure. They kept up the Christmas carol, sent true loveknots on Valentine morning, eat pancakes on Shrovetide, shewed their wit on the first of April, and religiously cracked nuts on Michaelmas eve. Being apprized of our approach, the whole neighbourhood came out to meet their minister, drest in their finest cloaths, and preceded by a pipe and tabor: also a feast was provided for our reception, at which we sat chearfully down; and what the conversation wanted in wit, we made up in laughter.

Our little habitation was situated at the foot of a sloping hill, sheltered with a beautiful underwood behind and a pratling river before; on one side a meadow, on the other a green. My farm consisted of about twenty acres of excellent land, having given an hundred pound for my predecessor's goodwill. Nothing could exceed the neatness of my little enclosures, the elms and hedge rows appearing with inexpressible beauty. My house consisted of but one story and was covered with thatch, which gave it an air of great snugness; the walls on the inside were nicely white-washed, and my daughters undertook to adorn them with pictures of their own designing. Though the same room served us for parlour and kitchen, that only made it the warmer. Besides, as it was kept with the utmost neatness, the dishes, plates, and coppers being well scoured and all disposed in bright rows on the shelves, the eye was agreeably relieved and did not seem to want richer furniture. There were three other apartments, one for my wife and me, another for our two daughters within our own, and the third, with two beds, for the rest of my children.

The little republic to which I gave laws was regulated in the following manner: by sun-rise we all assembled in our common appartment, the fire being previously kindled by the servant. After we had saluted each other with proper ceremony, for I always thought fit to keep up some mechanical forms of good breeding without which freedom ever destroys friendship, we all bent in gratitude to that Being who gave us another day. This duty being performed, my son and I went to pursue our usual industry abroad, while my wife and daughters employed themselves in providing breakfast, which was always ready at a certain time. I allowed half an hour for this meal, and an hour for dinner; which time was taken up in innocent mirth between my wife and daughters, and in philosophical arguments between my son and me.

As we rose with the sun, so we never pursued our labours after it was gone down, but returned home to the expecting family, where smiling looks, a neat hearth, and pleasant fire were prepared for our reception. Nor were we without other guests: sometimes farmer Flamborough, our talkative neighbour, and often the blind piper would pay us a visit and taste our gooseberry wine, for the making of which we had lost neither the receipt nor the reputation. These harmless people had several ways of being good company; while one played the pipes, another would sing some soothing ballad, Johnny Armstrong's last good night, or the cruelty of Barbara Allen. The night was concluded in the manner we began the morning, my youngest boys being appointed to read the lessons of the day; and he that read loudest, distinctest, and best, was to have an halfpenny on Sunday to put in the poor's box.

When Sunday came, it was indeed a day of finery, which all my sumptuary edicts could not restrain. How well so ever I fancied my lectures against pride had conquered the vanity of my daughters, yet I still found them secretly attached to all their former finery; they still loved laces, ribbands, bugles and catgut; my wife herself retained a passion for her crimson paduasoy because I formerly happened to say it became her.

The first Sunday in particular their behaviour served to mortify me. I had desired my girls the preceding night to be drest early the next day, for I always loved to be at church a good while before the rest of the congregation. They punctually obeyed my directions; but when we were to assemble in the morning at breakfast, down came my wife and daughters drest out in all their former splendour: their hair plaistered up with pomatum, their faces patched to taste, their trains bundled up into an heap behind, and rustling at every motion. I could not help smiling at their vanity, particularly that of my wife, from whom I expected more discretion. In this exigence, therefore, my only resource was to order my son, with an important air, to call our coach. The girls were amazed at the command; but I repeated it with more solemnity than before.—"Surely, my dear, you jest," cried my wife; "we can walk it perfectly well: we want no coach to carry us now." —"You mistake, child," returned I, "we do want a coach; for if we walk to church in this trim, the very children in the parish will hoot after us for a show."—"Indeed," replied my wife, "I always imagined that my Charles was fond of seeing his children neat and handsome about him."—"You may be as neat as you please," interrupted I, "and I shall love you the better for it; but all this is not neatness, but frippery. These rufflings, and pinkings, and patchings, will only make us hated by all the wives of all our neighbours. No, my children," continued I, more gravely, "those gowns may be altered into something of a plainer cut; for finery is very unbecoming in us who want the means of decency. I do not know whether such flouncing and shredding is becoming even in the rich, if we consider upon a moderate calculation that the nakedness of the indigent world may be cloathed from the trimmings of the vain."

This remonstrance had the proper effect; they went with great composure, that very instant, to change their dress; and the next day I had the satisfaction of finding my daughters, at their own request, employed in cutting up their trains into Sunday waistcoats for Dick and Bill, the two little ones, and what was still more satisfactory, the gowns seemed improved by being thus curtailed.

CHAPTER FIVE

A new and great acquaintance introduced. *What we place most hopes upon, generally proves most fatal.*

At a small distance from the house my predecessor had made a seat, overshaded by an hedge of hawthorn and honeysuckle. Here, when the weather was fine and our labour soon finished, we usually all sate together, to enjoy an extensive landscape, in the calm of the evening. Here too we drank tea, which now was become an occasional banquet; and as we had it but seldom, it diffused a new joy, the preparations for it being made with no small share of bustle and ceremony. On these occasions, our two little ones always read for us, and they were regularly served after we had done. Sometimes, to give a variety to our amusements, the girls sung to the guitar; and while they thus formed a little concert, my wife and I would stroll down the sloping field that was embellished with blue-bells and centaury, talk of our children with rapture, and enjoy the breeze that wafted both health and harmony.

In this manner we began to find that every situation in life may bring its own peculiar pleasures; every morning waked us to a repetition of toil, but the evening repaid it with vacant hilarity.

It was about the beginning of autumn on a holiday, for I kept such as intervals of relaxation from labour, that I had drawn out my family to our usual place of amusement, and our young musicians began their usual concert. As we were thus engaged, we saw a stag bound nimbly by within about twenty paces of where we were sitting, and by its panting it seemed prest by the hunters. We had not much time to reflect upon the poor animal's distress when we perceived the dogs and horsemen come sweeping along at some distance behind, and making the very path it had taken. I was instantly for returning in with my family; but either curiosity or surprize, or some more hidden motive, held my wife and daughters to their seats. The huntsman, who rode foremost, past us with great swiftness, followed by four or five persons more who seemed in equal haste. At last, a young gentleman of a more genteel appearance than the rest came forward, and for a while regarding us, instead of pursuing the chace, stopt short, and giving his horse to a servant who attended, approached us with a careless superior air. He seemed to want no introduction, but was going to salute my daughters as one certain of a kind reception; but they had early learnt the lesson of looking presumption out of countenance. Upon which he let us know that his name was Thornhill, and that he was owner of the estate that lay for some extent round us. He again, therefore, offered to salute the female part of the family; and such was the power of fortune and fine cloaths that he found no second repulse. As his address, though confident, was easy, we soon became more familiar; and perceiving musical instruments lying near, he begged to be favoured with a song. As I did not approve of such disproportioned acquaintances, I

winked upon my daughters in order to prevent their compliance; but my hint was counteracted by one from their mother,
so that with a chearful air they gave us a favourite song of
Dryden's. Mr. Thornhill seemed highly delighted with their
performance and choice and then took up the guitar himself. He played but very indifferently; however, my eldest
daughter repaid his former applause with interest and assured
him that his tones were louder than even those of her master.
At this compliment he bowed, which she returned with a curtesy. He praised her taste, and she commended his understanding: an age could not have made them better acquainted. While the fond mother, too, equally happy, insisted
upon her landlord's stepping in and tasting a glass of her
gooseberry. The whole family seemed earnest to please him:
my girls attempted to entertain him with topics they thought
most modern, while Moses, on the contrary, gave him a question or two from the ancients, for which he had the satisfaction of being laughed at, for he always ascribed to his wit
that laughter which was lavished at his simplicity; my little
ones were no less busy, and fondly stuck close to the stranger. All my endeavours could scarce keep their dirty fingers
from handling and tarnishing the lace on his cloaths and lifting up the flaps of his pocket holes to see what was there. At
the approach of evening he took leave; but not till he had requested permission to renew his visit, which, as he was our
landlord, we most readily agreed to.

As soon as he was gone, my wife called a council on the
conduct of the day. She was of opinion that it was a most
fortunate hit, for that she had known even stranger things at
last brought to bear. She hoped again to see the day in which
we might hold up our heads with the best of them; and concluded, she protested she could see no reason why the two
Miss Wrinklers should marry great fortunes, and her children
get none. As this last argument was directed to me, I protested I could see no reason for it neither, nor why one got
the ten thousand pound prize in the lottery and another
sate down with a blank. "But those," added I, "who either
aim at husbands greater than themselves or at the ten thousand pound prize have been fools for their ridiculous claims,
whether successful or not."—"I protest, Charles," cried my

wife, "this is the way you always damp my girls and me when we are in Spirits. Tell me, Sophy, my dear, what do you think of our new visitor? Don't you think he seemed to be good-natured?"—"Immensely so, indeed, mamma," replied she. "I think he has a great deal to say upon every thing, and is never at a loss; and the more trifling the subject, the more he has to say; and what is more, I protest he is very handsome."—"Yes," cried Olivia, "he is well enough for a man; but for my part, I don't much like him, he is so extremely impudent and familiar; but on the guitar he is shocking." These two last speeches I interpreted by contraries. I found by this that Sophia internally despised, as much as Olivia secretly admired him.—"Whatever may be your opinions of him, my children," cried I, "to confess a truth, he has not prepossest me in his favour. Disproportioned friendships ever terminate in disgust; and I thought, notwithstanding all his ease, that he seemed perfectly sensible of the distance between us. Let us keep to companions of our own rank. There is no character among men more contemptible than that of a fortune-hunter; and I can see no reason why fortune-hunting women should not be contemptible too. Thus, at best, it will be contempt if his views are honourable; but if they are otherwise! I should shudder but to think of that, for though I have no apprehensions from the conduct of my children, I think there are some from his character."—I would have proceeded but for the interruption of a servant from the 'Squire, who with his compliments sent us a side of venison and a promise to dine with us some days after. This well-timed present pleaded more powerfully in his favour than any thing I had to say could obviate. I therefore continued silent, satisfied with just having pointed out danger, and leaving it to their own discretion to avoid it. That virtue which requires to be ever guarded is scarce worth the centinel.

CHAPTER SIX

The happiness of a country fire-side.

As we carried on the former dispute with some degree of warmth, in order to accommodate matters it was universally concluded upon that we should have a part of the venison for supper, and the girls undertook the task with alacrity. "I am sorry," cried I, "that we have no neighbour or stranger to take part in this good cheer; feasts of this kind acquire a double relish from hospitality."—"Bless me," cried my wife, "here comes our good friend Mr. Burchell, that saved our Sophia, and that run you down fairly in the argument."—"Confute me in argument, child!" cried I. "You mistake there, my dear. I believe there are but few that can do that. I never dispute your abilities at making a goose-pye, and I beg you'll leave argument to me."—As I spoke, poor Mr. Burchell entered the house and was welcomed by the family, who shook him heartily by the hand, while little Dick officiously reached him a chair.

I was pleased with the poor man's friendship for two reasons; because I knew that he wanted mine, and I knew him to be friendly as far as he was able. He was known in our neighbourhood by the character of the poor Gentleman that would do no good when he was young, though he was not yet above thirty. He would at intervals talk with great good sense; but in general he was fondest of the company of children, whom he used to call harmless little men. He was famous, I found, for singing them ballads and telling them stories, and seldom went without something in his pockets for them, a piece of ginger-bread or an halfpenny whistle. He generally came into our neighbourhood once a year and lived upon the neighbours hospitality. He sate down to supper among us, and my wife was not sparing of her gooseberry wine. The tale went round; he sung us old songs, and gave the children the story of the Buck of Beverland, with the history of Patient Grissel. The adventures of Catskin next entertained them, and then Fair Rosamond's bower. Our cock, which always crew at eleven, now told us it was time for repose; but an unforeseen difficulty started about lodging the stranger: all our beds were already taken up, and it was too late to send him to the next alehouse. In this dilemma little Dick offered him his part of the bed if his brother Moses would let him lie with him; "And I," cried Bill, "will give Mr. Burchell my part if my sisters will take me to theirs."— "Well done, my good children," cried I, "hospitality is one of the first christian duties. The beast retires to its shelter, and the bird flies to its nest; but helpless man can only find refuge from his fellow creature. The greatest stranger in this world was he that came to save it. He never had an house, as if willing to see what hospitality was left remaining amongst us. Deborah, my dear," cried I to my wife, "give those boys a lump of sugar each, and let Dick's be the largest, because he spoke first."

In the morning early I called out my whole family to help at saving an after-growth of hay, and our guest offering his assistance, he was accepted among the number. Our labours went on lightly, we turned the swath to the wind, I went foremost, and the rest followed in due succession. I could not avoid, however, observing the assiduity of Mr. Burchell in assisting my daughter Sophia in her part of the task. When he had finished his own, he would join in her's, and enter into a close conversation; but I had too good an opinion of Sophia's understanding and was too well convinced of her ambition to be under any uneasiness from a man of broken fortune. When we were finished for the day, Mr. Burchell was invited as on the night before; but he refused, as he was to lie that night at a neighbour's to whose child he was carrying a whistle. When gone, our conversation at supper turned upon our late unfortunate guest. "What a strong instance," said I, "is that poor man of the miseries attending a youth of levity and extravagance. He by no means wants sense, which only serves to aggravate his former folly. Poor forlorn creature, where are now the revellers, the flatterers, that he could once inspire and command! Gone, perhaps, to attend the bagnio pander, grown rich by his extravagance. They once praised him, and now they applaud the pander; their former raptures at his wit are now converted into sarcasms at his folly; he is poor and perhaps deserves poverty, for he has neither the ambition to be independent, nor the skill to be useful." Prompted perhaps by some secret reasons I delivered this observation with too much acrimony, which my Sophia gently reproved. "Whatsoever his former conduct may be, pappa, his circumstances should exempt him from censure now. His present indigence is a sufficient punishment for former folly; and I have heard my pappa himself say that we should never strike one unnecessary blow at a victim over whom providence already holds the scourge of its resentment."—"You are right, Sophy," cried my son Moses, "and one of the antients finely represents so malicious a conduct by the attempts of a rustic to flay Marsyas, whose skin, the fable tells us, had been wholly stript off by another. Besides I don't know if this poor man's situation be so bad as my father would represent it. We are not to judge of the feelings of others by what we might feel if in their place. However dark the habitation of the mole to our eyes, yet the animal itself finds the apartment sufficiently lightsome. And to confess a truth, this man's mind seems fitted to his station; for I never heard any one more sprightly than he was to-day when he conversed with you." —This was said without the least design; however it excited a blush, which she strove to cover by an affected laugh, assuring him that she scarce took any notice of what he said to her, but that she believed he might once have been a very fine gentleman. The readiness with which she undertook to vindicate herself and her blushing were symptoms I did not internally approve; but I represt my suspicions.

As we expected our landlord the next day, my wife went to make the venison pasty; Moses sate reading, while I taught the little ones; my daughters seemed equally busy with the rest, and I observed them for a good while cooking something over the fire. I at first supposed they were assisting their mother; but little Dick informed me in a whisper that they were making a *wash* for the face. Washes of all kinds I had a natural antipathy to, for I knew that instead of mending the complexion they spoiled it. I therefore approached my chair by sly degrees to the fire, and grasping the poker, as if it wanted mending, seemingly by accident overturned the whole composition, and it was too late to begin another.

CHAPTER SEVEN

A town wit described. The dullest fellows may learn to be comical for a night or two.

When the morning arrived on which we were to entertain our young landlord, it may be easily supposed what provisions were exhausted to make an appearance. It may also be conjectured that my wife and daughters expanded their gayest plumage upon this occasion. Mr. Thornhill came with a couple of friends, his chaplain and feeder.[61] The servants, who were numerous, he politely ordered to the next ale-house, but my wife in the triumph of her heart insisted on entertaining them all, for which, by the bye, our family was pinched for three weeks after. As Mr. Burchell had hinted to us the day before that he was making some proposals of marriage to Miss Wilmot, my son George's former mistress, this a good deal damped the heartiness of his reception, but accident, in some measure, relieved our embarrassment; for one of the company happening to mention her name, Mr. Thornhill observed with an oath that he never knew any thing more absurd than calling such a fright a beauty: "For strike me ugly," continued he, "if I should not find as much pleasure in choosing my mistress by the information of a lamp under the clock at St. Dunstan's." At this he laughed, and so did we—the jests of the rich are ever successful. Olivia too could not avoid whispering, loud enough to be heard, that he had an infinite fund of humour.

After dinner I began with my usual toast, the Church; for this I was thanked by the chaplain, as he said the church was the only mistress of his affections.—"Come tell us honestly, Frank," said the 'Squire with his usual archness, "suppose the church, your present mistress, drest in lawn sleeves on one hand, and Miss Sophia with no lawn about her on the other, which would you be for?" "For both, to be sure," cried the chaplain.—"Right, Frank," cried the 'Squire; "for may this glass suffocate me but a fine girl is worth all the priestcraft in the nation. For what are tythes and tricks but an imposition, all a confounded imposture, and I can prove it."—"I wish you would," cried my son Moses, "and I think," continued he, "that I should be able to combat in the opposition." —"Very well, Sir," cried the 'Squire, who immediately smoaked[62] him, and winking on the rest of the company to prepare us for the sport, "if you are for a cool argument upon that subject, I am ready to accept the challenge. And first, whether are you for managing it analogically or dialogically?" "I am for managing it rationally," cried Moses, quite happy at being permitted to dispute. "Good again," cried the 'Squire; "and firstly, of the first. I hope you'll not deny that whatever

is, is. If you don't grant me that, I can go no further."—
"Why," returned Moses, "I think I may grant that, and make
the best of it."—"I hope too," returned the other, "you'll grant
that a part is less than the whole."—"I grant that too," cried
Moses, "it is but just and reasonable."—"I hope," cried the
'Squire, "you will not deny that the two angles of a triangle
are equal to two right ones."—"Nothing can be plainer," returned t'other, and looked round with his usual importance.
—"Very well," cried the 'Squire, speaking very quick, "the
premises being thus settled, I proceed to observe, that the
concatenation of self existences, proceeding in a reciprocal
duplicate ratio, naturally produce a problematical dialogism,
which in some measure proves that the essence of spir-
ituality may be referred to the second predicable."—"Hold,
hold," cried the other, "I deny that. Do you think I can thus
tamely submit to such heterodox doctrines?"—"What!" replied
the 'Squire, as if in a passion, "not submit! Answer me one
plain question: Do you think Aristotle right when he says
that relatives are related?" "Undoubtedly," replied the other.
—"If so then," cried the 'Squire, "answer me directly to what
I propose: Whether do you judge the analytical investigation
of the first part of my enthymem deficient secundum quoad,
or quoad minus, and give me your reasons too, give me your
reasons, I say, directly."—"I protest," cried Moses, "I don't
rightly comprehend the force of your reasoning; but if it be
reduced to one simple proposition, I fancy it may then have
an answer."—"O, Sir," cried the 'Squire, "I am your most
humble servant, I find you want me to furnish you with argument and intellects both. No, Sir, there I protest you are too
hard for me." This effectually raised the laugh against poor
Moses, who sate the only dismal figure in a groupe of merry
faces; nor did he offer a single syllable more during the whole
entertainment.

But though all this gave me no pleasure, it had a very different effect upon Olivia, who mistook this humour, which
was a mere act of memory, for real wit. She thought him
therefore a very fine gentleman; and such as consider what
powerful ingredients a good figure, fine cloaths, and fortune
are in that character will easily forgive her. Mr. Thornhill,
notwithstanding his real ignorance, talked with ease, and

could expatiate upon the common topics of conversation with fluency. It is not surprising then that such talents should win the affections of a girl who by education was taught to value an appearance in herself, and consequently to set a value upon it when found in another.

Upon his departure we again entered into a debate upon the merits of our young landlord. As he directed his looks and conversation to Olivia, it was no longer doubted but that she was the object that induced him to be our visitor. Nor did she seem to be much displeased at the innocent raillery of her brother and sister upon this occasion. Even Deborah herself seemed to share the glory of the day, and exulted in her daughter's victory as if it were her own. "And now, my dear," cried she to me, "I'll fairly own that it was I that instructed my girls to encourage our landlord's addresses. I had always some ambition, and you now see that I was right; for who knows how this may end?" "Ay, who knows that indeed," answered I, with a groan: "for my own part I don't much like it; and I could have been better pleased with one that was poor and honest than this fine gentleman with his fortune and infidelity; for depend on't, if he be what I suspect him, no free-thinker shall ever have a child of mine."

"Sure, father," cried Moses, "you are too severe in this; for heaven will never arraign him for what he thinks, but for what he does. Every man has a thousand vicious thoughts which arise without his power to suppress. Thinking freely of religion may be involuntary with this gentleman: so that allowing his sentiments to be wrong, yet as he is purely passive in their reception he is no more to be blamed for their incursions than the governor of a city without walls for the shelter he is obliged to afford an invading enemy."

"True, my son," cried I; "but if the governor invites the enemy, there he is justly culpable. And such is always the case with those who embrace error. The vice does not lie in assenting to the proofs they see; but in being blind to many of the proofs that offer. Like corrupt judges on a bench, they determine right on that part of the evidence they hear; but they will not hear all the evidence. Thus, my son, though our erroneous opinions be involuntary when formed, yet as we have been wilfully corrupt or very negligent in forming them, we deserve punishment for our vice or contempt for our folly."

My wife now kept up the conversation, though not the argument; she observed that several very prudent men of our acquaintance were free-thinkers and made very good husbands; and she knew some sensible girls that had skill enough to make converts of their spouses: "And who knows, my dear," continued she, "what Olivia may be able to do. The girl has a great deal to say upon every subject, and to my knowledge is very well skilled in controversy."

"Why, my dear, what controversy can she have read?" cried I. "It does not occur to my memory that I ever put such books into her hands; you certainly over-rate her merit."—"Indeed, pappa," replied Olivia, "she does not. I have read a great deal of controversy. I have read the disputes between Thwackum and Square; the controversy between Robinson Crusoe and Friday the savage, and I am now employed in reading the controversy in Religious courtship." [63]—"Very well," cried I, "that's a good girl. I find you are perfectly qualified for making converts, and so go help your mother to make the gooseberry-pye."

CHAPTER EIGHT

An amour, which promises little good fortune, yet may be productive of much.

The next morning we were again visited by Mr. Burchell, though I began, for certain reasons, to be displeased with the frequency of his return; but I could not refuse him my company and fire-side. It is true his labour more than requited his entertainment; for he wrought among us with vigour, and either in the meadow or at the hay-rick put himself foremost. Besides, he had always something amusing to say that lessened our toil, and was at once so out of the way and yet so sensible, that I loved, laughed at, and pitied him. My only dislike arose from an attachment he discovered to my daughter; he would, in a jesting manner, call her his little mistress, and when he bought each of the girls a set of ribbands, her's was the finest. I knew not how, but he every day seemed to become more amiable, his wit to improve, and his simplicity to assume the superior airs of wisdom.

Our family dined in the field, and we sate, or rather reclined, round a temperate repast, our cloth spread upon the hay, while Mr. Burchell seemed to give chearfulness to the feast. To heighten our satisfaction two blackbirds answered each other from opposite hedges, the familiar redbreast came and pecked the crumbs from our hands, and every sound seemed but the echo of tranquillity. "I never sit thus," says Sophia, "but I think of the two lovers, so sweetly described by Mr. Gay, who were struck dead in each other's arms under a barley mow. There is something so pathetic in the description that I have read it an hundred times with new rapture." —"In my opinion," cried my son, "the finest strokes in that description are much below those in the Acis and Galatea of Ovid. The Roman poet understands the use of *contrast* better, and upon that figure artfully managed all strength in the pathetic depends."—"It is remarkable," cried Mr. Burchell, "that both the poets you mention have equally contributed to introduce a false taste into their respective countries, by loading all their lines with epithet. Men of little genius found them most easily imitated in their defects, and English poetry, like that in the latter empire of Rome, is nothing at present but a combination of luxuriant images without plot or connexion, a string of epithets that improve the sound without carrying on the sense. But perhaps, madam, while I thus reprehend others, you'll think it just that I should give them an opportunity to retaliate, and indeed I have made this remark only to have an opportunity of introducing to the company a ballad which, whatever be its other defects, is I think at least free from those I have mentioned."

A BALLAD

"Turn, gentle hermit of the dale,
   And guide my lonely way,
To where yon taper cheers the vale,
   With hospitable ray.

"For here, forlorn and lost I tread,
  With fainting steps and slow;
Where wilds immeasurably spread,
  Seem lengthening as I go."

"Forbear, my son," the hermit cries,
  "To tempt the dangerous gloom;
For yonder phantom only flies
  To lure thee to thy doom.

"Here to the houseless child of want,
  My door is open still;
And tho' my portion is but scant,
  I give it with good will.

"Then turn to-night, and freely share
  Whate'er my cell bestows;
My rushy couch, and frugal fare,
  My blessing and repose.

"No flocks that range the valley free,
  To slaughter I condemn:
Taught by that power that pities me,
  I learn to pity them.

"But from the mountain's grassy side
  A guiltless feast I bring;
A scrip with herbs and fruits supply'd,
  And water from the spring.

"Then, pilgrim, turn, thy cares forego;
  All earth-born cares are wrong:
Man wants but little here below,
  Nor wants that little long."

Soft as the dew from heav'n descends,
  His gentle accents fell:
The grateful stranger lowly bends,
  And follows to the cell.

Far shelter'd in a glade obscure
   The modest mansion lay;
A refuge to the neighbouring poor
   And strangers led astray.

No stores beneath its humble thatch
   Requir'd a master's care;
The door just opening with a latch,
   Receiv'd the harmless pair.

And now when worldly crowds retire
   To revels or to rest,
The hermit trimm'd his little fire,
   And cheer'd his pensive guest;

And spread his vegetable store,
   And gayly prest, and smil'd,
And skill'd in legendary lore,
   The lingering hours beguil'd.

Around in sympathetic mirth
   Its tricks the kitten tries,
The cricket chirrups in the hearth;
   The crackling faggot flies.

But nothing could a charm impart
   To sooth the stranger's woe;
For grief was heavy at his heart,
   And tears began to flow.

His rising cares the hermit spy'd,
   With answering care opprest:
"And whence, unhappy youth," he cry'd,
   "The sorrows of thy breast?

"From better habitations spurn'd,
   Reluctant dost thou rove;
Or grieve for friendship unreturn'd,
   Or unregarded love?

"Alas! the joys that fortune brings
    Are trifling, and decay;
And those who prize the paltry things,
    More trifling still than they.

"And what is friendship but a name,
    A charm that lulls to sleep;
A shade that follows wealth or fame,
    But leaves the wretch to weep?

"And love is still an emptier sound,
    The haughty fair one's jest,
On earth unseen, or only found
    To warm the turtle's nest.

"For shame, fond youth, thy sorrows hush,
    And spurn the sex," he said:
But, while he spoke, a rising blush
    The bashful guest betray'd.

He sees unnumber'd beauties rise
    Expanding to the view,
Like clouds that deck the morning skies,
    As bright, as transient too.

Her looks, her lips, her panting breast
    Alternate spread alarms,
The lovely stranger stands confest
    A maid in all her charms.

And "ah, forgive a stranger rude,
    A wretch forlorn," she cry'd,
"Whose feet unhallowed thus intrude
    Where heaven and you reside.

"But let a maid thy pity share,
    Whom love has taught to stray;
Who seeks for rest, but finds despair
    Companion of her way.

"My father liv'd beside the Tyne,
    A wealthy Lord was he;
And all his wealth was mark'd as mine,
    He had but only me.

"To win me from his tender arms,
    Unnumber'd suitors came;
Who prais'd me for imputed charms,
    And felt or feign'd a flame.

"Each morn the gay phantastic crowd
    With richest proffers strove:
Amongst the rest young Edwin bow'd,
    But never talk'd of love.

"In humble simplest habit clad,
    No wealth nor power had he;
A constant heart was all he had,
    But that was all to me.

"The blossom opening to the day,
    The dews of heaven refin'd,
Could nought of purity display
    To emulate his mind.

"The dew, the blossom on the tree,
    With charms inconstant shine;
Their charms were his, but woe to me,
    Their constancy was mine.

"For still I try'd each fickle art,
    Importunate and vain;
And while his passion touch'd my heart,
    I triumph'd in his pain.

"Till quite dejected with my scorn,
    He left me to my pride;
And sought a solitude forlorn,
    In secret where he died.

"But mine the sorrow, mine the fault,
    And well my life shall pay,
I'll seek the solitude he sought,
    And stretch me where he lay—

"And there forlorn despairing hid,
    I'll lay me down and die:
'Twas so for me that Edwin did,
    And so for him will I."

"Thou shalt not thus," the hermit cry'd,
    And clasp'd her to his breast:
The wondering fair one turn'd to chide,
    'Twas Edwin's self that prest.

"Turn, Angelina, ever dear,
    My charmer, turn to see,
Thy own, thy long-lost Edwin here,
    Restor'd to love and thee.

"Thus let me hold thee to my heart,
    And every care resign:
And shall we never, never part,
    O thou,—my all that's mine.

"No, never, from this hour to part,
    We'll live and love so true;
The sigh that rends thy constant heart,
    Shall break thy Edwin's too."

While this ballad was reading, Sophia seemed to mix an air of tenderness with her approbation. But our tranquillity was soon disturbed by the report of a gun just by us, and immediately after a man was seen bursting through the hedge to take up the game he had killed. This sportsman was the 'Squire's chaplain, who had shot one of the blackbirds that so agreeably entertained us. So loud a report, and so near, startled my daughters; and I could perceive that Sophia in the fright had thrown herself into Mr. Burchell's arms for protection. The gentleman came up and asked pardon for having disturbed us, affirming that he was ignorant of our being so near. He therefore sate down by my youngest daughter, and sportsman like offered her what he had killed that morning. She was going to refuse, but a private look from her mother soon induced her to correct the mistake and accept his present, though with some reluctance. My wife, as usual, discovered her pride in a whisper, observing that Sophy had made a conquest of the chaplain as well as her sister had of the 'Squire. I suspected, however, with more probability, that her affections were placed upon a different object. The chaplain's errand was to inform us that Mr. Thornhill had provided music and refreshments and intended that night giving the young ladies a ball by moon-light on the grass-plot before our door. "Nor can I deny," continued he, "but I have an interest in being first to deliver this message, as I expect for my reward to be honoured with Miss Sophy's hand as a partner." To this my girl replied that she should have no objection, if she could do it with honour: "But here," continued she, "is a gentleman," looking at Mr. Burchell, "who has been my companion in the task for the day, and it is fit he should share in its amusements." Mr. Burchell returned her a compliment for her intentions; but resigned her up to the chaplain, adding that he was to go that night five miles, being invited to an harvest supper. His refusal appeared to me a little extraordinary, nor could I conceive how so sensible a girl as my youngest could thus prefer a middle aged man of broken fortune to a sprightly young fellow of twenty-two. But as men are most capable of distinguishing merit in women, so the ladies often form the truest judgments upon us. The two sexes seem placed as spies upon each other, and are furnished with different abilities, adapted for mutual inspection.

CHAPTER NINE

Two ladies of great distinction introduced. Superior finery ever seems to confer superior breeding.

Mr. Burchell had scarce taken leave, and Sophia consented to dance with the chaplain, when my little ones came running out to tell us that the 'Squire was come with a crowd of company. Upon our return we found our landlord with a couple of un-

der gentlemen and two young ladies richly drest, whom he introduced as women of very great distinction and fashion from
town. We happened not to have chairs enough for the whole
company; but Mr. Thornhill immediately proposed that every gentleman should sit in a lady's lap. This I positively objected to, notwithstanding a look of disapprobation from my
wife. Moses was therefore dispatched to borrow a couple of
chairs; and as we were in want of ladies also to make up a
set at country dances, the two gentlemen went with him in
quest of a couple of partners. Chairs and partners were
soon provided. The gentlemen returned with my neighbour
Flamborough's rosy daughters, flaunting with red top-knots.
But there was an unlucky circumstance which was not adverted
to; though the Miss Flamboroughs were reckoned the very
best dancers in the parish and understood the jig and the
round-about to perfection, yet they were totally unacquainted
with country dances. This at first discomposed us; however,
after a little shoving and dragging, they began to go merrily
on. Our music consisted of two fiddles, with a pipe and tabor.
The moon shone bright, Mr. Thornhill and my eldest daughter led up the ball, to the great delight of the spectators; for
the neighbours hearing what was going forward came flocking
about us. My girl moved with so much grace and vivacity that
my wife could not avoid discovering the pride of her heart
by assuring me that though the little chit did it so cleverly,
all the steps were stolen from herself. The ladies of the town
strove hard to be equally easy, but without success. They
swam, sprawled, languished, and frisked; but all would not do;
the gazers indeed owned that it was fine, but neighbour Flamborough observed that Miss Livy's feet seemed as pat to the
music as its echo. After the dance had continued about an
hour, the two ladies, who were apprehensive of catching cold,
moved to break up the ball. One of them, I thought, expressed
her sentiments upon this occasion in a very coarse manner,
when she observed that by the *living jingo, she was all of a
muck of sweat.* Upon our return to the house, we found a very
elegant cold supper which Mr. Thornhill had ordered to be
brought with him. The conversation at this time was more reserved than before. The two ladies threw my girls quite into
the shade, for they would talk of nothing but high life and

high lived company, with other fashionable topics, such as pictures, taste, Shakespear, and the musical glasses. 'Tis true they once or twice mortified us sensibly by slipping out an oath; but that appeared to me as the surest symptom of their distinction, (tho' I am since informed swearing is now perfectly unfashionable.) Their finery, however, threw a veil over any grossness in their conversation. My daughters seemed to regard their superior accomplishments with envy, and what appeared amiss was ascribed to tip-top quality breeding. But the condescension of the ladies was still superior to their other accomplishments. One of them observed that had Miss Olivia seen a little more of the world, it would greatly improve her. To which the other added that a single winter in town would make her little Sophia quite another thing. My wife warmly assented to both, adding that there was nothing she more ardently wished than to give her girls a single winter's polishing. To this I could not help replying that their breeding was already superior to their fortune, and that greater refinement would only serve to make their poverty ridiculous and give them a taste for pleasures they had no right to possess.—"And what pleasures," cried Mr. Thornhill, "do they not deserve, who have so much in their power to bestow? As for my part," continued he, "my fortune is pretty large; love, liberty, and pleasure are my maxims; but curse me if a settlement of half my estate could give my charming Olivia pleasure, it should be hers; and the only favour I would ask in return would be to add myself to the benefit." I was not such a stranger to the world as to be ignorant that this was the fashionable cant to disguise the insolence of the basest proposal, but I made an effort to suppress my resentment. "Sir," cried I, "the family which you now condescend to favour with your company has been bred with as nice a sense of honour as you. Any attempts to injure that, may be attended with very dangerous consequences. Honour, Sir, is our only possession at present, and of that last treasure we must be particularly careful."—I was soon sorry for the warmth with which I had spoken this, when the young gentleman, grasping my hand, swore he commended my spirit, though he disapproved my suspicions. "As to your present hint," continued he, "I protest nothing was farther from my heart than such a thought. No, by all that's tempting, the virtue that will stand a regular siege was never to my taste; for all my amours are carried by a coup de main."

The two ladies, who affected to be ignorant of the rest, seemed highly displeased with this last stroke of freedom, and began a very discreet and serious dialogue upon virtue; in this my wife, the chaplain, and I soon joined; and the 'Squire himself was at last brought to confess a sense of sorrow for his former excesses. We talked of the pleasures of temperance, and the sun-shine in the mind unpolluted with guilt. I was well pleased that my little ones were kept up beyond the usual time to be edified by such good conversation. Mr. Thornhill even went beyond me, and demanded if I had any objection to giving prayers. I joyfully embraced the proposal, and in this manner the night was passed in a most comfortable way, till at last the company began to think of returning. The ladies seemed very unwilling to part from my daughters, for whom they had conceived a particular affection, and joined in a request to have the pleasure of their company home. The 'Squire seconded the proposal, and my wife added her entreaties; the girls too looked upon me as if they wished to go. In this perplexity I made two or three excuses, which my daughters as readily removed; so that at last I was obliged to give a peremptory refusal, for which we had nothing but sullen looks and short answers the whole day ensuing.

CHAPTER TEN

The family endeavours to cope with their betters. The miseries of the poor when they attempt to appear above their circumstances.

I now began to find that all my long and painful lectures upon temperance, simplicity, and contentment, were entirely disregarded. The distinctions lately paid us by our betters awaked that pride which I had laid asleep, but not removed. Our windows now again, as formerly, were filled with washes for the neck and face. The sun was dreaded as an enemy to the skin without doors, and the fire as a spoiler of the complexion within. My wife observed that rising too early would hurt her daughters' eyes, that working after dinner would redden their noses, and convinced me that the hands never

looked so white as when they did nothing. Instead therefore
of finishing George's shirts, we now had them new modelling
their old gauzes, or flourishing upon catgut. The poor Miss
Flamboroughs, their former gay companions, were cast off as
mean acquaintance, and the whole conversation ran upon
high life and high lived company, with pictures, taste, Shakespear, and the musical glasses.

But we could have borne all this, had not a fortune-telling
gypsey come to raise us into perfect sublimity. The tawney
sybil no sooner appeared than my girls came running to me
for a shilling a piece to cross her hand with silver. To say
the truth I was tired of being always wise, and could not help
gratifying their request, because I loved to see them happy. I
gave each of them a shilling; though for the honour of the
family it must be observed that they never went without
money themselves, as my wife always generously let them
have a guinea each to keep in their pockets, but with strict in-
junctions never to change it. After they had been closetted up
with the fortune-teller for some time, I knew by their looks
upon their returning that they had been promised something
great.—"Well, my girls, how have you sped? Tell me, Livy,
has the fortune-teller given thee a pennyworth?"—"I protest,
pappa," says the girl, with a serious face, "I believe she deals
with some body that's not right; for she positively declared
that I am to be married to a great 'Squire in less than a
twelvemonth!"—"Well, now, Sophy, my child," said I, "and
what sort of a husband are you to have?" "Sir," replied she, "I
am to have a Lord soon after my sister has been married to
the 'Squire."—"How," cried I, "is that all you are to have for
your two shillings! Only a Lord and a 'Squire for two shillings! You fools, I could have promised you a Prince and a
Nabob for half the money."

This curiosity of theirs, however, was attended with very
serious effects; we now began to think ourselves designed by
the stars to something exalted, and already anticipated our
future grandeur.

It has been a thousand times observed, and I must observe it
once more, that the hours we pass with happy prospects in
view are more pleasing than those crowned with fruition. In
the first case we cook the dish to our own appetite; in the

latter nature cooks it for us. It is impossible to repeat the train of agreeable reveries we called up for our entertainment. We looked upon our fortunes as once more rising; and as the whole parish asserted that the 'Squire was in love with my daughter, she was actually so with him; for they persuaded her into passion. In this agreeable interval my wife had the most lucky dreams in the world, which she took care to tell us every morning with great solemnity and exactness. It was one night a coffin and cross bones, the sign of an approaching wedding; at another time she imagined her daughter's pockets filled with farthings, a certain sign of their being one day stuffed with gold. The girls had their omens too; they felt strange kisses on their lips; they saw rings in the candle, purses bounced from the fire, and true love-knots lurked in the bottom of every tea-cup.

Towards the end of the week we received a card from the town ladies, in which, with their compliments, they hoped to see all our family at church the Sunday following. All Saturday morning I could perceive, in consequence of this, my wife and daughters in close conference together, and now and then glancing at me with looks that betrayed a latent plot. To be sincere, I had strong suspicions that some absurd proposal was preparing for appearing with splendor the next day. In the evening they began their operations in a very regular manner, and my wife undertook to conduct the siege. After tea, when I seemed in spirits, she began thus.—"I fancy, Charles, my dear, we shall have a great deal of good company at our church to-morrow."—"Perhaps we may, my dear," returned I; "though you need be under no uneasiness about that, you shall have a sermon whether there be or not." —"That is what I expect," returned she; "but I think, my dear, we ought to appear there as decently as possible, for who knows what may happen?" "Your precautions," replied I, "are highly commendable. A decent behaviour and appearance in church is what charms me. We should be devout, and humble, chearful and serene."—"Yes," cried she, "I know that; but I mean we should go there in as proper a manner as possible; not altogether like the scrubs about us." "You are quite right, my dear," returned I, "and I was going to make the very same proposal. The proper manner of going is to go there as early as possible, to have time for meditation before the service begins."—"Phoo, Charles," interrupted she, "all that is very true; but not what I would be at. I mean, we should go there genteelly. You know the church is two miles off, and I protest I don't like to see my daughters trudging up to their pew all blowzed and red with walking, and looking for all the world as if they had been winners at a smock race. Now, my dear, my proposal is this: there are our two plow horses, the Colt that has been in our family these nine years and his companion Blackberry, that have scarce done an earthly thing for this month past and are both grown fat and lazy. Why should not they do something as well as we? And let me tell you, when Moses has trimmed them a little, they will not be so contemptible."

To this proposal I objected that walking would be twenty times more genteel than such a paltry conveyance, as Blackberry was wall-eyed and the Colt wanted a tail; that they had never been broke to the rein, but had an hundred vicious tricks; and that we had but one saddle and pillion in the whole house. All these objections, however, were over-ruled, so that I was obliged to comply. The next morning I perceived them not a little busy in collecting such materials as might be necessary for the expedition; but as I found it would be a business of much time, I walked on to the church before, and they promised speedily to follow. I waited near an hour in the reading desk for their arrival; but not finding them come as expected, I was obliged to begin, and went through the service not without some uneasiness at finding them absent. This was encreased when all was finished and no appearance of the family. I therefore walked back by the horse-way, which was five miles round, tho' the foot-way was but two, and when got about half way home, perceived the procession marching slowly forward towards the church, my son, my wife, and the two little ones exalted upon one horse, and my two daughters upon the other. I demanded the cause of their delay; but I soon found by their looks they had met with a thousand misfortunes on the road. The horses had at first refused to move from the door, till Mr. Burchell was kind enough to beat them forward for about two hundred yards with his cudgel. Next the straps of my wife's pillion broke down, and they were obliged to stop to repair them before they could proceed. After that, one of the horses took it into his head to stand still, and neither blows nor entreaties could prevail with him to proceed. It was just recovering from this dismal situation that I found them; but perceiving every thing safe, I own their present mortification did not much displease me, as it would give me many opportunities of future triumph, and teach my daughters more humility.

CHAPTER ELEVEN

The family still resolve to hold up their heads.

Michaelmas eve happening on the next day, we were invited to burn nuts and play tricks at neighbour Flamborough's. Our late mortifications had humbled us a little, or it is probable we might have rejected such an invitation with contempt; however, we suffered ourselves to be happy. Our honest neighbour's goose and dumplings were fine, and the lamb's-wool,[64] even in the opinion of my wife, who was a connoisseur, was thought excellent. It is true, his manner of telling stories was not quite so well. They were very long, and very dull, and all about himself, and we had laughed at them ten times before; however, we were kind enough to laugh at them once more.

Mr. Burchell, who was of the party, was always fond of seeing some innocent amusement going forward, and set the boys and girls to blind man's buff. My wife too was persuaded to join in the diversion, and it gave me pleasure to think she was not yet too old. In the mean time, my neighbour and I looked on, laughed at every feat, and praised our own dexterity when we were young. Hot cockles succeeded next, questions and commands followed that, and last of all they sate down to hunt the slipper. As every person may not be acquainted with this primæval pastime, it may be necessary to observe that the company at this play plant themselves in a ring upon the ground, all except one who stands in the middle, whose business it is to catch a shoe which the company shove about under their hams from one to another, something like a weaver's shuttle. As it is impossible, in this case, for the lady who is up to face all the company at once, the great beauty of the play lies in hitting her a thump with the heel of the shoe on that side least capable of making a defence. It was in this manner that my eldest daughter was hemmed in, and thumped about, all blowzed, in spirits, and bawling for fair play, fair play, with a voice that might deafen a ballad singer, when confusion on confusion, who should enter the room but our two great acquaintances from town, Lady Blarney and Miss Carolina Wilelmina Amelia Skeggs! Description would but beggar, therefore it is unnecessary to describe this new mortification. Death! To be seen by ladies of such high breeding in such vulgar attitudes! Nothing better could ensue from such a vulgar play of Mr. Flamborough's proposing. We seemed stuck to the ground for some time, as if actually petrified with amazement.

The two ladies had been at our house to see us, and finding us from home, came after us hither, as they were uneasy to know what accident could have kept us from church the day before. Olivia undertook to be our prolocutor and delivered the whole in a summary way, only saying, "We were thrown from our horses." At which account the ladies were greatly concerned; but being told the family received no hurt, they were extremely glad; but being informed that we were almost killed by the fright, they were vastly sorry; but hearing that we had a very good night, they were extremely glad again. Nothing could exceed their complaisance to my daughters; their professions the last evening were warm, but now they were ardent. They protested a desire of having a more lasting acquaintance. Lady Blarney was particularly attached to Olivia; Miss Carolina Wilelmina Amelia Skeggs (I love to give the whole name) took a greater fancy to her sister. They supported the conversation between themselves, while my daughters sate silent, admiring their exalted breeding. But as every reader, however beggarly himself, is fond of high-lived dialogues, with anecdotes of Lords, Ladies, and Knights of the Garter, I must beg leave to give him the concluding part of the present conversation.

"All that I know of the matter," cried Miss Skeggs, "is this, that it may be true, or it may not be true; but this I can assure your Ladyship, that the whole rout was in amaze; his Lordship turned all manner of colours, my Lady fell into a swoon;

but Sir Tomkyn, drawing his sword, swore he was hers to the last drop of his blood."

"Well," replied our Peeress, "this I can say, that the Dutchess never told me a syllable of the matter, and I believe her Grace would keep nothing a secret from me. But this you may depend on as fact, that the next morning my Lord Duke cried out three times to his valet de chambre, Jernigan, Jernigan, Jernigan, bring me my garters."

But previously I should have mentioned the very impolite behaviour of Mr. Burchell, who, during this discourse, sate with his face turned to the fire, and at the conclusion of every sentence would cry out *fudge,* an expression which displeased us all and in some measure damped the rising spirit of the conversation.

"Besides, my dear Skeggs," continued our Peeress, "there is nothing of this in the copy of verses that Dr. Burdock made upon the occasion." [*Fudge!*]

"I am surprised at that," cried Miss Skeggs; "for he seldom leaves any thing out, as he writes only for his own amusement. But can your Ladyship favour me with a sight of them?" [*Fudge!*]

"My dear creature," replied our Peeress, "do you think I carry such things about me? Though they are very fine to be sure, and I think myself something of a judge; at least I know what pleases myself. Indeed I was ever an admirer of all Doctor Burdock's little pieces; for except what he does, and our dear Countess at Hanover-Square, there's nothing comes out but the most lowest stuff in nature; not a bit of high life among them." [*Fudge!*]

"Your Ladyship should except," says t'other, "your own things in the Lady's Magazine. I hope you'll say there's nothing low lived there? But I suppose we are to have no more from that quarter?" [*Fudge!*]

"Why, my dear," says the Lady, "you know my reader and companion has left me, to be married to Captain Roch, and as my poor eyes won't suffer me to write myself, I have been for some time looking out for another. A proper person is no easy matter to find, and to be sure thirty pounds a year is a small stipend for a well-bred girl of character that can read, write, and behave in company; as for the chits about town, there is no bearing them about one." [*Fudge!*]

"That I know," cried Miss Skeggs, "by experience. For of the three companions I had this last half year, one of them refused to do plain-work an hour in the day, another thought twenty-five guineas a year too small a salary, and I was obliged to send away the third, because I suspected an intrigue with the chaplain. Virtue, my dear Lady Blarney, virtue is worth any price; but where is that to be found?" [*Fudge!*]

My wife had been for a long time all attention to this discourse; but was particularly struck with the latter part of it. Thirty pounds and twenty-five guineas a year made fifty-six pounds five shillings English money, all which was in a manner going a-begging, and might easily be secured in the family. She for a moment studied my looks for approbation; and, to own a truth, I was of opinion that two such places would fit our two daughters exactly. Besides, if the 'Squire had any real affection for my eldest daughter, this would be the way to make her every way qualified for her fortune. My wife therefore was resolved that we should not be deprived of such advantages for want of assurance and undertook to harangue for the family. "I hope," cried she, "your Ladyships will pardon my present presumption. It is true we have no right to pretend to such favours; but yet it is natural for me to wish putting my children forward in the world. And I will be bold to say my two girls have had a pretty good education, and capacity, at least the country can't shew better. They can read, write, and cast accompts; they understand their needle, breadstitch, cross and change, and all manner of plain-work; they can pink, point, and frill; and know something of music; they can do up small cloaths, work upon catgut; my eldest can cut paper, and my youngest has a very pretty manner of telling fortunes upon the cards." [*Fudge!*]

When she had delivered this pretty piece of eloquence, the two ladies looked at each other a few minutes in silence, with an air of doubt and importance. At last Miss Carolina Wilelmina Amelia Skeggs condescended to observe that the young ladies, from the opinion she could form of them from so slight an acquaintance, seemed very fit for such employments,

"But a thing of this kind, Madam," cried she, addressing my spouse, "requires a thorough examination into characters and a more perfect knowledge of each other. Not, Madam," continued she, "that I in the least suspect the young ladies virtue, prudence and discretion; but there is a form in these things, Madam, there is a form."

My wife approved her suspicions very much, observing that she was very apt to be suspicious herself, but referred her to all the neighbours for a character; but this our Peeress declined as unnecessary, alledging that her cousin Thornhill's recommendation would be sufficient, and upon this we rested our petition.

CHAPTER TWELVE

Fortune seems resolved to humble the family of Wakefield.
Mortifications are often more painful than real calamities.

When we were returned home, the night was dedicated to schemes of future conquest. Deborah exerted much sagacity in conjecturing which of the two girls was likely to have the best place, and most opportunities of seeing good company. The only obstacle to our preferment was in obtaining the 'Squire's recommendation; but he had already shewn us too many instances of his friendship to doubt of it now. Even in bed my wife kept up the usual theme: "Well, faith, my dear Charles, between ourselves, I think we have made an excellent day's work of it."—"Pretty well," cried I, not knowing what to say.—"What only pretty well!" returned she. "I think it is very well. Suppose the girls should come to make acquaintances of taste in town! And this I am assured of, that London is the only place in the world for all manner of husbands. Besides, my dear, stranger things happen every day; and as ladies of quality are so taken with my daughters, what will not men of quality be! Entre nous, I protest I like my Lady Blarney vastly, so very obliging. However, Miss Carolina Wilelmina Amelia Skeggs has my warm heart. But yet, when they came to talk of places in town, you saw at once how I nailed them. Tell me, my dear, don't you think I did for my children there?"—"Ay," returned I, not knowing well what to think of the matter, "heaven grant they may be both the better for it this day three months!" This was one of those observations I usually made to impress my wife with an opinion of my sagacity; for if the girls succeeded, then it was a pious wish fulfilled; but if any thing unfortunate ensued, then it might be looked upon as a prophecy. All this conversation, however, was only preparatory to another scheme, and indeed I dreaded as much. This was nothing less than that as we were now to hold up our heads a little higher in the world, it would be proper to sell the Colt, which was grown old, at a neighbouring fair, and buy us an horse that would carry single or double upon an occasion, and make a pretty appearance at church or upon a visit. This at first I opposed stoutly; but it was as stoutly defended. However, as I weakened, my antagonist gained strength, till at last it was resolved to part with him.

As the fair happened on the following day, I had intentions of going myself; but my wife persuaded me that I had got a cold, and nothing could prevail upon her to permit me from home. "No, my dear," said she, "our son Moses is a discreet boy, and can buy and sell to very good advantage; you know all our great bargains are of his purchasing. He always stands out and higgles, and actually tires them till he gets a bargain."

As I had some opinion of my son's prudence, I was willing enough to entrust him with this commission; and the next morning I perceived his sisters mighty busy in fitting out Moses for the fair; trimming his hair, brushing his buckles, and cocking his hat with pins. The business of the toilet being over, we had at last the satisfaction of seeing him mounted upon the Colt, with a deal box before him to bring home groceries in. He had on a coat made of that cloth they call thunder and lightning, which, though grown too short, was much too good to be thrown away. His waistcoat was of gosling green, and his sisters had tied his hair with a broad black ribband. We all followed him several paces from the door, bawling after him, good luck, good luck, till we could see him no longer.

He was scarce gone, when Mr. Thornhill's butler came to

congratulate us upon our good fortune, saying that he over-
heard his young master mention our names with great commendations.

Good fortune seemed resolved not to come alone. Another
footman from the same family followed with a card for my
daughters, importing that the two ladies had received such a
pleasing account from Mr. Thornhill of us all, that, after a
few previous enquiries more, they hoped to be perfectly satisfied. "Ay," cried my wife, "I now see it is no easy matter to
get into the families of the great; but when one once gets in,
then, as Moses says, they may go sleep." To this piece of humour, for she intended it for wit, my daughters assented with
a loud laugh of pleasure. In short, such was her satisfaction at
this message that she actually put her hand to her pocket,
and gave the messenger seven-pence halfpenny.

This was to be our visiting-day. The next that came was Mr.
Burchell, who had been at the fair. He brought my little ones
a pennyworth of gingerbread each, which my wife undertook
to keep for them, and give them by letters at a time. He
brought my daughters also a couple of boxes in which they
might keep wafers, snuff, patches, or even money, when they
got it. My wife was usually fond of a weesel skin purse, as being the most lucky; but this by the bye. We had still a regard
for Mr. Burchell, though his late rude behaviour was in some
measure displeasing; nor could we now avoid communicating
our happiness to him and asking his advice; although we seldom followed advice, we were all ready enough to ask it.
When he read the note from the two ladies, he shook his head
and observed that an affair of this sort demanded the utmost
circumspection.—This air of diffidence highly displeased my
wife. "I never doubted, Sir," cried she, "your readiness to be
against my daughters and me. You have more circumspection
than is wanted. However, I fancy when we come to ask advice,
we shall apply to persons who seem to have made use of it
themselves."—"Whatever my own conduct may have been,
madam," replied he, "is not the present question; tho' as I have
made no use of advice myself, I should in conscience give it to
those that will."—As I was apprehensive this answer might
draw on a repartee, making up by abuse what it wanted in wit,
I changed the subject by seeming to wonder what could keep

our son so long at the fair, as it was now almost nightfall.— "Never mind our son," cried my wife, "depend upon it he knows what he is about. I'll warrant we'll never see him sell his hen of a rainy day. I have seen him buy such bargains as would amaze one. I'll tell you a good story about that, that will make you split your sides with laughing.—But as I live, yonder comes Moses, without an horse, and the box at his back."

As she spoke, Moses came slowly on foot, and sweating under the deal box, which he had strapt round his shoulders.— "Welcome, welcome, Moses; well, my boy, what have you brought us from the fair?"—"I have brought you myself," cried Moses, with a sly look, and resting the box on the dresser. —"Ay, Moses," cried my wife, "that we know, but where is the horse?" "I have sold him," cried Moses, "for three pounds five shillings and two-pence."—"Well done, my good boy," returned she, "I knew you would touch them off. Between ourselves, three pounds five shillings and two-pence is no bad day's work. Come, let us have it then."—"I have brought back no money," cried Moses again. "I have laid it all out in a bargain, and here it is," pulling out a bundle from his breast: "here they are; a groce of green spectacles, with silver rims and shagreen cases."—"A groce of green spectacles!" repeated my wife in a faint voice. "And you have parted with the Colt, and brought us back nothing but a groce of green paltry spectacles!"—"Dear mother," cried the boy, "why won't you listen to reason? I had them a dead bargain, or I should not have bought them. The silver rims alone will sell for double the money."—"A fig for the silver rims," cried my wife, in a passion: "I dare swear they won't sell for above half the money at the rate of broken silver, five shillings an ounce."— "You need be under no uneasiness," cried I, "about selling the rims, for I perceive they are only copper varnished over."— "What," cried my wife, "not silver, the rims not silver!" "No," cried I, "no more silver than your sauce-pan."—"And so," returned she, "we have parted with the Colt, and have only got a groce of green spectacles, with copper rims and shagreen cases! A murrain take such trumpery. The blockhead has been imposed upon, and should have known his company better." —"There, my dear," cried I, "you are wrong, he should not have known them at all."—"Marry, hang the ideot," returned she again, "to bring me such stuff; if I had them, I would throw them in the fire." "There again you are wrong, my dear," cried I; "for though they be copper, we will keep them by us, as copper spectacles, you know, are better than nothing."

By this time the unfortunate Moses was undeceived. He now saw that he had indeed been imposed upon by a prowling sharper, who, observing his figure, had marked him for an easy prey. I therefore asked the circumstances of his deception. He sold the horse, it seems, and walked the fair in search of another. A reverent looking man brought him to a tent, under a pretence of having one to sell. "Here," continued Moses, "we met another man, very well drest, who desired to borrow twenty pounds upon these, saying that he wanted money and would dispose of them for a third of the value. The first gentleman, who pretended to be my friend, whispered me to buy them and cautioned me not to let so good an offer pass. I sent for Mr. Flamborough, and they talked him up as finely as they did me, and so at last we were persuaded to buy the two groce between us."

CHAPTER THIRTEEN

Mr. Burchell is found to be an enemy; for he has the confidence to give disagreeable advice.

Our family had now made several attempts to be fine; but some unforeseen disaster demolished each as soon as projected. I endeavoured to take the advantage of every disappointment, to improve their good sense in proportion as they were frustrated in ambition. "You see, my children," cried I, "how little is to be got by attempts to impose upon the world, in coping with our betters. Such as are poor and will associate with none but the rich are hated by those they avoid and despised by those they follow. Unequal combinations are always disadvantageous to the weaker side, the rich having the pleasure and the poor the inconveniencies that result from them. But come, Dick, my boy, and repeat the fable that you were reading to-day, for the good of the company."

"Once upon a time," cried the child, "a Giant and a Dwarf were friends, and kept together. They made a bargain that they would never forsake each other, but go seek adventures.

The first battle they fought was with two Saracens, and the Dwarf, who was very courageous, dealt one of the champions a most angry blow. It did the Saracen but very little injury, who lifting up his sword, fairly struck off the poor Dwarf's arm. He was now in a woeful plight; but the Giant coming to his assistance in a short time left the two Saracens dead on the plain, and the Dwarf cut off the dead man's head out of spite. They then travelled on to another adventure. This was against three bloody-minded Satyrs who were carrying away a damsel in distress. The Dwarf was not quite so fierce now as before, but for all that struck the first blow, which was returned by another that knocked out his eye; but the Giant was soon up with them, and had they not fled, would certainly have killed them every one. They were all very joyful for this victory, and the damsel who was relieved fell in love with the Giant and married him. They now travelled far, and farther than I can tell, till they met with a company of robbers. The Giant, for the first time, was foremost now; but the Dwarf was not far behind. The battle was stout and long. Wherever the Giant came all fell before him; but the Dwarf had like to have been killed more than once. At last the victory declared for the two adventurers; but the Dwarf lost his leg. The Dwarf was now without an arm, a leg, and an eye, while the Giant, who was without a single wound, cried out to him, 'Come on, my little heroe, this is glorious sport; let us get one victory more, and then we shall have honour for ever.'—'No,' cries the Dwarf, who was by this time grown wiser, 'no, I declare off; I'll fight no more; for I find in every battle that you get all the honour and rewards, but all the blows fall upon me.' "

I was going to moralize this fable, when our attention was called off to a warm dispute between my wife and Mr. Burchell, upon my daughters intended expedition to town. My wife very strenuously insisted upon the advantages that would result from it. Mr. Burchell, on the contrary, dissuaded her with great ardor, and I stood neuter. His present dissuasions seemed but the second part of those which were received with so ill a grace in the morning. The dispute grew high, while poor Deborah, instead of reasoning stronger, talked louder, and at last was obliged to take shelter from a defeat in clamour. The conclusion of her harangue, however, was highly dis-

pleasing to us all; she knew, she said, of some who had their
own secret reasons for what they advised; but for her part she
wished such to stay away from her house for the future.—
"Madam," cried Burchell, with looks of great composure,
which tended to enflame her the more, "as for secret reasons,
you are right; I have secret reasons, which I forbear to
mention because you are not able to answer those of which I
make no secret; but I find my visits here are become troublesome; I'll take my leave therefore now, and perhaps come
once more to take a final farewell when I am quitting the
country." Thus saying, he took up his hat, nor could the
attempts of Sophia, whose looks seemed to upbraid his pre-
cipitancy, prevent his going.

When gone, we all regarded each other for some minutes
with confusion. My wife, who knew herself to be the cause,
strove to hide her concern with a forced smile and an air of
assurance which I was willing to reprove: "How, woman,"
cried I to her, "is it thus we treat strangers? Is it thus we return their kindness? Be assured, my dear, that these were the
harshest words and to me the most unpleasing that ever escaped your lips!"—"Why would he provoke me then?" replied
she; "but I know the motives of his advice perfectly well. He
would prevent my girls from going to town, that he may have
the pleasure of my youngest daughter's company here at home.
But whatever happens, she shall chuse better company than
such low-lived fellows as he."—"Low-lived, my dear, do you
call him?" cried I; "it is very possible we may mistake this
man's character: for he seems upon some occasions the most
finished gentleman I ever knew.—Tell me, Sophia, my girl,
has he ever given you any secret instances of his attachment?"
—"His conversation with me, sir," replied my daughter, "has
ever been sensible, modest, and pleasing. As to aught else, no,
never. Once indeed, I remember to have heard him say he
never knew a woman who could find merit in a man that
seemed poor." "Such, my dear," cried I, "is the common cant
of all the unfortunate or idle. But I hope you have been taught
to judge properly of such men, and that it would be even
madness to expect happiness from one who has been so very
bad an œconomist of his own. Your mother and I have now
better prospects for you. The next winter, which you will

probably spend in town, will give you opportunities of making a more prudent choice."

What Sophia's reflections were upon this occasion, I can't pretend to determine; but I was not displeased at the bottom that we were rid of a guest from whom I had much to fear. Our breach of hospitality went to my conscience a little; but I quickly silenced that monitor by two or three specious reasons, which served to satisfy and reconcile me to myself. The pain which conscience gives the man who has already done wrong is soon got over. Conscience is a coward, and those faults it has not strength enough to prevent, it seldom has justice enough to punish by accusing.

CHAPTER FOURTEEN

Fresh mortifications, or a demonstration that seeming calamities may be real blessings.

The journey of my daughters to town was now resolved upon, Mr. Thornhill having kindly promised to inspect their conduct himself, and inform us by letter of their behaviour. But it was thought indispensably necessary that their appearance should equal the greatness of their expectations, which could not be done without some expence. We debated therefore in full council what were the easiest methods of raising money, or, more properly speaking, what we could most conveniently sell. The deliberation was soon finished; it was found that our remaining horse was utterly useless for the plow without his companion, and equally unfit for the road as wanting an eye; it was therefore determined that we should dispose of him for the purposes above-mentioned, at the neighbouring fair, and, to prevent imposition, that I should go with him myself. Though this was one of the first mercantile transactions of my life, yet I had no doubt about acquitting myself with reputation. The opinion a man forms of his own prudence is measured by that of the company he keeps; and as mine was mostly in the family way, I had conceived no unfavourable sentiments of my worldly wisdom. My wife, however, next morning at parting, after I had got some paces from the door, called me back to advise me, in a whisper, to have all my eyes about me.

I had, in the usual forms, when I came to the fair, put my horse through all his paces; but for some time had no bidders. At last a chapman approached and, after he had for a good while examined the horse round, finding him blind of one eye, would have nothing to say to him; a second came up, but observing he had a spavin, declared he would not take him for the driving home; a third perceived he had a windgall, and would bid no money; a fourth knew by his eye that he had the botts; a fifth, more impertinent than all the rest, wondered what a plague I could do to the fair with a blind, spavined, galled hack that was only fit to be cut up for a dog kennel. By this time I began to have a most hearty contempt for the poor animal myself, and was almost ashamed at the approach of every customer; for though I did not entirely believe all the fellows told me, yet I reflected that the number of witnesses was a strong presumption they were right, and St. Gregory, upon good works, professes himself to be of the same opinion.

I was in this mortifying situation when a brother clergy-man, an old acquaintance, who had also business to the fair, came up and shaking me by the hand proposed adjourning to a public-house and taking a glass of whatever we could get. I readily closed with the offer, and entering an ale-house, we were shewn into a little back room, where there was only a venerable old man, who sat wholly intent over a large book which he was reading. I never in my life saw a figure that pre-possessed me more favourably. His locks of silver grey vener-ably shaded his temples, and his green old age seemed to be the result of health and benevolence. However, his presence did not interrupt our conversation; my friend and I discoursed on the various turns of fortune we had met: the Whistonian controversy, my last pamphlet, the archdeacon's reply, and the hard measure that was dealt me. But our attention was in a short time taken off by the appearance of a youth who, enter-ing the room, respectfully said something softly to the old stranger. "Make no apologies, my child," said the old man; "to do good is a duty we owe to all our fellow creatures; take this, I wish it were more; but five pounds will relieve your distress, and you are welcome." The modest youth shed tears of gratitude, and yet his gratitude was scarce equal to mine. I could have hugged the good old man in my arms, his benevolence pleased me so. He continued to read, and we resumed our conversation, until my companion, after some time, recollecting that he had business to transact in the fair, promised to be soon back, adding that he always desired to have as much of Dr. Primrose's company as possible. The old gentleman, hearing my name mentioned, seemed to look at me with attention, and when my friend was gone, most respectfully demanded if I was any way related to the great Primrose, that couragious monogamist, who had been the bulwark of the church. Never did my heart feel sincerer rapture than at that moment. "Sir," cried I, "the applause of so good a man, as I am sure you are, adds to that happiness in my breast which your benevolence has already excited. You behold before you, Sir, that Doctor Primrose, the monogamist, whom you have been pleased to call great. You here see that unfortunate Divine who has so long, and it would ill become me to say successfully, fought against the deuterogamy of the age." "Sir," cried the stranger, struck with awe, "I fear I have been too familiar; but you'll forgive my curiosity, Sir, I beg pardon." "Sir," cried I, grasping his hand, "you are so far from displeasing me by your familiarity that I must beg you'll accept my friendship, as you already have all my esteem."—"Then with gratitude I accept the offer," cried he, squeezing me by the hand, "thou glorious pillar of unshaken orthodoxy; and do I behold"——I here interrupted what he was going to say; for tho', as an author, I could digest no small share of flattery, yet now my modesty would permit no more. However, no lovers in romance ever cemented a more instantaneous friendship. We talked upon several subjects; at first I thought he seemed rather devout than learned, and began to think he despised all human doctrines as dross. Yet this no way lessened him in my esteem; for I had for some time begun privately to harbour such an opinion myself. I therefore took occasion to observe that the world in general began to be blameably indifferent as to doctrinal matters and followed human speculations too much—"Ay, Sir," replied he, as if he had reserved all his learning to that moment, "Ay, Sir, the world is in its dotage, and yet the cosmogony or creation of the world has puzzled philosophers of all ages. What a medley of opinions have they not broached upon the creation of the world? Sanconiathon, Manetho, Berosus, and Ocellus

Lucanus, have all attempted it in vain. The latter has these
words, *Anarchon ara kai atelutaion to pan,* which imply that
all things have neither beginning nor end. Manetho also, who
lived about the time of Nebuchadon-Asser, Asser being a Syr-
iac word usually applied as a sirname to the kings of that
country, as Teglat Phael-Asser, Nabon-Asser, he, I say, formed
a conjecture equally absurd; for as we usually say, *ek to bib-
lion kubernetes,* which implies that books will never teach the
world; so he attempted to investigate——But, Sir, I ask pardon, I am straying from the question."—That he actually was;
nor could I for my life see how the creation of the world had
any thing to do with the business I was talking of; but it was
sufficient to shew me that he was a man of letters, and I now
reverenced him the more. I was resolved therefore to bring
him to the touch-stone; but he was too mild and too gentle
to contend for victory. Whenever I made any observation that
looked like a challenge to controversy, he would smile, shake
his head, and say nothing; by which I understood he could say
much, if he thought proper. The subject therefore insensibly
changed from the business of antiquity to what which brought
us both to the fair; mine I told him was to sell an horse, and
very luckily, indeed, his was to buy one for one of his tenants.
My horse was soon produced, and in fine we struck a bargain.
Nothing now remained but to pay me, and he accordingly
pulled out a thirty pound note, and bid me change it. Not being in a capacity of complying with his demand, he ordered
the landlady to call up his footman, who made his appearance
in a very genteel livery. "Here, Abraham," cried he, "go and
get gold for this; you'll do it at neighbour Jackson's, or any
where." While the fellow was gone, he entertained me with a
pathetic harangue on the great scarcity of silver, which I undertook to improve, by deploring also the great scarcity of
gold; so that by the time Abraham returned, we had both
agreed that money was never so hard to be come at as now.
Abraham returned to inform us, that he had been over the
whole fair and could not get change, tho' he had offered half
a crown for doing it. This was a very great disappointment to
us all; but the old gentleman having paused a little, asked me
if I knew one Solomon Flamborough in my part of the
country; upon replying that he was my next door neighbour,

"If that be the case then," returned he, "I believe we shall deal. You shall have a draught upon him, payable at sight; and let me tell you he is as warm a man as any within five miles round him. Honest Solomon and I have been acquainted for many years together. I remember I always beat him at three jumps; but he could hop upon one leg farther than I." A draught upon my neighbour was to me the same as money; for I was sufficiently convinced of his ability; the draught was signed and put into my hands, and Mr. Jenkinson, the old gentleman, his man Abraham, and my horse, old Blackberry, trotted off very well pleased with each other.

Being now left to reflection, I began to recollect that I had done wrong in taking a draught from a stranger, and so prudently resolved upon having back my horse and following the purchaser. But this was now too late. I therefore made directly homewards, resolving to get the draught changed into money at my friend's as fast as possible. I found my honest neighbour smoking his pipe at his own door, and informing him that I had a small bill upon him, he read it twice over. "You can read the name, I suppose," cried I, "Ephraim Jenkinson." "Yes," returned he, "the name is written plain enough, and I know the gentleman too, the greatest rascal under the canopy of heaven. This is the very same rogue who sold us the spectacles. Was he not a venerable looking man, with grey hair, and no flaps to his pocket-holes? And did he not talk a long string of learning about Greek and cosmogony and the world?" To this I replied with a groan. "Aye," continued he, "he has but that one piece of learning in the world, and he always talks it away whenever he finds a scholar in company; but I know the rogue, and will catch him yet."

Though I was already sufficiently mortified, my greatest struggle was to come in facing my wife and daughters. No truant was ever more afraid of returning to school, there to behold the master's sweet visage, than I was of going home. I was determined, however, to anticipate their fury by first falling into a passion myself.

But, alas! upon entering, I found the family no way disposed for battle. My wife and girls were all in tears, Mr. Thornhill having been there that day to inform them that their journey to town was entirely over. The two ladies having heard reports of us from some malicious person about us were that day set out for London. He could neither discover the tendency, nor the author of these, but whatever they might be or whoever might have broached them, he continued to assure our family of his friendship and protection. I found, therefore, that they bore my disappointment with great resignation, as it was eclipsed in the greatness of their own. But what perplexed us most was to think who could be so base as to asperse the character of a family so harmless as ours, too humble to excite envy, and too inoffensive to create disgust.

CHAPTER FIFTEEN

All Mr. Burchell's villainy at once detected. The folly of being
over-wise.

That evening and a part of the following day was employed in fruitless attempts to discover our enemies; scarce a family in the neighbourhood but incurred our suspicions, and each of us had reasons for our opinion best known to ourselves. As we were in this perplexity, one of our little boys, who had been playing abroad, brought in a letter-case which he found on the green. It was quickly known to belong to Mr. Burchell, with whom it had been seen, and upon examination contained some hints upon different subjects; but what particularly engaged our attention was a sealed note, superscribed, *the copy of a letter to be sent to the two ladies at Thornhill-castle.* It instantly occurred that he was the base informer, and we deliberated whether the note should not be broke open. I was against it; but Sophia, who said she was sure that of all men he would be the last to be guilty of so much baseness, insisted upon its being read. In this she was seconded by the rest of the family, and, at their joint solicitation, I read as follows:

"LADIES,
The bearer will sufficiently satisfy you as to the person from whom this comes: one at least the friend of innocence, and ready to prevent its being seduced. I am informed for a truth that you have some intentions of bringing two young ladies to town whom I have some knowledge of, under the character of

companions. As I would neither have simplicity imposed upon, nor virtue contaminated, I must offer it as my opinion, that the impropriety of such a step will be attended with dangerous consequences. It has never been my way to treat the infamous or the lewd with severity; nor should I now have taken this method of explaining myself, or reproving folly, did it not aim at guilt. Take therefore the admonition of a friend, and seriously reflect on the consequences of introducing infamy and vice into retreats where peace and innocence have hitherto resided."

Our doubts were now at an end. There seemed indeed something applicable to both sides in this letter, and its censures might as well be referred to those to whom it was written, as to us; but the malicious meaning was obvious, and we went no farther. My wife had scarce patience to hear me to the end, but railed at the writer with unrestrained resentment. Olivia was equally severe, and Sophia seemed perfectly amazed at his baseness. As for my part, it appeared to me one of the vilest instances of unprovoked ingratitude I had met with. Nor could I account for it in any other manner than by imputing it to his desire of detaining my youngest daughter in the country, to have the more frequent opportunities of an interview. In this manner we all sate ruminating upon schemes of vengeance, when our other little boy came running in to tell us that Mr. Burchell was approaching at the other end of the field. It is easier to conceive than describe the complicated sensations which are felt from the pain of a recent injury, and the pleasure of approaching revenge. Tho' our intentions were only to upbraid him with his ingratitude, yet it was resolved to do it in a manner that would be perfectly cutting. For this purpose we agreed to meet him with our usual smiles, to chat in the beginning with more than ordinary kindness, to amuse him a little, and then in the midst of the flattering calm to burst upon him like an earthquake and overwhelm him with the sense of his own baseness. This being resolved upon, my wife undertook to manage the business herself, as she really had some talents for such an undertaking. We saw him approach, he entered, drew a chair, and sate down.—"A fine day, Mr. Burchell."—"A very fine day, Doctor; though I fancy we shall have some rain by the shooting of my corns."—"The shooting of your horns," cried my wife in a loud fit of laughter, and then asked pardon for being fond of a joke.—"Dear madam," replied he, "I pardon you with all my heart; for I protest I should not have thought it a joke till you told me."—"Perhaps not, Sir," cried my wife, winking at us, "and yet I dare say you can tell us how many jokes go to an ounce."—"I fancy, madam," returned Burchell, "you have been reading a jest book this morning, that ounce of jokes is so very good a conceit; and yet, madam, I had rather see half an ounce of understanding."—"I believe you might," cried my wife, still smiling at us, though the laugh was against her; "and yet I have seen some men pretend to understanding that have very little."—"And no doubt," replied her antagonist, "you have known ladies set up for wit that had none."—I quickly began to find that my wife was likely to gain but little at this business; so I resolved to treat him in a stile of more severity myself. "Both wit and understanding," cried I, "are trifles without integrity; it is that which gives value to every character. The ignorant peasant, without fault, is greater than the philosopher with many; for what is genius or courage without an heart? *An honest man is the noblest work of God.*"

"I always held that favourite maxim of Pope," returned Mr. Burchell, "as very unworthy a man of genius, and a base desertion of his own superiority. As the reputation of books is raised not by their freedom from defect, but the greatness of their beauties, so should that of men be prized not for their exemption from fault, but the size of those virtues they are possessed of. The scholar may want prudence, the statesman may have pride, and the champion ferocity; but shall we prefer to these men the low mechanic, who laboriously plods on through life without censure or applause? We might as well prefer the tame correct paintings of the Flemish school to the erroneous, but sublime animations of the Roman pencil."

"Sir," replied I, "your present observation is just, when there are shining virtues and minute defects; but when it appears that great vices are opposed in the same mind to as extraordinary virtues, such a character deserves contempt."

"Perhaps," cried he, "there may be some such monsters as you describe, of great vices joined to great virtues; yet in my progress through life, I never yet found one instance of their existence; on the contrary, I have ever perceived that where the mind was capacious, the affections were good. And indeed Providence seems kindly our friend in this particular, thus to debilitate the understanding where the heart is corrupt, and diminish the power where there is the will to do mischief. This rule seems to extend even to other animals: the little vermin race are ever treacherous, cruel, and cowardly, whilst those endowed with strength and power are generous, brave, and gentle."

"These observations sound well," returned I, "and yet it would be easy this moment to point out a man," and I fixed my eye stedfastly upon him, "whose head and heart form a most detestable contrast. Ay, Sir," continued I, raising my voice, "and I am glad to have this opportunity of detecting him in the midst of his fancied security. Do you know this, Sir, this pocket-book?"—"Yes, Sir," returned he, with a face of impenetrable assurance, "that pocket-book is mine, and I am glad you have found it."—"And do you know," cried I, "this letter? Nay, never falter, man; but look me full in the face; I say, do you know this letter?"—"That letter," returned he, "yes, it was I that wrote that letter."—"And how could you," said I, "so basely, so ungratefully presume to write this letter?"—"And how came you," replied he, with looks of unparalleled effrontery, "so basely to presume to break open this letter? Don't you know, now, I could hang you all for this? All that I have to do is to swear at the next justice's that you have been guilty of breaking open the lock of my pocketbook, and so hang you all up at his door." This piece of unexpected insolence raised me to such a pitch that I could scarce govern my passion. "Ungrateful wretch, begone, and no longer pollute my dwelling with thy baseness. Begone, and never let me see thee again; go from my doors, and the only punishment I wish thee is an alarmed conscience, which will be a sufficient tormentor!" So saying, I threw him his pocketbook, which he took up with a smile, and shutting the clasps with the utmost composure, left us quite astonished at the serenity of his assurance. My wife was particularly enraged that nothing could make him angry or make him seem ashamed of his villainies: "My dear," cried I, willing to calm those passions that had been raised too high among us, "we are not to be surprised that bad men want shame; they only blush at being detected in doing good, but glory in their vices. "Guilt and shame, says the allegory, were at first companions, and in the beginning of their journey inseparably kept together. But their union was soon found to be disagreeable and inconvenient to both; guilt gave shame frequent uneasiness, and shame often betrayed the secret conspiracies of guilt. After long disagreement, therefore, they at length consented to part for ever. Guilt boldly walked forward alone to overtake fate, that went before in the shape of an executioner; but shame being naturally timorous, returned back to keep company with virtue, which, in the beginning of their journey, they had left behind. Thus, my children, after men have travelled through a few stages in vice, they no longer continue to have shame at doing evil, and shame attends only upon their virtues."

[margin note: Personification]

CHAPTER SIXTEEN

The family use art, which is opposed with still greater.

Whatever might have been Sophia's sensations, the rest of the family was easily consoled for Mr. Burchell's absence by the company of our landlord, whose visits now became more frequent and longer. Though he had been disappointed in procuring my daughters the amusements of the town, as he designed, he took every opportunity of supplying them with those little recreations which our retirement would admit of. He usually came in the morning, and while my son and I followed our occupations abroad, he sat with the family at home and amused them by describing the town, with every part of which he was particularly acquainted. He could repeat all the observations that were retailed in the atmosphere of the playhouses, and had all the good things of the high wits by rote long before they made way into the jest-books. The intervals between conversation were employed in teaching my daughters piquet, or sometimes in setting my two little ones to box to make them *sharp*, as he called it; but the hopes of having him for a son-in-law in some measure blinded us to all his defects. It must be owned that my wife laid a thousand schemes to entrap him, or, to speak it more tenderly, used every art to magnify the merit of her daughter. If the cakes at tea eat short and crisp, they were made by Olivia; if the gooseberry wine was well knit, the gooseberries were of her gathering: it was her fingers gave the pickles their peculiar green; and in the composition of a pudding, her judgment was infallible. Then the poor woman would sometimes tell the 'Squire that she thought him and Olivia extremely like each other, and would bid both stand up to see which was tallest. These instances of cunning, which she thought impenetrable yet which every body saw through, were very pleasing to our benefactor, who gave every day some new proofs of his passion, which though they had not arisen to proposals of marriage, yet we thought fell but little short of it; and his slowness was attributed sometimes to native bashfulness, and sometimes to his fear of offending a rich uncle. An occurrence, however, which happened soon after, put it beyond a doubt, that he designed to become one of the family; my wife even regarded it as an absolute promise.

My wife and daughters happening to return a visit to neighbour Flamborough's found that family had lately got their pictures drawn by a limner, who travelled the country, and did them for fifteen shillings a head. As this family and ours had long a sort of rivalry in point of taste, our spirit took the alarm at this stolen march upon us, and notwithstanding all I could say, and I said much, it was resolved that we should have our pictures done too. Having, therefore, engaged the limner, for what could I do? our next deliberation was to shew the superiority of our taste in the attitudes. As for our neighbour's family, there were seven of them, and they were drawn with seven oranges, a thing quite out of taste, no variety in life, no composition in the world. We desired to have something in a brighter style, and after many debates, at length came to an unanimous resolution to be drawn together, in one large historical family piece. This would be cheaper, since one frame would serve for all, and it would be infinitely more genteel; for all families of any taste were now drawn in the same manner. As we did not immediately recollect an historical subject to hit us, we were contented each with being drawn as independent historical figures. My wife desired to be represented as Venus, with a stomacher richly set with diamonds and her two little ones as Cupids by her side, while I, in my gown and band, was to present her with my books on the Whistonian[65] controversy. Olivia would be drawn as an Amazon, sitting upon a bank of flowers, drest in a green joseph[66] laced with gold, and a whip in her hand. Sophia was to be a shepherdess, with as many sheep as the painter could spare; and Moses was to be drest out with an hat and white feather. Our taste so much pleased the 'Squire, that he insisted on being put in as one of the family in the character of Alexander the great, at Olivia's feet. This was considered by us all as an indication of his desire to be introduced into the family in reality, nor could we refuse his request. The painter was therefore set to work, and as he wrought with assiduity and expedition, in less than four days the whole was compleated. The piece was large, and it must be owned he did not spare his colours; for which my wife gave him great encomiums. We were all perfectly satisfied with his performance; but an unfortunate circumstance had not occurred till the picture was finished, which now struck us with dismay. It was so very large that we had no place in the house to fix it. How we all came to disregard so material a point is inconceivable; but certain it is, we were this time all greatly overseen. Instead, therefore, of gratifying our vanity, as we hoped, there it leaned, in a most mortifying manner, against the kitchen wall where the canvas was stretched and painted, much too large to be got through any of the doors, and the jest of all our neighbours. One compared it to Robinson Crusoe's longboat, too large to be removed; another thought it more resembled a reel in a bottle; some wondered how it should be got out, and still more were amazed how it ever got in.

But though it excited the ridicule of some, it effectually raised more ill-natured suggestions in many. The 'Squire's portrait being found united with ours was an honour too great to escape envy. Malicious whispers began to circulate at our expence, and our tranquillity continually to be disturbed by persons who came as friends to tell us what was said of us by enemies. These reports we always resented with becoming spirit; but scandal ever improves by opposition. We again therefore entered into a consultation upon obviating the malice of our enemies, and at last came to a resolution which had too much cunning to give me entire satisfaction. It was this: as our principal object was to discover the honour of Mr. Thornhill's addresses, my wife undertook to sound him, by pretending to ask his advice in the choice of an husband for her eldest daughter. If this was not found sufficient to induce him to a declaration, it was then fixed upon to terrify him with a rival which it was thought would compel him, though never so refractory. To this last step, however, I would by no means give my consent, till Olivia gave me the most solemn assurances that she would marry the person provided to rival him upon this occasion, if Mr. Thornhill did not prevent it by taking her himself. Such was the scheme laid, which though I did not strenuously oppose, I did not entirely approve.

The next time, therefore, that Mr. Thornhill came to see us, my girls took care to be out of the way in order to give their mamma an opportunity of putting her scheme in execution; but they only retired to the next room, from whence they could over-hear the whole conversation, which my wife artfully introduced by observing that one of the Miss Flamboroughs was like to have a very good match of it in Mr. Spanker. To this the 'Squire assenting, she proceeded to remark, that they who had warm fortunes were always sure of getting good husbands; "But heaven help," continued she, "the girls that have none. What signifies beauty, Mr. Thornhill? or what signifies all the virtue, and all the qualifications in the world, in this age of self-interest? It is not, what is she? but what has she? is all the cry."

"Madam," returned he, "I highly approve the justice, as well as the novelty, of your remarks, and if I were a king, it should be otherwise. It should then, indeed, be fine times with the girls without fortunes; our two young ladies should be the first for whom I would provide."

"Ah, Sir!" returned my wife, "you are pleased to be facetious; but I wish I were a queen, and then I know where they should look for an husband. But now, that you have put it into my head, seriously, Mr. Thornhill, can't you recommend me a proper husband for my eldest girl? She is now nineteen years old, well grown and well educated, and, in my humble opinion, does not want for parts."

"Madam," replied he, "if I were to chuse, I would find out a person possessed of every accomplishment that can make an angel happy. One with prudence, fortune, taste, and sincerity; such, madam, would be in my opinion the proper husband." "Ay, Sir," said she, "but do you know of any such person?"— "No, madam," returned he, "it is impossible to know any person that deserves to be her husband; she's too great a treasure for one man's possession: she's a goddess. Upon my soul, I speak what I think, she's an angel."—"Ah, Mr. Thornhill, you only flatter my poor girl; but we have been thinking of marrying her to one of your tenants, whose mother is lately dead and who wants a manager; you know whom I mean, farmer Williams; a warm man, Mr. Thornhill, able to give her good bread; ay, and who has several times made her proposals"; (which was actually the case) "but, Sir," concluded she, "I should be glad to have your approbation of our choice."— "How, madam," replied he, "my approbation! My approbation of such a choice! Never. What! Sacrifice so much beauty, and sense, and goodness, to a creature insensible of the blessing! Excuse me, I can never approve of such a piece of injustice! And I have my reasons!"—"Indeed, Sir," cried Deborah, "if you have your reasons, that's another affair; but I should be glad to know those reasons."—"Excuse me, madam," returned he, "they lie too deep for discovery"; (laying his hand upon his bosom) "they remain buried, rivetted here."

After he was gone, upon general consultation we could not tell what to make of these fine sentiments. Olivia considered them as instances of the most exalted passion, but I was not quite so sanguine; it seemed to me pretty plain that they had more of love than matrimony in them; yet, whatever they might portend, it was resolved to prosecute the scheme of farmer Williams, who, since my daughter's first appearance in the country, had paid her his addresses.

CHAPTER SEVENTEEN

Scarce any virtue found to resist the power of long and pleasing temptation.

As I only studied my child's real happiness, the assiduity of Mr. Williams pleased me, as he was in easy circumstances,

prudent, and sincere. It required but very little encouragement to revive his former passion; so that in an evening or
two after he and Mr. Thornhill met at our house, and surveyed each other for some time with looks of anger; but Williams owed his landlord no rent, and little regarded his indignation. Olivia, on her side, acted the coquet to perfection, if
that might be called acting which was her real character, pretending to lavish all her tenderness on her new lover. Mr.
Thornhill appeared quite dejected at this preference, and with
a pensive air took leave, though I own it puzzled me to find
him so much in pain as he appeared to be when he had it in
his power so easily to remove the cause, by declaring an honourable passion. But whatever uneasiness he seemed to endure, it could easily be perceived that Olivia's anguish was
still greater. After any of these interviews between her lovers,
of which there were several, she usually retired to solitude,
and there indulged her grief. It was in such a situation I
found her one evening, after she had been for some time supporting a fictitious gayety.—"You now see, my child," said I,
"that your confidence in Mr. Thornhill's passion was all a
dream; he permits the rivalry of another, every way his inferior, though he knows it lies in his power to secure you by
a candid declaration himself."—"Yes, pappa," returned she,
"but he has his reasons for this delay. I know he has. The sincerity of his looks and words convince me of his real esteem.
A short time, I hope, will discover the generosity of his sentiments, and convince you that my opinion of him has been
more just than yours."—"Olivia, my darling," returned I, "every scheme that has been hitherto pursued to compel him to a
declaration has been proposed and planned by yourself, nor
can you in the least say that I have constrained you. But you
must not suppose, my dear, that I will be ever instrumental
in suffering his honest rival to be the dupe of your ill-placed
passion. Whatever time you require to bring your fancied admirer to an explanation shall be granted; but at the expiration
of that term, if he is still regardless, I must absolutely insist
that honest Mr. Williams shall be rewarded for his fidelity.
The character which I have hitherto supported in life demands this from me, and my tenderness, as a parent, shall
never influence my integrity as a man. Name then your day,

let it be as distant as you think proper, and in the mean time take care to let Mr. Thornhill know the exact time on which I design delivering you up to another. If he really loves you, his own good sense will readily suggest that there is but one method alone to prevent his losing you for ever."—This proposal, which she could not avoid considering as perfectly just, was readily agreed to. She again renewed her most positive promise of marrying Mr. Williams, in case of the other's insensibility; and at the next opportunity, in Mr. Thornhill's presence, that day month was fixed upon for her nuptials with his rival.

Such vigorous proceedings seemed to redouble Mr. Thornhill's anxiety; but what Olivia really felt gave me some uneasiness. In this struggle between prudence and passion, her vivacity quite forsook her, and every opportunity of solitude was sought, and spent in tears. One week passed away; but her lover made no efforts to restrain her nuptials. The succeeding week he was still assiduous; but not more open. On the third he discontinued his visits entirely, and instead of my daughter testifying any impatience, as I expected, she seemed to retain a pensive tranquillity which I looked upon as resignation. For my own part, I was now sincerely pleased with thinking that my child was going to be secured in a continuance of competence and peace, and frequently applauded her resolution. It was within about four days of her intended nuptials, that my little family at night were gathered round a charming fire, telling stories of the past, and laying schemes for the future. Busied in forming a thousand projects, and laughing at whatever folly came uppermost, "Well, Moses," cried I, "we shall soon, my boy, have a wedding in the family; what is your opinion of matters and things in general?"— "My opinion, father, is that all things go on very well; and I was just now thinking, that when sister Livy is married to farmer Williams, we shall then have the loan of his cyderpress and brewing tubs for nothing."—"That we shall, Moses," cried I, "and he will sing us Death and the Lady to raise our spirits into the bargain."—"He has taught that song to our Dick," cried Moses; "and I think he goes thro' it very prettily."—"Does he so?" cried I, "then let us have it; where's little Dick? let him up with it boldly."—"My brother Dick," cried Bill my youngest, "is just gone out with sister Livy; but Mr. Williams has taught me two songs, and I'll sing them for you, pappa. Which song do you chuse, *the dying Swan,* or the *Elegy on the death of a mad dog?*" "The elegy, child, by all means," said I; "I never heard that yet; and Deborah, my life, grief you know is dry, let us have a bottle of the best gooseberry wine, to keep up our spirits. I have wept so much at all sorts of elegies of late that without an enlivening glass I am sure this will overcome me; and Sophy, love, take your guitar, and thrum in with the boy a little."

AN ELEGY ON THE DEATH OF A MAD DOG

Good people all, of every sort,
    Give ear unto my song;
And if you find it wond'rous short,
    It cannot hold you long.

In Isling town there was a man,
    Of whom the world might say,
That still a godly race he ran,
    Whene'er he went to pray.

A kind and gentle heart he had,
    To comfort friends and foes;
The naked every day he clad,
    When he put on his cloaths.

And in that town a dog was found,
    As many dogs there be,
Both mungrel, puppy, whelp and hound,
    And curs of low degree.

This dog and man at first were friends;
    But when a pique began,
The dog, to gain some private ends,
    Went mad and bit the man.

> Around from all the neighbouring streets,
>   The wondering neighbours ran,
> And swore the dog had lost his wits,
>   To bite so good a man.
>
> The wound it seem'd both sore and sad,
>   To every christian eye;
> And while they swore the dog was mad,
>   They swore the man would die.
>
> But soon a wonder came to light,
>   That shew'd the rogues they lied,
> The man recovered of the bite,
>   The dog it was that dy'd.

"A very good boy, Bill, upon my word, and an elegy that may truly be called tragical. Come, my children, here's Bill's health, and may he one day be a bishop."

"With all my heart," cried my wife; "and if he but preaches as well as he sings, I make no doubt of him. The most of his family, by the mother's side, could sing a good song; it was a common saying in our country that the family of the Blenkin-sops could never look straight before them, nor the Hug-ginses blow out a candle; that there were none of the Grog-rams but could sing a song, or of the Marjorams but could tell a story."—"However that be," cried I, "the most vulgar ballad of them all generally pleases me better than the fine modern odes and things that petrify us in a single stanza, productions that we at once detest and praise. Put the glass to your brother, Moses. The great fault of these elegists is that they are in despair for griefs that give the sensible part of mankind very little pain. A lady loses her lap-dog, and so the silly poet runs home to versify the disaster."

"That may be the mode," cried Moses, "in sublimer compo-sitions; but the Ranelagh songs that come down to us are per-fectly familiar, and all cast in the same mold: Colin meets Dolly, and they hold a dialogue together; he gives her a fair-ing to put in her hair, and she presents him with a nosegay; and then they go together to church, where they give good advice to young nymphs and swains to get married as fast as they can."

"And very good advice too," cried I, "and I am told there is not a place in the world where advice can be given with so much propriety as there; for, as it persuades us to marry, it also furnishes us with a wife; and surely that must be an excellent market, my boy, where we are told what we want and supplied with it when wanting."

"Yes, Sir," returned Moses, "and I know but of two such markets for wives in Europe,—Ranelagh in England, and Fontarabia in Spain. The Spanish market is open once a year, but our English wives are saleable every night."

"You are right, my boy," cried his mother, "Old England is the only place in the world for husbands to get wives."—"And for wives to manage their husbands," interrupted I. "It is a proverb abroad, that if a bridge were built across the sea, all the ladies of the Continent would come over to take pattern from ours; for there are no such wives in Europe as our own.

"But let us have one bottle more, Deborah, my life, and Moses give us a good song. What thanks do we not owe to heaven for thus bestowing tranquillity, health, and competence. I think myself happier now than the greatest monarch upon earth. He has no such fire-side, nor such pleasant faces about it. Yes, Deborah my dear, we are now growing old; but the evening of our life is likely to be happy. We are descended from ancestors that knew no stain, and we shall leave a good and virtuous race of children behind us. While we live they will be our support and our pleasure here, and when we die they will transmit our honour untainted to posterity. Come, my son, we wait for your song; let us have a chorus. But where is my darling Olivia? That little cherub's voice is always sweetest in the concert."—Just as I spoke Dick came running in, "O pappa, pappa, she is gone from us, she is gone from us, my sister Livy is gone from us for ever."—"Gone, child!"—"Yes, she is gone off with two gentlemen in a post chaise, and one of them kissed her, and said he would die for her; and she cried very much, and was for coming back; but he persuaded her again, and she went into the chaise, and said, 'O, what will my poor pappa do when he knows I am un-

done!' "—"Now, then," cried I, "my children, go and be miserable; for we shall never enjoy one hour more. And O may
heaven's everlasting fury light upon him and his! Thus to rob
me of my child! And sure it will, for taking back my sweet
innocent that I was leading up to heaven. Such sincerity as
my child was possest of. But all our earthly happiness is now
over! Go, my children, go, and be miserable and infamous;
for my heart is broken within me!"—"Father," cried my son,
"is this your fortitude?"—"Fortitude, child! Yes, he shall see I
have fortitude! Bring me my pistols. I'll pursue the traitor.
While he is on earth I'll pursue him. Old as I am, he shall
find I can sting him yet. The villain! the perfidious villain."
—I had by this time reached down my pistols, when my poor
wife, whose passions were not so strong as mine, caught me
in her arms. "My dearest, dearest husband," cried she, "the
bible is the only weapon that is fit for your old hands now.
Open that, my love, and read our anguish into patience, for
she has vilely deceived"—her sorrow represt the rest in silence. "Indeed, Sir," resumed my son, after a pause, "your rage
is too violent and unbecoming. You should be my mother's
comforter, and you encrease her pain. It ill suited you and
your reverend character thus to curse your greatest enemy;
you should not have curst the wretch, villain as he is."—"I did
not curse him, child, did I?"—"Indeed, Sir, you did; you curst
him twice."—"Then may heaven forgive me and him if I did.
And now, my son, I see it was more than human benevolence
that first taught us to bless our enemies! Blest be his holy
name for all the good he hath given, and for that he has
taken away. But it is not, it is not a small distress that can
wring tears from these old eyes, that have not wept for so
many years. My Child!—To undo my darling! May confusion
seize!——Heaven forgive me, what am I about to say! You
may remember, my love, how good she was, and how charming; till this vile moment all her care was to make us happy.
Had she but died! But she is gone, the honour of our family
contaminated, and I must look out for happiness in other
worlds than here. But my child, you saw them go off: perhaps
he forced her away? If he forced her, she may yet be innocent."—"Ah no, Sir!" cried the child; "he only kissed her, and
called her his angel, and she wept very much, and leaned

upon his arm, and they drove off very fast."—"She's an ungrateful creature," cried my wife, who could scarce speak for weeping, "to use us thus. She never had the least constraint put upon her affections. The vile strumpet has basely deserted her parents without any provocation, thus to bring your grey hairs to the grave, and I must shortly follow."

In this manner that night, the first of our real misfortunes, was spent in the bitterness of complaint, and ill supported sallies of enthusiasm. I determined, however, to find out our betrayer, wherever he was, and reproach his baseness. The next morning we missed our wretched child at breakfast, where she used to give life and chearfulness to us all. My wife, as before, attempted to ease her heart by reproaches. "Never," cried she, "shall that vilest stain of our family again darken those harmless doors. I will never call her daughter more. No, let the strumpet live with her vile seducer: she may bring us to shame, but she shall never more deceive us."

"Wife," said I, "do not talk thus hardly; my detestation of her guilt is as great as yours, but ever shall this house and this heart be open to a poor returning repentant sinner. The sooner she returns from her transgression, the more welcome shall she be to me. For the first time the very best may err; art may persuade, and novelty spread out its charm. The first fault is the child of simplicity; but every other the offspring of guilt. Yes, the wretched creature shall be welcome to this heart and this house, tho' stained with ten thousand vices. I will again hearken to the music of her voice, again will I hang fondly on her bosom, if I find but repentance there. My son, bring hither my bible and my staff; I will pursue her, wherever she is, and tho' I cannot save her from shame, I may prevent the continuance of iniquity."

CHAPTER EIGHTEEN

The pursuit of a father to reclaim a lost child to virtue.

Tho' the child could not describe the gentleman's person who handed his sister into the post-chaise, yet my suspicions fell entirely upon our young landlord, whose character for such intrigues was but too well known. I therefore directed my steps towards Thornhill-castle, resolving to upbraid him and, if possible, to bring back my daughter; but before I had reached his seat I was met by one of my parishioners, who said he saw a young lady resembling my daughter in a post-chaise with a gentleman whom, by the description, I could only guess to be Mr. Burchell, and that they drove very fast. This information, however, did by no means satisfy me. I therefore went to the young 'Squire's, and though it was yet early, insisted upon seeing him immediately; he soon appeared with the most open familiar air and seemed perfectly amazed at my daughter's elopement, protesting upon his honour that he was quite a stranger to it. I now therefore condemned my former suspicions, and could turn them only on Mr. Burchell, who I recollected had of late several private conferences with her; but the appearance of another witness left me no room to doubt of his villainy, who averred that he and my daughter were actually gone towards the wells, about thirty miles off, where there was a great deal of company. [Being driven to that state of mind in which we are more ready to act precipitately than to reason right, I never debated with myself whether these accounts might not have been given by persons purposely placed in my way to mislead me, but resolved to pursue my daughter and her fancied deluder thither.] I walked along with earnestness, and enquired of several by the way; but received no accounts, till entering the town, I was met by a person on horseback whom I remembered to have seen at the 'Squire's, and he assured me that if I followed them to the races, which were but thirty miles farther, I might depend upon overtaking them; for he had seen them dance there the night before, and the whole assembly seemed charmed with my daughter's performance. Early the next day I walked forward to the races, and about four in the afternoon I came upon the course. The company made a very brilliant appearance, all earnestly employed in one pursuit, that of pleasure; how different from mine, that of reclaiming a lost child to virtue! I thought I perceived Mr. Burchell at some distance from me; but, as if he dreaded an interview, upon my approaching him, he mixed among a crowd, and I saw him no more. I now reflected that it would be to no purpose to continue my pursuit farther, and resolved to return home to an innocent family, who wanted my assistance. But the agitations of my mind and the fatigue I had undergone threw me into a fever, the symptoms of which I perceived before I came off the course. This was another unexpected stroke, as I was more than seventy miles distant from home; however, I retired to a little ale-house by the road-side, and in this place, the usual retreat of indigence and frugality, I laid me down patiently to wait the issue of my disorder. I languished here for near three weeks; but at last my constitution prevailed, though I was unprovided with money to defray the expenses of my entertainment. It is possible the anxiety from this last circumstance alone might have brought on a relapse, had I not been supplied by a traveller, who stopt to take a cursory refreshment. This person was no other than the philanthropic bookseller in St. Paul's church-yard,[67] who has written so many little books for children; he called himself their friend; but he was the friend of all mankind. He was no sooner alighted, but he was in haste to be gone; for he was ever on business of the utmost importance, and was at that time actually compiling materials for the history of one Mr. Thomas Trip. I immediately recollected this good-natured man's red pimpled face, for he had published for me against the Deuterogamists of the age, and from him I borrowed a few pieces to be paid at my return. Leaving the inn, therefore, as I was yet but weak, I resolved to return home by easy journies of ten miles a day. My health and usual tranquillity were almost restored, and I now condemned that pride which had made me refractory to the hand of correction. Man little knows what calamities are beyond his patience to bear till he tries them; as in ascending the heights of ambition, which look bright from below, every step we rise shews us some new prospect of hidden disappointment, so in our descent to the vale of wretchedness, which from the summits of pleasure appears dark and gloomy, the busy mind, still attentive to its own amusement, finds something to flatter and surprise it. Still as we descend, the objects appear to brighten, unexpected prospects amuse, and the mental eye becomes adapted to its gloomy situation.

I now proceeded forwards, and had walked about two hours, when I perceived what appeared at a distance like the waggon, which I was resolved to overtake: but when I came up with it, found it to be a strolling company's cart that was carrying their scenes and other theatrical furniture to the next village, where they were to exhibit. The cart was attended only by the person who drove it and one of the company, as the rest of the players were to follow the ensuing day. Good company upon the road, says the proverb, is always the shortest cut. I therefore entered into conversation with the poor player; and as I once had some theatrical powers myself, I disserted on such topics with my usual freedom, but as I was pretty much unacquainted with the present state of the stage, I demanded who were the present theatrical writers in vogue, who the Drydens and Otways of the day.—"I fancy, Sir," cried the player, "few of our modern dramatists would think themselves much honoured by being compared to the writers you mention. Dryden and Row's manner, Sir, are quite out of fashion; our taste has gone back a whole century, Fletcher, Ben Johnson, and all the plays of Shakespear, are the only things that go down."—"How," cried I, "is it possible the present age can be pleased with that antiquated dialect, that obsolete humour, those over-charged characters, which abound in the works you mention?"—"Sir," returned my companion, "the public think nothing about dialect, or humour, or character; for that is none of their business, they only go to be amused, and find themselves happy when they can enjoy a pantomime under the sanction of Johnson's or Shakespear's name."—"So then, I suppose," cried I, "that our modern dramatists are rather imitators of Shakespeare than of nature."— "To say the truth," returned my companion, "I don't know that they imitate any thing at all; nor indeed does the public require it of them; it is not the composition of the piece, but the number of starts and attitudes that may be introduced into it that elicits applause. I have known a piece with not one jest in the whole shrugged into popularity, and another saved by the poet's throwing in a fit of the gripes. No, Sir, the works of Congreve and Farquhar have too much wit in them for the present taste; our modern dialogue is much more natural."

By this time the equipage of the strolling company was arrived at the village, which, it seems, had been apprised of our approach and was come out to gaze at us; for my companion observed that strollers always have more spectators without

taste in drama

doors than within. I did not consider the impropriety of my being in such company till I saw a mob gather about me. I therefore took shelter, as fast as possible, in the first ale-house that offered, and being shewn into the common room, was accosted by a very well-drest gentleman who demanded whether I was the real chaplain of the company or whether it was only to be my masquerade character in the play. Upon informing him of the truth, and that I did not belong to the company, he was condescending enough to desire me and the player to partake in a bowl of punch, over which he discussed modern politics with great earnestness and seeming interest. I set him down in my own mind for nothing less than a parliament-man at least; but was almost confirmed in my conjectures, when upon my asking what there was in the house for supper, he insisted that the player and I should sup with him at his house, with which request, after some entreaties, I was prevailed on to comply.

CHAPTER NINETEEN

The description of a person discontented with the present
government and apprehensive of the loss of our liberties.

The house where we were to be entertained, lying at a small distance from the village, our inviter observed that as the coach was not ready, he would conduct us on foot, and we soon arrived at one of the most magnificent mansions I had seen in the country. The apartment into which we were shewn was perfectly elegant and modern; he went to give orders for supper, while the player with a wink observed that we were perfectly in luck. Our entertainer soon returned, an elegant supper was brought in, two or three ladies in an easy deshabille were introduced, and the conversation began with some sprightliness. Politics, however, was the subject on which our entertainer chiefly expatiated; for he asserted that liberty was at once his boast and his terror. After the cloth was removed, he asked me if I had seen the last Monitor, to which replying in the negative, "What, nor the Auditor, I suppose?" cried he. "Neither, Sir," returned I. "That's strange, very strange," replied my entertainer. "Now, I read all the politics that come out. The Daily, the Public, the Ledger, the Chronicle, the

London Evening, the Whitehall Evening, the seventeen magazines, and the two reviews; and though they hate each other,
I love them all. Liberty, Sir, liberty is the Briton's boast, and
by all my coal mines in Cornwall, I reverence its guardians."
"Then it is to be hoped," cried I, "you reverence the King."
"Yes," returned my entertainer, "when he does what we would
have him; but if he goes on as he has done of late, I'll never
trouble myself more with his matters. I say nothing. I think
only. I could have directed some things better. I don't think
there has been a sufficient number of advisers; he should advise with every person willing to give him advice, and then
we should have things done in another manner."

"I wish," cried I, "that such intruding advisers were fixed
in the pillory. It should be the duty of honest men to assist
the weaker side of our constitution, that sacred power that has
for some years been every day declining, and losing its due
share of influence in the state. But these ignorants still continue the cry of liberty, and if they have any weight, basely
throw it into the subsiding scale."

"How," cried one of the ladies, "do I live to see one so
base, so sordid, as to be an enemy to liberty and a defender
of tyrants? Liberty, that sacred gift of heaven, that glorious
privilege of Britons!"

"Can it be possible," cried our entertainer, "that there
should be any found at present advocates for slavery? Any
who are for meanly giving up the privileges of Britons? Can
any, Sir, be so abject?"

"No, Sir," replied I, "I am for liberty, that attribute of
Gods! Glorious liberty! that theme of modern declamation. I
would have all men kings. I would be a king myself. We have
all naturally an equal right to the throne: we are all originally
equal. This is my opinion, and was once the opinion of a set
of honest men who were called Levellers. They tried to erect
themselves into a community, where all should be equally free.
But, alas! it would never answer; for there were some among
them stronger, and some more cunning than others, and these
became masters of the rest; for as sure as your groom rides
your horses because he is a cunninger animal than they, so
surely will the animal that is cunninger or stronger than he
sit upon his shoulders in turn. Since then it is entailed upon

humanity to submit, and some are born to command and others to obey, the question is, as there must be tyrants, whether it is better to have them in the same house with us, or in the same village, or still farther off, in the metropolis. Now, Sir, for my own part, as I naturally hate the face of a tyrant, the farther off he is removed from me, the better pleased am I. The generality of mankind also are of my way of thinking and have unanimously created one king, whose election at once diminishes the number of tyrants, and puts tyranny at the greatest distance from the greatest number of people. Now those who were tyrants themselves before the election of one tyrant are naturally averse to a power raised over them, and whose weight must ever lean heaviest on the subordinate orders. It is the interest of the great, therefore, to diminish kingly power as much as possible; because whatever they take from it is naturally restored to themselves; and all they have to do in a state, is to undermine the single tyrant, by which they resume their primæval authority. Now a state may be so constitutionally circumstanced, its laws may be so disposed, and its men of opulence so minded, as all to conspire to carry on this business of undermining monarchy. If the circumstances of the state be such, for instance, as to favour the accumulation of wealth, and make the opulent still more rich, this will encrease their strength and their ambition. But an accumulation of wealth must necessarily be the consequence in a state when more riches flow in from external commerce than arise from internal industry, for external commerce can only be managed to advantage by the rich, and they have also at the same time all the emoluments arising from internal industry; so that the rich, in such a state, have two sources of wealth, whereas the poor have but one. Thus wealth, in all commercial states, is found to accumulate, and such have hitherto in time become aristocratical. Besides this the very laws of a country may contribute to the accumulation of wealth; as when those natural ties that bind the rich and poor together are broken, and it is ordained that the rich shall only marry among each other; or when the learned are held unqualified to serve their country as counsellors merely from a defect of opulence, and wealth is thus made the object of a wise man's ambition; by these means, I say, and such means as these, riches will accumulate. The possessor of accumulated wealth, when furnished with the necessaries and pleasures of life, can employ the superfluity of fortune only in purchasing power. That is, differently speaking, in making dependants, in purchasing the liberty of the needy or the venal, of men who are willing to bear the mortification of contiguous tyranny for bread. Thus each very opulent man generally gathers round him a circle of the poorest of the people; and the polity abounding in accumulated wealth, may be compared to a Cartesian system, each orb with a vortex of its own. Those, however, who are willing to move in a great man's vortex are only such as must be slaves, the rabble of mankind, whose souls and whose education are adapted to servitude, and who know nothing of liberty except the name. But there must still be a large number of the people without the sphere of the opulent man's influence, namely, that order of men which subsists between the very rich and the very rabble, those men who are possest of too large fortunes to submit to the neighbouring man in power and yet are too poor to set up for tyranny themselves. In this middle order of mankind are generally to be found all the arts, wisdom, and virtues of society. This order alone is known to be the true preserver of freedom, and may be called the People. Now it may happen that this middle order of mankind may lose all its influence in a state, and its voice be in a manner drowned in that of the rabble, for if the fortune sufficient for qualifying a person at present to give his voice in state affairs be ten times less than was judged sufficient upon forming the constitution, it is evident that greater numbers of the rabble will thus be introduced into the political system, and they ever moving in the vortex of the great will follow where greatness shall direct. In such a state, therefore, all that the middle order has left is to preserve the prerogative and privileges of the one principal tyrant with the most sacred circumspection. For he divides the power of the rich and calls off the great from falling with tenfold weight on the middle order placed beneath them. The middle order may be compared to a town of which the opulent are forming the siege, and which the tyrant is hastening to relieve. While the besiegers are in dread of the external enemy, it is but natural to offer the townsmen the most specious terms, to flatter them with sounds and amuse them with privileges; but if they once defeat the tyrant, the walls of the town will be but a small defence to its inhabitants. What they may then expect may be seen by turning our eyes to Holland, Genoa, or Venice where the laws govern the poor, and the rich govern the law. I am then for, and would die for, monarchy, sacred monarchy; for if there be any thing sacred amongst men, it must be the anointed sovereign of his people, and every diminution of his power in war or in peace is an infringement upon the real liberties of the subject. The sounds of liberty, patriotism, and Britons, have already done *much;* it is to be hoped that the true sons of freedom will prevent their ever doing more. I have known many of those bold champions for liberty in my time, yet do I not remember one that was not in his heart and in his family a tyrant."

My warmth I found had lengthened this harangue beyond the rules of good breeding; but the impatience of my entertainer, who often strove to interrupt it, could be restrained no longer. "What," cried he, "then I have been all this while entertaining a Jesuit in parson's cloaths; but by all the coal mines of Cornwall, out he shall pack, if my name be Wilkinson." I now found I had gone too far, and asked pardon for the warmth with which I had spoken. "Pardon," returned he in a fury; "I think such principles demand ten thousand pardons. What, give up liberty, property, and, as the Gazetteer says, lie down to be saddled with wooden shoes! Sir, I insist upon your marching out of this house immediately, to prevent worse consequences, Sir, I insist upon it." I was going to repeat my remonstrances; but just then we heard a footman's rap at the door, and the two ladies cried out, "As sure as death there is our master and mistress come home." It seems my entertainer was all this while only the butler, who, in his master's absence, had a mind to cut a figure and be for a while the gentleman himself; and, to say the truth, he talked politics as well as most country gentlemen do. But nothing could now exceed my confusion upon seeing the gentleman with his lady enter, nor was their surprize at finding such company and good cheer less than ours. "Gentlemen," cried the real master of the house to me and my companion, "I am your most humble servant; but I protest this is so unexpected a favour that I almost sink under the obligation." However unexpected our company might be to him, his I am sure, was still more so to us, and I was struck dumb with the apprehensions of my own absurdity, when whom should I next see enter the room but my dear miss Arabella Wilmot, who was formerly designed to be married to my son George, but whose match was broken off, as already related. As soon as she saw me, she flew to my arms with the utmost joy. "My dear sir," cried she, "to what happy accident is it that we owe so unexpected a visit? I am sure my uncle and aunt will be in raptures when they find they have the good Dr. Primrose for their guest." Upon hearing my name, the old gentleman and lady very politely stept up and welcomed me with most cordial hospitality. Nor could they forbear smiling upon being informed of the nature of my present visit; but the unfortunate butler, whom they at first seemed disposed to turn away, was at my intercession forgiven.

Mr. Arnold and his lady, to whom the house belonged, now insisted upon having the pleasure of my stay for some days, and as their niece, my charming pupil, whose mind in some measure had been formed under my own instructions, joined in their entreaties, I complied. That night I was shewn to a magnificent chamber, and the next morning early Miss Wilmot desired to walk with me in the garden, which was decorated in the modern manner. After some time spent in pointing out the beauties of the place, she enquired, with seeming unconcern, when last I had heard from my son George. "Alas! Madam," cried I, "he has now been near three years absent, without ever writing to his friends or me. Where he is I know not; perhaps I shall never see him or happiness more. No, my dear Madam, we shall never more see such pleasing hours as were once spent by our fire-side at Wakefield. My little family are now dispersing very fast, and poverty has brought not only want but infamy upon us." The good-natured girl let fall a tear at this account; but as I saw her possessed of too much sensibility, I forbore a more minute detail of our sufferings. It was, however, some consolation to me to find that time had made no alteration in her affections, and that she had rejected several matches that had been made her since our leaving her part of the country. She led me round all the extensive improvements of the place, pointing to the several walks and arbours, and at the same time catching from every object a hint for some new question relative to my son. In this manner we spent the forenoon, till the bell summoned us in to dinner, where we found the manager of the strolling company, who was come to dispose of tickets for the Fair Penitent, which was to be acted that evening, the part of Horatio by a young gentleman who had never appeared on any stage before. He seemed to be very warm in the praises of the new performer, and averred that he never saw any who bid so fair for excellence. Acting, he observed, was not learned in a day; "But this gentleman," continued he, "seems born to tread the stage. His voice, his figure, and attitudes, are all admirable. We caught him up accidentally in our journey down." This account, in some measure, excited our curiosity, and at the entreaty of the ladies I was prevailed upon to accompany them to the play-house, which was no other than a barn. As the company with which I went was incontestably the chief of the place, we were received with the greatest respect and placed in the front seat of the theatre, where we sate for some time with no small impatience to see Horatio make his appearance. The new performer advanced at last, and I found it was my unfortunate son. He was going to begin, when, turning his eyes upon the audience, he perceived us, and stood at once speechless and immoveable. The actors behind the scene, who ascribed this pause to his natural timidity, attempted to encourage him; but instead of going on, he burst into a flood of tears and retired off the stage. I don't know what were the sensations I felt, for they succeeded with too much rapidity for description; but I was soon awaked from this disagreeable reverie by Miss Wilmot, who, pale and with a trembling voice, desired me to conduct her back to her uncle's. When got home, Mr. Arnold, who was as yet a stranger to our extraordinary behaviour, being informed that the new performer was my son, sent his coach and an invitation for him; and as he persisted in his refusal to appear again upon the stage, the players put another in his place, and we soon had him with us. Mr. Arnold gave him the kindest reception, and I received him with my usual transport; for I could never counterfeit false resentment. Miss Wilmot's reception was mixed with seeming neglect, and yet I could perceive she acted a studied part. The tumult in her mind seemed not yet abated; she said twenty giddy things that looked like joy, and then laughed loud at her own want of meaning. At intervals she would take a sly peep at the glass, as if happy in the consciousness of unresisting beauty, and often would ask questions, without giving any manner of attention to the answers.

CHAPTER TWENTY

The history of a philosophic vagabond, pursuing novelty, but
losing content.

After we had supped, Mrs. Arnold politely offered to send a couple of her footmen for my son's baggage, which he at first seemed to decline; but upon her pressing the request, he was obliged to inform her that a stick and wallet were all the moveable things upon this earth that he could boast of. "Why, aye my son," cried I, "you left me but poor, and poor I find you are come back; and yet I make no doubt you have seen a great deal of the world."—"Yes, Sir," replied my son, "but travelling after fortune is not the way to secure her; and, indeed, of late I have desisted from the pursuit."—"I fancy, Sir," cried Mrs. Arnold, "that the account of your adventures would be amusing; the first part of them I have often heard from my niece, but could the company prevail for the rest, it would be an additional obligation."—"Madam," replied my son, "I promise you the pleasure you have in hearing will not be half so great as my vanity in the recital, and yet in the whole narrative I can scarce promise you one adventure, as my account is not of what I did, but what I saw. The first misfortune of my life, which you all know, was great; but tho' it distrest, it could not sink me. No person ever had a better knack at hoping than I. The less kind I found fortune then, the more I expected from her another time, and being now at the bottom of her wheel, every new revolution might lift, but could not depress me. I proceeded, therefore, towards London in a fine morning, no way uneasy about to-morrow, but chearful as the birds that caroll'd by the road. I comforted myself with various reflections, that London was the true mart where abilities of every kind were sure of meeting distinction and reward.

"Upon my arrival in town, Sir, my first care was to deliver your letter of recommendation to our cousin, who was himself in little better circumstances than me. My first scheme, you know, Sir, was to be usher at an academy, and I asked his advice on the affair. Our cousin received the proposal with a true Sardonic grin. 'Aye,' cried he, 'this is a pretty career indeed that has been chalked out for you. I have been once an usher[68] at a boarding school myself; and may I die by an anodyne necklace,[69] but I had rather be an under turnkey in Newgate. I was up early and late. I was brow-beat by the master, hated for my ugly face by the mistress, worried by the boys within, and never permitted to stir out to meet civility abroad. But are you sure you are fit for a school? Let me examine you a little. Have you been bred apprentice to the business? No. Then you won't do for a school. Can you dress the boys hair? No. Then you won't do for a school. Have you had the small-pox? No. Then you won't do for a school. Can you lie three in a bed? No. Then you will never do for a school. Have you got a good stomach? Yes. Then you will by no means do for a school. No, Sir, if you are for a genteel easy profession, bind yourself seven years as an apprentice to turn a cutler's wheel; but avoid a school by any means. But come,' continued he, 'I see you are a lad of spirit and some learning, what do you think of commencing author, like me? You have read in books, no doubt, of men of genius starving at the trade, but at present I'll shew you forty very dull fellows about town that live by it in opulence. All honest joggtrot men, who go on smoothly and dully, and write history and politics, and are praised; and who, had they been bred coblers, would all their lives have only mended shoes, but never made them.'

"Finding that there was no great degree of gentility affixed to the character of an usher, I resolved to accept his proposal; and having the highest respect for literature, I hailed the antiqua mater of Grubstreet with reverence. I thought it my glory to pursue a track which Dryden and Otway trod before me. In fact, I considered the goddess of this region as the parent of excellence; and however an intercourse with the world might give us good sense, the poverty she granted was the nurse of genius! Big with these reflections I sate down, and finding that the best things remained to be said on the wrong side, I resolved to write a book that should be wholly new. I therefore drest up three paradoxes with some ingenuity. They were false, indeed, but they were new. The jewels of truth have been so often imported by others that nothing was left for me to import but some splendid things that at a distance looked every bit as well. Witness you powers what fancied importance sate perched upon my quill while I was writing. The whole learned world, I made no doubt, would rise to oppose my systems; but then I was prepared to oppose the whole learned world. Like the porcupine I sate self collected, with a quill pointed against every opposer."

"Well said, my boy," cried I, "and what subject did you treat upon? I hope you did not pass over the importance of Hierarchical monogamy. But I interrupt, go on; you published your paradoxes; well, and what did the learned world say to your paradoxes?"

"Sir," replied my son, "the learned world said nothing to my paradoxes; nothing at all, Sir. Every man of them was employed in praising his friends and himself, or condemning his enemies; and unfortunately, as I had neither, I suffered the cruellest mortification, neglect.

"As I was meditating one day in a coffee-house on the fate of my paradoxes, a little man happening to enter the room placed himself in the box before me, and after some preliminary discourse, finding me to be a scholar, drew out a bundle of proposals, begging me to subscribe to a new edition he was going to give the world of Propertius, with notes. This demand necessarily produced a reply that I had no money; and that concession led him to enquire into the nature of my expectations. Finding that my expectations were just as great as my purse, 'I see,' cried he, 'you are unacquainted with the town. I'll teach you a part of it. Look at these proposals; upon these very proposals I have subsisted very comfortably for twelve years. The moment a nobleman returns from his travels, a Creolian arrives from Jamaica, or a dowager from her country seat, I strike for a subscription. I first besiege their hearts with flattery and then pour in my proposals at the breach. If they subscribe readily the first time, I renew my request to beg a dedication fee. If they let me have that, I smite them once more for engraving their coat of arms at the top. Thus,' continued he, 'I live by vanity, and laugh at it. But between ourselves, I am now too well known. I should be glad to borrow your face a bit; a nobleman of distinction has just returned from Italy; my face is familiar to his porter; but if you bring this copy of verses, my life for it you succeed, and we divide the spoil.' "

"Bless us, George," cried I, "and is that the employment of poets now! Do men of their exalted talents thus stoop to beggary! Can they so far disgrace their calling as to make a vile traffic of praise for bread?"

"O no, Sir," returned he, "a true poet can never be so base; for wherever there is genius there is pride. The creatures I now describe are only beggars in rhyme. The real poet, as he braves every hardship for fame, so he is equally a coward to contempt, and none but those who are unworthy protection condescend to solicit it.

"Having a mind too proud to stoop to such indignities, and yet a fortune too humble to hazard a second attempt for fame, I was now obliged to take a middle course and write for bread. But I was unqualified for a profession where mere industry alone could ensure success. I could not suppress my lurking passion for applause, but usually consumed that time in efforts after excellence which takes up but little room, when it should have been more advantageously employed in the diffusive productions of fruitful mediocrity. My little piece would come forth in the mist of periodical publication, unnoticed and unknown. The public were more importantly employed than to observe the easy simplicity of my style, or the harmony of my periods. Sheet after sheet was thrown off to oblivion. My essays were buried among the essays upon liberty, eastern tales, and cures for the bite of a mad dog; while Philautos, Philalethes, Philelutheros and Philanthropos, all wrote better, because they wrote faster, than I.

"Now, therefore, I began to associate with none but disappointed authors like myself, who praised, deplored, and despised each other. The satisfaction we found in every celebrated writer's attempts was inversely as their merits. I found

that no genius in another could please me. My unfortunate
paradoxes had entirely dried up that source of comfort. I could
neither read nor write with satisfaction, for excellence in another was my aversion, and writing was my trade.

"In the midst of these gloomy reflections, as I was one day
sitting on a bench in St. James's Park, a young gentleman of
distinction, who had been my intimate acquaintance at the
university, approached me. We saluted each other with some
hesitation, he almost ashamed of being known to one who
made so shabby an appearance, and I afraid of a repulse. But
my suspicions soon vanished; for Ned Thornhill was at the
bottom a very good-natured fellow."

"What did you say, George?" interrupted I. "Thornhill,
was not that his name? It can certainly be no other than my
landlord."—"Bless me," cried Mrs. Arnold, "is Mr. Thornhill
so near a neighbour of yours? He has long been a friend in
our family, and we expect a visit from him shortly."

"My friend's first care," continued my son, "was to alter
my appearance by a very fine suit of his own cloaths, and then
I was admitted to his table upon the footing of half friend,
half underling. My business was to attend him at auctions, to
put him in spirits when he sate for his picture, to take the left
hand in his chariot when not filled by another, and to assist
at tattering a kip,[70] as the phrase was, when he had a mind for
a frolic. Besides this, I had twenty other little employments
in the family. I was to do many small things without bidding:
to carry the cork screw, to stand godfather to all the butler's
children, to sing when I was bid, to be never out of humour,
always to be humble, and, if I could, to be very happy.

"In this honourable post, however, I was not without a rival.
A captain of marines, who seemed formed for the place by
nature, opposed me in my patron's affections. His mother had
been laundress to a man of quality, and thus he early acquired
a taste for pimping and pedigree. As this gentleman made it
the study of his life to be acquainted with lords, though he
was dismissed from several for his stupidity, yet he found
many of them who permitted his assiduities, being as dull as
himself. As flattery was his trade, he practised it with the
easiest address imaginable; but it came aukward and stiff from
me; and as every day my patron's desire of flattery encreased,

so every hour being better acquainted with his defects, I became more unwilling to give it. Thus I was once more fairly going to give up the field to the captain, when my friend found occasion for my assistance. This was nothing less than to fight a duel for him with a gentleman whose sister it was pretended he had used ill. I readily complied with his request, and tho' I see you are displeased at my conduct, yet as it was a debt indispensably due to friendship, I could not refuse. I undertook the affair, disarmed my antagonist, and soon after had the pleasure of finding that the lady was only a woman of the town and the fellow her bully and a sharper. This piece of service was repaid with the warmest professions of gratitude; but as my friend was to leave town in a few days, he knew no other method to serve me, but by recommending me to his uncle Sir William Thornhill and another nobleman of great distinction who enjoyed a post under the government. When he was gone, my first care was to carry his recommendatory letter to his uncle, a man whose character for every virtue was universal, yet just. I was received by his servants with the most hospitable smiles; for the looks of the domestics ever transmit their master's benevolence. Being shewn into a grand apartment where Sir William soon came to me, I delivered my message and letter, which he read and after pausing some minutes, 'Pray, Sir,' cried he, 'inform me what you have done for my kinsman, to deserve this warm recommendation? But I suppose, Sir, I guess at your merits, you have fought for him; and so you would expect a reward from me, for being the instrument of his vices. I wish, sincerely wish, that my present refusal may be some punishment for your guilt; but still more, that it may be some inducement to your repentance.'—The severity of this rebuke I bore patiently, because I knew it was just. My whole expectations now, therefore, lay in my letter to the great man. As the doors of the nobility are almost ever beset with beggars all ready to thrust in some sly petition, I found it no easy matter to gain admittance. However, after bribing the servants with half my worldly fortune, I was at last shewn into a spacious apartment, my letter being previously sent up for his lordship's inspection. During this anxious interval I had full time to look round me. Every thing was grand and of happy contrivance; the paintings, the furniture, the gildings, petrified me with awe and raised my idea of the owner. Ah, thought I to myself, how very great must the possessor of all these things be, who carries in his head the business of the state and whose house displays half the wealth of a kingdom; sure his genius must be unfathomable! During these awful reflections I heard a step come heavily forward. Ah, this is the great man himself! No, it was only a chambermaid. Another foot was heard soon after. This must be He! No, it was only the great man's valet de chambre. At last his lordship actually made his appearance. 'Are you,' cried he, 'the bearer of this here letter?' I answered with a bow. 'I learn by this,' continued he, 'as how that——' But just at that instant a servant delivered him a card, and without taking farther notice, he went out of the room and left me to digest my own happiness at leisure. I saw no more of him, till told by a footman that his lordship was going to his coach at the door. Down I immediately followed and joined my voice to that of three or four more who came, like me, to petition for favours. His lordship, however, went too fast for us and was gaining his Chariot door with large strides, when I hallowed out to know if I was to have any reply. He was by this time got in and muttered an answer, half of which only I heard, the other half was lost in the rattling of his chariot wheels. I stood for some time with my neck stretched out, in the posture of one that was listening to catch the glorious sounds, till looking round me, I found myself alone at his lordship's gate.

"My patience," continued my son, "was now quite exhausted; stung with the thousand indignities I had met with, I was willing to cast myself away, and only wanted the gulph to receive me. I regarded myself as one of those vile things that nature designed should be thrown by into her lumber room, there to perish in unpitied obscurity. I had still, however, half a guinea left, and of that I thought fortune herself should not deprive me; but in order to be sure of this, I was resolved to go instantly and spend it while I had it, and then trust to occurrences for the rest. As I was going along with this resolution, it happened that Mr. Crispe's office seemed invitingly open, to give me a welcome reception. In this office Mr. Crispe kindly offers all his majesty's subjects a generous promise of 30 l. a year, for which promise all they give in return is their liberty for life and permission to let him transport them to America as slaves. I was happy at finding a place where I could lose my fears in desperation, and therefore entered this cell, for it had the appearance of one, being dark, damp, and dirty. Here I found a number of poor creatures, all in circumstances like myself, expecting the arrival of Mr. Crispe, presenting a true epitome of English impatience. Each untractable soul at variance with fortune wreaked her injuries on their own hearts; but Mr. Crispe at last came down, and all our murmurs were hushed. He deigned to regard me with an air of peculiar approbation, and indeed he was the first man who for a month past had talked to me with smiles. After a few questions, he found I was fit for every thing in the world. He paused a while upon the properest means of providing for me, and slapping his forehead, as if he had found it, assured me that there was at that time an embassy talked of from the synod of Pensylvania to the Chickasaw Indians, and that he would use his interest to get me made secretary. I knew in my own heart that the fellow lied, and yet his promise gave me pleasure, there was something so magnificent in the sound. I fairly, therefore, divided my half-guinea, one-half of which went to be added to his thirty thousand pound, and with the other half I resolved to go to the next tavern, to be there more happy than he.

"As I was going out with that resolution, I was met at the door by the captain of a ship with whom I had formerly some little acquaintance, and he agreed to be my companion over a bowl of punch. As I never chose to make a secret of my circumstances, he assured me that I was upon the very point of ruin in listening to the office-keeper's promises, for that he only designed to sell me to the plantations. 'But,' continued he, 'I fancy you might, by a much shorter voyage, be very easily put into a genteel way of bread. Take my advice. My ship sails to-morrow for Amsterdam; what if you go in her as a passenger? The moment you land all you have to do is to teach the Dutchmen English, and I'll warrant you'll get pupils and money enough. I suppose you understand English,' added he, 'by this time, or the deuce is in it.' I confidently assured him of that; but expressed a doubt whether the Dutch would be willing to learn English. He affirmed with an oath that they were fond of it to distraction; and upon that affirmation I agreed with his proposal and embarked the next day to teach the Dutch English in Holland. The wind was fair, our voyage short, and after having paid my passage with half my moveables, I found myself, fallen as if from the skies, a stranger in one of the principal streets of Amsterdam. In this situation I was unwilling to let any time pass unemployed in teaching. I addressed myself therefore to two or three of those I met, whose appearance seemed most promising; but it was impossible to make ourselves mutually understood. It was not till this very moment I recollected that in order to teach Dutchmen English, it was necessary that they should first teach me Dutch. How I came to overlook so obvious an objection is to me amazing, but certain it is I overlooked it.

"This scheme thus blown up, I had some thoughts of fairly shipping back to England again; but happening into company with an Irish student, who was returning from Louvain, our conversation turning upon topics of literature, (for by the way it may be observed that I always forgot the meanness of my circumstances when I could converse upon such subjects) from him I learned that there were not two men in his whole university who understood Greek. This amazed me. I instantly resolved to travel to Louvain and there live by teaching Greek; and in this design I was heartened by my brother student, who threw out some hints that a fortune might be got by it.

"I set boldly forward the next morning. Every day lessened the burthen of my moveables, like Æsop and his basket of bread; for I paid them for my lodgings to the Dutch as I travelled on. When I came to Louvain, I was resolved not to go sneaking to the lower professors, but openly tendered my talents to the principal himself. I went, had admittance, and offered him my service as a master of the Greek language, which I had been told was a desideratum in this university. The *principal* seemed at first to doubt of my abilities; but of these I offered to convince him, by turning a part of any Greek author he should fix upon into Latin. Finding me perfectly earnest in my proposal, he addressed me thus: 'You see me, young man,' continued he, 'I never learned Greek, and I don't find that I ever missed it. I have had a doctor's cap and gown without Greek; I have ten thousand florins a year without Greek; and I eat heartily without Greek. In short,' continued he, 'I don't know Greek, and I do not believe there is any use in it.'

"I was now too far from home to think of returning; so I resolved to go forward. I had some knowledge of music, with a tolerable voice, and now turned what was once my amusement into a present means of bare subsistence. I passed among the harmless peasants of Flanders and among such of the French as were poor enough to be very merry; for I ever found them sprightly in proportion to their wants. Whenever I approached a peasant's house, towards night-fall, I played one of my most merry tunes, and that procured me not only a lodging, but subsistence for the next day. I once or twice attempted to play for people of fashion; but they still thought my performance odious and never rewarded me even with a trifle. This was to me the more extraordinary, as whenever I used formerly to play for company, when playing was my amusement, my music never failed to throw them into raptures, and the ladies especially; but as it was now my only means, it was received with contempt; a proof how ready the world is to under-rate those talents which a man lives by.

"In this manner I proceeded to Paris, with no design but just to look about me, and then to go forward. The people of Paris are much fonder of strangers that have money, than of those that have wit. You may imagine, then, as I could not boast much of either, that I was no great favourite. After I had walked about the town four or five days, and seen the outsides of the best houses, I was preparing to leave this retreat of venal hospitality, when passing through one of the principal streets, whom should I meet but our cousin, to whom you first recommended me. This meeting was very agreeable to me, and I believe not displeasing to him. He enquired into the nature of my journey to Paris and informed me of his business there, which was to collect pictures, medals, intaglios, and antiques of all kinds, for a gentleman in London who had just stept into taste and a large fortune. I was still more surprised at seeing our cousin pitched upon for this office, as himself had often assured me he knew nothing of the matter. Upon my asking how he had been taught the art of a connoscento so very suddenly, he assured me that nothing was more easy. The whole secret consisted in a strict adherence to two rules: the one always to observe that the picture might have been better if the painter had taken more pains; and the other, to praise the works of Pietro Perugino. 'But,' says he, 'as I once taught you how to be an author in London, I'll now undertake to instruct you in the art of picture buying at Paris.'

"With this proposal I very readily closed, as it was a living, and now all my ambition was to live. I went therefore to his lodgings, improved my dress by his assistance, and after some time, accompanied him to auctions of pictures, where the English gentry were expected to be purchasers. I was not a little surprised at his intimacy with people of the best fashion, who referred themselves to his judgment upon every picture or medal, as to an unerring standard of taste. He made very good use of my assistance upon these occasions; for when asked his opinion, he would gravely take me aside and ask mine, shrug, look wise, return, and assure the company that he could give no opinion upon an affair of so much importance. Yet there was sometimes an occasion for a more supported assurance. I remember to have seen him, after giving his opinion that the colouring of a picture was not mellow enough, very deliberately take a brush with brown varnish, that was accidentally lying in the place, and rub it over the piece with great composure before all the company, and then ask if he had not improved the tints.

"When he had finished his commission in Paris, he left me strongly recommended to several men of distinction, as a person very proper for a travelling tutor; and I was after some time employed in that capacity by a gentleman who brought his ward to Paris, in order to set him forward on his tour through Europe. I was to be the young gentleman's governor, with this injunction, that he should always be permitted to direct himself. My pupil in fact understood the art of guiding, in money concerns, much better than I. He was heir to a fortune of about two hundred thousand pounds, left him by an uncle in the West-Indies; and his guardians, to qualify him for the management of it, had bound him apprentice to an attorney. Thus avarice was his prevailing passion; all his questions on the road were how money might be saved: which was the least expensive course of travel, whether any thing could be bought that would turn to account when disposed of again in London. Such curiosities on the way as could be seen for nothing he was ready enough to look at; but if the sight was to be paid for, he usually asserted that he had been told it was not worth seeing. He never paid a bill that he would not observe, how amazingly expensive travelling was, and all this though he was not yet come to the age of twenty-one. When arrived at Leghorn, as we took a walk to look at the port and shipping, he enquired the expense of the passage by sea home to England. This he was informed was but a trifle, compared to his returning by land; he was therefore unable to withstand the temptation; so paying me the small part of my salary that was then due, he took leave and embarked with only one attendant for London.

"I now therefore was left once more upon the world at large; but then it was a thing I was used to. However my skill in music could avail me nothing in a country where every peasant was a better musician than I; but by this time I had acquired another talent, which answered my purpose as well, and this was a skill in disputation. In all the foreign universities and convents there are upon certain days philosophical theses maintained against every adventitious disputant; for which, if the champion opposes with any dexterity, he can claim a gratuity in money, a dinner, and a bed for one night. In this manner therefore I fought my way towards England, walked along from city to city, examined mankind more nearly, and, if I may so express it, saw both sides of the picture. My remarks, however, were few: I found that monarchy was the best government for the poor to live in, and commonwealths for the rich. I found that riches in general were in every country another name for freedom; and that no man is so fond of freedom himself that he would not chuse to subject the will of some individuals of society to his own.

"Upon my arrival in England I resolved to pay my respects first to you, and then to enlist as a volunteer in the first expedition that was sent out; but on my journey down my resolutions were changed by meeting an old acquaintance who I found belonged to a company of comedians that were going to make a summer campaign in the country. The company seemed not much to disapprove of me for an associate. They all, however, apprized me of the importance of the task at which I aimed, that the public was a many headed monster, and that only such as had very good heads could please it, that acting was not to be learnt in a day, and that without some traditional shrugs, which had been on the stage, and only on the stage, these hundred years, I could never pretend to please. The next difficulty was in fitting me with parts, as almost every character was in keeping. I was driven for some time from one character to another, till at last Horatio was fixed upon, which the presence of the present company happily hindered me from acting."

CHAPTER TWENTY-ONE

The short continuance of friendship amongst the vicious, which is coeval only with mutual satisfaction.

My son's account was too long to be delivered at once; the first part of it was begun that night and he was concluding the rest after dinner the next day, when the appearance of Mr. Thornhill's equipage at the door seemed to make a pause in the general satisfaction. The butler, who was now become my friend in the family, informed me with a whisper that the 'Squire had already made some overtures to Miss Wilmot and that her aunt and uncle seemed highly to approve the match. Upon Mr. Thornhill's entering, he seemed, at seeing my son and me, to start back; but I readily imputed that to surprize, and not displeasure. However, upon our advancing to salute him, he returned our greeting with the most apparent candour; and after a short time his presence seemed only to encrease the general good humour.

After tea he called me aside, to enquire after my daughter; but upon my informing him that my enquiry was unsuccessful, he seemed greatly surprised; adding that he had been since frequently at my house, in order to comfort the rest of my family, whom he left perfectly well. He then asked if I had communicated her misfortune to Miss Wilmot or my son; and upon my replying that I had not told them as yet, he greatly approved my prudence and precaution, desiring me by all means to keep it a secret: "For, at best," cried he, "it is but divulging one's own infamy; and perhaps Miss Livy may not be so guilty as we all imagine." We were here interrupted by a servant who came to ask the 'Squire in, to stand up at country dances; so that he left me quite pleased with the interest he seemed to take in my concerns. His addresses, however, to Miss Wilmot were too obvious to be mistaken; and yet she seemed not perfectly pleased, but bore them rather in compliance to the will of her aunt than from real inclination. I had even the satisfaction to see her lavish some kind looks upon my unfortunate son, which the other could neither extort by his fortune nor assiduity. Mr. Thornhill's seeming composure, however, not a little surprised me; we had now continued here a week, at the pressing instances of Mr. Arnold; but each day the more tenderness Miss Wilmot shewed my son, Mr. Thornhill's friendship seemed proportionably to encrease for him.

He had formerly made us the most kind assurances of using his interest to serve the family, but now his generosity was not confined to promises alone; the morning I designed for my departure, Mr. Thornhill came to me with looks of real pleasure to inform me of a piece of service he had done for his friend George. This was nothing less than his having procured him an ensign's commission in one of the regiments that was going to the West Indies, for which he had promised but one hundred pounds, his interest having been sufficient to get an abatement of the other two. "As for this trifling piece of service," continued the young gentleman, "I desire no other reward but the pleasure of having served my friend; and as for the hundred pound to be paid, if you are unable to raise it yourselves, I will advance it, and you shall repay me at your leisure." This was a favour we wanted words to express our sense of. I readily therefore gave my bond for the money and testified as much gratitude as if I never intended to pay.

George was to depart for town the next day to secure his commission in pursuance of his generous patron's directions, who judged it highly expedient to use dispatch lest in the mean time another should step in with more advantageous proposals. The next morning, therefore, our young soldier was early prepared for his departure and seemed the only person among us that was not affected by it. Neither the fatigues and dangers he was going to encounter, nor the friends and mistress, for Miss Wilmot actually loved him, he was leaving behind, any way damped his spirits. After he had taken leave of the rest of the company, I gave him all I had, my blessing. "And now, my boy," cried I, "thou art going to fight for thy country, remember how thy brave grandfather fought for his sacred king, when loyalty among Britons was a virtue. Go, my boy, and imitate him in all but his misfortunes, if it was a misfortune to die with Lord Falkland. Go, my boy, and if you fall, tho' distant, exposed and unwept by those that love you, the most precious tears are those with which heaven bedews the unburied head of a soldier."

The next morning I took leave of the good family that had been kind enough to entertain me so long, not without several expressions of gratitude to Mr. Thornhill for his late bounty. I left them in the enjoyment of all that happiness which affluence and good breeding procure and returned towards home, despairing of ever finding my daughter more, but sending a sigh to heaven to spare and to forgive her. I was now come within about twenty miles of home, having hired an horse to carry me, as I was yet but weak, and comforted myself with the hopes of soon seeing all I held dearest upon earth. But the night coming on, I put up at a little public house by the road-side, and asked for the landlord's company over a pint of wine. We sate beside his kitchen fire, which was the best room in the house, and chatted on politics and the news of the country. We happened, among other topics, to talk of young 'Squire Thornhill, whom the host assured me was hated as much as an uncle of his, who sometimes came down to the country, was loved. He went on to observe that he made it his whole study to betray the daughters of such as received him to their houses, and after a fortnight or three weeks possession, he turned them out unrewarded and abandoned to the world. As we continued our discourse in this manner, his wife, who had been out to get change, returned, and perceiving that her husband was enjoying a pleasure in which she was not a sharer, she asked him in an angry tone what he did there, to which he only replied in an ironical way by drinking her health. "Mr. Symmonds," cried she, "you use me very ill, and I'll bear it no longer. Here three parts of the business is left for me to do and the fourth left unfinished, while you do nothing but soak with the guests all day long, whereas if a spoonful of liquor were to cure me of a fever, I never touch a drop." I now found what she would be at and immediately poured her out a glass, which she received with a curtesy, and drinking towards my good health, "Sir," resumed she, "it is not so much for the value of the liquor I am angry, but one cannot help it, when the house is going out of the windows. If the customers or guests are to be dunned, all the burthen lies upon my back; he'd as lief eat that glass as budge after them himself. There now above stairs we have a young woman who has come to take up her lodgings here, and I don't believe she has got any money by her over civility. I am certain she is very slow of payment, and I wish she were put in mind of it."—"What signifies minding her," cried the host, "if she be slow, she is sure."—"I don't know that," replied the wife; "but I know that I am sure she has been here a fortnight, and we have not yet seen the cross of her money." —"I suppose, my dear," cried he, "we shall have it all in a lump."—"In a lump!" cried the other, "I hope we may get it any way; and that I am resolved we shall this very night, or out she tramps, bag and baggage."—"Consider, my dear," cried the husband, "she is a gentlewoman, and deserves more respect."—"As for the matter of that," returned the hostess, "gentle or simple, out she shall pack with a sassarara.[71] Gentry may be good things where they take; but for my part I never saw much good of them at the sign of the Harrow."—Thus saying, she ran up a narrow flight of stairs that went from the kitchen to a room over-head, and I soon perceived by the loudness of her voice and the bitterness of her reproaches, that no money was to be had from her lodger. I could hear her remonstrances very distinctly: "Out I say, pack out this moment, tramp thou infamous strumpet, or I'll give thee a mark thou won't be the better for this three months. What! you trumpery, to come and take up an honest house, without cross or coin to bless yourself with; come along I say."—"O dear madam," cried the stranger, "pity me, pity a poor abandoned creature for one night, and death will soon do the rest."—I

instantly knew the voice of my poor ruined child Olivia. I flew
to her rescue, while the woman was dragging her along by the
hair, and I caught the dear forlorn wretch in my arms.—"Welcome, any way welcome, my dearest lost one, my treasure, to
your poor old father's bosom. Tho' the vicious forsake thee,
there is yet one in the world that will never forsake thee; tho'
thou hadst ten thousand crimes to answer for, he will forget
them all."—"O my own dear,"—for minutes she could no
more—"my own dearest good papa! Could angels be kinder!
How do I deserve so much! The villain, I hate him and myself to be a reproach to such goodness. You can't forgive me.
I know you cannot."—"Yes, my child, from my heart I do
forgive thee! Only repent, and we both shall yet be happy.
We shall see many pleasant days yet, my Olivia."—"Ah!
never, sir, never. The rest of my wretched life must be infamy abroad and shame at home. But, alas! papa, you look
much paler than you used to do. Could such a thing as I am
give you so much uneasiness? Sure you have too much wisdom to take the miseries of my guilt upon yourself."—"Our
wisdom, young woman," replied I.—"Ah, why so cold a name,
papa?" cried she. "This is the first time you ever called me
by so cold a name."—"I ask pardon, my darling," returned I;
"but I was going to observe, that wisdom makes but a slow
defence against trouble, though at last a sure one." The
landlady now returned to know if we did not chuse a more
genteel apartment, to which assenting, we were shewn a room
where we could converse more freely. After we had talked
ourselves into some degree of tranquillity, I could not avoid
desiring some account of the gradations that led to her present wretched situation. "That villain, sir," said she, "from the
first day of our meeting made me honourable, though private,
proposals."

"Villain indeed!" cried I: "and yet it in some measure sur-
prizes me how a person of Mr. Burchell's good sense and
seeming honour could be guilty of such deliberate baseness,
and thus step into a family to undo it."

"My dear papa," returned my daughter, "you labour under a
strange mistake. Mr. Burchell never attempted to deceive me.
Instead of that he took every opportunity of privately admon-
ishing me against the artifices of Mr. Thornhill, whom now

I find was even worse than he represented him."—"Mr. Thornhill," interrupted I; "can it be?"—"Yes, Sir," returned she, "it was Mr. Thornhill who seduced me, who employed the two ladies, as he called them, but who in fact were abandoned women of the town, without breeding or pity, to decoy us up to London. Their artifices, you may remember, would have certainly succeeded, but for Mr. Burchell's letter, who directed those reproaches at them which we all applied to ourselves. How he came to have so much influence as to defeat their intentions still remains a secret to me; but I am convinced he was ever our warmest, sincerest friend."

"You amaze me, my dear," cried I; "but now I find my first suspicions of Mr. Thornhill's baseness were too well grounded; but he can triumph in security, for he is rich, and we are poor. But tell me, my child, sure it was no small temptation that could thus obliterate all the impressions of such an education, and so virtuous a disposition as thine?"

"Indeed, Sir," replied she, "he owes all his triumph to the desire I had of making him, and not myself, happy. I knew that the ceremony of our marriage, which was privately performed by a popish priest, was no way binding, and that I had nothing to trust to but his honour."—"What," interrupted I, "and were you indeed married by a priest, and in orders?" —"Indeed, Sir, we were," replied she, "though we were both sworn to conceal his name."—"Why then, my child, come to my arms again, and now you are a thousand times more welcome than before; for you are now his wife to all intents and purposes; nor can all the laws of man, tho' written upon tables of adamant, lessen the force of that sacred connexion."

"Alas, Papa," replied she, "you are but little acquainted with his villainies; he has been married already, by the same priest, to six or eight wives more, whom, like me, he has deceived and abandoned."

"Has he so?" cried I, "then we must hang the priest, and you shall inform against him to-morrow."—"But, Sir," returned she, "will that be right, when I am sworn to secrecy?"— "My dear," I replied, "if you have made such a promise, I cannot, nor will not, tempt you to break it. Even tho' it may benefit the public, you must not inform against him. In all human institutions a smaller evil is allowed to procure a greater good;

as in politics, a province may be given away to secure a kingdom; in medicine, a limb may be lopt off to preserve the body. But in religion the law is written and inflexible, *never* to do evil. And this law, my child, is right, for otherwise, if we commit a smaller evil to procure a greater good, certain guilt would be thus incurred in expectation of contingent advantage. And though the advantage should certainly follow, yet the interval between commission and advantage, which is allowed to be guilty, may be that in which we are called away to answer for the things we have done, and the volume of human actions is closed for ever. But I interrupt you, my dear; go on."

"The very next morning," continued she, "I found what little expectations I was to have from his sincerity. That very morning he introduced me to two unhappy women more, whom, like me, he had deceived, but who lived in contented prostitution. I loved him too tenderly to bear such rivals in his affections, and strove to forget my infamy in a tumult of pleasures. With this view, I danced, dressed, and talked; but still was unhappy. The gentlemen who visited there told me every moment of the power of my charms, and this only contributed to encrease my melancholy, as I had thrown all their power quite away. Thus each day I grew more pensive, and he more insolent, till at last the monster had the assurance to offer me to a young Baronet of his acquaintance. Need I describe, Sir, how his ingratitude stung me. My answer to this proposal was almost madness. I desired to part. As I was going he offered me a purse; but I flung it at him with indignation and burst from him in a rage that for a while kept me insensible of the miseries of my situation. But I soon looked round me and saw myself a vile, abject, guilty thing, without one friend in the world to apply to.

"Just in that interval, a stage coach happening to pass by, I took a place, it being my only aim to be driven at a distance from a wretch I despised and detested. I was set down here, where since my arrival, my own anxiety and this woman's unkindness have been my only companions. The hours of pleasure that I have passed with my mamma and sister now grow painful to me. Their sorrows are much; but mine is greater than theirs, for mine is guilt and infamy."

"Have patience, my child," cried I, "and I hope things will

yet be better. Take some repose to-night, and to-morrow I'll carry you home to your mother and the rest of the family, from whom you will receive a kind reception. Poor woman, this has gone to her heart; but she loves you still, Olivia, and will forget it."

CHAPTER TWENTY-TWO

Offences are easily pardoned where there is love at bottom.

The next morning I took my daughter behind me, and set out on my return home. As we travelled along, I strove by every persuasion to calm her sorrows and fears and to arm her with resolution to bear the presence of her offended mother. I took every opportunity, from the prospect of a fine country through which we passed, to observe how much kinder heaven was to us than we were to each other, and that the misfortunes of nature's making were very few. I assured her that she should never perceive any change in my affections, and that during my life, which yet might be long, she might depend upon a guardian and an instructor. I armed her against the censures of the world, shewed her that books were sweet unreproaching companions to the miserable, and that if they could not bring us to enjoy life, they would teach us to endure it.

The hired horse that we rode was to be put up that night at an inn by the way, within about five miles from my house, and as I was willing to prepare my family for my daughter's reception, I determined to leave her that night at the inn and to come for her, accompanied by my daughter Sophia, early the next morning. It was night before we reached our appointed stage; however, after seeing her provided with a decent apartment and having ordered the hostess to prepare proper refreshments, I kissed her and proceeded towards home. My heart caught new sensations of pleasure the nearer I approached that peaceful mansion. As a bird that has been frighted from its nest, my affections out-went my haste, and hovered round my little fire-side with all the rapture of expectation. I called up the many fond things I had to say, and anticipated the welcome I was to receive. I already felt my wife's tender embrace, and smiled at the joy of my little ones.

As I walked but slowly, the night wained apace. The labourers of the day were all retired to rest; the lights were out in every cottage; no sounds were heard but of the shrilling cock and the deep-mouthed watch-dog, at hollow distance. I approached my little abode of pleasure, and before I was within a furlong of the place, our honest mastiff came running to welcome me.

It was now near mid-night that I came to knock at my door; all was still and silent; my heart dilated with unutterable happiness, when, to my amazement, the house was bursting out in a blaze of fire and every aperture was red with conflagration! I gave a loud convulsive outcry, and fell upon the pavement insensible. This alarmed my son, who perceiving the flames, instantly waked my wife and daughter, and all running out, naked, and wild with apprehension, recalled me to life with their anguish. But it was only to objects of new terror; for the flames had, by this time, caught the roof of our dwelling, part after part continuing to fall in, while the family stood with silent agony, looking on as if they enjoyed the blaze. I gazed upon them and upon it by turns, and then looked round me for my two little ones; but they were not to be seen. O misery! "Where," cried I, "where are my little ones?"—"They are burnt to death in the flames," says my wife calmly, "and I will die with them."—That moment I heard the cry of the babes within, who were just awaked by the fire, and nothing could have stopped me. "Where, where are my children?" cried I, rushing through the flames and bursting the door of the chamber in which they were confined, "Where are my little ones?"—"Here, dear papa, here we are," cried they together, while the flames were just catching the bed where they lay. I caught them both in my arms and snatched them through the fire as fast as possible, while just as I was got out, the roof sunk in. "Now," cried I, holding up my children, "now let the flames burn on, and all my possessions perish. Here they are, I have saved my treasure. Here, my dearest, here are our treasures, and we shall yet be happy." We kissed our little darlings a thousand times, they clasped us round the neck and seemed to share our transports, while their mother laughed and wept by turns.

I now stood a calm spectator of the flames, and after some

time, began to perceive that my arm to the shoulder was scorched in a terrible manner. It was therefore out of my power to give my son any assistance, either in attempting to save our goods or preventing the flames spreading to our corn. By this time the neighbours were alarmed and came running to our assistance; but all they could do was to stand, like us, spectators of the calamity. My goods, among which were the notes I had reserved for my daughters fortunes, were entirely consumed, except a box with some papers that stood in the kitchen and two or three things more of little consequence, which my son brought away in the beginning. The neighbours contributed, however, what they could to lighten our distress. They brought us cloaths and furnished one of our out-houses with kitchen utensils; so that by daylight we had another, tho' a wretched, dwelling to retire to. My honest next neighbour and his children were not the least assiduous in providing us with every thing necessary and offering whatever consolation untutored benevolence could suggest.

When the fears of my family had subsided, curiosity to know the cause of my long stay began to take place; having therefore informed them of every particular, I proceeded to prepare them for the reception of our lost one, and tho' we had nothing but wretchedness now to impart, yet to procure her a welcome to what we had. This task would have been more difficult but for our recent calamity, which had humbled my wife's pride and blunted it by more poignant afflictions. Being unable to go for my poor child myself, as my arm now grew very painful, I sent my son and daughter, who soon returned, supporting the wretched delinquent, who had not courage to look up at her mother, whom no instructions of mine could persuade to a perfect reconciliation; for women have a much stronger sense of female error than men. "Ah, madam," cried her mother, "this is but a poor place you are come to after so much finery. My daughter Sophy and I can afford but little entertainment to persons who have kept company only with people of distinction. Yes, Miss Livy, your poor father and I have suffered very much of late; but I hope heaven will forgive you."—During this reception, the unhappy victim stood pale and trembling, unable to weep or to reply, but I could not continue a silent spectator of her distress;

wherefore assuming a degree of severity in my voice and manner which was ever followed with instant submission, "I entreat, woman, that my words may be now marked once for all. I have here brought you back a poor deluded wanderer; her return to duty demands the revival of our tenderness. The real hardships of life are now coming fast upon us; let us not therefore encrease them by dissention among each other. If we live harmoniously together, we may yet be contented, as there are enough of us here to shut out the censuring world and keep each other in countenance. The kindness of heaven is promised to the penitent, and let ours be directed by the example. Heaven, we are assured, is much more pleased to view a repentant sinner, than many persons who have supported a course of undeviating rectitude. And this is right; for that single effort by which we stop short in the down-hill path to perdition is itself a greater exertion of virtue than an hundred acts of justice."

CHAPTER TWENTY-THREE

None but the guilty can be long and completely miserable.

Some assiduity was now required to make our present abode as convenient as possible, and we were soon again qualified to enjoy our former serenity. Being disabled myself from assisting my son in our usual occupations, I read to my family from the few books that were saved, and particularly from such as, by amusing the imagination, contributed to ease the heart. Our good neighbours too came every day with the kindest condolence and fixed a time in which they were all to assist at repairing my former dwelling. Honest farmer Williams was not last among these visitors, but heartily offered his friendship. He would even have renewed his addresses to my daughter; but she rejected them in such a manner as totally represt his future solicitations. Her grief seemed formed for continuing, and she was the only person of our little society that a week did not restore to chearfulness. She now lost that unblushing innocence which once taught her to respect herself and to seek pleasure by pleasing. Anxiety now had taken strong possession of her mind, her beauty began to be impaired with her constitution, and neglect still more contributed to diminish it. Every tender epithet bestowed on her sister brought a pang to her heart and a tear to her eye; and as one vice, tho' cured, almost ever plants others where it has been, so her former guilt, tho' driven out by repentance, left jealousy and envy behind. I strove a thousand ways to lessen her care and even forgot my own pain in a concern for her's, collecting such amusing passages of history as a strong memory and some reading could suggest. "Our happiness, my dear," I would say, "is in the power of one who can bring it about a thousand unforeseen ways that mock our foresight. If example be necessary to prove this, I'll give you a story, my child, told us by a grave, tho' sometimes a romancing, historian.

"Matilda was married very young to a Neapolitan nobleman of the first quality and found herself a widow and a mother at the age of fifteen. As she stood one day caressing her infant son in the open window of an apartment, which hung over the river Volturna, the child with a sudden spring leaped from her arms into the flood below and disappeared in a moment. The mother, struck with instant surprize and making an effort to save him, plunged in after; but far from being able to assist the infant, she herself with great difficulty escaped to the opposite shore, just when some French soldiers were plundering the country on that side who immediately made her their prisoner.

"As the war was then carried on between the French and Italians with the utmost inhumanity, they were going at once to perpetrate those two extremes suggested by appetite and cruelty. This base resolution, however, was opposed by a young officer who, tho' their retreat required the utmost expedition, placed her behind him and brought her in safety to his native city. Her beauty at first caught his eye, her merit soon after his heart. They were married; he rose to the highest posts; they lived long together and were happy. But the felicity of a soldier can never be called permanent; after an interval of several years, the troops which he commanded having met with a repulse, he was obliged to take shelter in the city where he had lived with his wife. Here they suffered a siege, and the city at length was taken. Few histories can produce more various instances of cruelty than those which the French

and Italians at that time exercised upon each other. It was resolved by the victors upon this occasion to put all the French
prisoners to death; but particularly the husband of the unfortunate Matilda, as he was principally instrumental in protracting the siege. Their determinations were, in general, executed
almost as soon as resolved upon. The captive soldier was led
forth, and the executioner with his sword stood ready, while
the spectators in gloomy silence awaited the fatal blow, which
was only suspended till the general who presided as judge
should give the signal. It was in this interval of anguish and
expectation that Matilda came to take her last farewell of her
husband and deliverer, deploring her wretched situation and
the cruelty of fate that had saved her from perishing by a premature death in the river Volturna, to be the spectator of still
greater calamities. The general, who was a young man, was
struck with surprize at her beauty, and pity at her distress;
but with still stronger emotions when he heard her mention
her former dangers. He was her son, the infant for whom she
had encounter'd so much danger. He acknowledged her at
once as his mother, and fell at her feet. The rest may be easily
supposed: the captive was set free, and all the happiness that
love, friendship, and duty could confer on each, were united."

In this manner I would attempt to amuse my daughter, but
she listened with divided attention; for her own misfortunes
engrossed all the pity she once had for those of another, and
nothing gave her ease. In company she dreaded contempt, and
in solitude she only found anxiety. Such was the colour of her
wretchedness when we received certain information that Mr.
Thornhill was going to be married to Miss Wilmot, for whom
I always suspected he had a real passion, tho' he took every
opportunity before me to express his contempt both of her
person and fortune. This news only served to encrease poor
Olivia's affliction; such a flagrant breach of fidelity was more
than her courage could support. I was resolved, however, to
get more certain information and to defeat, if possible, the
completion of his designs, by sending my son to old Mr. Wilmot's with instructions to know the truth of the report, and
to deliver Miss Wilmot a letter intimating Mr. Thornhill's
conduct in my family. My son went, in pursuance of my directions, and in three days returned, assuring us of the truth

of the account; but that he had found it impossible to deliver the letter, which he was therefore obliged to leave, as Mr. Thornhill and Miss Wilmot were visiting round the country. They were to be married, he said, in a few days, having appeared together at church the Sunday before he was there, in great splendour, the bride attended by six young ladies drest in white and he by as many gentlemen. Their approaching nuptials filled the whole country with rejoicing, and they usually rode out together in the grandest equipage that had been seen in the country for many years. All the friends of both families, he said, were there, particularly the 'Squire's uncle, Sir William Thornhill, who bore so good a character. He added that nothing but mirth and feasting were going forward, that all the country praised the young bride's beauty and the bridegroom's fine person, and that they were immensely fond of each other, concluding that he could not help thinking Mr. Thornhill one of the most happy men in the world.

"Why let him if he can," returned I, "but, my son, observe this bed of straw and unsheltering roof, those mouldering walls and humid floor, my wretched body thus disabled by fire and my children weeping round me for bread; you have come home, my child, to all this; yet here, even here, you see a man that would not for a thousand worlds exchange situations. O, my children, if you could but learn to commune with your own hearts and know what noble company you can make them, you would little regard the elegance and splendours of the worthless. Almost all men have been taught to call life a passage, and themselves the travellers. The similitude still may be improved when we observe that the good are joyful and serene, like travellers that are going towards home, the wicked but by intervals happy, like travellers that are going into exile."

The Traveller

My compassion for my poor daughter, overpowered by this new disaster, interrupted what I had farther to observe. I bade her mother support her, and after a short time she recovered. She appeared from this time more calm, and I imagined had gained a new degree of resolution; but appearances deceived me, for her tranquility was the langour of over-wrought resentment. A supply of provisions, charitably sent us by my kind parishioners, seemed to diffuse chearfulness amongst the rest of the family, nor was I displeased at seeing them once more sprightly and at ease. It would have been unjust to damp their satisfactions, merely to condole with resolute melancholy, or to burthen them with a sadness they did not feel. Once more, therefore, the tale went round and the song was demanded, and chearfulness condescended to hover round our little habitation.

CHAPTER TWENTY-FOUR

Fresh calamities.

The next morning the sun arose with peculiar warmth for the season; so that we agreed to breakfast together at the honey-suckle bank, where, while we sate, my youngest daughter, at my request, joined her voice to the concert on the trees about us. It was here my poor Olivia first met her seducer, and every object served to recall her sadness. But that melancholy which is excited by objects of pleasure or inspired by sounds of harmony sooths the heart instead of corroding it. Her mother too upon this occasion felt a pleasing distress and wept, and loved her daughter as before. "Do, my pretty Olivia," cried she, "let us have that little melancholy air your pappa was so fond of; your sister Sophy has already obliged us. Do child; it will please your old father." She complied in a manner so exquisitely pathetic as moved me.

> When lovely woman stoops to folly,
>   And finds too late that men betray,
> What charm can sooth her melancholy,
>   What art can wash her guilt away?
>
> The only art her guilt to cover,
>   To hide her shame from every eye,
> To give repentance to her lover,
>   And wring his bosom—is to die.

As she was concluding the last stanza, to which an interruption in her voice from sorrow gave peculiar softness, the appearance of Mr. Thornhill's equipage at a distance alarmed us all but particularly encreased the uneasiness of my eldest daughter, who, desirous of shunning her betrayer, returned to the house with her sister. In a few minutes he was alighted from his chariot, and making up to the place where I was still sitting, enquired after my health with his usual air of familiarity. "Sir," replied I, "your present assurance only serves to aggravate the baseness of your character; and there was a time when I would have chastised your insolence for presuming thus to appear before me. But now you are safe; for age has cooled my passions, and my calling restrains them."

"I vow, my dear sir," returned he, "I am amazed at all this; nor can I understand what it means! I hope you don't think your daughter's late excursion with me had any thing criminal in it."

"Go," cried I, "thou art a wretch, a poor, pitiful wretch, and every way a lyar; but your meanness secures you from my anger! Yet, sir, I am descended from a family that would not have borne this! And so, thou vile thing, to gratify a momentary passion thou hast made one poor creature wretched for life, and polluted a family that had nothing but honour for their portion."

"If she or you," returned he, "are resolved to be miserable, I cannot help it. But you may still be happy; and whatever opinion you may have formed of me, you shall ever find me ready to contribute to it. We can readily marry her to another, and what is more, she may keep her lover beside; for I protest I shall ever continue to have a true regard for her."

I found all my passions awakened at this new degrading proposal; for though the mind may often be calm under great injuries, little villainy can at any time get within the soul and sting it into rage.—"Avoid my sight, thou reptile," cried I, "nor continue to insult me with thy presence. Were my brave son at home, he would not suffer this; but I am old, and disabled, and every way undone."

"I find," cried he, "you are bent upon obliging me to talk in an harsher manner than I intended. But as I have shewn you what may be hoped from my friendship, it may not be improper to represent what may be the consequences of my resentment. My attorney, to whom your late bond has been transferred, threatens hard, nor do I know how to prevent the course of justice except by paying the money myself, which, as I have been at some expenses lately previous to my intended marriage, it is not so easy to be done. And then my steward talks of driving for the rent; it is certain he knows his duty, for I never trouble myself with affairs of that nature. Yet still I could wish to serve you, and even to have you and your daughter present at my marriage, which is shortly to be solemnized with Miss Wilmot; it is even the request of my charming Arabella herself, whom I hope you will not refuse."

"Mr. Thornhill," replied I, "hear me once for all: as to your marriage with any but my daughter, that I never will consent to; and though your friendship could raise me to a throne or your resentment sink me to the grave, yet would I despise both. Thou hast once wofully, irreparably, deceived me. I reposed my heart upon thine honour and have found its baseness. Never more, therefore, expect friendship from me. Go, and possess what fortune has given thee, beauty, riches, health, and pleasure. Go, and leave me to want, infamy, disease, and sorrow. Yet humbled as I am, shall my heart still vindicate its dignity, and though thou hast my forgiveness, thou shalt ever have my contempt."

"If so," returned he, "depend upon it you shall feel the effects of this insolence, and we shall shortly see which is the fittest object of scorn, you or me."—Upon which he departed abruptly.

My wife and son, who were present at this interview, seemed terrified with the apprehension. My daughters also, finding that he was gone, came out to be informed of the result of our conference which, when known, alarmed them not less than the rest. But as to myself, I disregarded the utmost stretch of his malevolence; he had already struck the blow, and now I stood prepared to repel every new effort, like one of those instruments used in the art of war, which, however thrown, still presents a point to receive the enemy.

We soon, however, found that he had not threatened in vain; for the very next morning his steward came to demand my annual rent, which, by the train of accidents already related, I was unable to pay. The consequence of my incapacity was his driving my cattle that evening, and their being appraised and sold the next day for less than half their value. My wife and children now therefore entreated me to comply upon any terms, rather than incur certain destruction. They even begged of me to admit his visits once more and used all their little eloquence to paint the calamities I was going to endure: the terrors of a prison in so rigorous a season as the present, with the danger that threatened my health from the late accident that happened by the fire. But I continued inflexible.

"Why, my treasures," cried I, "why will you thus attempt to persuade me to the thing that is not right! My duty has taught me to forgive him; but my conscience will not permit me to approve. Would you have me applaud to the world what my heart must internally condemn? Would you have me tamely sit down and flatter our infamous betrayer; and to avoid a prison continually suffer the more galling bonds of mental confinement! No, never. If we are to be taken from this abode, only let us hold to the right, and wherever we are thrown, we can still retire to a charming apartment and look round our own hearts with intrepidity and with pleasure!"

In this manner we spent that evening. Early the next morning, as the snow had fallen in great abundance in the night, my son was employed in clearing it away and opening a passage before the door. He had not been thus engaged long, when he came running in with looks all pale to tell us that two strangers, whom he knew to be officers of justice, were making towards the house.

Just as he spoke they came in, and approaching the bed where I lay, after previously informing me of their employment and business, made me their prisoner, bidding me prepare to go with them to the county gaol, which was eleven miles off.

"My friends," said I, "this is severe weather in which you have come to take me to a prison; and it is particularly unfortunate at this time, as one of my arms has lately been burnt in a terrible manner, and it has thrown me into a slight fever, and I want cloaths to cover me, and I am now too weak and old to walk far in such deep snow; but if it must be so, I'll try to obey you."

I then turned to my wife and children and directed them to get together what few things were left us and to prepare immediately for leaving this place. I entreated them to be expeditious and desired my son to assist his elder sister, who, from a consciousness that she was the cause of all our calamities, was fallen and had lost anguish in insensibility. I encouraged my wife, who, pale and trembling, clasped our affrighted little ones in her arms, that clung to her bosom in silence, dreading to look round at the strangers. In the mean time my youngest daughter prepared for our departure, and as she received several hints to use dispatch, in about an hour we were ready to depart.

CHAPTER TWENTY-FIVE

No situation, however wretched it seems, but has some sort of comfort attending it.

We set forward from this peaceful neighbourhood, and walked on slowly. My eldest daughter being enfeebled by a slow fever which had begun for some days to undermine her constitution, one of the officers, who had an horse, kindly took her behind him; for even these men cannot entirely divest themselves of humanity. My son led one of the little ones by the hand and my wife the other, while I leaned upon my youngest girl, whose tears fell not for her own but my distresses.

We were now got from my late dwelling about two miles, when we saw a crowd running and shouting behind us, consisting of about fifty of my poorest parishioners. These, with dreadful imprecations, soon seized upon the two officers of justice, and swearing they would never see their minister go to gaol while they had a drop of blood to shed in his defence, were going to use them with great severity. The consequence might have been fatal, had I not immediately interposed and with some difficulty rescued the officers from the hands of the enraged multitude. My children, who looked upon my delivery now as certain, appeared transported with joy and were incapable of containing their raptures. But they were soon undeceived upon hearing me address the poor deluded people, who came, as they imagined, to do me service.

"What! my friends," cried I, "and is this the way you love me! Is this the manner you obey the instructions I have given you from the pulpit! Thus to fly in the face of justice and bring down ruin on yourselves and me! Which is your ring-leader? Shew me the man that has thus seduced you. As sure as he lives he shall feel my resentment. Alas! my dear deluded flock, return back to the duty you owe to God, to your country, and to me. I shall yet perhaps one day see you in greater felicity here and contribute to make your lives more happy. But let it at least be my comfort when I pen my fold for immortality, that not one here shall be wanting."

They now seemed all repentance, and melting into tears, came one after the other to bid me farewell. I shook each tenderly by the hand, and leaving them my blessing, proceeded forward without meeting any farther interruption. Some hours before night we reached the town, or rather village; for it consisted but of a few mean houses, having lost all its former opulence and retaining no marks of its ancient superiority but the gaol.

Upon entering, we put up at an inn, where we had such refreshments as could most readily be procured, and I supped with my family with my usual chearfulness. After seeing them properly accommodated for that night, I next attended the sheriff's officers to the prison, which had formerly been built for the purposes of war and consisted of one large apartment, strongly grated and paved with stone, common to both felons and debtors at certain hours in the four and twenty. Besides this, every prisoner had a separate cell, where he was locked in for the night.

I expected upon my entrance to find nothing but lamentations and various sounds of misery; but it was very different. The prisoners seemed all employed in one common design, that of forgetting thought in merriment or clamour. I was apprized of the usual perquisite required upon these occasions, and immediately complied with the demand, though the little money I had was very near being all exhausted. This was immediately sent away for liquor, and the whole prison soon was filled with riot, laughter, and prophaneness.

"How," cried I to myself, "shall men so very wicked be chearful, and shall I be melancholy! I feel only the same confinement with them, and I think I have more reason to be happy."

With such reflections I laboured to become chearful; but

chearfulness was never yet produced by effort, which is itself painful. As I was sitting therefore in a corner of the gaol in a pensive posture, one of my fellow prisoners came up, and sitting by me, entered into conversation. It was my constant rule in life never to avoid the conversation of any man who seemed to desire it: for if good, I might profit by his instruction; if bad, he might be assisted by mine. I found this to be a knowing man, of strong unlettered sense, but a thorough knowledge of the world, as it is called, or more properly speaking, of human nature on the wrong side. He asked me if I had taken care to provide myself with a bed, which was a circumstance I had never once attended to.

"That's unfortunate," cried he, "as you are allowed here nothing but straw, and your apartment is very large and cold. However you seem to be something of a gentleman, and as I have been one myself in my time, part of my bed-cloaths are heartily at your service."

I thanked him, professing my surprize at finding such humanity in a gaol in misfortunes; adding, to let him see that I was a scholar, "That the sage ancient seemed to understand the value of company in affliction, when he said, Ton kosman aire, ei dos ton etairon; and in fact," continued I, "what is the World if it affords only solitude?"

"You talk of the world, Sir," returned my fellow prisoner; "the world is in its dotage, and yet the cosmogony or creation of the world has puzzled the philosophers of every age. What a medley of opinions have they not broached upon the creation of the world. Sanconiathon, Manetho, Berosus and Ocellus Lucanus have all attempted it in vain. The latter has these words, Anarchon ara kai atelutaion to pan, which implies"— "I ask pardon, Sir," cried I, "for interrupting so much learning; but I think I have heard all this before. Have I not had the pleasure of once seeing you at Welbridge fair, and is not your name Ephraim Jenkinson?" At this demand he only sighed. "I suppose you must recollect," resumed I, "one Doctor Primrose, from whom you bought a horse?"

He now at once recollected me; for the gloominess of the place and the approaching night had prevented his distinguishing my features before.—"Yes, Sir," returned Mr. Jenkinson, "I remember you perfectly well. I bought an horse, but forgot to pay for him. Your neighbour Flamborough is the only prosecutor I am any way afraid of at the next assizes, for he intends to swear positively against me as a coiner. I am heartily sorry, Sir, I ever deceived you, or indeed any man; for you see," continued he, shewing his shackles, "what my tricks have brought me to."

"Well, sir," replied I, "your kindness in offering me assistance, when you could expect no return, shall be repaid with my endeavours to soften or totally suppress Mr. Flamborough's evidence, and I will send my son to him for that purpose the first opportunity; nor do I in the least doubt but he will comply with my request; and as to my own evidence, you need be under no uneasiness about that."

"Well, sir," cried he, "all the return I can make shall be yours. You shall have more than half my bed-cloaths to night, and I'll take care to stand your friend in the prison, where I think I have some influence."

I thanked him, and could not avoid being surprised at the present youthful change in his aspect; for at the time I had seen him before he appeared at least sixty.—"Sir," answered he, "you are little acquainted with the world; I had at that time false hair, and have learnt the art of counterfeiting every age from seventeen to seventy. Ah sir, had I but bestowed half the pains in learning a trade that I have in learning to be a scoundrel, I might have been a rich man at this day. But rogue as I am, still I may be your friend, and that perhaps when you least expect it."

We were now prevented from further conversation by the arrival of the gaoler's servants, who came to call over the prisoners' names and lock up for the night. A fellow also with a bundle of straw for my bed attended, who led me along a dark narrow passage into a room paved like the common prison, and in one corner of this I spread my bed and the cloaths given me by my fellow prisoner; which done, my conductor, who was civil enough, bade me a good-night. After my usual meditations, and having praised my heavenly corrector, I laid myself down and slept with the utmost tranquility till morning.

CHAPTER TWENTY-SIX

A reformation in the gaol. To make laws complete, they should
reward as well as punish.

The next morning early I was awakened by my family, whom
I found in tears at my bed-side. The gloomy strength of every
thing about us, it seems, had daunted them. I gently rebuked
their sorrow, assuring them I had never slept with greater
tranquillity, and next enquired after my eldest daughter, who
was not among them. They informed me that yesterday's uneasiness and fatigue had encreased her fever, and it was
judged proper to leave her behind. My next care was to send
my son to procure a room or two to lodge the family in, as
near the prison as conveniently could be found. He obeyed,
but could only find one apartment, which was hired at a small
expence, for his mother and sisters, the gaoler with humanity
consenting to let him and his two little brothers lie in the
prison with me. A bed was therefore prepared for them in a
corner of the room, which I thought answered very conveniently. I was willing however previously to know whether my
little children chose to lie in a place which seemed to fright
them upon entrance.

"Well," cried I, "my good boys, how do you like your bed?
I hope you are not afraid to lie in this room, dark as it appears."

"No, papa," says Dick, "I am not afraid to lie any where
where you are."

"And I," says Bill, who was yet but four years old, "love every place best that my papa is in."

After this I allotted to each of the family what they were
to do. My daughter was particularly directed to watch her declining sister's health; my wife was to attend me; my little
boys were to read to me: "And as for you, my son," continued I, "it is by the labour of your hands we must all hope
to be supported. Your wages, as a day-labourer, will be full
sufficient, with proper frugality, to maintain us all, and comfortably too. Thou art now sixteen years old and hast strength,
and it was given thee, my son, for very useful purposes; for
it must save from famine your helpless parents and family.

Prepare then this evening to look out for work against to-morrow, and bring home every night what money you earn, for our support."

Having thus instructed him and settled the rest, I walked down to the common prison, where I could enjoy more air and room. But I was not long there when the execrations, lewdness, and brutality that invaded me on every side, drove me back to my apartment again. Here I sate for some time, pondering upon the strange infatuation of wretches, who finding all mankind in open arms against them, were, however, labouring to make themselves a future and a tremendous enemy.

Their insensibility excited my highest compassion and blotted my own uneasiness a while from my mind. It even appeared as a duty incumbent upon me to attempt to reclaim them. I resolved therefore once more to return, and in spite of their contempt to give them my advice, and conquer them by perseverance. Going therefore among them again, I informed Mr. Jenkinson of my design, at which he laughed, but communicated it to the rest. The proposal was received with the greatest good-humour, as it promised to afford a new fund of entertainment to persons who had now no other resource for mirth, but what could be derived from ridicule or debauchery.

I therefore read them a portion of the service with a loud unaffected voice, and found my audience perfectly merry upon the occasion. Lewd whispers, groans of contrition burlesqued, winking and coughing, alternately excited laughter. However, I continued with my natural solemnity to read on, sensible that what I did might amend some, but could itself receive no contamination from any.

After reading, I entered upon my exhortation, which was rather calculated at first to amuse them than to reprove. I previously observed, that no other motive but their welfare could induce me to this; that I was their fellow prisoner, and now gained nothing by preaching. I was sorry, I said, to hear them so very prophane; because they got nothing by it but might lose a great deal: "For be assured, my friends," cried I, "for you are my friends, however the world may disclaim your friendship, though you swore twelve thousand oaths in a day,

it would not put one penny in your purse. Then what signifies calling every moment upon the devil and courting his
friendship, since you find how scurvily he uses you. He has
given you nothing here, you find, but a mouthful of oaths and
an empty belly; and by the best accounts I have of him, he
will give you nothing that's good hereafter.

"If used ill in our dealings with one man, we naturally go
elsewhere. Were it not worth your while then, just to try how
you may like the usage of another master, who gives you fair
promises at least to come to him. Surely, my Friends, of all
stupidity in the world his must be greatest, who after robbing
an house, runs to the thieftakers for protection. And yet how
are you more wise? You are all seeking comfort from him
that has already betrayed you, applying to a more malicious
being than any thieftaker of them all; for they only decoy
and then hang you; but he decoys and hangs, and what is
worst of all, will not let you loose after the hangman has
done."

When I had concluded, I received the compliments of my
audience, some of whom came and shook me by the hand,
swearing that I was a very honest fellow, and that they desired my further acquaintance. I therefore promised to repeat
my lecture next day, and actually conceived some hopes of
making a reformation here; for it had ever been my opinion
that no man was past the hour of amendment, every heart lying open to the shafts of reproof if the archer could but take
a proper aim. When I had thus satisfied my mind, I went back
to my apartment, where my wife had prepared a frugal meal,
while Mr. Jenkinson begged leave to add his dinner to ours
and partake of the pleasure, as he was kind enough to express
it, of my conversation. He had not yet seen my family, for as
they came to my apartment by a door in the narrow passage,
already described, by this means they avoided the common
prison. Jenkinson at the first interview therefore seemed not
a little struck with the beauty of my youngest daughter, which
her pensive air contributed to heighten, and my little ones
did not pass unnoticed.

"Alas, Doctor," cried he, "these children are too handsome
and too good for such a place as this!"

"Why, Mr. Jenkinson," replied I, "thank heaven, my children are pretty tolerable in morals, and if they be good, it matters little for the rest."

"I fancy, sir," returned my fellow prisoner, "that it must give you great comfort to have this little family about you."

"A comfort, Mr. Jenkinson," replied I, "yes it is indeed a comfort, and I would not be without them for all the world; for they can make a dungeon seem a palace. There is but one way in this life of wounding my happiness, and that is by injuring them."

"I am afraid then, sir," cried he, "that I am in some measure culpable; for I think I see here" (looking at my son Moses) "one that I have injured, and by whom I wish to be forgiven."

My son immediately recollected his voice and features, though he had before seen him in disguise, and taking him by the hand, with a smile forgave him. "Yet," continued he, "I can't help wondering at what you could see in my face, to think me a proper mark for deception."

"My dear sir," returned the other, "it was not your face, but your white stockings and the black ribband in your hair, that allured me. But no disparagement to your parts, I have deceived wiser men than you in my time; and yet, with all my tricks, the blockheads have been too many for me at last."

"I suppose," cried my son, "that the narrative of such a life as yours must be extremely instructive and amusing."

"Not much of either," returned Mr. Jenkinson. "Those relations which describe the tricks and vices only of mankind, by increasing our suspicion in life, retard our success. The traveller that distrusts every person he meets, and turns back upon the appearance of every man that looks like a robber, seldom arrives in time to his journey's end.

"Indeed I think from my own experience I may say that the knowing one is the silliest fellow under the sun. I was thought cunning from my very childhood; when but seven years old the ladies would say that I was a perfect little man; at fourteen I knew the world, cocked my hat, and loved the ladies; at twenty, though I was perfectly honest, yet every one thought me so cunning that not one would trust me. Thus I was at last obliged to turn sharper in my own defence, and have lived ever since, my head throbbing with schemes to deceive, and my heart palpitating with fears of detection.

"I used often to laugh at your honest simple neighbour Flamborough, and one way or another generally cheated him once a year. Yet still the honest man went forward without suspicion and grew rich, while I still continued tricksy and cunning, and was poor without the consolation of being honest.

"However," continued he, "let me know your case, and what has brought you here; perhaps, though I have not skill to avoid a gaol myself, I may extricate my friends."

In compliance with his curiosity, I informed him of the whole train of accidents and follies that had plunged me into my present troubles, and my utter inability to get free.

After hearing my story and pausing some minutes, he slapt his forehead, as if he had hit upon something material, and took his leave, saying he would try what could be done.

CHAPTER TWENTY-SEVEN

The same subject continued.

The next morning I communicated to my wife and children the scheme I had planned of reforming the prisoners, which they received with universal disapprobation, alledging the impossibility and impropriety of it, adding that my endeavours would no way contribute to their amendment, but might probably disgrace my calling.

"Excuse me," returned I, "these people, however fallen, are still men, and that is a very good title to my affections. Good council rejected returns to enrich the giver's bosom; and though the instruction I communicate may not mend them, yet it will assuredly mend myself. If these wretches, my children, were princes, there would be thousands ready to offer their ministry; but, in my opinion, the heart that is buried in a dungeon is as precious as that seated upon a throne. Yes, my treasures, if I can mend them I will; perhaps they will not all despise me. Perhaps I may catch up even one from the gulph, and that will be great gain; for is there upon earth a gem so precious as the human soul?"

Thus saying, I left them and descended to the common prison, where I found the prisoners very merry, expecting my arrival, and each prepared with some gaol trick to play upon the doctor. Thus, as I was going to begin, one turned my wig awry, as if by accident, and then asked my pardon. A second, who stood at some distance, had a knack of spitting through his teeth, which fell in showers upon my book. A third would cry amen in such an affected tone as gave the rest great delight. A fourth had slyly picked my pocket of my spectacles. But there was one whose trick gave more universal pleasure than all the rest; for observing the manner in which I had disposed my books on the table before me, he very dexterously displaced one of them and put an obscene jest-book of his own in the place. However I took no notice of all that this mischievous groupe of little beings could do, but went on, perfectly sensible that what was ridiculous in my attempt would excite mirth only the first or second time, while what was serious would be permanent. My design succeeded, and in less than six days some were penitent, and all attentive.

It was now that I applauded my perseverance and address at thus giving sensibility to wretches divested of every moral feeling, and now began to think of doing them temporal services also by rendering their situation somewhat more comfortable. Their time had hitherto been divided between famine and excess, tumultuous riot and bitter repining. Their only employment was quarrelling among each other, playing cribbage, and cutting tobacco stoppers. From this last mode of idle industry I took the hint of setting such as chose to work at cutting pegs for tobacconists and shoemakers, the proper wood being bought by a general subscription and when manufactured, sold by my appointment; so that each earned something every day: a trifle indeed, but sufficient to maintain him.

I did not stop here, but instituted fines for the punishment of immorality and rewards for peculiar industry. Thus, in less than a fortnight, I had formed them into something social and humane, and had the pleasure of regarding myself as a legislator who had brought men from their native ferocity into friendship and obedience.

And it were highly to be wished that legislative power would thus direct the law rather to reformation than severity. That it would appear convinced that the work of eradicating crimes is not by making punishments familiar, but formidable. Instead of our present prisons, which find or make men guilty, which enclose wretches for the commission of one crime, and return them, if returned alive, fitted for the perpetration of thousands, it were to be wished we had, as in other parts of Europe, places of penitence and solitude, where the accused might be attended by such as could give them repentance if guilty, or new motives to virtue if innocent. And this, but not the increasing punishments, is the way to mend a state; nor can I avoid even questioning the validity of that right which social combinations have assumed of capitally punishing offences of a slight nature. In cases of murder their right is obvious, as it is the duty of us all, from the law of self-defence, to cut off that man who has shewn a disregard for the life of another. Against such, all nature rises in arms; but it is not so against him who steals my property. Natural law gives me no right to take away his life, as by that the horse he steals is as much his property as mine. If then I have any right, it must be from a compact made between us that he who deprives the other of his horse shall die. But this is a false compact, because no man has a right to barter his life, no more than to take it away, as it is not his own. And next, the compact is inadequate and would be set aside even in a court of modern equity, as there is a great penalty for a very trifling convenience, since it is far better that two men should live than that one man should ride. But a compact that is false between two men is equally so between an hundred, or an hundred thousand; for as ten millions of circles can never make a square, so the united voice of myriads cannot lend the smallest foundation to falsehood. It is thus that reason speaks, and untutored nature says the same thing. Savages that are directed nearly by natural law alone are very tender of the lives of each other; they seldom shed blood but to retaliate former cruelty.

Our Saxon ancestors, fierce as they were in war, had but few executions in times of peace; and in all commencing governments that have the print of nature still strong upon them, scarce any crime is held capital.

It is among the citizens of a refined community that penal laws, which are in the hands of the rich, are laid upon the poor. Government, while it grows older, seems to acquire the moroseness of age; and as if our possessions were become

Primitivism (handwritten annotation in left margin)

anti-luxury

dearer in proportion as they increased, as if the more enormous our wealth, the more extensive our fears, our possessions are paled up with new edicts every day, and hung round with gibbets to scare every invader.

Whether is it from the number of our penal laws or the licentiousness of our people that this country should shew more convicts in a year than half the dominions of Europe united? Perhaps it is owing to both; for they mutually produce each other. When by indiscriminate penal laws a nation beholds the same punishment affixed to dissimilar degrees of guilt, from perceiving no distinction in the penalty the people are led to lose all sense of distinction in the crime, and this distinction is the bulwark of all morality; thus the multitude of laws produce new vices, and new vices call for fresh restraints.

It were to be wished then that power, instead of contriving new laws to punish vice, instead of drawing hard the cords of society till a convulsion come to burst them, instead of cutting away wretches as useless before we have tried their utility, instead of converting correction into vengeance, it were to be wished that we tried the restrictive arts of government, and made law the protector but not the tyrant of the people. We should then find that creatures whose souls are held as dross only wanted the hand of a refiner; we should then find that wretches, now stuck up for long tortures lest luxury should feel a momentary pang, might, if properly treated, serve to sinew the state in times of danger; that as their faces are like ours, their hearts are so too; that few minds are so base as that perseverance cannot amend; that a man may see his last crime without dying for it; and that very little blood will serve to cement our security.

CHAPTER TWENTY-EIGHT

Happiness and misery rather the result of prudence than of virtue in this life. Temporal evils or felicities being regarded by heaven as things merely in themselves trifling and unworthy its care in the distribution.

I had now been confined more than a fortnight, but had not since my arrival been visited by my dear Olivia, and I greatly longed to see her. Having communicated my wishes to my wife, the next morning the poor girl entered my apartment, leaning on her sister's arm. The change which I saw in her countenance struck me. The numberless graces that once resided there were now fled, and the hand of death seemed to have molded every feature to alarm me. Her temples were sunk, her forehead was tense, and a fatal paleness sate upon her cheek.

"I am glad to see thee, my dear," cried I; "but why this dejection, Livy? I hope, my love, you have too great a regard for me to permit disappointment thus to undermine a life which I prize as my own. Be chearful, child, and we may yet see happier days."

"You have ever, sir," replied she, "been kind to me, and it adds to my pain that I shall never have an opportunity of sharing that happiness you promise. Happiness, I fear, is no longer reserved for me here; and I long to be rid of a place where I have only found distress. Indeed, Sir, I wish you would make a proper submission to Mr. Thornhill; it may, in some measure, induce him to pity you, and it will give me relief in dying."

"Never, child," replied I, "I never shall be brought to acknowledge my daughter a prostitute; for tho' the world may look upon your offence with scorn, let it be mine to regard it as a mark of credulity, not of guilt. My dear, I am no way miserable in this place, however dismal it may seem, and be assured that while you continue to bless me by living, he shall never have my consent to make you more wretched by marrying another."

After the departure of my daughter, my fellow prisoner, who was by at this interview, sensibly enough expostulated on my obstinacy, in refusing a submission which promised to give me freedom. He observed that the rest of my family was not to be sacrificed to the peace of one child alone, and she the only one who had offended me. "Beside," added he, "I don't know if it be just thus to obstruct the union of man and wife, which you do at present, by refusing to consent to a match you cannot hinder but may render unhappy."

"Sir," replied I, "you are unacquainted with the man that oppresses us. I am very sensible that no submission I can make could procure me liberty even for an hour. I am told that even in this very room a debtor of his, no later than last year, died for want. But though my submission and approbation could transfer me from hence to the most beautiful apartment he is possessed of, yet I would grant neither, as something whispers me that it would be giving a sanction to adultery. While my daughter lives, no other marriage of his shall ever be legal in my eye. Were she removed, indeed, I should be the basest of men, from any resentment of my own, to attempt putting asunder those who wish for an union. No, villain as he is, I should then wish him married, to prevent the consequences of his future debaucheries. But should I not now be the most cruel of all fathers, to sign an Instrument which must send my child to the grave, merely to avoid a prison myself; and thus to escape one pang, break my child's heart with a thousand?"

He acquiesced in the justice of this answer, but could not avoid observing that he feared my daughter's life was already too much wasted to keep me long a prisoner. "However," continued he, "though you refuse to submit to the nephew, I hope you have no objections to laying your case before the uncle, who has the first character in the kingdom for every thing that is just and good. I would advise you to send him a letter by the post, intimating all his nephew's ill usage, and my life for it, that in three days you shall have an answer." I thank'd him for the hint and instantly set about complying, but I wanted paper, and unluckily all our money had been laid out that morning in provisions; however, he supplied me.

For the three ensuing days I was in a state of anxiety, to know what reception my letter might meet with; but in the mean time was frequently solicited by my wife to submit to any conditions rather than remain here, and every hour received repeated accounts of the decline of my daughter's health. The third day and the fourth arrived, but I received no answer to my letter; the complaints of a stranger against a favourite nephew were no way likely to succeed, so that these hopes soon vanished like all my former. My mind, however, still supported itself, though confinement and bad air began to make a visible alteration in my health, and my arm that had suffered in the fire grew worse. But my children sate by me, and while I was stretched on my straw, read to me by turns or listened and wept at my instructions. But my daughter's health declined faster than mine; every message from her contributed to encrease my apprehensions and pain. The fifth morning after I had written the letter which was sent to sir William Thornhill, I was alarmed with an account that she was speechless. Now it was, that confinement was truly painful to me; my soul was bursting from its prison to be near the pillow of my child, to comfort, to strengthen her, to receive her last wishes and teach her soul the way to heaven! Another account came. She was expiring, and yet I was debarred the small comfort of weeping by her. My fellow prisoner, some time after, came with the last account. He bade me be patient. She was dead!——The next morning he returned and found me with my two little ones, now my only companions, who were using all their innocent efforts to comfort me. They entreated to read to me, and bid me not to cry, for I was now too old to weep. "And is not my sister an angel, now, pappa," cried the eldest, "and why then are you sorry for her? I wish I were an angel out of this frightful place, if my pappa were with me." "Yes," added my youngest darling, "Heaven, where my sister is, is a finer place than this, and there are none but good people there, and the people here are very bad."

Mr. Jenkinson interrupted their harmless prattle by observing that now my daughter was no more, I should seriously think of the rest of my family and attempt to save my own life, which was every day declining for want of necessaries and wholesome air. He added that it was now incumbent on me to sacrifice any pride or resentment of my own to the welfare of those who depended on me for support; and that I was now, both by reason and justice, obliged to try to reconcile my landlord.

"Heaven be praised," replied I, "there is no pride left me now. I should detest my own heart if I saw either pride or resentment lurking there. On the contrary, as my oppressor has been once my parishioner, I hope one day to present him up an unpolluted soul at the eternal tribunal. No, sir, I have no resentment now, and though he has taken from me what I held dearer than all his treasures, though he has wrung my heart, for I am sick almost to fainting, very sick, my fellow prisoner, yet that shall never inspire me with vengeance. I am now willing to approve his marriage, and if this submission can do him any pleasure, let him know that if I have done him any injury, I am sorry for it." Mr. Jenkinson took pen and ink and wrote down my submission nearly as I have exprest it, to which I signed my name. My son was employed to carry the letter to Mr. Thornhill, who was then at his seat in the country. He went and in about six hours returned with a verbal answer. He had some difficulty, he said, to get a sight of his landlord, as the servants were insolent and suspicious; but he accidentally saw him as he was going out upon business, preparing for his marriage, which was to be in three days. He continued to inform us that he stept up in the humblest manner and delivered the letter, which, when Mr. Thornhill had read, he said that all submission was now too late and unnecessary; that he had heard of our application to his uncle, which met with the contempt it deserved; and as for the rest, that all future applications should be directed to his attorney, not to him. He observed, however, that as he had a very good opinion of the discretion of the two young ladies, they might have been the most agreeable intercessors.

"Well, sir," said I to my fellow prisoner, "you now discover the temper of the man that oppresses me. He can at once be facetious and cruel; but let him use me as he will, I shall soon be free in spite of all his bolts to restrain me. I am now drawing towards an abode that looks brighter as I approach it; this expectation cheers my afflictions, and though I shall leave an helpless family of orphans behind me, yet they will not be utterly forsaken; some friend, perhaps, will be found to assist them for the sake of their poor father, and some may charitably relieve them for the sake of their heavenly father."

Just as I spoke, my wife, whom I had not seen that day before, appeared with looks of terror, and making efforts, but unable to speak. "Why, my love," cried I, "why will you thus encrease my affliction by your own? what though no submissions can turn our severe master, tho' he has doomed me to die in this place of wretchedness, and though we have lost a darling child, yet still you will find comfort in your other children when I shall be no more." "We have indeed lost," returned she, "a darling child. My Sophia, my dearest, is gone, snatched from us, carried off by ruffians!" "How, madam," cried my fellow prisoner, "miss Sophia carried off by villains; sure it cannot be?"

She could only answer with a fixed look and a flood of tears. But one of the prisoners' wives, who was present, and came in with her, gave us a more distinct account; she informed us that as my wife, my daughter, and herself, were taking a walk together on the great road a little way out of the village, a post-chaise and four drove up to them and instantly stopt. Upon which a well drest man, but not Mr. Thornhill, stepping out, clasped my daughter round the waist, and forcing her in, bid the postillion drive on, so that they were out of sight in a moment.

"Now," cried I, "the sum of my miseries is made up, nor is it in the power of any thing on earth to give me another pang. What! not one left! not to leave me one! the monster! the child that was next my heart! she had the beauty of an angel and almost the wisdom of an angel. But support that woman, nor let her fall. Not to leave me one!"—"Alas, my husband," said my wife, "you seem to want comfort even more than I. Our distresses are great; but I could bear this and more if I saw you but easy. They may take away my children and all the world, if they leave me but you."

My Son, who was present, endeavoured to moderate our grief; he bade us take comfort, for he hoped that we might still have reason to be thankful.—"My child," cried I, "look round the world and see if there be any happiness left me now. Is not every ray of comfort shut out; while all our bright prospects only lie beyond the grave!"—"My dear father," returned he, "I hope there is still something that will give you an interval of satisfaction, for I have a letter from my brother George."—"What of him, child," interrupted I, "does he know of our misery? I hope my boy is exempt from any part of what his wretched family suffers?"—"Yes, sir," returned he, "he is perfectly gay, chearful, and happy. His letter brings nothing but good news; he is the favourite of his colonel, who promises to procure him the very next lieutenancy that becomes vacant!"

"And are you sure of all this," cried my wife, "are you sure that nothing ill has befallen my boy?"—"Nothing indeed, madam," returned my son; "you shall see the letter, which will give you the highest pleasure; and if any thing can procure you comfort, I am sure that will." "But are you sure," still repeated she, "that the letter is from himself, and that he is really so happy?"—"Yes, Madam," replied he, "it is certainly his, and he will one day be the credit and the support of our family!"—"Then I thank providence," cried she, "that my last letter to him has miscarried. Yes, my dear," continued she, turning to me, "I will now confess that though the hand of heaven is sore upon us in other instances, it has been favourable here. By the last letter I wrote my son, which was in the bitterness of anger, I desired him, upon his mother's blessing, and if he had the heart of a man, to see justice done his father and sister, and avenge our cause. But thanks be to him that directs all things, it has miscarried, and I am at rest." "Woman," cried I, "thou hast done very ill, and at another time my reproaches might have been more severe. Oh! what a tremendous gulph hast thou escaped, that would have buried both thee and him in endless ruin. Providence, indeed, has here been kinder to us than we to ourselves. It has reserved that son to be the father and protector of my children when I shall be away. How unjustly did I complain of being stript of every comfort when still I hear that he is happy and insensible of our afflictions, still kept in reserve to support his widowed mother, to protect his brothers and sisters. But what sisters has he left, he has no sisters now, they are all gone, robbed from me, and I am undone."—"Father," interrupted my son, "I beg you will give me leave to read his letter. I know it will please you." Upon which, with my permission, he read as follows:

Honoured Sir,
I have called off my imagination a few moments from the pleasures that surround me to fix it upon objects that are still more pleasing, the dear little fire-side at home. My fancy draws that harmless groupe as listening to every line of this with great composure. I view those faces with delight which never felt the deforming hand of ambition or distress! But whatever your happiness may be at home, I am sure it will be some addition to it, to hear that I am perfectly pleased with my situation, and every way happy here.

Our regiment is countermanded and is not to leave the kingdom; the colonel, who professes himself my friend, takes me with him to all companies where he is acquainted, and after my first visit I generally find myself received with encreased respect upon repeating it. I danced last night with lady G—, and could I forget you know whom, I might be perhaps successful. But it is my fate still to remember others, while I am myself forgotten by most of my absent friends, and in this number, I fear, Sir, that I must consider you; for I have long expected the pleasure of a letter from home to no purpose. Olivia and Sophia too, promised to write, but seem to have forgotten me. Tell them they are two arrant little baggages, and that I am at this moment in a most violent passion with them; yet still, I know not how, tho' I want to bluster a little, my heart is respondent only to softer emotions. Then tell them, sir, that after all, I love them affectionately, and be assured of my ever remaining

Your dutiful son.

"In all our miseries," cried I, "what thanks have we not to return, that one at least of our family is exempted from what we suffer. Heaven be his guard, and keep my boy thus happy to be the supporter of his widowed mother, and the father of these two babes, which is all the patrimony I can now bequeath him. May he keep their innocence from the temptations of want, and be their conductor in the paths of honour." I had scarce said these words, when a noise like that of a tumult seemed to proceed from the prison below; it died away soon after, and a clanking of fetters was heard along the passage that led to my apartment. The keeper of the prison entered, holding a man all bloody, wounded and fettered with the heaviest irons. I looked with compassion on the wretch as he approached me, but with horror when I found it was my own son.—"My George! My George! and do I behold thee thus. Wounded! Fettered! Is this thy happiness! Is this the manner you return to me? O that this sight could break my heart at once and let me die!"

"Where, sir, is your fortitude?" returned my son with an intrepid voice. "I must suffer; my life is forfeited, and let them take it; it is my last happiness that I have committed no murder, tho' I have lost all hopes of pardon."

I tried to restrain my passions for a few minutes in silence, but I thought I should have died with the effort.—"O my boy, my heart weeps to behold thee thus, and I cannot, cannot help it. In the moment that I thought thee blest and prayed for thy safety, to behold thee thus again! Chained, wounded. And yet the death of the youthful is happy. But I am old, a very old man, and have lived to see this day. To see my children all untimely falling about me, while I continue a wretched survivor in the midst of ruin! May all the curses that ever sunk a soul fall heavy upon the murderer of my children. May he live, like me, to see—"

"Hold, Sir," replied my son, "or I shall blush for thee. How, Sir, forgetful of your age, your holy calling, thus to arrogate the justice of heaven and fling those curses upward that must soon descend to crush thy own grey head with destruction! No, Sir, let it be your care now to fit me for that vile death I must shortly suffer, to arm me with hope and resolution, to give me courage to drink of that bitterness which must shortly be my portion."

"My child, you must not die. I am sure no offence of thine can deserve so vile a punishment. My George could never be guilty of any crime to make his ancestors ashamed of him."

"Mine, Sir," returned my son, "is, I fear, an unpardonable one. I have sent a challenge, and that is death by a late act of parliament. When I received my mother's letter from home, I immediately came down, determined to punish the betrayer of our honour, and sent him an order to meet me, which he answered, not in person, but by his dispatching four of his domestics to seize me. I wounded one, but the rest made me their prisoner. The coward is determined to put the law in execution against me; the proofs are undeniable, and as I am the first transgressor upon the statute,[72] I see no hopes of pardon. But you have often charmed me with the lessons of fortitude; let me now, Sir, find them in your example."

"And, my son, you shall find them. I am now raised above this world and all the pleasures it can produce. From this moment I break from my heart all the ties that held it down to earth and will prepare to fit us both for eternity. Yes, my son, I will point out the way, and my soul shall guide yours in the ascent, for we will take our flight together. I now see and am convinced you can expect no pardon here, and I can only exhort you to seek it at that greatest tribunal where we both shall shortly answer. But let us not be niggardly in our exhortation, but let all our fellow prisoners have a share; good gaoler, let them be permitted to stand here, while I attempt to improve them." Thus saying, I made an effort to rise from my straw, but wanted strength, and was able only to recline against the wall. The prisoners assembled according to my directions, for they loved to hear my council; my son and his mother supported me on either side; I looked and saw that none were wanting, and then addressed them with the following exhortation.

CHAPTER TWENTY-NINE

The equal dealings of providence demonstrated with regard to the happy and the miserable here below. That from the nature of pleasure and pain, the wretched must be repaid the balance of their sufferings in the life hereafter.

My friends, my children, and fellow sufferers, when I reflect on the distribution of good and evil here below, I find that much has been given man to enjoy, yet still more to suffer. Though we should examine the whole world, we shall not find one man so happy as to have nothing left to wish for; but we daily see thousands who by suicide shew us they have nothing left to hope. In this life then it appears that we cannot be entirely blest, but yet we may be completely miserable.

Why man should thus feel pain, why our wretchedness should be requisite in the formation of universal felicity, why, when all other systems are made perfect only by the perfection of their subordinate parts, the great system should require for its perfection, parts that are not only subordinate to others, but imperfect in themselves? These are questions that never can be explained, and might be useless if known. On this subject providence has thought fit to elude our curiosity, satisfied with granting us motives to consolation.

In this situation man has called in the friendly assistance

of philosophy, and heaven seeing the incapacity of that to console him has given him the aid of religion. The consolations of philosophy are very amusing, but often fallacious. It tells us that life is filled with comforts, if we will but enjoy them; and on the other hand, that though we unavoidably have miseries here, life is short, and they will soon be over. Thus do these consolations destroy each other; for if life is a place of comfort, its shortness must be misery, and if it be long, our griefs are protracted. Thus philosophy is weak; but religion comforts in an higher strain. Man is here, it tells us, fitting up his mind and preparing it for another abode. When the good man leaves the body and is all a glorious mind, he will find he has been making himself a heaven of happiness here, while the wretch that has been maimed and contaminated by his vices shrinks from his body with terror and finds that he has anticipated the vengeance of heaven. To religion then we must hold in every circumstance of life for our truest comfort; for if already we are happy, it is a pleasure to think that we can make that happiness unending; and if we are miserable, it is very consoling to think that there is a place of rest. Thus to the fortunate religion holds out a continuance of bliss, to the wretched a change from pain.

But though religion is very kind to all men, it has promised peculiar reward to the unhappy; the sick, the naked, the houseless, the heavy-laden, and the prisoner, have ever most frequent promises in our sacred law. The author of our religion every where professes himself the wretch's friend, and unlike the false ones of this world, bestows all his caresses upon the forlorn. The unthinking have censured this as partiality, as a preference without merit to deserve it. But they never reflect that it is not in the power even of heaven itself to make the offer of unceasing felicity as great a gift to the happy as to the miserable. To the first eternity is but a single blessing, since at most it but encreases what they already possess. To the latter it is a double advantage; for it diminishes their pain here and rewards them with heavenly bliss hereafter.

But providence is in another respect kinder to the poor than the rich; for as it thus makes the life after death more desirable, so it smooths the passage there. The wretched have long familiarity with every face of terror. The man of sorrows lays himself quietly down; he has no possessions to regret, and but few ties to stop his departure; he feels only nature's pang in the final separation, and this is no way greater than he has often fainted under before; for after a certain degree of pain, every new breach that death opens in the constitution nature kindly covers with insensibility.

Thus providence has given the wretched two advantages over the happy in this life, greater felicity in dying, and in heaven all that superiority of pleasure which arises from contrasted enjoyment. And this superiority, my friends, is no small advantage and seems to be one of the pleasures of the poor man in the parable; for though he was already in heaven and felt all the raptures it could give, yet it was mentioned as an addition to his happiness that he had once been wretched and now was comforted, that he had known what it was to be miserable and now felt what it was to be happy.

Thus, my friends, you see religion does what philosophy could never do; it shews the equal dealings of heaven to the happy and the unhappy and levels all human enjoyments to nearly the same standard. It gives to both rich and poor the same happiness hereafter, and equal hopes to aspire after it; but if the rich have the advantage of enjoying pleasure here, the poor have the endless satisfaction of knowing what it was once to be miserable, when crowned with endless felicity hereafter; and even though this should be called a small advantage, yet being an eternal one, it must make up by duration what the temporal happiness of the great may have exceeded by intenseness.

These are therefore the consolations which the wretched have peculiar to themselves, and in which they are above the rest of mankind; in other respects they are below them. They who would know the miseries of the poor, must see life and endure it. To declaim on the temporal advantages they enjoy is only repeating what none either believe or practise. The men who have the necessaries of living are not poor, and they who want them must be miserable. Yes, my friends, we must be miserable. No vain efforts of a refined imagination can sooth the wants of nature, can give elastic sweetness to the dank vapour of a dungeon, or ease to the throbbings of a woe-worn heart. Let the philosopher from his couch of softness tell us that we can resist all these. Alas! the effort by which we resist them is still the greatest pain! Death is slight, and any man may sustain it; but torments are dreadful, and these no man can endure.

To us then, my friends, the promises of happiness in heaven should be peculiarly dear; for if our reward be in this life alone, we are then indeed of all men the most miserable. When I look round these gloomy walls, made to terrify as well as to confine us, this light that only serves to shew the horrors of the place, those shackles that tyranny has imposed or crime made necessary, when I survey these emaciated looks and hear those groans, O, my friends, what a glorious exchange would heaven be for these! To fly through regions unconfined as air, to bask in the sunshine of eternal bliss, to carol over endless hymns of praise, to have no master to threaten or insult us, but the form of goodness himself for ever in our eyes; when I think of these things, death becomes the messenger of very glad tidings; when I think of these things, his sharpest arrow becomes the staff of my support; when I think of these things, what is there in life worth having? when I think of these things, what is there that should not be spurned away? kings in their palaces should groan for such advantages; but we, humbled as we are, should yearn for them.

And shall these things be ours? Ours they will certainly be if we but try for them; and what is a comfort, we are shut out from many temptations that would retard our pursuit. Only let us try for them, and they will certainly be ours, and what is still a comfort, shortly too; for if we look back on past life, it appears but a very short span, and whatever we may think of the rest of life, it will yet be found of less duration; as we grow older the days seem to grow shorter, and our intimacy with time ever lessens the perception of his stay. Then let us take comfort now, for we shall soon be at our journey's end; we shall soon lay down the heavy burthen laid by heaven upon us; and though death, the only friend of the wretched, for a little while mocks the weary traveller with the view, and like his horizon, still flies before him, yet the time will certainly and shortly come, when we shall cease from our toil; when the luxurious great ones of the world shall no more tread us to the earth; when we shall think with pleasure of our sufferings below; when we shall be surrounded with all our friends, or such as deserved our friendship; when our bliss shall be unutterable, and still, to crown all, unending.

CHAPTER THIRTY

Happier prospects begin to appear. Let us be inflexible, and fortune will at last change in our favour.

When I had thus finished, and my audience was retired, the gaoler, who was one of the most humane of his profession, hoped I would not be displeased, as what he did was but his duty, observing that he must be obliged to remove my son into a stronger cell, but that he should be permitted to revisit me every morning. I thanked him for his clemency, and grasping my boy's hand, bade him farewell and be mindful of the great duty that was before him.

I again, therefore, laid me down, and one of my little ones sate by my bedside reading, when Mr. Jenkinson entering, informed me that there was news of my daughter; for that she was seen by a person about two hours before in a strange gentleman's company, and that they had stopt at a neighbouring village for refreshment and seemed as if returning to town. He had scarce delivered this news when the gaoler came with looks of haste and pleasure to inform me that my daughter was found. Moses came running in a moment after, crying out that his Sister Sophy was below and coming up with our old friend Mr. Burchell.

Just as he delivered this news my dearest girl entered and with looks almost wild with pleasure ran to kiss me in a transport of affection. Her mother's tears and silence also shewed her pleasure.—"Here, pappa," cried the charming girl, "here is the brave man to whom I owe my delivery; to this gentleman's intrepidity I am indebted for my happiness and safety——" A kiss from Mr. Burchell, whose pleasure seemed even greater than hers, interrupted what she was going to add.

"Ah, Mr. Burchell," cried I, "this is but a wretched habitation you now find us in, and we are now very different from what you last saw us. You were ever our friend; we have long discovered our errors with regard to you and repented of our ingratitude. After the vile usage you then received at my hands, I am almost ashamed to behold your face; yet I hope you'll forgive me, as I was deceived by a base ungenerous wretch who under the mask of friendship has undone me."

"It is impossible," cried Mr. Burchell, "that I should forgive you, as you never deserved my resentment. I partly saw your delusion then, and as it was out of my power to restrain, I could only pity it!"

"It was ever my conjecture," cried I, "that your mind was noble; but now I find it so. But tell me, my dear child, how hast thou been relieved, or who the ruffians were who carried thee away?"

"Indeed, Sir," replied she, "as to the villain who brought me off, I am yet ignorant. For as my mamma and I were walking out, he came behind us, and almost before I could call for help, forced me into the post chaise, and in an instant the horses drove away. I met several on the road to whom I cried out for assistance, but they disregarded my entreaties. In the mean time the ruffian himself used every art to hinder me from crying out; he flattered and threatened by turns, and swore that if I continued but silent, he intended no harm. In the mean time I had broken the canvas that he had drawn up, and whom should I perceive at some distance but your old friend Mr. Burchell, walking along with his usual swiftness, with the great stick for which we used so much to ridicule him. As soon as we came within hearing, I called out to him by name and entreated his help. I repeated my exclamations several times, upon which with a very loud voice he bid the postillion stop; but the boy took no notice but drove on with still greater speed. I now thought he could never overtake us, when in less than a minute I saw Mr. Burchell come running up by the side of the horses and with one blow knock the postillion to the ground. The horses when he was fallen soon stopt of themselves, and the ruffian stepping out, with oaths and menaces drew his sword and ordered him at his peril to retire; but Mr. Burchell running up, shivered his sword to pieces and then pursued him for near a quarter of a mile; but he made his escape. I was at this time come out myself, willing to assist my deliverer; but he soon returned to me in triumph. The postillion, who was recovered, was going to make his escape too, but Mr. Burchell ordered him at his peril to mount again and drive back to town. Finding it impossible to resist, he reluctantly complied, though the wound he had received seemed, to me at least, to be dangerous. He continued to complain of the pain as we drove along, so that he at last excited Mr. Burchell's compassion, who at my request exchanged him for another at an inn where we called on our return."

"Welcome, then," cried I, "my child, and thou her gallant deliverer, a thousand welcomes. Though our chear is but wretched, yet our hearts are ready to receive you. And now, Mr. Burchell, as you have delivered my girl, if you think her a recompence she is yours; if you can stoop to an alliance with a family so poor as mine, take her, obtain her consent, as I know you have her heart, and you have mine. And let me tell you, Sir, that I give you no small treasure; she has been celebrated for beauty it is true, but that is not my meaning. I give you up a treasure in her mind."

"But, I suppose, Sir," cried Mr. Burchell, "that you are apprized of my circumstances and of my incapacity to support her as she deserves?"

"If your present objection," replied I, "be meant as an evasion of my offer, I desist; but I know no man so worthy to deserve her as you; and if I could give her thousands, and thousands sought her from me, yet my honest brave Burchell should be my dearest choice."

To all this his silence alone seemed to give a mortifying refusal, and without the least reply to my offer he demanded if we could not be furnished with refreshments from the next inn, to which being answered in the affirmative, he ordered them to send in the best dinner that could be provided upon such short notice. He bespoke also a dozen of their best wine and some cordials for me. Adding, with a smile, that he would stretch a little for once, and tho' in a prison, asserted he was never better disposed to be merry. The waiter soon made his appearance with preparations for dinner; a table was lent us by the gaoler, who seemed remarkably assiduous, the wine was disposed in order, and two very well-dressed dishes were brought in.

My daughter had not yet heard of her poor brother's melancholy situation, and we all seemed unwilling to damp her chearfulness by the relation. But it was in vain that I attempted to appear chearful, the circumstances of my unfortunate son broke through all efforts to dissemble, so that I was at last obliged to damp our mirth by relating his misfortunes and wishing that he might be permitted to share with us in this little interval of satisfaction. After my guests were recovered from the consternation my account had produced, I requested also that Mr. Jenkinson, a fellow prisoner, might be admitted, and the gaoler granted my request with an air of unusual submission. The clanking of my son's irons was no sooner heard along the passage than his sister ran impatiently to meet him, while Mr. Burchell in the mean time asked me if my son's name were George; to which replying in the affirmative, he still continued silent. As soon as my boy entered the room, I could perceive he regarded Mr. Burchell with a look of astonishment and reverence. "Come on," cried I, "my son, though we are fallen very low, yet providence has been pleased to grant us some small relaxation from pain. Thy sister is restored to us, and there is her deliverer; to that brave man it is that I am indebted for yet having a daughter; give him, my boy, the hand of friendship, he deserves our warmest gratitude."

My son seemed all this while regardless of what I said and still continued fixed at a respectful distance.—"My dear brother," cried his sister, "why don't you thank my good deliverer? the brave should ever love each other."

He still continued his silence and astonishment, till our guest at last perceived himself to be known, and assuming all his native dignity, desired my son to come forward. Never before had I seen anything so truly majestic as the air he assumed upon this occasion. The greatest object in the universe, says a certain philosopher, is a good man struggling with adversity; yet there is still a greater, which is the good man that comes to relieve it. After he had regarded my son for some time with a superior air, "I again find," said he, "unthinking boy, that the same crime"—— But here he was interrupted by one of the gaoler's servants, who came to inform us that a person of distinction who had driven into town with a chariot and several attendants sent his respects to the gentleman that was with us and begged to know when he should think proper to be waited upon.—"Bid the fellow wait," cried our guest, "till I shall have leisure to receive him"; and then turning to my son, "I again find, Sir," proceeded he, "that you are guilty of the same offence for which you once had my reproof, and for which the law is now preparing its justest punishments. You imagine, perhaps, that a contempt for your own life gives you a right to take that of another, but where, Sir, is the difference between a duelist who hazards a life of no value and the murderer who acts with greater security? Is it any diminution of the gamester's fraud when he alledges that he has staked a counter?"

"Alas, Sir," cried I, "whoever you are, pity the poor misguided creature; for what he has done was in obedience to a deluded mother, who in the bitterness of her resentment required him upon her blessing to avenge her quarrel. Here, Sir, is the letter, which will serve to convince you of her imprudence, and diminish his guilt."

He took the letter, and hastily read it over. "This," says he, "though not a perfect excuse, is such a palliation of his fault as induces me to forgive him. And now, Sir," continued he, kindly taking my son by the hand, "I see you are surprised at finding me here; but I have often visited prisons upon occasions less interesting. I am now come to see justice done a worthy man, for whom I have the most sincere esteem. I have long been a disguised spectator of thy father's benevolence. I have at his little dwelling enjoyed respect uncontaminated by flattery and have received that happiness that courts could not give, from the amusing simplicity around his fireside. My nephew has been apprised of my intentions of coming here, and I find is arrived; it would be wronging him and you to condemn him without examination; if there be injury, there shall be redress; and this I may say without boasting, that none have ever taxed the injustice of Sir William Thornhill."

We now found the personage whom we had so long entertained as an harmless amusing companion was no other than the celebrated Sir William Thornhill, to whose virtues and singularities scarce any were strangers. The poor Mr. Burchell was in reality a man of large fortune and great interest, to whom senates listened with applause, and whom party heard with conviction; who was the friend of his country, but loyal to his king. My poor wife recollecting her former familiarity seemed to shrink with apprehension; but Sophia, who a few moments before thought him her own, now perceiving the immense distance to which he was removed by fortune, was unable to conceal her tears.

"Ah, Sir," cried my wife with a piteous aspect, "how is it possible that I can ever have your forgiveness; the slights you received from me the last time I had the honour of seeing you at our house, and the jokes which I audaciously threw out, these jokes, Sir, I fear can never be forgiven."

"My dear good lady," returned he with a smile, "if you had your joke, I had my answer. I'll leave it to all the company if mine were not as good as yours. To say the truth, I know no body whom I am disposed to be angry with at present but the fellow who so frighted my little girl here. I had not even time to examine the rascal's person so as to describe him in an advertisement. Can you tell me, Sophia, my dear, whether you should know him again?"

"Indeed, Sir," replied she, "I can't be positive; yet now I recollect he had a large mark over one of his eye-brows."—"I ask pardon, madam," interrupted Jenkinson, who was by, "but be so good as to inform me if the fellow wore his own red hair?"—"Yes, I think so," cried Sophia. "And did your honour," continued he, turning to Sir William, "observe the length of his legs?"—"I can't be sure of their length," cried the Baronet, "but I am convinced of their swiftness; for he out-ran me, which is what I thought few men in the kingdom could have done."—"Please your honour," cried Jenkinson, "I know the man; it is certainly the same; the best runner in England; he has beaten Pinwire of Newcastle, Timothy Baxter is his name, I know him perfectly and the very place of his retreat this moment. If your honour will bid Mr. Gaoler let two of his men go with me, I'll engage to produce him to you in an hour at farthest." Upon this the gaoler was called, who instantly appearing, Sir William demanded if he knew him. "Yes, please your honour," reply'd the gaoler, "I know Sir William Thornhill well, and every body that knows any thing of him, will desire to know more of him."—"Well then," said the Baronet, "my request is that you will permit this man and two of your servants to go upon a message by my authority, and as I am in the commission of the peace, I undertake to secure you."—"Your promise is sufficient," replied the other, "and you may at a minute's warning send them over England whenever your honour thinks fit."

In pursuance of the gaoler's compliance, Jenkinson was dispatched in search of Timothy Baxter, while we were amused with the assiduity of our youngest boy Bill, who had just come in and climbed up to Sir William's neck in order to kiss him. His mother was immediately going to chastise his familiarity, but the worthy man prevented her; and taking the child, all ragged as he was, upon his knee, "What, Bill, you chubby rogue," cried he, "do you remember your old friend Burchell? and Dick too, my honest veteran, are you here, you shall find I have not forgot you." So saying, he gave each a large piece of gingerbread, which the poor fellows eat very heartily, as they had got that morning but a very scanty breakfast.

We now sate down to dinner, which was almost cold; but previously, my arm still continuing painful, Sir William wrote a prescription, for he had made the study of physic his amusement and was more than moderately skilled in the profession; this being sent to an apothecary who lived in the place, my arm was dressed, and I found almost instantaneous relief. We were waited upon at dinner by the gaoler himself, who was willing to do our guest all the honour in his power. But before we had well dined, another message was brought from his nephew, desiring permission to appear in order to vindicate his innocence and honour, with which request the Baronet complied and desired Mr. Thornhill to be introduced.

CHAPTER THIRTY-ONE

Former benevolence now repaid with unexpected interest.

Mr. Thornhill made his appearance with a smile, which he seldom wanted, and was going to embrace his uncle, which the other repulsed with an air of disdain. "No fawning, Sir, at present," cried the Baronet with a look of severity, "the only way to my heart is by the road of honour; but here I only see complicated instances of falsehood, cowardice, and oppression. How is it, Sir, that this poor man, for whom I know you professed a friendship, is used thus hardly? His daughter vilely seduced, as a recompence for his hospitality, and he himself thrown into a prison perhaps but for resenting the insult? His son too, whom you feared to face as a man——"

"Is it possible, Sir," interrupted his nephew, "that my uncle could object that as a crime which his repeated instructions alone have persuaded me to avoid."

"Your rebuke," cried Sir William, "is just; you have acted in this instance prudently and well, though not quite as your father would have done; my brother indeed was the soul of honour, but thou—— yes you have acted in this instance perfectly right, and it has my warmest approbation."

"And I hope," said his nephew, "that the rest of my conduct will not be found to deserve censure. I appeared, Sir, with this gentleman's daughter at some places of public amusement; thus what was levity scandal called by a harsher name, and it was reported that I had debauched her. I waited on her father in person, willing to clear the thing to his satisfaction, and he received me only with insult and abuse. As for the rest, with regard to his being here, my attorney and steward can best inform you, as I commit the management of business entirely to them. If he has contracted debts and is unwilling or even unable to pay them, it is their business to proceed in this manner, and I see no hardship or injustice in pursuing the most legal means of redress."

"If this," cried Sir William, "be as you have stated it, there is nothing unpardonable in your offence; and though your conduct might have been more generous in not suffering this gentleman to be oppressed by subordinate tyranny, yet it has been at least equitable."

"He cannot contradict a single particular," replied the 'Squire, "I defy him to do so, and several of my servants are ready to attest what I say. Thus, Sir," continued he, finding that I was silent, for in fact I could not contradict him, "thus, Sir, my own innocence is vindicated; but though at your entreaty I am ready to forgive this gentleman every other offence, yet his attempts to lessen me in your esteem excite a resentment that I cannot govern. And this too at a time when his son was actually preparing to take away my life; this, I say, was such guilt that I am determined to let the law take its course. I have here the challenge that was sent me, and two witnesses to prove it, and even though my uncle himself should dissuade me, which I know he will not, yet I will see public justice done, and he shall suffer for it."

"Thou monster," cried my wife, "hast thou not had vengeance enough already, but must my poor boy feel thy cruelty? I hope that good Sir William will protect us, for my son is as innocent as a child; I am sure he is, and never did harm to man."

"Madam," replied the good man, "your wishes for his safety are not greater than mine; but I am sorry to find his guilt too plain; and if my nephew persists——" But the appearance of Jenkinson and the gaoler's two servants now called off our attention, who entered, haling in a tall man, very genteelly drest and answering the description already given of the ruffian who had carried off my daughter.—"Here," cried Jenkinson, pulling him in, "here we have him; and if ever there was a candidate for Tyburn, this is one."

The moment Mr. Thornhill perceived the prisoner and Jenkinson, who had him in custody, he seemed to shrink back with terror. His face became pale with conscious guilt, and he would have withdrawn; but Jenkinson, who perceived his design, stopt him.—"What, 'Squire," cried he, "are you ashamed of your two old acquaintances, Jenkinson and Baxter? but this is the way that all great men forget their friends, though I am resolved we will not forget you. Our prisoner, please your honour," continued he, turning to Sir William, "has already confessed all. He declares that it was Mr. Thornhill who first put him upon this affair, that he gave him the cloaths he now wears to appear like a gentleman and furnished him with the post-chaise. The plan was laid between them that he should carry off the young lady to a place of safety and that there he should threaten and terrify her, but Mr. Thornhill was to come in in the mean time, as if by accident, to her rescue, and that they should fight awhile, and then he was to run off, by which Mr. Thornhill would have the better opportunity of gaining her affections himself under the character of her defender."

Sir William remembered the coat to have been frequently worn by his nephew, and all the rest the prisoner himself confirmed by a more circumstantial account, concluding that Mr. Thornhill had often declared to him that he was in love with both sisters at the same time.

"Heavens," cried Sir William, "what a viper have I been fostering in my bosom! And so fond of public justice too as he seemed to be. But he shall have it; secure him, Mr. Gaoler —yet hold, I fear there is not legal evidence to detain him."

Upon this, Mr. Thornhill, with the utmost humility, entreated that two such abandoned wretches might not be admitted as evidences against him, but that his servants should be examined.—"Your servants!" replied Sir William, "wretch, call them yours no longer, but come let us hear what those fellows have to say, let his butler be called."

When the butler was introduced, he soon perceived by his former master's looks that all his power was now over. "Tell me," cried Sir William sternly, "have you ever seen your master and that fellow drest up in his cloaths in company together?" "Yes, please your honour," cried the butler, "a thousand times; he was the man that always brought him his ladies."—"How," interrupted young Mr. Thornhill, "this to my face!"—"Yes," replied the butler, "or to any man's face. To tell you a truth, Master Thornhill, I never either loved you or liked you, and I don't care if I tell you now a piece of my mind."—"Now then," cried Jenkinson, "tell his honour whether you know any thing of me."—"I can't say," replied the butler, "that I know much good of you. The night that gentleman's daughter was deluded to our house, you were one of them."—"So then," cried Sir William, "I find you have brought a very fine witness to prove your innocence; thou stain to humanity! to associate with such wretches!" (But continuing his examination) "You tell me, Mr. Butler, that this was the person who brought him this old gentleman's daughter?"—"No, please your honour," replied the butler, "he did not bring her, for the 'Squire himself undertook that business; but he brought the priest that pretended to marry them."

—"It is but too true," cried Jenkinson, "I cannot deny it; that was the employment assigned me, and I confess it to my confusion."

"Good heavens!" exclaimed the Baronet, "how every new discovery of his villainy alarms me. All his guilt is now too plain, and I find his present prosecution was dictated by tyranny, cowardice and revenge; at my request, Mr. Gaoler, set this young officer, now your prisoner, free, and trust to me for the consequences. I'll make it my business to set the affair in a proper light to my friend the magistrate who has committed him. But where is the unfortunate young lady herself? let her appear to confront this wretch; I long to know by what arts he has seduced her honour. Entreat her to come in. Where is she?"

"Ah, Sir," said I, "that question stings me to the heart. I was once indeed happy in a daughter, but her miseries——" Another interruption here prevented me; for who should make her appearance but Miss Arabella Wilmot, who was next day to have been married to Mr. Thornhill. Nothing could equal her surprize at seeing Sir William and his nephew here before her, for her arrival was quite accidental. It happened that she and the old gentleman her father were passing through the town on the way to her aunt's, who had insisted that her nuptials with Mr. Thornhill should be consummated at her house; but stopping for refreshment, they put up at an inn at the other end of the town. It was there from the window that the young lady happened to observe one of my little boys playing in the street, and instantly sending a footman to bring the child to her, she learnt from him some account of our misfortunes, but was still kept ignorant of young Mr. Thornhill's being the cause. Though her father made several remonstrances on the impropriety of going to a prison to visit us, yet they were ineffectual; she desired the child to conduct her, which he did, and it was thus she surprised us at a juncture so unexpected.

Nor can I go on without a reflection on those accidental meetings which, though they happen every day, seldom excite our surprize but upon some extraordinary occasion. To what a fortuitous concurrence do we not owe every pleasure and convenience of our lives. How many seeming accidents must unite before we can be cloathed or fed. The peasant must be disposed to labour, the shower must fall, the wind fill the merchant's sail, or numbers must want the usual supply.

We all continued silent for some moments, while my charming pupil, which was the name I generally gave this young lady, united in her looks compassion and astonishment which gave new finishings to her beauty. "Indeed, my dear Mr. Thornhill," cried she to the 'Squire, who she supposed was come here to succour and not to oppress us, "I take it a little unkindly that you should come here without me, or never inform me of the situation of a family so dear to us both; you know I should take as much pleasure in contributing to the relief of my reverend old master here, whom I shall ever esteem, as you can. But I find that, like your uncle, you take a pleasure in doing good in secret."

"He find pleasure in doing good!" cried Sir William, interrupting her. "No, my dear, his pleasures are as base as he is. You see in him, madam, as complete a villain as ever disgraced humanity. A wretch who after having deluded this poor man's daughter, after plotting against the innocence of her sister, has thrown the father into prison and the eldest son into fetters, because he had courage to face his betrayer. And give me leave, madam, now to congratulate you upon an escape from the embraces of such a monster."

"O goodness," cried the lovely girl, "how have I been deceived! Mr. Thornhill informed me for certain that this gentleman's eldest son, Captain Primrose, was gone off to America with his new-married lady."

"My sweetest miss," cried my wife, "he has told you nothing but falsehoods. My son George never left the kingdom, nor never was married. Tho' you have forsaken him, he has always loved you too well to think of any body else; and I have heard him say he would die a batchellor for your sake." She then proceeded to expatiate upon the sincerity of her son's passion, she set his duel with Mr. Thornhill in a proper light, from thence she made a rapid digression to the 'Squire's debaucheries, his pretended marriages, and ended with a most insulting picture of his cowardice.

"Good heavens!" cried Miss Wilmot, "how very near have I been to the brink of ruin! But how great is my pleasure to have escaped it! Ten thousand falsehoods has this gentleman told me! He had at last art enough to persuade me that my promise to the only man I esteemed was no longer binding, since he had been unfaithful. By his falsehoods I was taught to detest one equally brave and generous!"

But by this time my son was freed from the incumbrances of justice. Mr. Jenkinson also, who had acted as his valet de chambre, had dressed up his hair and furnished him with whatever was necessary to make a genteel appearance. He now therefore entered, handsomely drest in his regimentals, and, without vanity, (for I am above it) he appeared as handsome a fellow as ever wore a military dress. As he entered, he made Miss Wilmot a modest and distant bow, for he was not as yet acquainted with the change which the eloquence of his mother had wrought in his favour. But no decorums could restrain the impatience of his blushing mistress to be forgiven. Her tears, her looks, all contributed to discover the real sensations of her heart for having forgotten her former promise and having suffered herself to be deluded by an impostor. My son appeared amazed at her condescension and could scarce believe it real.—"Sure, madam," cried he, "this is but delusion! I can never have merited this! To be blest thus is to be too happy."—"No, Sir," replied she, "I have been deceived, basely deceived, else nothing could have ever made me unjust to my promise. You know my friendship, you have long known it; but forget what I have done, and as you once had my warmest vows of constancy, you shall now have them repeated; and be assured that if your Arabella cannot be yours, she shall never be another's."—"And no other's you shall be," cried Sir William, "if I have any influence with your father."

This hint was sufficient for my son Moses, who immediately flew to the inn where the old gentleman was, to inform him of every circumstance that had happened. But in the mean time the 'Squire perceiving that he was on every side undone, now finding that no hopes were left from flattery or dissimulation, concluded that his wisest way would be to turn and face his pursuers. Thus laying aside all shame, he appeared the open hardy villain. "I find then," cried he, "that I am to expect no justice here; but I am resolved it shall be done me.

You shall know, Sir," turning to Sir William, "I am no longer a poor dependant upon your favours. I scorn them. Nothing can keep Miss Wilmot's fortune from me, which, I thank her father's assiduity, is pretty large. The articles and a bond for her fortune are signed and safe in my possession. It was her fortune, not her person, that induced me to wish for this match; and possessed of the one, let who will take the other."

This was an alarming blow. Sir William was sensible of the justice of his claims, for he had been instrumental in drawing up the marriage articles himself. Miss Wilmot therefore perceiving that her fortune was irretrievably lost, turning to my son, she asked if the loss of fortune could lessen her value to him. "Though fortune," said she, "is out of my power, at least I have my hand to give."

"And that, madam," cried her real lover, "was indeed all that you ever had to give; at least all that I ever thought worth the acceptance. And I now protest, my Arabella, by all that's happy, your want of fortune this moment encreases my pleasure, as it serves to convince my sweet girl of my sincerity."

Mr. Wilmot now entering, he seemed not a little pleased at the danger his daughter had just escaped, and readily consented to a dissolution of the match. But finding that her fortune, which was secured to Mr. Thornhill by bond, would not be given up, nothing could exceed his disappointment. He now saw that his money must all go to enrich one who had no fortune of his own. He could bear his being a rascal, but to want an equivalent to his daughter's fortune was wormwood. He sate therefore, for some minutes, employed in the most mortifying speculations, till Sir William attempted to lessen his anxiety.—"I must confess, Sir," cried he, "that your present disappointment does not entirely displease me. Your immoderate passion for wealth is now justly punished. But tho' the young lady cannot be rich, she has still a competence sufficient to give content. Here you see an honest young soldier, who is willing to take her without fortune; they have long loved each other, and for the friendship I bear his father, my interest shall not be wanting for his promotion. Leave then that ambition which disappoints you, and for once admit that happiness which courts your acceptance."

"Sir William," replied the old gentleman, "be assured I

never yet forced her inclinations, nor will I now. If she still continues to love this young gentleman, let her have him with all my heart. There is still, thank heaven, some fortune left, and your promise will make it something more. Only let my old friend here (meaning me) give me a promise of settling six thousand pounds upon my girl, if ever he should come to his fortune, and I am ready this night to be the first to join them together."

As it now remained with me to make the young couple happy, I readily gave a promise of making the settlement he required, which, to one who had such little expectations as I, was no great favour. We had now therefore the satisfaction of seeing them fly into each other's arms in a transport. "After all my misfortunes," cried my son George, "to be thus rewarded! Sure this is more than I could ever have presumed to hope for. To be possessed of all that's good, and after such an interval of pain! My warmest wishes could never rise so high!" —"Yes, my George," returned his lovely bride, "now let the wretch take my fortune; since you are happy without it so am I. O what an exchange have I made from the basest of men to the dearest, best! Let him enjoy our fortune, I now can be happy even in indigence."—"And I promise you," cried the 'Squire, with a malicious grin, "that I shall be very happy with what you despise."—"Hold, hold, Sir," cried Jenkinson, "there are two words to that bargain. As for that lady's fortune, Sir, you shall never touch a single stiver of it. Pray your honour," continued he to Sir William, "can the 'Squire have this lady's fortune if he be married to another?"—"How can you make such a simple demand?" replied the Baronet, "undoubtedly he cannot."—"I am sorry for that," cried Jenkinson; "for as this gentleman and I have been old fellow sporters, I have a friendship for him. But I must declare, well as I love him, that his contract is not worth a tobacco stopper, for he is married already."—"You lie, like a rascal," returned the 'Squire, who seemed roused by this insult; "I never was legally married to any woman."—"Indeed, begging your honour's pardon," replied the other, "you were; and I hope you will shew a proper return of friendship to your own honest Jenkinson, who brings you a wife, and if the company restrains their curiosity a few minutes, they shall see her."—So saying he went off with his usual celerity and left us all unable to form any probable conjecture as to his design.—"Ay let him go," cried the 'Squire; "whatever else I may have done I defy him there. I am too old now to be frightened with squibs."

"I am surprised," said the Baronet, "what the fellow can intend by this. Some low piece of humour I suppose!"—"Perhaps, Sir," replied I, "he may have a more serious meaning. For when we reflect on the various schemes this gentleman laid to seduce innocence, perhaps some one more artful than the rest has been found able to deceive him. When we consider what numbers he has ruined, how many parents now feel with anguish the infamy and the contamination which he has brought into their families, it would not surprise me if some one of them——Amazement! Do I see my lost daughter! Do I hold her! It is, it is my life, my happiness. I thought thee lost, my Olivia, yet still I hold thee,—and still thou shalt live to bless me." The warmest transports of the fondest lover were not greater than mine when I saw him introduce my child, and held my daughter in my arms, whose silence only spoke her raptures. "And art thou returned to me, my darling," cried I, "to be my comfort in age!"—"That she is," cried Jenkinson; "and make much of her, for she is your own honourable child, and as honest a woman as any in the whole room, let the other be who she will. And as for you, 'Squire, as sure as you stand there, this young lady is your lawful wedded wife. And to convince you that I speak nothing but truth, here is the licence by which you were married together."—— So saying, he put the licence into the Baronet's hands, who read it and found it perfect in every respect. "And now, gentlemen," continued he, "I find you are surprised at all this; but a few words will explain the difficulty. That there 'Squire of renown, for whom I have a great friendship, but that's between ourselves, has often employed me in doing odd little things for him. Among the rest he commissioned me to procure him a false licence and a false priest, in order to deceive this young lady. But as I was very much his friend, what did I do but went and got a true licence and a true priest and married them both as fast as the cloth could make them. Perhaps you'll think it was generosity that made me do all this. But no.

To my shame I confess it, my only design was to keep the licence and let the 'Squire know that I could prove it upon him whenever I thought proper, and so make him come down whenever I wanted money." A burst of pleasure now seemed to fill the whole apartment; our joy reached even to the common room, where the prisoners themselves sympathized,

> *And shook their chains*
> *In transport and rude harmony.*

Happiness expanded upon every face, and even Olivia's cheek seemed flushed with pleasure. To be thus restored to reputation, to friends and fortune at once, was a rapture sufficient to stop the progress of decay and restore former health and vivacity. But perhaps among all there was not one who felt sincerer pleasure than I. Still holding the dear-loved child in my arms, I asked my heart if these transports were not delusion. "How could you," cried I, turning to Mr. Jenkinson, "how could you add to my miseries by the story of her death? But it matters not; my pleasure at finding her again is more than a recompence for the pain."

"As to your question," replied Jenkinson, "that is easily answered. I thought the only probable means of freeing you from prison was by submitting to the 'Squire and consenting to his marriage with the other young lady. But these you had vowed never to grant while your daughter was living; there was therefore no other method to bring things to bear but by persuading you that she was dead. I prevailed on your wife to join in the deceit, and we have not had a fit opportunity of undeceiving you till now."

In the whole assembly now there only appeared two faces that did not glow with transport. Mr. Thornhill's assurance had entirely forsaken him; he now saw the gulph of infamy and want before him, and trembled to take the plunge. He therefore fell on his knees before his uncle and in a voice of piercing misery implored compassion. Sir William was going to spurn him away but at my request he raised him, and after pausing a few moments, "Thy vices, crimes and ingratitude," cried he, "deserve no tenderness; yet thou shalt not be entirely forsaken, a bare competence shall be supplied, to support the wants of life but not its follies. This young lady, thy wife, shall be put in possession of a third part of that fortune which once was thine, and from her tenderness alone thou art to expect any extraordinary supplies for the future." He was going to express his gratitude for such kindness in a set speech; but the Baronet prevented him by bidding him not aggravate his meanness, which was already but too apparent. He ordered him at the same time to be gone, and from all his former domestics to chuse one such as he should think proper, which was all that should be granted to attend him.

As soon as he left us, Sir William very politely stept up to his new niece with a smile and wished her joy. His example was followed by Miss Wilmot and her father; my wife too kissed her daughter with much affection, as, to use her own expression, she was now made an honest woman of. Sophia and Moses followed in turn, and even our benefactor Jenkinson desired to be admitted to that honour. Our satisfaction seemed scarce capable of increase. Sir William, whose greatest pleasure was in doing good, now looked round with a countenance open as the sun and saw nothing but joy in the looks of all except that of my daughter Sophia, who, for some reasons we could not comprehend, did not seem perfectly satisfied. "I think now," cried he, with a smile, "that all the company, except one or two, seem perfectly happy. There only remains an act of justice for me to do. You are sensible, Sir," continued he, turning to me, "of the obligations we both owe Mr. Jenkinson for his late assiduity in detecting a scoundrel. It is but just we should both reward him for it. Your youngest daughter, Miss Sophia, will, I am sure, make him very happy, and he shall have from me five hundred pounds as her fortune, and upon this I am sure they can live very comfortably together. Come, Miss Sophia, what say you to this match of my making? Will you have him?"—My poor girl seemed almost sinking into her mother's arms at the hideous proposal.—"Have him, Sir!" cried she faintly. "No, Sir, never."—"What!" cried he again, "not have Mr. Jenkinson, your benefactor, an handsome young fellow, with five hundred pounds and good expectations!"—"I beg, Sir," returned she, scarce able to speak, "that you'll desist, and not make me so very wretched."—"Was ever such obstinacy known," cried he again, "to refuse a man whom the family has such infinite obligations to, who has preserved your sister. What! not have him!"—"No, Sir, never!" replied she angrily, "I'd sooner die first."—"If that be the case then," cried he, "if you will not have him—I think I must have you myself." And so saying, he caught her to his breast with ardour. "My loveliest, my most sensible of girls," cried he, "how could you ever think your own Burchell could deceive you, or that Sir William Thornhill could ever cease to admire a mistress that loved him for himself alone? I have for some years sought for a woman who, a stranger to my fortune, could think that I had merit as a man. After having tried in vain, even amongst the pert and the ugly, how great at last must be my rapture to have made a conquest over such sense and such heavenly beauty." Then turning to Jenkinson, "As I cannot, Sir, part with this young lady myself, for she has taken a fancy to the cut of my face, all the recompence I can make is to give you her fortune, and you may call upon my steward to-morrow for five hundred pounds." Thus we had all our compliments to repeat, and Lady Thornhill underwent the same round of ceremony that her sisters had done before. In the mean time Sir William's gentleman appeared to tell us that the equipages were ready to carry us to the inn, where every thing was prepared for our reception. My wife and I led the van and left those gloomy mansions of sorrow. The generous Baronet ordered forty pounds to be distributed among the prisoners, and Mr. Wilmot, induced by his example, gave half that sum. We were received below by the shouts of the villagers, and I saw and shook by the hand two or three of my honest parishioners, who were among the number. They attended us to our inn, where a sumptuous entertainment was provided, and coarser provisions distributed in great quantities among the populace.

After supper, as my spirits were exhausted by the alternation of pleasure and pain which they had sustained during the day, I asked permission to withdraw, and leaving the company in the midst of their mirth, as soon as I found myself alone, I poured out my heart in gratitude to the giver of joy as well as of sorrow, and then slept undisturbed till morning.

CHAPTER THIRTY-TWO

The Conclusion.

The next morning as soon as I awaked, I found my eldest son sitting by my bedside, who came to encrease my joy with another turn of fortune in my favour. First having released me from the settlement that I had made the day before in his favour, he let me know that my merchant who had failed in town was arrested at Antwerp, and there had given up effects to a much greater amount than what was due to his creditors. My boy's generosity pleased me almost as much as this unlooked for good fortune. But I had some doubts whether I ought in justice to accept his offer. While I was pondering upon this, Sir William entered the room, to whom I communicated my doubts. His opinion was that as my son was already possessed of a very affluent fortune by his marriage, I might accept his offer without any hesitation. His business, however, was to inform me that as he had the night before sent for the licences and expected them every hour, he hoped that I would not refuse my assistance in making all the company happy that morning. A footman entered while we were speaking to tell us that the messenger was returned, and as I was by this time ready, I went down, where I found the whole company as merry as affluence and innocence could make them. However, as they were now preparing for a very solemn ceremony, their laughter entirely displeased me. I told them of the grave, becoming and sublime deportment they should assume upon this mystical occasion, and read them two homilies and a thesis of my own composing in order to prepare them. Yet they still seemed perfectly refractory and ungovernable. Even as we were going along to church, to which I led the way, all gravity had quite forsaken them, and I was often tempted to turn back in indignation. In church a new dilemma arose, which promised no easy solution. This was, which couple should be married first; my son's bride warmly insisted that Lady Thornhill (that was to be) should take the lead; but this the other refused with equal ardour, protesting she would not be guilty of such rudeness for the world. The argument was supported for some time between both with equal obstinacy and good breeding. But as I stood all this time with my book ready, I was at last quite tired of the contest, and shutting it, "I perceive," cried I, "that none of you have a mind to be married, and I think we had as good go back again; for I suppose there will be no business done here to-day."—This at once reduced them to reason. The Baronet and his Lady were first married, and then my son and his lovely partner.

I had previously that morning given orders that a coach should be sent for my honest neighbour Flamborough and his family, by which means, upon our return to the inn, we had the pleasure of finding the two Miss Flamboroughs alighted before us. Mr. Jenkinson gave his hand to the eldest and my son Moses led up the other; (and I have since found that he has taken a real liking to the girl, and my consent and bounty he shall have whenever he thinks proper to demand them.) We were no sooner returned to the inn but numbers of my parishioners, hearing of my success, came to congratulate me, but among the rest were those who rose to rescue me and whom I formerly rebuked with such sharpness. I told the story to Sir William, my son-in-law, who went out and reproved them with great severity; but finding them quite disheartened by his harsh reproof, he gave them half a guinea a piece to drink his health and raise their dejected spirits.

Soon after this we were called to a very genteel entertainment, which was drest by Mr. Thornhill's cook. And it may not be improper to observe with respect to that gentleman that he now resides in quality of companion at a relation's house, being very well liked and seldom sitting at the side-table except when there is no room at the other; for they make no stranger of him. His time is pretty much taken up in keeping his relation, who is a little melancholy, in spirits, and in learning to blow the French-horn. My eldest daughter, however, still remembers him with regret; and she has even told me, though I make a great secret of it, that when he reforms she may be brought to relent. But to return, for I am not apt to digress thus; when we were to sit down to dinner our ceremonies were going to be renewed. The question was, whether my eldest daughter, as being a matron, should not sit above the two young brides; but the debate was cut short by my son George, who proposed that the company should sit indiscriminately, every gentleman by his lady. This was received with great approbation by all, excepting my wife, who I could perceive was not perfectly satisfied, as she expected to have had the pleasure of sitting at the head of the table and carving all the meat for all the company. But notwithstanding this, it is impossible to describe our good humour. I can't say whether we had more wit amongst us now than usual; but I am certain we had more laughing, which answered the end as well. One jest I particularly remember: old Mr. Wilmot drinking to Moses, whose head was turned another way, my son replied, "Madam, I thank you." Upon which the old gentleman, winking upon the rest of the company, observed that he was thinking of his mistress. At which jest I thought the two Miss Flamboroughs would have died with laughing. As soon as dinner was over, according to my old custom, I requested that the table might be taken away, to have the pleasure of seeing all my family assembled once more by a chearful fireside. My two little ones sat upon each knee, the rest of the company by their partners. I had nothing now on this side of the grave to wish for, all my cares were over, my pleasure was unspeakable. It now only remained that my gratitude in good fortune should exceed my former submission in adversity.

Poems

[The first three of the following poems were first printed in Gold-smith's periodical, *The Bee,* in issues which were published in October 1759. The fourth was a song intended for *She Stoops to Conquer.* It was removed from the script because the actress who played the part of Kate could not sing. In the spring of 1773, not long after the play was first performed, Boswell dined with Gold-smith and heard him sing the song to "a pretty Irish air called *The Humours of Balamagairy.*" After Goldsmith's death Boswell published the song in the *London Magazine* for June 1774. The words, in Goldsmith's hand, are preserved in the Boswell Papers at Yale. *The Traveller,* based on experiences which Goldsmith had had nine years earlier, was first published in December 1764. The last ten lines, except for the penultimate couplet, were supplied by Johnson. *The Deserted Village* was first published in May 1770. Here again Johnson helped his friend by writing the last two couplets.]

THE GIFT

To Iris, in Bow-Street, Covent-Garden

Say, cruel Iris, pretty rake,
    Dear mercenary beauty,
What annual offering shall I make,
    Expressive of my duty?

My heart, a victim to thine eyes,
    Should I at once deliver,
Say, would the angry fair one prize
    The gift, who slights the giver?

A bill, a jewel, watch or toy,
    My rivals give—and let 'em.

If gems, or gold, impart a joy,
   I'll give them—when I get 'em.

I'll give—but not the full-blown rose,
   Or rose-bud more in fashion;
Such short-liv'd offerings but disclose
   A transitory passion.

I'll give thee something yet unpaid,
   Not less sincere, than civil:
I'll give thee——Ah! too charming maid;
   I'll give thee——To the Devil.

A SONNET

Weeping, murmuring, complaining,
   Lost to every gay delight;
Myra, too sincere for feigning,
   Fears th'approaching bridal night.

Yet why this killing soft dejection?
   Why dim thy beauty with a tear?
Had Myra followed my direction
   She long had wanted cause to fear.

AN ELEGY ON THAT GLORY OF HER SEX MRS. MARY BLAIZE

Good people all, with one accord,
   Lament for Madam Blaize,
Who never wanted a good word—
   From those who spoke her praise.

The needy seldom pass'd her door,
   And always found her kind;
She freely lent to all the poor,—
   Who left a pledge behind.

She strove the neighbourhood to please,
    With manners wond'rous winning,
And never follow'd wicked ways,—
    Unless when she was sinning.

At church, in silks and sattins new,
    With hoop of monstrous size,
She never slumber'd in her pew,—
    But when she shut her eyes.

Her love was sought, I do aver,
    By twenty beaus and more;
The king himself has follow'd her,—
    When she has walk'd before.

But now her wealth and finery fled,
    Her hangers-on cut short all;
The doctors found, when she was dead,—
    Her last disorder mortal.

Let us lament, in sorrow sore,
    For Kent-street well may say,
That had she liv'd a twelve-month more,—
    She had not dy'd to-day.

SONG

Ah, me! when shall I marry me?
    Lovers are plenty; but fail to relieve me.
He, fond youth, that could carry me,
    Offers to love, but means to deceive me.

But I will rally and combat the ruiner:
    Not a look, not a smile, shall my passion discover.
She that gives all to the false one pursuing her,
    Makes but a penitent, loses a lover.

THE TRAVELLER

or, A Prospect of Society

To the Rev. Henry Goldsmith

Dear Sir,

I am sensible that the friendship between us can acquire no new force from the ceremonies of a dedication; and perhaps it demands an excuse thus to prefix your name to my attempts, which you decline giving with your own. But as a part of this poem was formerly written to you from Switzerland, the whole can now with propriety be only inscribed to you. It will also throw a light upon many parts of it when the reader understands that it is addressed to a man who, despising fame and fortune, has retired early to happiness and obscurity, with an income of forty pounds a year.

I now perceive, my dear brother, the wisdom of your humble choice. You have entered upon a sacred office where the harvest is great and the labourers are but few, while you have left the field of ambition where the labourers are many and the harvest not worth carrying away. But of all kinds of ambition, as things are now circumstanced, perhaps that which pursues poetical fame is the wildest. What from the encreased refinement of the times, from the diversity of judgments produced by opposing systems of criticism, and from the more prevalent divisions of opinion influenced by party, the strongest and happiest efforts can expect to please but in a very narrow circle. Though the poet were as sure of his aim as the imperial archer of antiquity, who boasted that he never missed the heart, yet would many of his shafts now fly at random, for the heart is too often in the wrong place.

Poetry makes a principal amusement among unpolished nations; but in a country verging to the extremes of refinement, painting and music come in for a share. And as they offer the feeble mind a less laborious entertainment, they at first rival poetry, and at length supplant her; they engross all favour to themselves, and though but younger sisters, seize upon the elder's birth-right.

Yet, however this art may be neglected by the powerful, it

is still in greater danger from the mistaken efforts of the learned to improve it. What criticisms have we not heard of late in favour of blank verse, and Pindaric odes, chorusses, anapests and iambics, alliterative care and happy negligence! Every absurdity has now a champion to defend it, and as he is generally much in the wrong, so he has always much to say [for error is ever talkative].

But there is an enemy to this art still more dangerous, I mean party. Party entirely distorts the judgment, and destroys the taste. A mind capable of relishing general beauty, when once infected with this disease, can only find pleasure in what contributes to encrease the distemper. Like the tyger, that seldom desists from pursuing man after having once preyed upon human flesh, the reader who has once gratified his appetite with calumny, makes, ever after, the most agreeable feast upon murdered reputation. Such readers generally admire some half-witted thing, who wants to be thought a bold man, having lost the character of a wise one. Him they dignify with the name of poet; his lampoons are called satires, his turbulence is said to be force, and his phrenzy fire.[73]

What reception a poem may find which has neither abuse, party, nor blank verse to support it, I cannot tell, nor am I much sollicitous to know. My aims are right. Without espousing the cause of any party, I have attempted to moderate the rage of all. I have endeavoured to shew that there may be equal happiness in other states though differently governed from our own; that each state has a peculiar principle of happiness, and that this principle in each state, and in our own in particular, may be carried to a mischievous excess. There are few can judge better than yourself how far these positions are illustrated in this poem.

I am, Sir,

Your most affectionate brother,

Oliver Goldsmith

Remote, unfriended, melancholy, slow,
Or by the lazy Scheld, or wandering Po;
Or onward, where the rude Carinthian boor,
Against the houseless stranger shuts the door;
Or where Campania's plain forsaken lies,

A weary waste expanded to the skies:
Where'er I roam, whatever realms to see,
My heart untravell'd fondly turns to thee;
Still to my brother turns, with ceaseless pain,
And drags at each remove a lengthening chain. 10
    Eternal blessings crown my earliest friend,
And round his dwelling guardian saints attend;
Blest be that spot, where chearful guests retire
To pause from toil, and trim their ev'ning fire;
Blest that abode, where want and pain repair,
And every stranger finds a ready chair;
Blest be those feasts where mirth and peace abound,
Where all the ruddy family around,
Laugh at the jests or pranks that never fail,
Or sigh with pity at some mournful tale, 20
Or press the bashful stranger to his food,
And learn the luxury of doing good.
    But me, not destin'd such delights to share,
My prime of life in wand'ring spent and care,
Impell'd, with steps unceasing, to pursue
Some fleeting good, that mocks me with the view;
That, like the circle bounding earth and skies,
Allures from far, yet, as I follow, flies;
My fortune leads to traverse realms alone,
And find no spot of all the world my own. 30
    Even now, where Alpine solitudes ascend,
I sit me down a pensive hour to spend;
And, plac'd on high above the storm's career,
Look downward where an hundred realms appear;
Lakes, forests, cities, plains extended wide,
The pomp of kings, the shepherd's humbler pride.
    When thus Creation's charms around combine,
Amidst the store, 'twere thankless to repine.
'Twere affectation all, and school-taught pride,
To spurn the splendid things by heaven supply'd. 40
Let school-taught pride dissemble all it can,
These little things are great to little man;
And wiser he, whose sympathetic mind
Exults in all the good of all mankind.
Ye glittering towns, with wealth and splendour crown'd

Ye fields, where summer spreads profusion round,
Ye lakes, whose vessels catch the busy gale,
Ye bending swains, that dress the flow'ry vale,
For me your tributary stores combine;
Creation's heir, the world, the world is mine.   50
   As some lone miser visiting his store,
Bends at his treasure, counts, recounts it o'er;
Hoards after hoards his rising raptures fill,
Yet still he sighs, for hoards are wanting still:
Thus to my breast alternate passions rise,
Pleas'd with each good that heaven to man supplies:
Yet oft a sigh prevails, and sorrows fall,
To see the sum of human bliss so small;
And oft I wish, amidst the scene, to find
Some spot to real happiness consign'd,   60
Where my worn soul, each wand'ring hope at rest,
May gather bliss to see my fellows blest.
   Yet, where to find that happiest spot below,
Who can direct, when all pretend to know?
The shudd'ring tenant of the frigid zone
Boldly asserts that country for his own,
Extols the treasures of his stormy seas,
And live-long nights of revelry and ease;
The naked negro, panting at the line,
Boasts of his golden sands and palmy wine,   70
Basks in the glare, or stems the tepid wave,
And thanks his Gods for all the good they gave.
Nor less the patriot's boast, where'er we roam,
His first best country ever is at home.
   And yet, perhaps, if states with states we scan,
Or estimate their bliss on Reason's plan,
Though patriots flatter, and though fools contend,
We still shall find uncertainty suspend,
Find that each good, by Art or Nature given,
To these or those but makes the balance even;   80
Find that the bliss of all is much the same,
And patriotic boasting, reason's shame.
   Nature, a mother kind alike to all,
Still grants her bliss at Labour's earnest call;
[With food as well the peasant is supply'd

On Idra's cliffs as Arno's shelvy side;]
And though rough rocks or gloomy summits frown,
These rocks, by custom, turn to beds of down.
　　From Art more various are the blessings sent;
Wealth, splendours, honor, liberty, content.　　　　　90
Yet these each other's power so strong contest,
That either seems destructive of the rest.
[Where wealth and freedom reign contentment fails,
And honour sinks where commerce long prevails.]
Hence every state to one lov'd blessing prone,
Conforms and models life to that alone.
Each to the favourite happiness attends,
And spurns the plan that aims at other ends;
'Till, carried to excess in each domain,
This favourite good begets peculiar pain.　　　　　100
　　But let us view these truths with closer eyes,
And trace them through the prospect as it lies:
Here for a while my proper cares resign'd,
Here let me sit in sorrow for mankind,
Like yon neglected shrub at random cast,
That shades the steep, and sighs at every blast.
　　Far to the right where Appennine ascends,
Bright as the summer, Italy extends;
Her uplands sloping deck the mountain's side,
Woods over woods in gay theatric pride;　　　　　110
While oft some temple's mould'ring top between,
With venerable grandeur marks the scene.
　　Could Nature's bounty satisfy the breast,
The sons of Italy were surely blest.
Whatever fruits in different climes are found,
That proudly rise, or humbly court the ground;
Whatever blooms in torrid tracts appear,
Whose bright succession decks the varied year;
Whatever sweets salute the northern sky
With vernal lives that blossom but to die;　　　　　120
These here disporting own the kindred soil,
Nor ask luxuriance from the planter's toil;
While sea-born gales their gelid wings expand
To winnow fragrance round the smiling land.
　　But small the bliss that sense alone bestows,

And sensual bliss is all this nation knows.
In florid beauty groves and fields appear,
Men seem the only growth that dwindles here.
Contrasted faults through all their manners reign,
Though poor, luxurious, though submissive, vain,   130
Though grave, yet trifling, zealous, yet untrue,
And even in penance planning sins anew.
All evils here contaminate the mind,
That opulence departed leaves behind;
For wealth was theirs, not far remov'd the date,
When commerce proudly flourish'd through the state;
At her command the palace learnt to rise,
Again the long-fall'n column sought the skies;
The canvass glow'd beyond even Nature warm,
The pregnant quarry teem'd with human form.   140
But, more unsteady than the southern gale,
Soon commerce turn'd on other shores her sail;
[While nought remain'd of all that riches gave,
But towns unman'd, and lords without a slave:]
And late the nation found with fruitless skill
Their former strength was now plethoric ill.
Yet though to fortune lost, here still abide
Some splendid arts, the wrecks of former pride,
From which the feeble heart and long fall'n mind
An easy compensation seem to find.   150
Here may be seen, in bloodless pomp array'd,
The paste-board triumph and the cavalcade;
Processions form'd for piety and love,
A mistress or a saint in every grove.
By sports like these are all their cares beguil'd,
The sports of children satisfy the child;
At sports like these while foreign arms advance,
In passive ease they leave the world to chance.
When struggling virtue sinks by long controul,
She leaves at last, or feebly mans the soul;   160
While low delights, succeeding fast behind,
In happier meanness occupy the mind:
As in those domes, where Cæsars once bore sway,
Defac'd by time and tottering in decay,
Amidst the ruin, heedless of the dead,

The shelter-seeking peasant builds his shed,
And, wond'ring man could want the larger pile,
Exults, and owns his cottage with a smile.
   My soul turn from them, turn we to survey
Where rougher climes a nobler race display,   170
Where the bleak Swiss their stormy mansions tread,
And force a churlish soil for scanty bread;
No product here the barren hills afford,
But man and steel, the soldier and his sword.
No vernal blooms their torpid rocks array,
But winter lingering chills the lap of May;
No Zephyr fondly sooths the mountain's breast,
But meteors glare, and stormy glooms invest.
   Yet still, even here, content can spread a charm,
Redress the clime, and all its rage disarm.   180
Though poor the peasant's hut, his feasts though small,
He sees his little lot the lot of all;
Sees no contiguous palace rear its head
To shame the meanness of his humble shed;
No costly lord the sumptuous banquet deal
To make him loath his vegetable meal;
But calm, and bred in ignorance and toil,
Each wish contracting, fits him to the soil.
Chearful at morn he wakes from short repose,
Breasts the keen air, and carrols as he goes;   190
With patient angle trolls the finny deep,
Or drives his vent'rous plow-share to the steep;
Or seeks the den where snow tracks mark the way,
And drags the struggling savage into day.
At night returning, every labour sped,
He sits him down the monarch of a shed;
Smiles by his chearful fire, and round surveys
His children's looks, that brighten at the blaze;
While his lov'd partner, boastful of her hoard,
Displays the cleanly platter on the board: 200
And haply too some pilgrim, thither led,
With many a tale repays the nightly bed.
   Thus every good his native wilds impart,
Imprints the patriot passion on his heart,
[And even those ills, that round his mansion rise,

Enhance the bliss his scanty fund supplies.]
Dear is that shed to which his soul conforms,
And dear that hill which lifts him to the storms;
And as a babe, when scaring sounds molest,
Clings close and closer to the mother's breast,   210
So the loud torrent, and the whirlwind's roar,
But bind him to his native mountains more.

These are the charms to barren states assign'd;
Their wants are few, their wishes all confin'd.
Yet let them only share the praises due,
If few their wants, their pleasures are but few;
Since every want that stimulates the breast,
Becomes a source of pleasure when redrest.
Hence from such lands each pleasing science flies,
That first excites desire, and then supplies;   220
Unknown to them, when sensual pleasures cloy,
To fill the languid pause with finer joy;
Unknown those powers that raise the soul to flame,
Catch every nerve, and vibrate through the frame.
Their level life is but a smould'ring fire,
Nor quench'd by want, nor fan'd by strong desire;
Unfit for raptures, or, if raptures cheer
On some high festival of once a year,
In wild excess the vulgar breast takes fire,
Till, buried in debauch, the bliss expire.   230

But not their joys alone thus coarsly flow:
Their morals, like their pleasures, are but low,
For, as refinement stops, from sire to son
Unalter'd, unimprov'd their manners run,
And love's and friendship's finely pointed dart
Fall blunted from each indurated heart.
Some sterner virtues o'er the mountain's breast
May sit, like falcons cow'ring on the nest;
But all the gentler morals, such as play
Through life's more cultur'd walks, and charm our way,   240
These far dispers'd, on timorous pinions fly,
To sport and flutter in a kinder sky.

To kinder skies, where gentler manners reign,
We turn; and France displays her bright domain.
Gay sprightly land of mirth and social ease,

Pleas'd with thyself, whom all the world can please,
How often have I led thy sportive choir,
With tuneless pipe, beside the murmuring Loire?
Where shading elms along the margin grew,
And freshen'd from the wave the Zephyr flew;   250
And haply, tho' my harsh touch faltering still,
But mock'd all tune, and marr'd the dancer's skill;
Yet would the village praise my wond'rous power,
And dance, forgetful of the noon-tide hour.
Alike all ages. Dames of ancient days
Have led their children through the mirthful maze,
And the gay grandsire, skill'd in gestic lore,
Has frisk'd beneath the burthen of threescore.
  So blest a life these thoughtless realms display,
Thus idly busy rolls their world away: 260
Theirs are those arts that mind to mind endear,
For honour forms the social temper here.
Honour, that praise which real merit gains,
Or even imaginary worth obtains,
Here passes current; paid from hand to hand,
It shifts in splendid traffic round the land:
From courts, to camps, to cottages it strays,
And all are taught an avarice of praise;
They please, are pleas'd, they give to get esteem,
Till, seeming blest, they grow to what they seem.   270
  But while this softer art their bliss supplies,
It gives their follies also room to rise;
For praise too dearly lov'd, or warmly sought,
Enfeebles all internal strength of thought.
And the weak soul, within itself unblest,
Leans for all pleasure on another's breast.
Hence ostentation here, with tawdry art,
Pants for the vulgar praise which fools impart;
Here vanity assumes her pert grimace,
And trims her robes of frize with copper lace,   280
Here beggar pride defrauds her daily cheer,
To boast one splendid banquet once a year;
The mind still turns where shifting fashion draws,
Nor weighs the solid worth of self applause.
  To men of other minds my fancy flies,

Embosom'd in the deep where Holland lies,
Methinks her patient sons before me stand,
Where the broad ocean leans against the land,
And, sedulous to stop the coming tide,
Lift the tall rampire's artificial pride,   290
That spreads its arms amidst the watry roar,
Scoops out an empire, and usurps the shore.
Onward methinks, and diligently slow
The firm connected bulwark seems to go;
While ocean pent, and rising o'er the pile,
Sees an amphibious world beneath him smile;
The slow canal, the yellow blossom'd vale,
The willow tufted bank, the gliding sail,
The crowded mart, the cultivated plain,
A new creation rescu'd from his reign.   300
    Thus, while around the wave-subjected soil
Impels the native to repeated toil,
Industrious habits in each breast obtain
And industry begets a love of gain.
Hence all the good from opulence that springs,
With all those ills superfluous treasure brings,
Are here display'd. Their much-lov'd wealth imparts
Convenience, plenty, elegance, and arts;
But view them closer, craft and fraud appear,
Even liberty itself is barter'd here.[74]   310
At gold's superior charms all freedom flies,
The needy sell it, and the rich man buys;
A land of tyrants, and a den of slaves,
Here wretches seek dishonourable graves,
And calmly bent, to servitude conform,
Dull as their lakes that sleep beneath the storm.
    Heavens! how unlike their Belgic sires of old!
Rough, poor, content, ungovernably bold;
War in each breast, and freedom on each brow;
How much unlike the sons of Britain now!   320
    Fir'd at the sound my genius spreads her wing,
And flies where Britain broods the western spring;
Where lawns extend that scorn Arcadian pride,
And brighter streams than fam'd Hydaspis glide.
There all around the gentlest breezes stray,

There gentle music melts on every spray;
Creation's mildest charms are there combin'd,
Extremes are only in the master's mind!
Stern o'er each bosom reason holds her state,
With daring aims irregularly great,   330
I see the lords of human kind pass by,
Pride in their port, defiance in their eye,
Intent on high designs, a thoughtful band,
By forms unfashion'd, fresh from Nature's hand;
Fierce in their native hardiness of soul,
True to imagin'd right, above controul,
While even the peasant boasts these rights to scan,
And learns to venerate himself as man.
    Thine, Freedom, thine the blessings pictur'd here,
Thine are those charms that dazzle and endear;   340
Too blest indeed, were such without alloy,
But foster'd even by Freedom ills annoy:
That independence Britons prize too high,
Keeps man from man, and breaks the social tie;
[The self-dependent lordlings stand alone,
All claims that bind and sweeten life unknown;]
See, though by circling deeps together held,
Minds combat minds, repelling and repell'd.
Ferments arise, imprison'd factions roar,
Represt ambition struggles round her shore,   350
Whilst over-wrought, the general system feels
Its motions stop, or phrenzy fires the wheels.
    Nor this the worst. As social bonds decay,
As duty, love, and honour fail to sway,
Fictitious bonds, the bonds of wealth and law,
Still gather strength, and force unwilling awe.
Hence all obedience bows to these alone,
And talent sinks, and merit weeps unknown;
Till time may come, when stript of all her charms,
That land of scholars, and that nurse of arms;   360
Where noble stems transmit the patriot flame,
And monarchs toil, and poets pant for fame;
One sink of level avarice shall lie,
And scholars, soldiers, kings, unhonor'd die.
    Yet think not, thus when Freedom's ills I state,

I mean to flatter kings, or court the great;
Perish the wish; for, inly satisfy'd,
Above their pomps I hold my ragged pride.
But when contending chiefs blockade the throne,
Contracting regal power to stretch their own,   370
When I behold a factious band agree
To call it freedom when themselves are free;
Each wanton judge new penal statutes draw,
Laws grind the poor, and rich men rule the law;
The wealth of climes, where savage nations roam,
Pillag'd from slaves to purchase slaves at home;
Fear, pity, justice, indignation start,
Tear off reserve, and bare my swelling heart;
'Till half a patriot, half a coward grown,
I fly from petty tyrants to the throne.   380
    Yes, brother, curse with me that baleful hour,
When first ambition struck at regal power;
And thus polluting honour in its source,
Gave wealth to sway the mind with double force.
Have we not seen, round Britain's peopled shore,
Her useful sons exchang'd for useless ore?
Seen all her triumphs but destruction haste,
Like flaring tapers brightening as they waste;
Seen opulence, her grandeur to maintain,
Lead stern depopulation in her train,   390
And over fields where scatter'd hamlets rose,
In barren solitary pomp repose?
Have we not seen at pleasure's lordly call,
The smiling long-frequented village fall?
Beheld the duteous son, the sire decay'd,
The modest matron, and the blushing maid,
Forc'd from their homes, a melancholy train,
To traverse climes beyond the western main;
Where wild Oswego spreads her swamps around,
And Niagara stuns with thund'ring sound?   400
    Even now, perhaps, as there some pilgrim strays
Through tangled forests, and through dangerous ways;
Where beasts with man divided empire claim,
And the brown Indian takes a deadly aim;
There, while above the giddy tempest flies,

And all around distressful yells arise,
The pensive exile, bending with his woe,
To stop too fearful, and too faint to go,
Casts a fond look where England's glories shine,
And bids his bosom sympathize with mine.   410
 Vain, very vain, my weary search to find
That bliss which only centers in the mind:
Why have I stray'd, from pleasure and repose,
To seek a good each government bestows?
In every government, though terrors reign,
Though tyrant kings, or tyrant laws restrain,
How small of all that human hearts endure,
That part which laws or kings can cause or cure.
Still to ourselves in every place consign'd,
Our own felicity we make or find: 420
With secret course, which no loud storms annoy,
Glides the smooth current of domestic joy.
The lifted ax, the agonizing wheel,
Luke's iron crown, and Damien's[75] bed of steel,
To men remote from power but rarely known,
Leave reason, faith, and conscience, all our own.

THE DESERTED VILLAGE

To Sir Joshua Reynolds

Dear Sir,

I can have no expectations in an address of this kind, either to add to your reputation, or to establish my own. You can gain nothing from my admiration, as I am ignorant of that art in which you are said to excel; and I may lose much by the severity of your judgment, as few have a juster taste in poetry than you. Setting interest therefore aside, to which I never paid much attention, I must be indulged at present in following my affections. The only dedication I ever made was to my brother, because I loved him better than most other men. He is since dead. Permit me to inscribe this Poem to you.

 How far you may be pleased with the versification and mere mechanical parts of this attempt, I don't pretend to enquire; but I know you will object (and indeed several of our best and wisest friends concur in the opinion) that the depopulation it deplores is no where to be seen, and the disorders it laments are only to be found in the poet's own imagination. To this I can scarce make any other answer than that I sincerely believe what I have written; that I have taken all possible pains, in my country excursions, for these four or five years past, to be certain of what I alledge; and that all my views and enquiries have led me to believe those miseries real, which I here attempt to display. But this is not the place to enter into an enquiry, whether the country be depopulating, or not; the discussion would take up much room, and I should prove myself, at best, an indifferent politician, to tire the reader with a long preface, when I want his unfatigued attention to a long poem.

In regretting the depopulation of the country, I inveigh against the increase of our luxuries; and here also I expect the shout of modern politicians against me. For twenty or thirty years past, it has been the fashion to consider luxury as one of the greatest national advantages; and all the wisdom of antiquity in that particular, as erroneous. Still however, I must remain a professed ancient on that head, and continue to think those luxuries prejudicial to states, by which so many vices are introduced, and so many kingdoms have been undone. Indeed so much has been poured out of late on the other side of the question, that, merely for the sake of novelty and variety, one would sometimes wish to be in the right.

> I am,
> Dear Sir,
> Your sincere friend,
> and ardent admirer,
> *Oliver Goldsmith*

Sweet Auburn, loveliest village of the plain,
Where health and plenty cheared the labouring swain,
Where smiling spring its earliest visit paid,
And parting summer's lingering blooms delayed,
Dear lovely bowers of innocence and ease,
Seats of my youth, when every sport could please,
How often have I loitered o'er thy green,
Where humble happiness endeared each scene;
How often have I paused on every charm,
The sheltered cot, the cultivated farm,   10

The never failing brook, the busy mill,
The decent church that topt the neighbouring hill,
The hawthorn bush, with seats beneath the shade,
For talking age and whispering lovers made;
How often have I blest the coming day,
When toil remitting lent its turn to play,
And all the village train from labour free
Led up their sports beneath the spreading tree;
While many a pastime circled in the shade,
The young contending as the old surveyed;   20
And many a gambol frolicked o'er the ground,
And slights of art and feats of strength went round;
And still as each repeated pleasure tired,
Succeeding sports the mirthful band inspired;
The dancing pair that simply sought renown
By holding out to tire each other down;
The swain mistrustless of his smutted face,
While secret laughter tittered round the place;
The bashful virgin's side-long looks of love,
The matron's glance that would those looks reprove: 30
These were thy charms, sweet village; sports like these,
With sweet succession, taught even toil to please;
These round thy bowers their chearful influence shed,
These were thy charms—But all these charms are fled.
    Sweet smiling village, loveliest of the lawn,
Thy sports are fled, and all thy charms withdrawn;
Amidst thy bowers the tyrant's hand is seen,
And desolation saddens all thy green:
One only master grasps the whole domain,[76]
And half a tillage stints thy smiling plain;   40
No more thy glassy brook reflects the day,
But choaked with sedges, works its weedy way.
Along thy glades, a solitary guest,
The hollow sounding bittern guards its nest;
Amidst thy desert walks the lapwing flies,
And tires their ecchoes with unvaried cries.
Sunk are thy bowers, in shapeless ruin all,
And the long grass o'ertops the mouldering wall,
And trembling, shrinking from the spoiler's hand,
Far, far away thy children leave the land.   50

Ill fares the land, to hastening ills a prey,
Where wealth accumulates, and men decay:
Princes and lords may flourish, or may fade;
A breath can make them, as a breath has made;
But a bold peasantry, their country's pride,
When once destroyed, can never be supplied.

A time there was, ere England's griefs began,
When every rood of ground maintained its man;
For him light labour spread her wholesome store,
Just gave what life required, but gave no more: 60
His best companions, innocence and health;
And his best riches, ignorance of wealth.

But times are altered; trade's unfeeling train
Usurp the land and disposses the swain;
Along the lawn, where scattered hamlets rose,
Unwieldy wealth, and cumbrous pomp repose;
And every want to luxury allied,
And every pang that folly pays to pride.
These gentle hours that plenty bade to bloom,
Those calm desires that asked but little room,   70
Those healthful sports that graced the peaceful scene,
Lived in each look, and brightened all the green;
These far departing seek a kinder shore,
And rural mirth and manners are no more.

Sweet AUBURN! parent of the blissful hour,
Thy glades forlorn confess the tyrant's power.
Here as I take my solitary rounds,
Amidst thy tangling walks, and ruined grounds,
And, many a year elapsed, return to view
Where once the cottage stood, the hawthorn grew,   80
Here, as with doubtful, pensive steps I range,
Trace every scene, and wonder at the change,
Remembrance wakes with all her busy train,
Swells at my breast, and turns the past to pain.

In all my wanderings round this world of care,
In all my griefs—and GOD has given my share—
I still had hopes my latest hours to crown,
Amidst these humble bowers to lay me down;
My anxious day to husband near the close,
And keep life's flame from wasting by repose.   90

I still had hopes, for pride attends us still,
Amidst the swains to shew my book-learned skill,
Around my fire an evening groupe to draw,
And tell of all I felt, and all I saw;
And, as an hare whom hounds and horns pursue,
Pants to the place from whence at first she flew,
I still had hopes, my long vexations past,
Here to return—and die at home at last.

   O blest retirement, friend to life's decline,
Retreats from care that never must be mine,   100
How blest is he who crowns in shades like these,
A youth of labour with an age of ease;
Who quits a world where strong temptations try,
And, since 'tis hard to combat, learns to fly.
For him no wretches, born to work and weep,
Explore the mine, or tempt the dangerous deep;
No surly porter stands in guilty state
To spurn imploring famine from his gate,
But on he moves to meet his latter end,
Angels around befriending virtue's friend;   110
Sinks to the grave with unperceived decay,
While resignation gently slopes the way;
And all his prospects brightening to the last,
His Heaven commences ere the world be past!

   Sweet was the sound when oft at evening's close,
Up yonder hill the village murmur rose;
There as I past with careless steps and slow,
The mingling notes came softened from below;
The swain responsive as the milk-maid sung,
The sober herd that lowed to meet their young,   120
The noisy geese that gabbled o'er the pool,
The playful children just let loose from school,
The watch-dog's voice that bayed the whispering wind,
And the loud laugh that spoke the vacant mind,
These all in soft confusion sought the shade,
And filled each pause the nightingale had made.
But now the sounds of population fail,
No chearful murmurs fluctuate in the gale,
No busy steps the grass-grown foot-way tread,
But all the bloomy flush of life is fled.   130

All but yon widowed, solitary thing
That feebly bends beside the plashy spring;
She, wretched matron, forced, in age, for bread,
To strip the brook with mantling cresses spread,
To pick her wintry faggot from the thorn,
To seek her nightly shed, and weep till morn;
She only left of all the harmless train,
The sad historian of the pensive plain.

    Near yonder copse, where once the garden smil'd,
And still where many a garden flower grows wild;   140
There, where a few torn shrubs the place disclose,
The village preacher's modest mansion rose.
A man he was, to all the country dear,
And passing rich with forty pounds a year;
Remote from towns he ran his godly race,
Nor e'er had changed, nor wish'd to change his place;
Unskilful he to fawn, or seek for power,
By doctrines fashioned to the varying hour;
Far other aims his heart had learned to prize,
More bent to raise the wretched than to rise.   150
His house was known to all the vagrant train,
He chid their wanderings, but relieved their pain;
The long remembered beggar was his guest,
Whose beard descending swept his aged breast; ·
The ruined spendthrift, now no longer proud,
Claimed kindred there, and had his claims allowed;
The broken soldier, kindly bade to stay,
Sate by his fire, and talked the night away;
Wept o'er his wounds, or tales of sorrow done,
Shouldered his crutch, and shewed how fields were won. 160
Pleased with his guests, the good man learned to glow,
And quite forgot their vices in their woe;
Careless their merits, or their faults to scan,
His pity gave ere charity began.

    Thus to relieve the wretched was his pride,
And even his failings leaned to Virtue's side;
But in his duty prompt at every call,
He watched and wept, he prayed and felt, for all.
And, as a bird each fond endearment tries,
To tempt its new fledged offspring to the skies;   170

The Deserted Village 483

He tried each art, reproved each dull delay,
Allured to brighter worlds, and led the way.
   Beside the bed where parting life was layed,
And sorrow, guilt, and pain, by turns dismayed,
The reverend champion stood. At his control,
Despair and anguish fled the struggling soul;
Comfort came down the trembling wretch to raise,
And his last faultering accents whispered praise.
   At church, with meek and unaffected grace,
His looks adorned the venerable place;   180
Truth from his lips prevailed with double sway,
And fools, who came to scoff, remained to pray.
The service past, around the pious man,
With ready zeal each honest rustic ran;
Even children followed with endearing wile,
And plucked his gown, to share the good man's smile.
His ready smile a parent's warmth exprest,
Their welfare pleased him, and their cares distrest;
To them his heart, his love, his griefs were given,
But all his serious thoughts had rest in Heaven.   190
As some tall cliff that lifts its awful form,
Swells from the vale, and midway leaves the storm,
Tho' round its breast the rolling clouds are spread,
Eternal sunshine settles on its head.
   Beside yon straggling fence that skirts the way,
With blossomed furze unprofitably gay,
There, in his noisy mansion, skill'd to rule,
The village master taught his little school;
A man severe he was, and stern to view,
I knew him well, and every truant knew;   200
Well had the boding tremblers learned to trace
The day's disasters in his morning face;
Full well they laugh'd with counterfeited glee,
At all his jokes, for many a joke had he;
Full well the busy whisper circling round,
Conveyed the dismal tidings when he frowned;
Yet he was kind, or if severe in aught,
The love he bore to learning was in fault;
The village all declared how much he knew;
'Twas certain he could write, and cypher too;   210

Lands he could measure, terms and tides presage,
And even the story ran that he could gauge.
In arguing too, the parson owned his skill,
For e'en tho' vanquished, he could argue still;
While words of learned length, and thundering sound,
Amazed the gazing rustics ranged around;
And still they gazed, and still the wonder grew,
That one small head could carry all he knew.
 But past is all his fame. The very spot
Where many a time he triumphed, is forgot.   220
Near yonder thorn, that lifts its head on high,
Where once the sign-post caught the passing eye,
Low lies that house where nut-brown draughts inspired,
Where grey-beard mirth and smiling toil retired,
Where village statesmen talked with looks profound,
And news much older than their ale went round.
Imagination fondly stoops to trace
The parlour splendours of that festive place;
The white-washed wall, the nicely sanded floor,
The varnished clock that clicked behind the door;   230
The chest contrived a double debt to pay,
A bed by night, a chest of drawers by day;
The pictures placed for ornament and use,
The twelve good rules, the royal game of goose;
The hearth, except when winter chill'd the day,
With aspen boughs, and flowers, and fennel gay,
While broken tea-cups, wisely kept for shew,
Ranged o'er the chimney, glistened in a row.
 Vain transitory splendours! Could not all
Reprieve the tottering mansion from its fall!   240
Obscure it sinks, nor shall it more impart
An hour's importance to the poor man's heart;
Thither no more the peasant shall repair
To sweet oblivion of his daily care;
No more the farmer's news, the barber's tale,
No more the wood-man's ballad shall prevail;
No more the smith his dusky brow shall clear,
Relax his ponderous strength, and lean to hear;
The host himself no longer shall be found
Careful to see the mantling bliss go round;   250

Nor the coy maid, half willing to be prest,
Shall kiss the cup to pass it to the rest.
     Yes! let the rich deride, the proud disdain,
These simple blessings of the lowly train;
To me more dear, congenial to my heart,
One native charm, than all the gloss of art;
Spontaneous joys, where Nature has its play,
The soul adopts, and owns their first born sway;
Lightly they frolic o'er the vacant mind,
Unenvied, unmolested, unconfined.   260
But the long pomp, the midnight masquerade,
With all the freaks of wanton wealth arrayed,
In these, ere triflers half their wish obtain,
The toiling pleasure sickens into pain;
And, even while fashion's brightest arts decoy,
The heart distrusting asks, if this be joy.
     Ye friends to truth, ye statesmen, who survey
The rich man's joys encrease, the poor's decay,
'Tis yours to judge, how wide the limits stand
Between a splendid and an happy land.   270
Proud swells the tide with loads of freighted ore,
And shouting Folly hails them from her shore;
Hoards, even beyond the miser's wish abound,
And rich men flock from all the world around.
Yet count our gains. This wealth is but a name
That leaves our useful products still the same.
Not so the loss. The man of wealth and pride,
Takes up a space that many poor supplied;
Space for his lake, his park's extended bounds,
Space for his horses, equipage, and hounds;   280
The robe that wraps his limbs in silken sloth,
Has robbed the neighbouring fields of half their growth;
His seat, where solitary sports are seen,
Indignant spurns the cottage from the green;
Around the world each needful product flies,
For all the luxuries the world supplies.
While thus the land adorned for pleasure, all
In barren splendour feebly waits the fall.
     As some fair female unadorned and plain,
Secure to please while youth confirms her reign,   290

Slights every borrowed charm that dress supplies,
Nor shares with art the triumph of her eyes;
But when those charms are past, for charms are frail,
When time advances, and when lovers fail,
She then shines forth, sollicitous to bless,
In all the glaring impotence of dress;
Thus fares the land, by luxury betrayed;
In nature's simplest charms at first arrayed;
But verging to decline, its splendours rise,
Its vistas strike, its palaces surprize;   300
While scourged by famine from the smiling land,
The mournful peasant leads his humble band;
And while he sinks without one arm to save,
The country blooms—a garden, and a grave.
    Where then, ah where, shall poverty reside,
To scape the pressure of contiguous pride?
If to some common's fenceless limits strayed,
He drives his flock to pick the scanty blade,
Those fenceless fields the sons of wealth divide,
And even the bare-worn common is denied.   310
    If to the city sped—What waits him there?
To see profusion that he must not share;
To see ten thousand baneful arts combined
To pamper luxury, and thin mankind;
To see each joy the sons of pleasure know,
Extorted from his fellow-creature's woe.
Here, while the courtier glitters in brocade,
There the pale artist plies the sickly trade;
Here, while the proud their long drawn pomps display,
There the black gibbet glooms beside the way.   320
The dome where pleasure holds her midnight reign,
Here, richly deckt, admits the gorgeous train;
Tumultuous grandeur crowds the blazing square,
The rattling chariots clash, the torches glare.
Sure scenes like these no troubles e'er annoy!
Sure these denote one universal joy!
Are these thy serious thoughts?—Ah, turn thine eyes
Where the poor houseless shivering female lies.
She once, perhaps, in village plenty blest,
Has wept at tales of innocence distrest;   330

Her modest looks the cottage might adorn,
Sweet as the primrose peeps beneath the thorn;
Now lost to all; her friends, her virtue fled,
Near her betrayer's door she lays her head,
And pinch'd with cold, and shrinking from the shower,
With heavy heart deplores that luckless hour
When idly first, ambitious of the town,
She left her wheel and robes of country brown.
    Do thine, sweet AUBURN, thine, the loveliest train,
Do thy fair tribes participate her pain?   340
Even now, perhaps, by cold and hunger led,
At proud men's doors they ask a little bread!
    Ah, no. To distant climes, a dreary scene,
Where half the convex world intrudes between,
To torrid tracts with fainting steps they go,
Where wild Altama [77] murmurs to their woe.
Far different there from all that charm'd before,
The various terrors of that horrid shore;
Those blazing suns that dart a downward ray,
And fiercely shed intolerable day;   350
Those matted woods where birds forget to sing,
But silent bats in drowsy clusters cling,
Those poisonous fields with rank luxuriance crowned,
Where the dark scorpion gathers death around;
Where at each step the stranger fears to wake
The rattling terrors of the vengeful snake;
Where crouching tigers wait their hapless prey,
And savage men, more murderous still than they;
While oft in whirls the mad tornado flies,
Mingling the ravaged landshape with the skies.   360
Far different these from every former scene,
The cooling brook, the grassy vested green,
The breezy covert of the warbling grove,
That only sheltered thefts of harmless love.
    Good Heaven! what sorrows gloom'd that parting day,
That called them from their native walks away;
When the poor exiles, every pleasure past,
Hung round their bowers, and fondly looked their last,
And took a long farewell, and wished in vain
For seats like these beyond the western main;   370

And shuddering still to face the distant deep,
Returned and wept, and still returned to weep.
The good old sire, the first prepared to go
To new found worlds, and wept for others woe.
But for himself, in conscious virtue brave,
He only wished for worlds beyond the grave.
His lovely daughter, lovelier in her tears,
The fond companion of his helpless years,
Silent went next, neglectful of her charms,
And left a lover's for a father's arms.   380
With louder plaints the mother spoke her woes,
And blest the cot where every pleasure rose;
And kist her thoughtless babes with many a tear,
And claspt them close in sorrow doubly dear;
Whilst her fond husband strove to lend relief
In all the decent manliness of grief.

    O luxury! Thou curst by Heaven's decree,
How ill exchanged are things like these for thee!
How do thy potions, with insidious joy,
Diffuse their pleasures only to destroy!   390
Kingdoms, by thee, to sickly greatness grown,
Boast of a florid vigour not their own;
At every draught more large and large they grow,
A bloated mass of rank unwieldy woe;
Till sapped their strength, and every part unsound,
Down, down they sink, and spread a ruin round.

    Even now the devastation is begun,
And half the business of destruction done;
Even now, methinks, as pondering here I stand,
I see the rural virtues leave the land: 400
Down where yon anchoring vessel spreads the sail,
That idly waiting flaps with every gale,
Downward they move, a melancholy band,
Pass from the shore, and darken all the strand.
Contented toil, and hospitable care,
And kind connubial tenderness, are there;
And piety, with wishes placed above,
And steady loyalty, and faithful love:
And thou, sweet Poetry, thou loveliest maid,
Still first to fly where sensual joys invade;   410

Unfit in these degenerate times of shame,
To catch the heart, or strike for honest fame;
Dear charming nymph, neglected and decried,
My shame in crowds, my solitary pride;
Thou source of all my bliss, and all my woe,
That found'st me poor at first, and keep'st me so;
Thou guide by which the nobler arts excell,
Thou nurse of every virtue, fare thee well.
Farewell, and O where'er thy voice be tried,
On Torno's cliffs, or Pambamarca's side,   420
Whether where equinoctial fervours glow,
Or winter wraps the polar world in snow,
Still let thy voice prevailing over time,
Redress the rigours of the inclement clime;
Aid slighted truth, with thy persuasive strain,
Teach erring man to spurn the rage of gain;
Teach him that states of native strength possest,
Tho' very poor, may still be very blest;
That trade's proud empire hastes to swift decay,
As ocean sweeps the labour'd mole away;   430
While self dependent power can time defy,
As rocks resist the billows and the sky.

VERSES IN REPLY TO DR. BAKER'S INVITATION

[The dinner to which Goldsmith had been invited was held at the
home of Dr. George Baker, Sir Joshua's physician, and the others
mentioned, all from Devonshire, were members of Goldsmith's
personal circle, among them the three children of Mrs. Horneck
who are referred to as the Jessamy Bride, Little Comedy, and the
Captain in Lace, Joshua Reynolds and his sister Frances, and Angelica Kauffman, an artist who had just completed her portrait of
Reynolds which is now in the National Portrait Gallery in London.
At the end of the poem Goldsmith refers to the *Public Advertiser,*
which in January and February 1767 printed verses praising this
portrait by Angelica.]

This *is* a poem! This *is* a copy of verses!

   Your mandate I got;
   You may all go to pot;

Had your senses been right,
You'd have sent before night;
As I hope to be saved,
I put off being shaved;
For I could not make bold,
While the matter was cold,
To meddle in suds,
Or to put on my duds;
So tell Horneck and Nesbitt,
And Baker and his bit,
And Kauffman beside,
And the Jessamy bride,
With the rest of the crew,
The Reynoldses two,
Little Comedy's face,
And the Captain in lace,
(By the bye you may tell him
I have something to sell him,
Of use I insist,
When he comes to enlist.
Your worships must know
That a few days ago,
An order went out
For the foot guards so stout
To wear tails in high taste,
Twelve inches at least;
Now I've got him a scale
To measure each tail,
To lengthen a short tail,
And a long one to curtail.)—
　　Yet how can I when vext
Thus stray from my text?
Tell each other to rue
Your Devonshire crew,
For sending so late
To one of my state.
But 'tis Reynolds's way
From wisdom to stray,
And Angelica's whim

To be frolic like him,
But, alas! your good worships, how could they be wiser,
When both have been spoil'd in to-day's Advertiser?

Oliver Goldsmith

LETTER IN PROSE AND VERSE TO MRS. BUNBURY

[Catherine Horneck Bunbury, the "Little Comedy" of the preceding verse-letter, had late in 1773 invited Goldsmith, in verse, to spend the New Year's holiday with them at Barton, the Bunburys' family seat. Others referred to in Goldsmith's reply are her sister, Mary Horneck, her husband Henry, and her brother-in-law, Sir Charles Bunbury. In the game of Loo the Knave of Clubs (called Pam) took precedence over the Ace of trumps. If a player took no tricks, he was "loo'd."]

Madam.
I read your letter with all that allowance which critical candour would require, but after all find so much to object to, and so much to raise my indignation, that I cannot help giving it a serious reply. I am not so ignorant madam as not to see there are many sarcasms contain'd in it, and solœcisms also (solœcism is a word that comes from the town of Soleis in Attica among the Greeks, built by Solon, and applied as we use the word kidderminster for curtains from a town also of that name, but this is learning you have no taste for). I say madam there are sarcasms in it and solœcisms also. But not to seem an ill natured critic, Ill take leave to quote your own words and give you my remarks upon them as they occur. You begin as follows,

I hope my good Doctor you soon will be here,
And your spring velvet coat very smart will appear
To open our ball the first day in the year.

Pray, madam, where did you ever find the Epithet good applied to the title of Doctor? Had you calld me learned Doctor, or grave Doctor, or Noble Doctor it might be allowable because these belong to the profession. But not to cavil at

triffles; you talk of my spring velvet coat and advise me to
wear it the first day in the year, that is in the middle of
winter. A spring velvet in the middle of winter?!! That would
be a solœcism indeed. And yet to encrease the inconsistence,
in another part of your letter you call me a beau. Now on one
side or other you must be wrong. If I'm a beau I can never
think of wearing a spring velvet in winter, and if I be not a
beau—why—then—that explains itself. But let me go on to
your next two strange lines

> And bring with you a wig that is modish and gay
> To dance with the girls that are makers of hay.

The absurdity of making hay at Christmass you yourself
seem sensible of. You say your sister will laugh, and so indeed
she well may—the lattins have an expression for a contemptuous kind of laughter, *naso contemnere adunco,* that is, to
laugh with a crooked nose; she may laugh at you in the manner of the ancients if she thinks fit. But now I come to the
most extraordinary of all extraordinary propositions, which is
to take your and your sister's advice in playing at Loo. The
presumption of the offer raises my indignation beyond the
bounds of prose; it inspires me at once with verse and resentment. I take advice! And from who? You shall hear.

> First let me suppose what may shortly be true
> The company set, and the word to be Loo.
> All smirking, and pleasant, and big with adventure
> And ogling the stake which is fixd in the center.
> Round and round go the cards while I inwardly damn
> At never once finding a visit from Pam.
> I lay down my stake, apparently cool,
> While the harpies about me all pocket the pool.
> I fret in my gizzard, yet cautious and sly,
> I wish all my friends may be bolder than I.
> Yet still they sit snugg, not a creature will aim
> By losing their money to venture at fame.
> 'Tis in vain that at niggardly caution I scold,
> 'Tis in vain that I flatter the brave and the bold.
> All play in their own way, and think me an ass.
> "What does Mrs. Bunbury?" "I sir? I pass."

"Pray what does Miss Horneck? Take courage. Come
  do."
"Who I! Let me see sir. Why I must pass too."
Mr. Bunbury frets, and I fret like the devil
To see them so cowardly lucky and civil.
Yet still I sit snugg and continue to sigh on
Till, made by my losses as bold as a lion,
I venture at all, while my avarice regards
The whole pool as my own. "Come give me five cards."
"Well done," cry the ladies. "Ah Doctor that's good.
"The pool's very rich. Ah. The Doctor is loo'd."
Thus foild in my courage, on all sides perplext,
I ask for advice from the lady that's next.
"Pray mam be so good as to give your advice.
"Don't you think the best way is venture fort twice?"
"I advise," cries the lady, "to try it, I own.
"Ah! The Doctor is loo'd. Come Doctor, put down."
Thus playing and playing I still grow more eager
And so bold and so bold, I'm at last a bold beggar.
Now, ladies, I ask if law matters you're skill'd in,
Whether crimes such as yours should not come before
  Fielding,
For giving advice that is not worth a straw
May well be call'd picking of pockets in law;
And picking of pockets with which I now charge ye
Is by Quinto Elizabeth [78] death without Clergy.
What justice when both to the Old Baily brought!
By the gods, Ill enjoy it, tho' 'tis but in thought.
Both are placed at the bar with all proper decorum.
With bunches of Fennel and nosegays before 'em.
Both cover their faces with mobbs and all that,
But the judge bids them angrily take off their hat.
When uncovered a buzz of enquiry runs round:
"Pray what are their crimes?" "They've been pilfering
  found."
"But pray who have they pilfered?" "A Doctor I hear."
"What, yon solemn fac'd, odd looking man that stands
  near?"
"The same." "What a pitty. How does it surprize one!
"Two handsomer culprits I never set eyes on."

Then their friends all come round me with cringing
　　and leering
To melt me to pitty, and soften my swearing.
First Sir Charles advances, with phrases well strung:
"Consider, Dear Doctor, the girls are but young."
"The younger, the worse," I return him again,
"It shews that their habits are all dy'd in grain."
"But then they're so handsome, one's bosom it
　　grieves."
"What signifies handsome when people are thieves?"
"But where is your justice; their cases are hard."
"What signifies justice; I want the reward.—"

There's the parish of Edmonton offers forty pound; there's
the parish of St Leonard Shoreditch offers forty pound; there's
the parish of Tyburn from the hog in the pound to St Giles's
watch house offers forty pound. I shall have all that if I con-
vict them.

"But consider their case, It may yet be your own
And see how they kneel; is your heart made of stone?"
This moves, so at last I agree to relent
For ten pounds in hand, and ten pound to be spent.
The judge takes the hint, having seen what we drive at,
And lets them both off with correction in private.

I chalenge you all to answer this. I tell you you cannot. It cuts
deep. But now for the rest of the letter, and next—but I want
room—so I believe I shall battle the rest out at Barton some
day next week. I don't value you all.

THE HAUNCH OF VENISON

A Poetical Epistle to Lord Clare

[Robert Nugent, Lord Clare, a politician, a wit, and one of the
wealthiest men of his day, had sought out Goldsmith soon after the
publication of *The Traveller,* and became a close friend. The Mr.
Burne mentioned at the end of the opening paragraph was Clare's
nephew. The word *bounce* was slang for a boastful lie. The verses,
written late in Goldsmith's life, were not published until 1776, two
years after his death.]

Thanks, my Lord, for your ven'son, for finer or fatter
Never rang'd in a forest, or smok'd on a platter;
The haunch was a picture for painters to study,
The white was so white, and the red was so ruddy.
[Tho' my stomach was sharp, I could scarce help regretting,
To spoil such a delicate picture by eating;]
I had thoughts, in my chamber, to hang it in view,
To be shown to my friends as a piece of *Virtu;*
As in some *Irish* houses, where things are so-so,
One gammon of bacon hangs up for a show:
But for eating a rasher of what they take pride in,
They'd as soon think of eating the pan it is fry'd in.
But hold—let us pause—Don't I hear you pronounce
This tale of the bacon a damnable bounce?
Well, suppose it a bounce—sure a poet may try,
By a bounce now and then, to get courage to fly:
But, my Lord, it's no bounce: I protest in my turn,
It's a truth—and your Lordship may ask Mr. Burne.
   To go on with my tale—As I gaz'd on the haunch,
I thought of a friend that was trusty and staunch;
So I cut it, and sent it to Reynolds undrest,
To paint it, or eat it, just as he lik'd best.
Of the neck and the breast I had next to dispose;
'Twas a neck and a breast that might rival Monroe's:[79]
But in parting with these I was puzzled again,
With the *how,* and the *who,* and the *where,* and the *when.*
There's Coley, and Williams, and Howard, and Hiff,
I think they love ven'son—I know they love beef;
But hang it—to poets that seldom can eat,
Your very good mutton's a very good treat;
Such dainties to them—It *would* look like a flirt,
[It's] like sending them Ruffles, when wanting a Shirt.
   While thus I debated, in reverie center'd,
An acquaintance, a friend—as he call'd himself, enter'd;
A fine-spoken Custom-house Officer he,
Who smil'd, as he gazed on the ven'son and me.
"What have we got here?—Aye, this is *good eating!*
Your own, I suppose—or is it in waiting?"
"Why whose should it be, Sir?" cried I, with a flounce,
"I get these things often;"—but that was a bounce:

["Some Lords, my acquaintance, that settle the nation,
Are pleas'd to be kind—but I hate ostentation."]
"If that be the case, then," cried he, very gay,
"I'm glad I have taken this house in my way.
To-morrow you take a poor dinner with me;
No words—I insist on't—precisely at three:
And now that I think on't, as I am a sinner!
We wanted this ven'son to make up the dinner.
I'll take no denial—you shall—and you must,
And my wife, little Kitty, is famous for crust.
We'll have Johnson, and Burke, all the Wits will be there,
My acquaintance is slight, or I'd ask my Lord Clare.
Here, porter—this ven'son with me to Mile-end;
No words, my dear Goldsmith, my very good friend!"
Thus seizing his hat, he brush'd off like the wind,
And the porter and eatables follow'd behind.

Left alone to reflect, having empty'd my shelf,
And no body with me at sea, but myself,
Though I could not help thinking my gentleman hasty,
Yet Johnson, and Burke, and a good ven'son pasty,
Were things that I never dislik'd in my life,
Tho' clogg'd with a coxcomb, and Kitty his wife.
So next day in due splendor to make my approach,
I drove to his door in my own hackney-coach.

When come to the place where we all were to dine,
(A chair lumber'd closet just twelve feet by nine:)
My friend bade me welcome, but struck me quite dumb,
With tidings that Johnson, and Burke could not come.
"And I knew it," he cry'd, "both eternally fail,
The one at the House and the other with Thrale;
But I warrant for me, we shall make up the party,
With two full as clever, and ten times as hearty.
The one is a Scotchman, the other a Jew,
Who dabble and write in the Papers—like you;
The one writes the *Snarler*, the other the *Scourge;*
Some think he writes *Cinna*—he owns to *Panurge.*"

While thus he describ'd them by trade, and by name,
They enter'd, and dinner was serv'd as they came.
At the top a fry'd liver and bacon was seen,
At the bottom was tripe, in a swinging terrene;

At the sides there was spinage and pudding made hot;
In the middle—a place where the ven'son was not.
Now, my Lord, as for tripe it's my utter aversion,
And your bacon I hate like a *Turk* or a *Persian;*
[So there I sat stuck, like a horse in a pound,
While the bacon and liver went merrily round:]
But what vex'd me most was that damn'd Scottish rogue,
With his long-winded speeches, and smiles and his brogue.
"And Madam," says he, "may this bit be my poison,
If a prettier dinner I ever set eyes on;
Pray a slice of your liver, but may I be curst,
But I've eat of your tripe, till I'm ready to burst."
"Your Tripe," quoth the Jew, "if the truth I may speak,
I could eat of this tripe seven days in the week.
I like these here dinners, so pretty and small;
But your friend there, the Doctor, eats nothing at all."
"Oho!" quoth my friend, "he'll come on in a trice,
He's keeping a corner for something that's nice:
There's a pasty—" "A pasty!" returned the Scot,
"I don't care, if I keep a corner for thot."
"We'll all keep a corner," the Lady cry'd out;
"We'll all keep a corner" was eccho'd about.
While thus we resolv'd, and the pasty delay'd,
With looks quite astonishing, enter'd the maid;
A visage so sad, and so pale with affright,
Wak'd Priam in drawing his curtains by night.
But too soon we found out (for who could mistake her?)
That she came with some terrible news from the baker:
And so it fell out, for that negligent sloven,
Had shut out the pasty on shutting his oven.
Sad Philomel thus—but let similes drop—
And now that I think on't, the story may stop.
To be plain, my good Lord, 'tis but labour misplac'd,
To send such good verses to one of your taste;
You've got an odd something—a kind of discerning—
A relish—a taste—sicken'd over by learning;
At least it's your temper, 'tis very well known,
That you think very slightly of all that's your own:
So, perhaps, in your habits of thinking amiss,
You may make a mistake, and think slightly of this.

RETALIATION

[Early in 1774 some of Goldsmith's friends, little realizing that he was to die on April 4, amused themselves at the St. James's Coffee House by composing mock epitaphs on him. One that has survived was written by Garrick:

> Here lies Nolly Goldsmith, for shortness call'd Noll,
> Who wrote like an angel, but talk'd like poor Poll.

Goldsmith, who was rarely successful in extemporizing, did not reply at once, but retaliated by writing the following verses, which were first published two weeks after his death. Those whom he writes about are the Dean of Derry (Thomas Barnard); Edmund Burke, his relative William, and his brother Richard; Richard Cumberland, the dramatist; Dr. Douglas, a Scot who had exposed several literary forgeries; David Garrick, the great actor; John Ridge and Joseph Hickey, both lawyers; and Sir Joshua Reynolds.]

Of old, when Scarron his companions invited,
Each guest brought his dish, and the feast was united;
If our landlord supplies us with beef, and with fish,
Let each guest bring himself, and he brings the best dish:
Our Dean shall be venison, just fresh from the plains;
Our Burke shall be tongue, with a garnish of brains;
Our Will shall be wild fowl, of excellent flavour,
And Dick with his pepper, shall heighten their savour:
Our Cumberland's sweet-bread, its place shall obtain,
And Douglas is pudding, substantial and plain:
Our Garrick's a sallad, for in him we see
Oil, vinegar, sugar, and saltness agree:
To make out the dinner, full certain I am,
That Ridge is anchovy, and Reynolds is lamb;
That Hickey's a capon, and by the same rule,
Magnanimous Goldsmith, a goosberry fool:
At a dinner so various, at such a repast,
Who'd not be glutton, and stick to the last:
Here, waiter, more wine, let me sit while I'm able,
'Till all my companions sink under the table;
Then with chaos and blunders encircling my head,
Let me ponder, and tell what I think of the dead.

Here lies the good Dean, re-united to earth,
Who mixt reason with pleasure, and wisdom with mirth:
If he had any faults, he has left us in doubt,
At least, in six weeks, I could not find 'em out;
Yet some have declar'd, and it can't be denied 'em,
That sly-boots was cursedly cunning to hide 'em.

Here lies our good Edmund, whose genius was such,
We scarcely can praise it, or blame it too much;
Who, born for the Universe, narrow'd his mind,
And to party gave up, what was meant for mankind.
Tho' fraught with all learning, yet straining his throat,
To persuade Tommy Townsend to lend him a vote;
Who, too deep for his hearers, still went on refining,
And thought of convincing, while they thought of dining;
Tho' equal to all things, for all things unfit,
Too nice for a statesman, too proud for a wit:
For a patriot too cool; for a drudge, disobedient,
And too fond of the *right* to pursue the *expedient*.
In short, 'twas his fate, unemploy'd, or in place, Sir,
To eat mutton cold, and cut blocks with a razor.

Here lies honest William, whose heart was a mint,
While the owner ne'er knew half the good that was in't;
The pupil of impulse, it forced him along,
His conduct still right, with his argument wrong;
Still aiming at honour, yet fearing to roam,
The coachman was tipsy, the chariot drove home;
Would you ask for his merits, alas! he had none,
What was good was spontaneous, his faults were his own.

Here lies honest Richard, whose fate I must sigh at,
Alas, that such frolic should now be so quiet!
What spirits were his, what wit and what whim,
Now breaking a jest, and now breaking a limb;
Now wrangling and grumbling to keep up the ball,
Now teazing and vexing, yet laughing at all!
In short so provoking a Devil was Dick,
That we wish'd him full ten times a day at Old Nick,
But missing his mirth and agreeable vein,
As often we wish'd to have Dick back again.

Here Cumberland lies having acted his parts,
The Terence of England, the mender of hearts;

A flattering painter, who made it his care
To draw men as they ought to be, not as they are.
His gallants are all faultless, his women divine,
And comedy wonders at being so fine;
Like a tragedy queen he has dizen'd her out,
Or rather like tragedy giving a rout.
His fools have their follies so lost in a croud
Of virtues and feelings, that folly grows proud,
And coxcombs alike in their failings alone,
Adopting his portraits are pleas'd with their own.
Say, where has our poet this malady caught,
Or wherefore his characters thus without fault?
Say was it that vainly directing his view,
To find out men's virtues and finding them few,
Quite sick of pursuing each troublesome elf,
He grew lazy at last and drew from himself?

Here Douglas retires from his toils to relax,
The scourge of impostors, the terror of quacks:
Come all ye quack bards, and ye quacking divines,
Come and dance on the spot where your tyrant reclines,
When Satire and Censure encircl'd his throne,
I fear'd for your safety, I fear'd for my own;
But now he is gone, and we want a detector,
Our Dodds shall be pious, our Kenricks shall lecture;
Macpherson write bombast, and call it a style,
Our Townshend make speeches, and I shall compile;
New Lauders and Bowers the Tweed shall cross over,
No countryman living their tricks to discover;
Detection her taper shall quench to a spark,
And Scotchman meet Scotchman and cheat in the dark.

Here lies David Garrick, describe me who can,
An abridgment of all that was pleasant in man;
As an actor, confest without rival to shine,
As a wit, if not first, in the very first line,
Yet with talents like these, and an excellent heart,
The man had his failings, a dupe to his art;
Like an ill judging beauty, his colours he spread,
And beplaister'd with rouge his own natural red.
On the stage he was natural, simple, affecting,
'Twas only that, when he was off, he was acting:

With no reason on earth to go out of his way,
He turn'd and he varied full ten times a day;
Tho' secure of our hearts, yet confoundedly sick
If they were not his own by finessing and trick,
He cast off his friends, as a huntsman his pack,
For he knew when he pleased he could whistle them back.
Of praise a mere glutton, he swallowed what came,
And the puff of a dunce, he mistook it for fame;
'Till his relish grown callous, almost to disease,
Who pepper'd the highest, was surest to please.
But let us be candid, and speak out our mind,
If dunces applauded, he paid them in kind.
Ye Kenricks, ye Kellys, and Woodfalls so grave,
What a commerce was yours, while you got and you gave!
How did Grub-street re-echo the shouts that you rais'd,
While he was beroscius'd, and you were beprais'd!
But peace to his spirit, wherever it flies,
To act as an angel, and mix with the skies:
Those poets, who owe their best fame to his skill,
Shall still be his flatterers, go where he will.
Old Shakespeare, receive him, with praise and with love,
And Beaumonts and Bens be his Kellys above.
   Here Hickey reclines, a most blunt, pleasant creature,
And slander itself must allow him good-nature:
He cherish'd his friend, and he relish'd a bumper;
Yet one fault he had, and that one was a thumper:
Perhaps you may ask if the man was a miser?
I answer, no, no, for he always was wiser;
Too courteous, perhaps, or obligingly flat;
His very worst foe can't accuse him of that.
Perhaps he confided in men as they go;
And so was too foolishly honest; ah, no.
Then what was his failing? come tell it, and burn ye,
He was, could he help it? a special attorney.
   Here Reynolds is laid, and to tell you my mind,
He has not left a better or wiser behind;
His pencil was striking, resistless and grand,
His manners were gentle, complying and bland;
Still born to improve us in every part,
His pencil our faces, his manners our heart:

To coxcombs averse, yet most civilly steering,
When they judged without skill he was still hard of hearing:
When they talk'd of their Raphaels, Corregios and stuff,
He shifted his trumpet, and only took snuff.

She Stoops to Conquer

O R

THE MISTAKES OF A NIGHT

[*She Stoops to Conquer* was first acted at Covent Garden on 15 March 1773. Colman, the manager, was pessimistic, believing that Goldsmith's hostility to sentimental comedy would not be shared by theatre-goers, but the play was a success from the start. Garrick's prologue was spoken by Woodward, who had played Lofty in *The Good Natur'd Man* but who had refused to act in *She Stoops*. "Poor Ned" Shuter, mentioned in the prologue, was Woodward's fellow actor, who had played Croaker in the earlier comedy and took the part of Hardcastle in this. The italicized words at the beginning of the prologue are borrowed from *Hamlet* (I. ii. 77-86).]

To Samuel Johnson, L.L.D.

Dear Sir,

By inscribing this slight performance to you, I do not mean so much to compliment you as myself. It may do me some honour to inform the public that I have lived many years in intimacy with you. It may serve the interests of mankind also to inform them that the greatest wit may be found in a character, without impairing the most unaffected piety.

I have, particularly, reason to thank you for your partiality to this performance. The undertaking a comedy not merely sentimental was very dangerous; and Mr. Colman, who saw this piece in its various stages, always thought it so. However I ventured to trust it to the public; and, though it was necessarily delayed till late in the season, I have every reason to be grateful.

> I am, Dear Sir,
> Your most sincere friend,
> And admirer,
>
> *Oliver Goldsmith*

PROLOGUE

By David Garrick, Esq.

Enter MR. WOODWARD, *Dressed in black, and holding a Handkerchief to his Eyes.*

Excuse me, Sirs, I pray—I can't yet speak—
I'm crying now—and have been all the week!
'Tis not alone this mourning suit, good masters;
I've that within—for which there are no plaisters!
Pray wou'd you know the reason why I'm crying?
The comic muse, long sick, is now a dying!
And if she goes, my tears will never stop;
For as a play'r, I can't squeeze out one drop:
I am undone, that's all—shall lose my bread—
I'd rather, but that's nothing—lose my head.
When the sweet maid is laid upon the bier,
Shuter and I shall be chief mourners here.
To *her* a mawkish drab of spurious breed,
Who deals in *sentimentals* will succeed!
Poor Ned and I are dead to all intents,
We can as soon speak *Greek* as *sentiments!*
Both nervous grown, to keep our spirits up,
We now and then take down a hearty cup.
What shall we do?—If Comedy forsake us!
They'll turn us out, and no one else will take us,
But why can't I be moral?—Let me try—
My heart thus pressing—fix'd my face and eye—
With a sententious look that nothing means
(Faces are blocks in sentimental scenes)
Thus I begin—*All is not gold that glitters,*
Pleasure seems sweet, but proves a glass of bitters.
When ign'rance enters, folly is at hand;
Learning is better far than house and land.
Let not your virtue trip, who trips may stumble,
And virtue is not virtue if she tumble.
   I give it up—morals won't do for me;
To make you laugh I must play tragedy.

One hope remains—hearing the maid was ill,
A *doctor* comes this night to shew his skill.
To cheer her heart, and give your muscles motion,
He in *five draughts* prepar'd, presents a potion:
A kind of magic charm—for be assur'd,
If you will *swallow it,* the maid is cur'd:
But desp'rate the Doctor, and her case is,
If you reject the dose and make wry faces!
This truth he boasts, will boast it while he lives,
No *pois'nous drugs* are mix'd in what he gives;
Should he succeed, you'll give him his degree;
If not, within he will receive no fee!
The college *you,* must his pretentions back,
Pronounce him *regular,* or dub him *quack.*

ACT I

SCENE, *A Chamber in an old-fashioned House*

Enter MRS. HARDCASTLE *and* MR. HARDCASTLE

Mrs. Hardcastle. I vow, Mr. Hardcastle, you're very particular. Is there a creature in the whole country but ourselves that does not take a trip to town now and then, to rub off the rust a little? There's the two Miss Hoggs, and our neighbour, Mrs. Grigsby, go to take a month's polishing every winter.

Hardcastle. Ay, and bring back vanity and affectation to last them the whole year. I wonder why London cannot keep its own fools at home. In my time the follies of the town crept slowly among us, but now they travel faster than a stage-coach. Its fopperies come down, not only as inside passengers, but in the very basket.

Mrs. Hardcastle. Ay, *your* times were fine times, indeed; you have been telling us of *them* for many a long year. Here we live in an old rumbling mansion, that looks for all the world like an inn, but that we never see company. Our best visitors are old Mrs. Oddfish, the curate's wife, and little Cripplegate, the lame dancing-master: And all our entertain-

ment your old stories of Prince Eugene and the Duke of Marlborough. I hate such old-fashioned trumpery.

Hardcastle. And I love it. I love every thing that's old: old
friends, old times, old manners, old books, old wine; and, I
believe, Dorothy (*taking her hand*) you'll own I have been
pretty fond of an old wife.

Mrs. Hardcastle. Lord, Mr. Hardcastle, you're for ever at
your Dorothy's and your old wife's. You may be a Darby, but
I'll be no Joan, I promise you. I'm not so old as you'd make
me, by more than one good year. Add twenty to twenty, and
make money of that.

Hardcastle. Let me see; twenty added to twenty, makes just
fifty and seven.

Mrs. Hardcaste. It's false, Mr. Hardcastle: I was but twenty
when I was brought to bed of Tony, that I had by Mr. Lumpkin, my first husband; and he's not come to years of discretion
yet.

Hardcastle. Nor ever will, I dare answer for him. Ay, you
have taught *him* finely.

Mrs. Hardcastle. No matter, Tony Lumpkin has a good
fortune. My son is not to live by his learning. I don't think a
boy wants much learning to spend fifteen hundred a year.

Hardcastle. Learning, quotha! A mere composition of tricks
and mischief.

Mrs. Hardcastle. Humour, my dear: nothing but humour.
Come, Mr. Hardcastle, you must allow the boy a little humour.

Hardcastle. I'd sooner allow him an horse-pond. If burning
the footmens shoes, frighting the maids, and worrying the
kittens, be humour, he has it. It was but yesterday he fastened
my wig to the back of my chair, and when I went to make a
bow, I popt my bald head in Mrs. Frizzle's face.

Mrs. Hardcastle. And am I to blame? The poor boy was
always too sickly to do any good. A school would be his death.
When he comes to be a little stronger, who know what a year
or two's Latin may do for him?

Hardcastle. Latin for him! A cat and fiddle. No, no, the ale-
house and the stable are the only schools he'll ever go to.

Mrs. Hardcastle. Well, we must not snub the poor boy now,
for I believe we shan't have him long among us. Any body
that looks in his face may see he's consumptive.

Hardcastle. Ay, if growing too fat be one of the symptoms.

Mrs. Hardcastle. He coughs sometimes.

Hardcastle. Yes, when his liquor goes the wrong way.

Mrs. Hardcastle. I'm actually afraid of his lungs.

Hardcastle. And truly so am I; for he sometimes whoops like a speaking trumpet—(TONY *hallooing behind the Scenes*) —O there he goes—A very consumptive figure, truly.

Enter TONY, *crossing the Stage*

Mrs. Hardcastle. Tony, where are you going, my charmer? Won't you give papa and I a little of your company, lovee?

Tony. I'm in haste, mother. I cannot stay.

Mrs. Hardcastle. You shan't venture out this raw evening, my dear. You look most shockingly.

Tony. I can't stay, I tell you. The Three Pigeons expects me down every moment. There's some fun going forward.

Hardcastle. Ay; the ale-house, the old place. I thought so.

Mrs. Hardcastle. A low, paltry set of fellows.

Tony. Not so low neither. There's Dick Muggins the exciseman, Jack Slang the horse doctor, Little Aminadab that grinds the music box, and Tom Twist that spins the pewter platter.

Mrs. Hardcastle. Pray, my dear, disappoint them for one night at least.

Tony. As for disappointing *them,* I should not much mind; but I can't abide to disappoint *myself.*

Mrs. Hardcastle. (*detaining him*) You shan't go.

Tony. I will, I tell you.

Mrs. Hardcastle. I say you shan't.

Tony. We'll see which is strongest, you or I.

[*Exit, hawling her out.*

HARDCASTLE *Solus*

Hardcastle. Ay, there goes a pair that only spoil each other. But is not the whole age in a combination to drive sense and discretion out of doors? There's my pretty darling Kate; the fashions of the times have almost infected her too. By living a year or two in town, she is as fond of gauze and French frippery, as the best of them.

Enter MISS HARDCASTLE

Hardcastle. Blessings on my pretty innocence! Drest out as usual, my Kate. Goodness! What a quantity of superfluous silk hast thou got about thee, girl! I could never teach the fools of this age that the indigent world could be cloathed out of the trimmings of the vain.

Miss Hardcastle. You know our agreement, Sir. You allow me the morning to receive and pay visits, and to dress in my own manner; and in the evening I put on my housewife's dress to please you.

Hardcastle. Well, remember I insist on the terms of our agreement; and, by the bye, I believe I shall have occasion to try your obedience this very evening.

Miss Hardcastle. I protest, Sir, I don't comprehend your meaning.

Hardcastle. Then to be plain with you, Kate, I expect the young gentleman I have chosen to be your husband from town this very day. I have his father's letter, in which he informs me his son is set out, and that he intends to follow himself shortly after.

Miss Hardcastle. Indeed! I wish I had known something of this before. Bless me, how shall I behave? It's a thousand to one I shan't like him; our meeting will be so formal, and so like a thing of business, that I shall find no room for friendship or esteem.

Hardcastle. Depend upon it, child, I'll never controul your choice; but Mr. Marlow, whom I have pitched upon, is the son of my old friend, Sir Charles Marlow, of whom you have heard me talk so often. The young gentleman has been bred a scholar, and is designed for an employment in the service of his country. I am told he's a man of an excellent understanding.

Miss Hardcastle. Is he?

Hardcastle. Very generous.

Miss Hardcastle. I believe I shall like him.

Hardcastle. Young and brave.

Miss Hardcastle. I'm sure I shall like him.

Hardcastle. And very handsome.

Miss Hardcastle. My dear Papa, say no more (*kissing his hand*) he's mine, I'll have him.

Hardcastle. And to crown all, Kate, he's one of the most bashful and reserved young fellows in all the world.

Miss Hardcastle. Eh! you have frozen me to death again. That word reserved has undone all the rest of his accomplishments. A reserved lover, it is said, always makes a suspicious husband.

Hardcastle. On the contrary, modesty seldom resides in a breast that is not enriched with nobler virtues. It was the very feature in his character that first struck me.

Miss Hardcastle. He must have more striking features to catch me, I promise you. However, if he be so young, so handsome, and so every thing, as you mention, I believe he'll do still. I think I'll have him.

Hardcastle. Ay, Kate, but there is still an obstacle. It's more than an even wager, he may not have *you.*

Miss Hardcastle. My dear papa, why will you mortify one so?—Well, if he refuses, instead of breaking my heart at his indifference, I'll only break my glass for its flattery. Set my cap to some newer fashion, and look out for some less difficult admirer.

Hardcastle. Bravely resolved! In the mean time I'll go prepare the servants for his reception; as we seldom see company they want as much training as a company of recruits, the first day's muster. [*Exit.*

MISS HARDCASTLE *Sola*

Miss Hardcastle. Lud, this news of Papa's puts me all in a flutter. Young, handsome; these he put last; but I put them foremost. Sensible, good-natured; I like all that. But then reserved, and sheepish, that's much against him. Yet can't he be cured of his timidity, by being taught to be proud of his wife? Yes, and can't I—But I vow I'm disposing of the husband, before I have secured the lover.

Enter MISS NEVILLE

Miss Hardcastle. I'm glad you're come, Neville, my dear. Tell me, Constance, how do I look this evening? Is there any thing whimsical about me? Is it one of my well looking days, child? Am I in face to day?

Miss Neville. Perfectly, my dear. Yet now I look again—bless me!—sure no accident has happened among the canary birds or the gold fishes. Has your brother or the cat been meddling? Or has the last novel been too moving?

Miss Hardcastle. No; nothing of all this. I have been threatened—I can scarce get it out—I have been threatened with a lover.

Miss Neville. And his name——

Miss Hardcastle. Is Marlow.

Miss Neville. Indeed!

Miss Hardcastle. The son of Sir Charles Marlow.

Miss Neville. As I live, the most intimate friend of Mr. Hastings, *my* admirer. They are never asunder. I believe you must have seen him when we lived in town.

Miss Hardcastle. Never.

Miss Neville. He's a very singular character, I assure you. Among women of reputation and virtue, he is the modestest man alive; but his acquaintance give him a very different character among creatures of another stamp: you understand me.

Miss Hardcastle. An odd character, indeed. I shall never be able to manage him. What shall I do? Pshaw, think no more of him, but trust to occurrences for success. But how goes on your own affair my dear, has my mother been courting you for my brother Tony, as usual?

Miss Neville. I have just come from one of our agreeable tête-à-têtes. She has been saying a hundred tender things, and setting off her pretty monster as the very pink of perfection.

Miss Hardcastle. And her partiality is such that she actually thinks him so. A fortune like your's is no small temptation. Besides, as she has the sole management of it, I'm not surprized to see her unwilling to let it go out of the family.

Miss Neville. A fortune like mine, which chiefly consists in jewels, is no such mighty temptation. But at any rate if my dear Hastings be but constant, I make no doubt to be too hard for her at last. However, I let her suppose that I am in love with her son, and she never once dreams that my affections are fixed upon another.

Miss Hardcastle. My good brother holds out stoutly. I could almost love him for hating you so.

Miss Neville. It is a good natured creature at bottom, and I'm sure would wish to see me married to any body but himself. But my aunt's bell rings for our afternoon's walk round the improvements. Allons. Courage is necessary, as our affairs are critical.

Miss Hardcastle. Would it were bed time and all were well.[80]

[*Exeunt.*

SCENE, *An Alehouse Room. Several shabby fellows, with Punch and Tobacco.* TONY *at the head of the Table, a little higher than the rest: A mallet in his hand.*

Omnes. Hurrea, hurrea, hurrea, bravo.

First Fellow. Now, gentlemen, silence for a song. The 'Squire is going to knock himself down for a song.

Omnes. Ay, a song, a song.

Tony. Then I'll sing you, gentlemen, a song I made upon this ale-house, the Three Pigeons.

SONG

Let school-masters puzzle their brain,
With grammar, and nonsense, and learning;
Good liquor, I stoutly maintain,
Gives genus a better discerning.
Let them brag of their Heathenish Gods,
Their Lethes, their Styxes, and Stygians;
Their Quis, and their Quæs, and their Quods,
They're all but a parcel of Pigeons.
          Toroddle, toroddle, toroll.

When Methodist preachers come down,
A preaching that drinking is sinful,
I'll wager the rascals a crown,

> *They always preach best with a skinful.*
> *But when you come down with your pence,*
> *For a slice of their scurvy religion,*
> *I'll leave it to all men of sense,*
> *But you, my good friend, are the pigeon.*
>
> Toroddle, toroddle, toroll.

> *Then come, put the jorum about,*
> *And let us be merry and clever,*
> *Our hearts and our liquors are stout,*
> *Here's the Three Jolly Pigeons for ever.*
> *Let some cry up woodcock or hare,*
> *Your bustards, your ducks, and your widgeons;*
> *But of all the birds in the air,*
> *Here's a health to the Three Jolly Pigeons.*
>
> Toroddle, toroddle, toroll.

Omnes. Bravo, bravo.

First Fellow. The 'Squire has got spunk in him.

Second Fellow. I loves to hear him sing, bekeays he never gives us nothing that's *low*.[81]

Third Fellow. O damn anything that's *low,* I cannot bear it.

Fourth Fellow. The genteel thing is the genteel thing at any time. If so be that a gentleman bees in a concatenation accordingly.

Third Fellow. I like the maxum of it, Master Muggins. What, tho' I am obligated to dance a bear, a man may be a gentleman for all that. May this be my poison if my bear ever dances but to the very genteelest of tunes. Water Parted, or the minuet in Ariadne.[82]

Second Fellow. What a pitty it is the 'Squire is not come to his own. It would be well for all the publicans within ten miles round of him.

Tony. Ecod and so it would, Master Slang. I'd then shew what it was to keep choice of company.

Second Fellow. O, he takes after his own father for that. To be sure old 'Squire Lumpkin was the finest gentleman I ever set my eyes on. For winding the streight horn, or beating a thicket for a hare or a wench, he never had his fellow. It was a saying in the place that he kept the best horses, dogs, and girls in the whole county.

Tony. Ecod, and when I'm of age I'll be no bastard I promise you. I have been thinking of Bett Bouncer and the miller's grey mare to begin with. But come, my boys, drink about and be merry, for you pay no reckoning. Well Stingo, what's the matter?

Enter LANDLORD

Landlord. There be two gentlemen in a post-chaise at the door. They have lost their way upo' the forest; and they are talking something about Mr. Hardcastle.

Tony. As sure as can be one of them must be the gentleman that's coming down to court my sister. Do they seem to be Londoners?

Landlord. I believe they may. They look woundily[83] like Frenchmen.

Tony. Then desire them to step this way, and I'll set them right in a twinkling. (*Exit* LANDLORD.) Gentlemen, as they mayn't be good enough company for you, step down for a moment, and I'll be with you in the squeezing of a lemon.

[*Exeunt Mob.*

TONY *solus*

Tony. Father-in-law has been calling me whelp, and hound, this half year. Now if I pleased, I could be so revenged upon the old grumbletonian. But then I'm afraid—afraid of what! I shall soon be worth fifteen hundred a year, and let him frighten me out of *that* if he can.

Enter LANDLORD, *conducting* MARLOW *and* HASTINGS

Marlow. What a tedious uncomfortable day have we had of it! We were told it was but forty miles across the country, and we have come above threescore.

Hastings. And all Marlow, from that unaccountable reserve of yours, that would not let us enquire more frequently on the way.

Marlow. I own, Hastings, I am unwilling to lay myself under an obligation to every one I meet, and often stand the chance of an unmannerly answer.

Hastings. At present, however, we are not likely to receive any answer.

Tony. No offence, gentlemen. But I'm told you have been enquiring for one Mr. Hardcastle, in these parts. Do you know what part of the country you are in?

Hastings. Not in the least Sir, but should thank you for information.

Tony. Nor the way you came?

Hastings. No, Sir; but if you can inform us——

Tony. Why, gentlemen, if you know neither the road you are going, nor where you are, nor the road you came, the first thing I have to inform you is, that—You have lost your way.

Marlow. We wanted no ghost to tell us that.[84]

Tony. Pray, gentlemen, may I be so bold as to ask the place from whence you came?

Marlow. That's not necessary towards directing us where we are to go.

Tony. No offence; but question for question is all fair, you know. Pray, gentlemen, is not this same Hardcastle a cross-grain'd, old-fashion'd, whimsical fellow with an ugly face, a daughter, and a pretty son?

Hastings. We have not seen the gentleman, but he has the family you mention.

Tony. The daughter, a tall trapesing, trolloping, talkative maypole——The son, a pretty, well-bred, agreeable youth, that every body is fond of.

Marlow. Our information differs in this. The daughter is said to be well-bred and beautiful; the son, an aukward booby, reared up, and spoiled at his mother's apron-string.

Tony. He-he-hem—Then, gentlemen, all I have to tell you is, that you won't reach Mr. Hardcastle's house this night, I believe.

Hastings. Unfortunate!

Tony. It's a damn'd long, dark, boggy, dirty, dangerous way. Stingo, tell the gentlemen the way to Mr. Hardcastle's; (*winking upon the* LANDLORD) Mr. Hardcastle's, of Quagmire Marsh, you understand me.

Landlord. Master Hardcastle's! Lock-a-daisy, my masters, you're come a deadly deal wrong! When you came to the bottom of the hill, you should have cross'd down Squash-lane.

Marlow. Cross down Squash-lane!

Landlord. Then you were to keep streight forward, 'till you came to four roads.

Marlow. Come to where four roads meet!

Tony. Ay; but you must be sure to take only one of them.

Marlow. O Sir, you're facetious.

Tony. Then keeping to the right, you are to go sideways till you come upon Crack skull common: there you must look sharp for the track of the wheel, and go forward, 'till you come to farmer Murrain's barn. Coming to the farmer's barn, you are to turn to the right, and then to the left, and then to the right about again, till you find out the old mill——

Marlow. Zounds, man! we could as soon find out the longitude! [85]

Hastings. What's to be done, Marlow?

Marlow. This house promises but a poor reception; though perhaps the Landlord can accommodate us.

Landlord. Alack, master, we have but one spare bed in the whole house.

Tony. And to my knowledge, that's taken up by three lodgers already. (*after a pause, in which the rest seem disconcerted*) I have hit it. Don't you think, Stingo, our landlady could accommodate the gentlemen by the fire-side, with—— three chairs and a bolster?

Hastings. I hate sleeping by the fire-side.

Marlow. And I detest your three chairs and a bolster.

Tony. You do, do you?—then let me see—what—if you go on a mile further, to the Buck's Head; the old Buck's Head on the hill, one of the best inns in the whole county?

Hastings. O ho! so we have escaped an adventure for this night, however.

Landlord. (*apart to* TONY) Sure, you ben't sending them to your father's as an inn, be you?

Tony. Mum, you fool you. Let *them* find that out. (*to them*) You have only to keep on streight forward, till you come to a large old house by the road side. You'll see a pair of large horns over the door. That's the sign. Drive up the yard, and call stoutly about you.

Hastings. Sir, we are obliged to you. The servants can't miss the way?

Tony. No, no. But I tell you though, the landlord is rich, and going to leave off business; so he wants to be thought a gentleman, saving your presence, he! he! he! He'll be for giving you his company, and ecod if you mind him, he'll persuade you that his mother was an alderman, and his aunt a justice of the peace.

Landlord. A troublesome old blade to be sure; but a keeps as good wines and beds as any in the whole country.

Marlow. Well, if he supplies us with these, we shall want no further connexion. We are to turn to the right, did you say?

Tony. No, no; streight forward. I'll just step myself, and shew you a piece of the way. (*to the* LANDLORD) Mum.

Landlord. Ah, bless your heart, for a sweet, pleasant—— damn'd mischievous son of a whore.

[*Exeunt.*

ACT II

SCENE, *An old-fashioned House*

Enter HARDCASTLE, *followed by three or four aukward*
SERVANTS

Hardcastle. Well, I hope you're perfect in the table exercise I have been teaching you these three days. You all know your posts and your places, and can shew that you have been used to good company, without ever stirring from home.

Omnes. Ay, ay.

Hardcastle. When company comes, you are not to pop out and stare, and then run in again, like frighted rabbits in a warren.

Omnes. No, no.

Hardcastle. You, Diggory, whom I have taken from the barn, are to make a shew at the side-table; and you, Roger, whom I have advanced from the plough, are to place yourself behind *my* chair. But you're not to stand so, with your hands in your pockets. Take your hands from your pockets, Roger; and from your head, you blockhead you. See how Diggory carries his hands. They're a little too stiff, indeed, but that's no great matter.

Diggory. Ay, mind how I hold them. I learned to hold my hands this way, when I was upon drill for the militia. And so being upon drill——

Hardcastle. You must not be so talkative, Diggory. You must be all attention to the guests. You must hear us talk, and not think of talking; you must see us drink, and not think of drinking; you must see us eat, and not think of eating.

Diggory. By the laws, your worship, that's perfectly unpossible. Whenever Diggory sees yeating going forward, ecod he's always wishing for a mouthful himself.

Hardcastle. Blockhead! Is not a belly-full in the kitchen as good as a belly-full in the parlour? Stay your stomach with that reflection.

Diggory. Ecod I thank your worship, I'll make a shift to stay my stomach with a slice of cold beef in the pantry.

Hardcastle. Diggory, you are too talkative. Then if I happen to say a good thing, or tell a good story at table, you must not all burst out a-laughing, as if you made part of the company.

Diggory. Then ecod your worship must not tell the story of Ould Grouse in the gun-room: I can't help laughing at that—he! he! he!—for the soul of me. We have laughed at that these twenty years—ha! ha! ha!

Hardcastle. Ha! ha! ha! The story is a good one. Well, honest Diggory, you may laugh at that—but still remember to be attentive. Suppose one of the company should call for a glass of wine, how will you behave? A glass of wine, Sir, if you please (*to* DIGGORY)—Eh, why don't you move?

Diggory. Ecod, your worship, I never have courage till I see the eatables and drinkables brought upo' the table, and then I'm as bauld as a lion.

Hardcastle. What, will no body move?

First Servant. I'm not to leave this pleace.

Second Servant. I'm sure it's no pleace of mine.

Third Servant. Nor mine, for sartain.

Diggory. Wauns, and I'm sure it canna be mine.

Hardcastle. You numbskulls! and so while, like your betters, you are quarrelling for places, the guests must be starved. O

you dunces! I find I must begin all over again.—But don't I
hear a coach drive into the yard? To your posts you blockheads. I'll go in the mean time and give my old friend's son a
hearty reception at the gate.   [*Exit* HARDCASTLE.

Diggory. By the elevens, my pleace is gone quite out of my
head.

Roger. I know that my pleace is to be every where.

First Servant. Where the devil is mine?

Second Servant. My pleace is to be no where at all; and so
Ize go about my business.

[*Exeunt* SERVANTS, *running about as if frighted, different ways.*

Enter SERVANT *with Candles, shewing in* MARLOW *and*
HASTINGS

Servant. Welcome, gentlemen, very welcome. This way.

Hastings. After the disappointments of the day, welcome
once more, Charles, to the comforts of a clean room and a
good fire. Upon my word, a very well-looking house; antique
but creditable.

Marlow. The usual fate of a large mansion. Having first
ruined the master by good housekeeping, it at last comes to
levy contributions as an inn.

Hastings. As you say, we passengers are to be taxed to pay
all these fineries. I have often seen a good sideboard, or a
marble chimney-piece, tho' not actually put in the bill, enflame a reckoning confoundedly.

Marlow. Travellers, George, must pay in all places. The
only difference is, that in good inns you pay dearly for luxuries; in bad inns you are fleeced and starved.

Hastings. You have lived pretty much among them. In
truth, I have been often surprized that you who have seen so
much of the world, with your natural good sense, and your
many opportunities, could never yet acquire a requisite share
of assurance.

Marlow. The Englishman's malady. But tell me, George,
where could I have learned that assurance you talk of? My
life has been chiefly spent in a college or an inn, in seclusion
from that lovely part of the creation that chiefly teach men

confidence. I don't know that I was ever familiarly acquainted with a single modest woman—except my mother—But among females of another class you know—

Hastings. Ay, among them you are impudent enough of all conscience.

Marlow. They are of *us,* you know.

Hastings. But in the company of women of reputation I never saw such an ideot, such a trembler; you look for all the world as if you wanted an opportunity of stealing out of the room.

Marlow. Why man that's because I *do* want to steal out of the room. Faith, I have often formed a resolution to break the ice, and rattle away at any rate. But I don't know how, a single glance from a pair of fine eyes has totally overset my resolution. An impudent fellow may counterfeit modesty, but I'll be hanged if a modest man can ever counterfeit impudence.

Hastings. If you could but say half the fine things to them that I have heard you lavish upon the bar-maid of an inn, or even a college bed-maker—

Marlow. Why, George, I can't say fine things to them. They freeze, they petrify me. They may talk of a comet, or a burning mountain, or some such bagatelle. But to me, a modest woman, drest out in all her finery, is the most tremendous object of the whole creation.

Hastings. Ha! ha! ha! At this rate, man, how can you ever expect to marry!

Marlow. Never, unless as among kings and princes, my bride were to be courted by proxy. If, indeed, like an Eastern bridegroom, one were to be introduced to a wife he never saw before, it might be endured. But to go through all the terrors of a formal courtship, together with the episode of aunts, grandmothers and cousins, and at last to blurt out the broad staring question of *madam will you marry me?* No, no, that's a strain much above me I assure you.

Hastings. I pity you. But how do you intend behaving to the lady you are come down to visit at the request of your father?

Marlow. As I behave to all other ladies. Bow very low. Answer yes, or no, to all her demands—But for the rest, I don't think I shall venture to look in her face, till I see my father's again.

Hastings. I'm surprized that one who is so warm a friend can be so cool a lover.

Marlow. To be explicit, my dear Hastings, my chief inducement down was to be instrumental in forwarding your happiness, not my own. Miss Neville loves you, the family don't know you, as my friend you are sure of a reception, and let honour do the rest.

Hastings. My dear Marlow! But I'll suppress the emotion. Were I a wretch, meanly seeking to carry off a fortune, you should be the last man in the world I would apply to for assistance. But Miss Neville's person is all I ask, and that is mine, both from her deceased father's consent, and her own inclination.

Marlow. Happy man! You have talents and art to captivate any woman. I'm doom'd to adore the sex, and yet to converse with the only part of it I despise. This stammer in my address, and this aukward prepossessing visage of mine, can never permit me to soar above the reach of a milliner's 'prentice, or one of the dutchesses of Drury-lane.[86] Pshaw! this fellow here to interrupt us.

Enter HARDCASTLE

Hardcastle. Gentlemen, once more you are heartily welcome. Which is Mr. Marlow? Sir, you're heartily welcome. It's not my way, you see, to receive my friends with my back to the fire. I like to give them a hearty reception in the old stile at my gate. I like to see their horses and trunks taken care of.

Marlow. (*aside*) He has got our names from the servants already. (*to him.*) We approve your caution and hospitality, Sir. (*to* HASTINGS.) I have been thinking, George, of changing our travelling dresses in the morning. I am grown confoundedly ashamed of mine.

Hardcastle. I beg, Mr. Marlow, you'll use no ceremony in this house.

Hastings. I fancy, George, you're right: the first blow is half the battle. I intend opening the campaign with the white and gold.

Hardcastle. Mr. Marlow—Mr. Hastings—gentlemen—pray be under no constraint in this house. This is Liberty-hall, gentlemen. You may do just as you please here.

Marlow. Yet, George, if we open the campaign too fiercely at first, we may want ammunition before it is over. I think to reserve the embroidery to secure a retreat.

Hardcastle. Your talking of a retreat, Mr. Marlow, puts me in mind of the Duke of Marlborough, when we went to besiege Denain. He first summoned the garrison.

Marlow. Don't you think the *ventre dor* waistcoat will do with the plain brown?

Hardcastle. He first summoned the garrison, which might consist of about five thousand men——

Hastings. I think not. Brown and yellow mix but very poorly.

Hardcastle. I say, gentlemen, as I was telling you, he summoned the garrison, which might consist of about five thousand men——

Marlow. The girls like finery.

Hardcastle. Which might consist of about five thousand men, well appointed with stores, ammunition, and other implements of war. Now, says the Duke of Marlborough to George Brooks, that stood next to him—You must have heard of George Brooks; I'll pawn my Dukedom, says he, but I take that garrison without spilling a drop of blood. So——

Marlow. What, my good friend, if you gave us a glass of punch in the mean time, it would help us to carry on the siege with vigour.

Hardcastle. Punch, Sir! (*aside*) This is the most unaccountable kind of modesty I ever met with.

Marlow. Yes, Sir, punch. A glass of warm punch, after our journey, will be comfortable. This is Liberty-Hall, you know.

Hardcastle. Here's cup, Sir.

Marlow. (*aside*) So this fellow, in his Liberty-hall, will only let us have just what he pleases.

Hardcastle. (*taking the cup*) I hope you'll find it to your mind. I have prepared it with my own hands, and I believe you'll own the ingredients are tolerable. Will you be so good as to pledge me, Sir? Here, Mr. Marlow, here is to our better acquaintance. [*drinks.*

Marlow. (*aside*) A very impudent fellow this! but he's a character, and I'll humour him a little. Sir, my service to you. [*drinks.*

Hastings. (*aside*) I see this fellow wants to give us his company, and forgets that he's an innkeeper, before he has learned to be a gentleman.

Marlow. From the excellence of your cup, my old friend, I suppose you have a good deal of business in this part of the country. Warm work, now and then, at elections, I suppose.

Hardcastle. No, Sir, I have long given that work over. Since our betters have hit upon the expedient of electing each other, there's no business *for us that sell ale.*[87]

Hastings. So, then you have no turn for politics, I find.

Hardcastle. Not in the least. There was a time, indeed, I fretted myself about the mistakes of government, like other people; but finding myself every day grow more angry, and the government growing no better, I left it to mend itself. Since that, I no more trouble my head about *Heyder Ally,* or *Ally Cawn,* than about *Ally Croaker.*[88] Sir, my service to you.

Hastings. So that with eating above stairs, and drinking below, with receiving your friends within, and amusing them without, you lead a good pleasant bustling life of it.

Hardcastle. I do stir about a great deal, it's certain. Half the differences of the parish are adjusted in this very parlour.

Marlow. (*after drinking*) And you have an argument in your cup, old gentleman, better than any in Westminster-hall.

Hardcastle. Ay, young gentleman, that, and a little philosophy.

Marlow. (*aside*) Well, this is the first time I ever heard of an innkeeper's philosophy.

Hastings. So then, like an experienced general, you attack them on every quarter. If you find their reason manageable, you attack it with your philosophy; if you find they have no reason, you attack them with this. Here's your health, my philosopher. (*drinks*)

Hardcastle. Good, very good, thank you; ha, ha. Your Generalship puts me in mind of Prince Eugene, when he fought the Turks at the battle of Belgrade. You shall hear.

Marlow. Instead of the battle of Belgrade, I believe it's almost time to talk about supper. What has your philosophy got in the house for supper?

Hardcastle. For supper, Sir! (*aside*) Was ever such a request to a man in his own house!

Marlow. Yes, Sir, supper, Sir; I begin to feel an appetite. I shall make devilish work to-night in the larder, I promise you.

Hardcastle. (*aside*) Such a brazen dog sure never my eyes beheld. (*to him*) Why really, Sir, as for supper I can't well tell. My Dorothy, and the cook maid, settle these things between them. I leave these kind of things entirely to them.

Marlow. You do, do you?

Hardcastle. Entirely. By-the-bye, I believe they are in actual consultation upon what's for supper this moment in the kitchen.

Marlow. Then I beg they'll admit *me* as one of their privy council. It's a way I have got. When I travel, I always chuse to regulate my own supper. Let the cook be called. No offence I hope, Sir.

Hardcastle. O no, Sir, none in the least; yet, I don't know how: our Bridget, the cook maid, is not very communicative upon these occasions. Should we send for her, she might scold us all out of the house.

Hastings. Let's see your list of the larder then. I ask it as a favour. I always match my appetite to my bill of fare.

Marlow. (*to* HARDCASTLE, *who looks at them with surprize*) Sir, he's very right, and it's my way too.

Hardcastle. Sir, you have a right to command here. Here, Roger, bring us the bill of fare for to night's supper. I believe it's drawn out. Your manner, Mr. Hastings, puts me in mind of my uncle, Colonel Wallop. It was a saying of his, that no man was sure of his supper till he had eaten it.

Hastings. (*aside*) All upon the high ropes! His uncle a Colonel! We shall soon hear of his mother being a justice of peace. But let's hear the bill of fare.

Marlow. (*perusing*) What's here? For the first course; for the second course; for the desert. The devil, Sir, do you think we have brought down the whole Joiners Company, or the Corporation of Bedford, to eat up such a supper? Two or three little things, clean and comfortable, will do.

Hastings. But, let's hear it.

Marlow. (*reading*) For the first course at the top, a pig, and pruin sauce.

Hastings. Damn your pig, I say.

Marlow. And damn your pruin sauce, say I.

Hardcastle. And yet, gentlemen, to men that are hungry, pig, with pruin sauce is very good eating.

Marlow. At the bottom, a calve's tongue and brains.

Hastings. Let your brains be knock'd out, my good Sir; I don't like them.

Marlow. Or you may clap them on a plate by themselves. I do.

Hardcastle. (*aside*) Their impudence confounds me. (*to them*) Gentlemen, you are my guests, make what alterations you please. Is there any thing else you wish to retrench or alter, gentlemen?

Marlow. Item. A pork pie, a boiled rabbet and sausages, a florentine, a shaking pudding, and a dish of tiff—taff—taffety cream!

Hastings. Confound your made dishes, I shall be as much at a loss in this house as at a green and yellow dinner at the French ambassador's table. I'm for plain eating.

Hardcastle. I'm sorry, gentlemen, that I have nothing you like, but if there be any thing you have a particular fancy to——

Marlow. Why, really, Sir, your bill of fare is so exquisite, that any one part of it is full as good as another. Send us what you please. So much for supper. And now to see that our beds are air'd, and properly taken care of.

Hardcastle. I entreat you'll leave all that to me. You shall not stir a step.

Marlow. Leave that to you! I protest, Sir, you must excuse me, I always look to these things myself.

Hardcastle. I must insist, Sir, you'll make yourself easy on that head.

Marlow. You see I'm resolved on it. (*aside*) A very troublesome fellow this, as ever I met with.

Hardcastle. Well, Sir, I'm resolved at least to attend you. (*aside*) This may be modern modesty, but I never saw any thing look so like old-fashioned impudence.

[*Exeunt* MARLOW *and* HARDCASTLE.

HASTINGS *solus*

Hastings. So I find this fellow's civilities begin to grow troublesome. But who can be angry at those assiduities which are meant to please him? Ha! what do I see? Miss Neville, by all that's happy!

Enter MISS NEVILLE

Miss Neville. My dear Hastings! To what unexpected good fortune? to what accident am I to ascribe this happy meeting?

Hastings. Rather let me ask the same question, as I could never have hoped to meet my dearest Constance at an inn.

Miss Neville. An inn! sure you mistake! my aunt, my guardian, lives here. What could induce you to think this house an inn?

Hastings. My friend Mr. Marlow, with whom I came down, and I, have been sent here as to an inn, I assure you. A young fellow whom we accidentally met at a house hard by directed us hither.

Miss Neville. Certainly it must be one of my hopeful cousin's tricks, of whom you have heard me talk so often, ha! ha! ha! ha!

Hastings. He whom your aunt intends for you? He of whom I have such just apprehensions?

Miss Neville. You have nothing to fear from him, I assure you. You'd adore him if you knew how heartily he despises me. My aunt knows it too, and has undertaken to court me for him, and actually begins to think she has made a conquest.

Hastings. Thou dear dissembler! You must know, my Constance, I have just seized this happy opportunity of my friend's visit here to get admittance into the family. The horses that carried us down are now fatigued with their journey, but they'll soon be refreshed; and then if my dearest girl will trust in her faithful Hastings, we shall soon be landed in France, where even among slaves the laws of marriage are respected.[89]

Miss Neville. I have often told you, that though ready to obey you, I yet should leave my little fortune behind with reluctance. The greatest part of it was left me by my uncle, the India Director, and chiefly consists in jewels. I have been for some time persuading my aunt to let me wear them. I fancy I'm very near succeeding. The instant they are put into my possession you shall find me ready to make them and myself yours.

Hastings. Perish the baubles! Your person is all I desire. In the meantime, my friend Marlow must not be let into his mistake. I know the strange reserve of his temper is such, that if abruptly informed of it, he would instantly quit the house before our plan was ripe for execution.

Miss Neville. But how shall we keep him in the deception? Miss Hardcastle is just returned from walking; what if we still continue to deceive him?—This, this way—— [*they confer.*

Enter MARLOW

Marlow. The assiduities of these good people teize me beyond bearing. My host seems to think it ill manners to leave me alone, and so he claps not only himself but his old-fashioned wife on my back. They talk of coming to sup with us too; and then, I suppose, we are to run the gauntlet thro' all the rest of the family.—What have we got here!—

Hastings. My dear Charles! Let me congratulate you!—The most fortunate accident!—Who do you think is just alighted?

Marlow. Cannot guess.

Hastings. Our mistresses, boy, Miss Hardcastle and Miss Neville. Give me leave to introduce Miss Constance Neville to your acquaintance. Happening to dine in the neighbourhood, they called, on their return to take fresh horses, here. Miss Hardcastle has just stept into the next room, and will be back in an instant. Wasn't it lucky? eh!

Marlow. (*aside*) I have just been mortified enough of all conscience, and here comes something to complete my embarrassment.

Hastings. Well! but wasn't it the most fortunate thing in the world?

Marlow. Oh! yes. Very fortunate—a most joyful encounter——But our dresses, George, you know, are in disorder——What if we should postpone the happiness 'till tomorrow?——To-morrow at her own house——It will be every bit as convenient——And rather more respectful——To-morrow let it be.   [*offering to go.*

Miss Neville. By no means, Sir. Your ceremony will displease her. The disorder of your dress will shew the ardour of your impatience. Besides, she knows you are in the house, and will permit you to see her.

Marlow. O! the devil! how shall I support it? Hem! hem! Hastings, you must not go. You are to assist me, you know. I shall be confoundedly ridiculous. Yet, hang it! I'll take courage. Hem!

Hastings. Pshaw man! it's but the first plunge, and all's over. She's but a woman, you know.

Marlow. And of all women, she that I dread most to encounter!

Enter MISS HARDCASTLE *as returned from walking, a Bonnet, &c.*

Hastings. (*introducing them*) Miss Hardcastle, Mr. Marlow, I'm proud of bringing two persons of such merit together, that only want to know, to esteem each other.

Miss Hardcastle. (*aside*) Now, for meeting my modest gentleman with a demure face, and quite in his own manner. (*after a pause, in which he appears very uneasy and disconcerted.*) I'm glad of your safe arrival, Sir——I'm told you had some accidents by the way.

Marlow. Only a few, madam. Yes, we had some. Yes, Madam, a good many accidents, but should be sorry—Madam—or rather glad of any accidents—that are so agreeably concluded. Hem!

Hastings. (*to him*) You never spoke better in your whole life. Keep it up, and I'll insure you the victory.

Miss Hardcastle. I'm afraid you flatter, Sir. You that have seen so much of the finest company can find little entertainment in an obscure corner of the country.

Marlow. (*gathering courage*) I have lived, indeed, in the world, Madam; but I have kept very little company. I have been but an observer upon life, Madam, while others were enjoying it.

Miss Neville. But that, I am told, is the way to enjoy it at last.

Hastings. (*to him*) Cicero never spoke better. Once more, and you are confirm'd in assurance for ever.

Marlow. (*to him*) Hem! Stand by me then, and when I'm down, throw in a word or two to set me up again.

Miss Hardcastle. An observer, like you, upon life, were, I fear, disagreeably employed, since you must have had much more to censure than to approve.

Marlow. Pardon me, Madam. I was always willing to be amused. The folly of most people is rather an object of mirth than uneasiness.

Hastings. (*to him*) Bravo, bravo. Never spoke so well in your whole life. Well, Miss Hardcastle, I see that you and Mr. Marlow are going to be very good company. I believe our being here will but embarrass the interview.

Marlow. Not in the least, Mr. Hastings. We like your company of all things. (*to him*) Zounds! George, sure you won't go? How can you leave us?

Hastings. Our presence will but spoil conversation, so we'll retire to the next room. (*to him*) You don't consider, man, that we are to manage a little tête-à-tête of our own.

[*Exeunt.*

Miss Hardcastle. (*after a pause*) But you have not been wholly an observer, I presume, Sir. The ladies I should hope have employed some part of your addresses.

Marlow. (*relapsing into timidity*) Pardon me, Madam, I—I—I—as yet have studied—only—to—deserve them.

Miss Hardcastle. And that some say is the very worst way to obtain them.

Marlow. Perhaps so, madam. But I love to converse only with the more grave and sensible part of the sex.——But I'm afraid I grow tiresome.

Miss Hardcastle. Not at all, Sir; there is nothing I like so much as grave conversation myself; I could hear it for ever. Indeed I have often been surprized how a man of *sentiment* could ever admire those light airy pleasures, where nothing reaches the heart.

Marlow. It's—a disease—of the mind, madam. In the variety of tastes there must be some who, wanting a relish—for—um—a—um.

Miss Hardcastle. I understand you, Sir. There must be some, who wanting a relish for refined pleasures, pretend to despise what they are incapable of tasting.

Marlow. My meaning, madam, but infinitely better expressed. And I can't help observing—a——

Miss Hardcastle. (*aside*) Who could ever suppose this fellow impudent upon some occasions. (*to him*) You were going to observe, Sir——

Marlow. I was observing, madam——I protest, madam, I forget what I was going to observe.

Miss Hardcastle. (*aside*) I vow and so do I. (*to him*) You were observing, Sir, that in this age of hypocrisy—something about hypocrisy, Sir.

Marlow. Yes, madam. In this age of hypocrisy there are few who upon strict enquiry do not—a—a—a——

Miss Hardcastle. I understand you perfectly, Sir.

Marlow. (*aside*) Egad! and that's more than I do myself.

Miss Hardcastle. You mean that in this hypocritical age there are few that do not condemn in public what they practise in private, and think they pay every debt to virtue when they praise it.

Marlow. True, madam; those who have most virtue in their mouths, have least of it in their bosoms. But I'm sure I tire you, madam.

Miss Hardcastle. Not in the least, Sir; there's something so agreeable and spirited in your manner, such life and force—— pray, Sir, go on.

Marlow. Yes, madam. I was saying——that there are some occasions——when a total want of courage, madam, destroys all the——and puts us——upon a——a——a——

Miss Hardcastle. I agree with you entirely, a want of courage upon some occasions assumes the appearance of ignorance, and betrays us when we most want to excel. I beg you'll proceed.

Marlow. Yes, madam. Morally speaking, madam——But I see Miss Neville expecting us in the next room. I would not intrude for the world.

Miss Hardcastle. I protest, Sir, I never was more agreeably entertained in all my life. Pray go on.

Marlow. Yes, madam. I was——But she beckons us to join her. Madam, shall I do myself the honour to attend you?

Miss Hardcastle. Well then, I'll follow.

Marlow. (*aside*) This pretty smooth dialogue has done for me.   [*Exit.*

Miss HARDCASTLE *sola*

Miss Hardcastle. Ha! ha! ha! Was there ever such a sober
sentimental interview? I'm certain he scarce look'd in my face
the whole time. Yet the fellow, but for his unaccountable bashfulness, is pretty well too. He has good sense, but then so
buried in his fears, that it fatigues one more than ignorance.
If I could teach him a little confidence, it would be doing
somebody that I know of a piece of service. But who is that
somebody?—that, faith, is a question I can scarce answer.

[*Exit.*

Enter TONY *and* MISS NEVILLE, *followed by* MRS.
HARDCASTLE *and* HASTINGS

Tony. What do you follow me for, cousin Con? I wonder
you're not ashamed to be so very engaging.

Miss Neville. I hope, cousin, one may speak to one's own
relations, and not be to blame.

Tony. Ay, but I know what sort of a relation you want to
make me though; but it won't do. I tell you, cousin Con, it
won't do, so I beg you'll keep your distance, I want no nearer
relationship.   [*She follows coqueting him to the back scene.*

Mrs. Hardcastle. Well! I vow, Mr. Hastings, you are very
entertaining. There's nothing in the world I love to talk of so
much as London, and the fashions, though I was never there
myself.

Hastings. Never there! You amaze me! From your air and
manner, I concluded you had been bred all your life either at
Ranelagh, St. James's, or Tower Wharf.

Mrs. Hardcastle. O! Sir, you're only pleased to say so. We
country persons can have no manner at all. I'm in love with
the town, and that serves to raise me above some of our neighbouring rustics; but who can have a manner, that has never
seen the Pantheon, the Grotto Gardens, the Borough, and
such places where the Nobility chiefly resort? All I can do, is
to enjoy London at second-hand. I take care to know every
tête-à-tête from the Scandalous Magazine, and have all the
fashions as they come out, in a letter from the two Miss
Rickets of Crooked-lane. Pray how do you like this head, Mr.
Hastings?

Hastings. Extremely elegant and degagée, upon my word, Madam. Your Friseur is a Frenchman, I suppose?

Mrs. Hardcastle. I protest I dressed it myself from a print in the Ladies Memorandum-book for the last year.

Hastings. Indeed. Such a head in a side-box, at the Playhouse, would draw as many gazers as my Lady May'ress at a City Ball.

Mrs. Hardcastle. I vow, since inoculation began, there is no such thing to be seen as a plain woman; so one must dress a little particular or one may escape in the crowd.

Hastings. But that can never be your case, Madam, in any dress. (*bowing*)

Mrs. Hardcastle. Yet, what signifies *my* dressing when I have such a piece of antiquity by my side as Mr. Hardcastle; all I can say will never argue down a single button from his cloaths. I have often wanted him to throw off his great flaxen wig, and where he was bald, to plaister it over like my Lord Pately, with powder.

Hastings. You are right, Madam; for, as among the ladies there are none ugly, so among the men there are none old.

Mrs. Hardcastle. But what do you think his answer was? Why, with his usual Gothic vivacity, he said I only wanted him to throw off his wig to convert it into a tête for my own wearing.

Hastings. Intolerable! At your age you may wear what you please, and it must become you.

Mrs. Hardcastle. Pray, Mr. Hastings, what do you take to be the most fashionable age about town?

Hastings. Some time ago, forty was all the mode; but I'm told the ladies intend to bring up fifty for the ensuing winter.

Mrs. Hardcastle. Seriously. Then I shall be too young for the fashion.

Hastings. No lady begins now to put on jewels 'till she's past forty. For instance, Miss there, in a polite circle, would be considered as a child, as a mere maker of samplers.

Mrs. Hardcastle. And yet Mrs. Niece thinks herself as much a woman and is as fond of jewels as the oldest of us all.

Hastings. Your niece, is she? And that young gentleman, a brother of yours, I should presume?

Mrs. Hardcastle. My son, Sir. They are contracted to each

other. Observe their little sports. They fall in and out ten times a day, as if they were man and wife already. (*to them*) Well Tony, child, what soft things are you saying to your cousin Constance this evening?

Tony. I have been saying no soft things; but that it's very hard to be followed about so. Ecod! I've not a place in the house now that's left to myself but the stable.

Mrs. Hardcastle. Never mind him, Con, my dear. He's in another story behind your back.

Miss Neville. There's something generous in my cousin's manner. He falls out before faces to be forgiven in private.

Tony. That's a damned confounded——crack.

Mrs. Hardcastle. Ah! he's a sly one. Don't you think they're like each other about the mouth, Mr. Hastings? The Blenkinsop mouth to a T. They're of a size too. Back to back, my pretties, that Mr. Hastings may see you. Come Tony.

Tony. You had as good not make me, I tell you.

(*measuring.*)

Miss Neville. O lud! he has almost cracked my head.

Mrs. Hardcastle. O the monster! For shame, Tony. You a man, and behave so!

Tony. If I'm a man, let me have my fortin. Ecod! I'll not be made a fool of no longer.

Mrs. Hardcastle. Is this, ungrateful boy, all that I'm to get for the pains I have taken in your education? I that have rock'd you in your cradle, and fed that pretty mouth with a spoon! Did not I work that waistcoat to make you genteel? Did not I prescribe for you every day, and weep while the receipt was operating?

Tony. Ecod! you had reason to weep, for you have been dosing me ever since I was born. I have gone through every receipt in the complete huswife ten times over; and you have thoughts of coursing me through *Quincy*[90] next spring. But, Ecod! I tell you, I'll not be made a fool of no longer.

Mrs. Hardcastle. Wasn't it all for your good, viper? Wasn't it all for your good?

Tony. I wish you'd let me and my good alone then. Snubbing this way when I'm in spirits. If I'm to have any good, let it come of itself; not to keep dinging it, dinging it into one so.

Mrs. Hardcastle. That's false; I never see you when you're in spirits. No, Tony, you then go to the alehouse or kennel. I'm never to be delighted with your agreeable, wild notes, unfeeling monster!

Tony. Ecod! Mamma, your own notes are the wildest of the two.

Mrs. Hardcastle. Was ever the like? But I see he wants to break my heart, I see he does.

Hastings. Dear Madam, permit me to lecture the young gentleman a little. I'm certain I can persuade him to his duty.

Mrs. Hardcastle. Well! I must retire. Come, Constance, my love. You see, Mr. Hastings, the wretchedness of my situation: Was ever poor woman so plagued with a dear, sweet, pretty, provoking, undutiful boy.

[*Exeunt* MRS. HARDCASTLE *and* MISS NEVILLE.

HASTINGS, TONY

Tony (*singing*). *There was a young man riding by, and fain would have his will. Rang do didlo dee.* Don't mind her. Let her cry. It's the comfort of her heart. I have seen her and sister cry over a book for an hour together, and they said they liked the book the better the more it made them cry.

Hastings. Then you're no friend to the ladies, I find, my pretty young gentleman?

Tony. That's as I find 'um.

Hastings. Not to her of your mother's chusing, I dare answer? And yet she appears to me a pretty well-tempered girl.

Tony. That's because you don't know her as well as I. Ecod! I know every inch about her; and there's not a more bitter cantanckerous toad in all Christendom.

Hastings. (*aside*) Pretty encouragement this for a lover!

Tony. I have seen her since the height of that. She has as many tricks as a hare in a thicket, or a colt the first day's breaking.

Hastings. To me she appears sensible and silent!

Tony. Ay, before company. But when she's with her playmates she's as loud as a hog in a gate.

Hastings. But there is a meek modesty about her that charms me.

Tony. Yes, but curb her never so little, she kicks up, and you're flung in a ditch.

Hastings. Well, but you must allow her a little beauty.— Yes, you must allow her some beauty.

Tony. Bandbox! She's all a made up thing, mun. Ah! could you but see Bet Bouncer of these parts, you might then talk of beauty. Ecod, she has two eyes as black as sloes, and cheeks as broad and red as a pulpit cushion. She'd make two of she.

Hastings. Well, what say you to a friend that would take this bitter bargain off your hands?

Tony. Anon?

Hastings. Would you thank him that would take Miss Neville and leave you to happiness and your dear Betsy?

Tony. Ay; but where is there such a friend, for who would take *her?*

Hastings. I am he. If you but assist me, I'll engage to whip her off to France, and you shall never hear more of her.

Tony. Assist you! Ecod I will, to the last drop of my blood. I'll clap a pair of horses to your chaise that shall trundle you off in a twinkling, and may be get you a part of her fortin beside, in jewels, that you little dream of.

Hastings. My dear squire, this looks like a lad of spirit.

Tony. Come along then, and you shall see more of my spirit before you have done with me. (*singing*) *We are the boys that fears no noise where the thundering cannons roar.*

[*Exeunt.*

ACT III

Enter HARDCASTLE *Solus*

Hardcastle. What could my old friend Sir Charles mean by recommending his son as the modestest young man in town? To me he appears the most impudent piece of brass that ever spoke with a tongue. He has taken possession of the easy chair by the fire-side already. He took off his boots in the parlour, and desired me to see them taken care of. I'm desirous to know how his impudence affects my daughter.— She will certainly be shocked at it.

Enter MISS HARDCASTLE, *plainly dress'd*

Hardcastle. Well, my Kate, I see you have changed your dress as I bid you; and yet, I believe, there was no great occasion.

Miss Hardcastle. I find such a pleasure, Sir, in obeying your commands, that I take care to observe them without ever debating their propriety.

Hardcastle. And yet, Kate, I sometimes give you some cause, particularly when I recommended my *modest* gentleman to you as a lover to-day.

Miss Hardcastle. You taught me to expect something extraordinary, and I find the original exceeds the description.

Hardcastle. I was never so surprized in my life! He has quite confounded all my faculties!

Miss Hardcastle. I never saw any thing like it: And a man of the world, too!

Hardcastle. Ay, he learned it all abroad,—what a fool was I, to think a young man could learn modesty by travelling. He might as soon learn wit at a masquerade.

Miss Hardcastle. It seems all natural to him.

Hardcastle. A good deal assisted by bad company and a French dancing-master.

Miss Hardcastle. Sure you mistake, papa! a French dancing-master could never have taught him that timid look,—that aukward address,—that bashful manner——

Hardcastle. Whose look? whose manner? child!

Miss Hardcastle. Mr. Marlow's: his meauvaise honte, his timidity struck me at the first sight.

Hardcastle. Then your first sight deceived you; for I think him one of the most brazen first sights that ever astonished my senses.

Miss Hardcastle. Sure, Sir, you rally! I never saw any one so modest.

Hardcastle. And can you be serious! I never saw such a bouncing swaggering puppy since I was born. Bully Dawson [91] was but a fool to him.

Miss Hardcastle. Surprising! He met me with a respectful bow, a stammering voice, and a look fixed on the ground.

Hardcastle. He met me with a loud voice, a lordly air, and a familiarity that made my blood freeze again.

Miss Hardcastle. He treated me with diffidence and respect; censured the manners of the age; admired the prudence of girls that never laughed; tired me with apologies for being tiresome; then left the room with a bow, and, madam, I would not for the world detain you.

Hardcastle. He spoke to me as if he knew me all his life before. Asked twenty questions, and never waited for an answer. Interrupted my best remarks with some silly pun, and when I was in my best story of the Duke of Marlborough and Prince Eugene, he asked if I had not a good hand at making punch. Yes, Kate, he ask'd your father if he was a maker of punch!

Miss Hardcastle. One of us must certainly be mistaken.

Hardcastle. If he be what he has shewn himself, I'm determined he shall never have my consent.

Miss Hardcastle. And if he be the sullen thing I take him, he shall never have mine.

Hardcastle. In one thing then we are agreed—to reject him.

Miss Hardcastle. Yes. But upon conditions. For if you should find him less impudent, and I more presuming; if you find him more respectful, and I more importunate—I don't know—the fellow is well enough for a man—Certainly we don't meet many such at a horse race in the country.

Hardcastle. If we should find him so——But that's impossible. The first appearance has done my business. I'm seldom deceived in that.

Miss Hardcastle. And yet there may be many good qualities under that first appearance.

Hardcastle. Ay, when a girl finds a fellow's outside to her taste, she then sets about guessing the rest of his furniture. With her, a smooth face stands for good sense, and a genteel figure for every virtue.

Miss Hardcastle. I hope, Sir, a conversation begun with a compliment to my good sense won't end with a sneer at my understanding?

Hardcastle. Pardon me, Kate. But if young Mr. Brazen can find the art of reconciling contradictions, he may please us both, perhaps.

Miss Hardcastle. And as one of us must be mistaken, what if we go to make further discoveries?

Hardcastle. Agreed. But depend on't I'm in the right.

Miss Hardcastle. And depend on't I'm not much in the wrong.   [*Exeunt.*

Enter TONY *running in with a Casket*

Tony. Ecod! I have got them. Here they are. My Cousin Con's necklaces, bobs and all. My mother shan't cheat the poor souls out of their fortune neither. O! my genus, is that you?

Enter HASTINGS

Hastings. My dear friend, how have you managed with your mother? I hope you have amused her with pretending love for your cousin, and that you are willing to be reconciled at last? Our horses will be refreshed in a short time, and we shall soon be ready to set off.

Tony. And here's something to bear your charges by the way. (*giving the casket*) Your sweetheart's jewels. Keep them, and hang those, I say, that would rob you of one of them.

Hastings. But how have you procured them from your mother?

Tony. Ask me no questions, and I'll tell you no fibs. I procured them by the rule of thumb. If I had not a key to every drawer in mother's bureau, how could I go to the ale-house so often as I do? An honest man may rob himself of his own at any time.

Hastings. Thousands do it every day. But to be plain with you; Miss Neville is endeavouring to procure them from her aunt this very instant. If she succeeds, it will be the most delicate way at least of obtaining them.

Tony. Well, keep them, till you know how it will be. But I know how it will be well enough, she'd as soon part with the only sound tooth in her head.

Hastings. But I dread the effects of her resentment, when she finds she has lost them.

Tony. Never you mind her resentment, leave *me* to manage that. I don't value her resentment the bounce of a cracker. Zounds! here they are! Morrice, Prance.   [*Exit* HASTINGS.

TONY, MRS. HARDCASTLE, MISS NEVILLE

Mrs. Hardcastle. Indeed, Constance, you amaze me. Such a girl as you want jewels? It will be time enough for jewels, my dear, twenty years hence, when your beauty begins to want repairs.

Miss Neville. But what will repair beauty at forty, will certainly improve it at twenty, Madam.

Mrs. Hardcastle. Yours, my dear, can admit of none. That natural blush is beyond a thousand ornaments. Besides, child, jewels are quite out at present. Don't you see half the ladies of our acquaintance, my lady Killdaylight, and Mrs. Crump, and the rest of them, carry their jewels to town, and bring nothing but Paste and Marcasites back?

Miss Neville. But who knows, Madam, but somebody that shall be nameless would like me best with all my little finery about me?

Mrs. Hardcastle. Consult your glass, my dear, and then see, if with such a pair of eyes, you want any better sparklers. What do you think, Tony, my dear, does your cousin Con want any jewels, in your eyes, to set off her beauty?

Tony. That's as thereafter may be.

Miss Neville. My dear aunt, if you knew how it would oblige me.

Mrs. Hardcastle. A parcel of old-fashioned rose and table-cut things. They would make you look like the court of king Solomon at a puppet-shew. Besides, I believe I can't readily come at them. They may be missing, for aught I know to the contrary.

Tony. (*apart to* MRS. HARDCASTLE) Then why don't you tell her so at once, as she's so longing for them. Tell her they're lost. It's the only way to quiet her. Say they're lost, and call me to bear witness.

Mrs. Hardcastle. (*apart to* TONY) You know, my dear, I'm only keeping them for you. So if I say they're gone, you'll bear me witness, will you? He! he! he!

Tony. Never fear me. Ecod! I'll say I saw them taken out with my own eyes.

Miss Neville. I desire them but for a day, Madam. Just to be permitted to shew them as relicks, and then they may be lock'd up again.

Mrs. Hardcastle. To be plain with you, my dear Constance, if I could find them, you should have them. They're missing, I assure you. Lost, for aught I know; but we must have patience wherever they are.

Miss Neville. I'll not believe it; this is but a shallow pretence to deny me. I know they're too valuable to be so slightly kept, and as you are to answer for the loss.

Mrs. Hardcastle. Don't be alarm'd, Constance. If they be lost, I must restore an equivalent. But my son knows they are missing, and not to be found.

Tony. That I can bear witness to. They are missing, and not to be found, I'll take my oath on't.

Mrs. Hardcastle. You must learn resignation, my dear; for tho' we lose our fortune, yet we should not lose our patience. See me, how calm I am.

Miss Neville. Ay, people are generally calm at the misfortunes of others.

Mrs. Hardcastle. Now, I wonder a girl of your good sense should waste a thought upon such trumpery. We shall soon find them; and, in the mean time, you shall make use of my garnets till your jewels be found.

Miss Neville. I detest garnets.

Mrs. Hardcastle. The most becoming things in the world to set off a clear complexion. You have often seen how well they look upon me. You *shall* have them.   [*Exit.*

Miss Neville. I dislike them of all things. You shan't stir.— Was ever any thing so provoking to mislay my own jewels, and force me to wear her trumpery.

Tony. Don't be a fool. If she gives you the garnets, take what you can get. The jewels are your own already. I have stolen them out of her bureau, and she does not know it. Fly to your spark, he'll tell you more of the matter. Leave me to manage *her*.

Miss Neville. My dear cousin.

Tony. Vanish. She's here, and has missed them already. Zounds! how she fidgets and spits about like a Catharine wheel.[92]

Enter MRS. HARDCASTLE

Mrs. Hardcastle. Confusion! thieves! robbers! We are cheated, plundered broke open, undone.

Tony. What's the matter, what's the matter, mamma? I hope nothing has happened to any of the good family!

Mrs. Hardcastle. We are robbed. My bureau has been broke open, the jewels taken out, and I'm undone.

Tony. Oh! is that all? Ha, ha, ha. By the laws, I never saw it better acted in my life. Ecod, I thought you was ruin'd in earnest, ha, ha, ha.

Mrs. Hardcastle. Why, boy, I *am* ruined in earnest. My bureau has been broke open, and all taken away.

Tony. Stick to that; ha, ha, ha; stick to that. I'll bear witness, you know, call me to bear witness.

Mrs. Hardcastle. I tell you, Tony, by all that's precious, the jewels are gone, and I shall be ruin'd for ever.

Tony. Sure I know they're gone, and I am to say so.

Mrs. Hardcastle. My dearest Tony, but hear me. They're gone, I say.

Tony. By the laws, mamma, you make me for to laugh, ha, ha. I know who took them well enough, ha, ha, ha.

Mrs. Hardcastle. Was there ever such a blockhead, that can't tell the difference between jest and earnest. I tell you I'm not in jest, booby.

Tony. That's right, that's right: You must be in a bitter passion, and then nobody will suspect either of us. I'll bear witness that they are gone.

Mrs. Hardcastle. Was there ever such a cross-grain'd brute, that won't hear me! Can you bear witness that you're no better than a fool? Was ever poor woman so beset with fools on one hand, and thieves on the other!

Tony. I can bear witness to that.

Mrs. Hardcastle. Bear witness again, you blockhead you, and I'll turn you out of the room directly. My poor niece, what will become of *her!* Do you laugh, you unfeeling brute, as if you enjoy'd my distress?

Tony. I can bear witness to that.

Mrs. Hardcastle. Do you insult me, monster? I'll teach you to vex your mother, I will.

Tony. I can bear witness to that.

[*He runs off, she follows him.*

Enter MISS HARDCASTLE *and* MAID

Miss Hardcastle. What an unaccountable creature is that brother of mine, to send them to the house as an inn, ha, ha. I don't wonder at his impudence.

Maid. But what is more, madam, the young gentleman as you passed by in your present dress, ask'd me if you were the bar maid? He mistook you for the bar maid, madam.

Miss Hardcastle. Did he? Then as I live I'm resolved to keep up the delusion. Tell me, Pimple, how do you like my present dress? Don't you think I look something like Cherry[93] in the Beaux Stratagem?

Maid. It's the dress, madam, that every lady wears in the country, but when she visits or receives company.

Miss Hardcastle. And are you sure he does not remember my face or person?

Maid. Certain of it.

Miss Hardcastle. I vow I thought so; for though we spoke for some time together, yet his fears were such, that he never once looked up during the interview. Indeed, if he had, my bonnet would have kept him from seeing me.

Maid. But what do you hope from keeping him in his mistake?

Miss Hardcastle. In the first place, I shall be *seen,* and that is no small advantage to a girl who brings her face to market. Then I shall perhaps make an acquaintance, and that's no small victory gained over one who never addresses any but the wildest of her sex. But my chief aim is to take my gentleman off his guard, and like an invisible champion of romance examine the giant's force before I offer to combat.

Maid. But you are sure you can act your part, and disguise your voice, so that he may mistake that, as he has already mistaken your person?

Miss Hardcastle. Never fear me. I think I have got the true bar cant.—Did your honour call?——Attend the Lion there.——Pipes and tobacco for the Angel.—The Lamb has been outrageous this half hour.[94]

Maid. It will do, madam. But he's here. [*Exit* MAID.

Enter MARLOW

Marlow. What a bawling in every part of the house; I have scarce a moment's repose. If I go to the best room, there I find my host and his story. If I fly to the gallery, there we have my hostess with her curtesy down to the ground. I have at last got a moment to myself, and now for recollection.

[*Walks and muses.*

Miss Hardcastle. Did you call, Sir? did your honour call?

Marlow (*musing*). As for Miss Hardcastle, she's too grave and sentimental for me.

Miss Hardcastle. Did your honour call?

[*She still places herself before him, he turning away.*

Marlow. No, child. (*musing*) Besides from the glimpse I had of her, I think she squints.

Miss Hardcastle. I'm sure, Sir, I heard the bell ring.

Marlow. No, no. (*musing*) I have pleased my father, however, by coming down, and I'll to-morrow please myself by returning.   [*Taking out his tablets, and perusing.*

Miss Hardcastle. Perhaps the other gentleman called, Sir?

Marlow. I tell you, no.

Miss Hardcastle. I should be glad to know, Sir. We have such a parcel of servants.

Marlow. No, no, I tell you. (*looks full in her face*) Yes, child, I think I did call. I wanted——I wanted——I vow, child, you are vastly handsome!

Miss Hardcastle. O la, Sir, you'll make one asham'd.

Marlow. Never saw a more sprightly malicious eye. Yes, yes, my dear, I did call. Have you got any of your——a——what d'ye call it in the house?

Miss Hardcastle. No, Sir, we have been out of that these ten days.

Marlow. One may call in this house, I find, to very little purpose. Suppose I should call for a taste, just by way of trial, of the nectar of your lips; perhaps I might be disappointed in that too.

Miss Hardcastle. Nectar! nectar! that's a liquor there's no call for in these parts. French, I suppose. We keep no French wines here, Sir.

Marlow. Of true English growth, I assure you.

Miss Hardcastle. Then it's odd I should not know it. We brew all sorts of wines in this house, and I have lived here these eighteen years.

Marlow. Eighteen years! Why one would think, child, you kept the bar before you were born. How old are you?

Miss Hardcastle. O! Sir, I must not tell my age. They say women and music should never be dated.

Marlow. To guess at this distance, you can't be much above forty. (*approaching*) Yet nearer I don't think so much. (*approaching*) By coming close to some women they look younger still; but when we come very close indeed. (*attempting to kiss her*)

Miss Hardcastle. Pray, Sir, keep your distance. One would think you wanted to know one's age as they do horses, by mark of mouth.

Marlow. I protest, child, you use me extremely ill. If you keep me at this distance, how is it possible you and I can be ever acquainted?

Miss Hardcastle. And who wants to be acquainted with you? I want no such acquaintance, not I. I'm sure you did not treat Miss Hardcastle that was here awhile ago in this obstropalous manner. I'll warrant me, before her you look'd dash'd, and kept bowing to the ground, and talk'd, for all the world, as if you was before a justice of peace.

Marlow. (*aside*) Egad! she has hit it, sure enough. (*to her*) In awe of her, child? Ha! ha! ha! A mere, aukward, squinting thing, no, no. I find you don't know me. I laugh'd, and rallied her a little; but I was unwilling to be too severe. No, I could not be too severe, *curse me!*

Miss Hardcastle. O! then, Sir, you are a favourite, I find, among the ladies?

Marlow. Yes, my dear, a great favourite. And yet, hang me, I don't see what they find in me to follow. At the Ladies Club in town I'm called their agreeable Rattle. Rattle, child, is not my real name, but one I'm known by. My name is Solomons. Mr. Solomons, my dear, at your service. (*Offering to salute her*)

Miss Hardcastle. Hold, Sir; you were introducing me to your club, not to yourself. And you're so great a favourite there you say?

Marlow. Yes, my dear. There's Mrs. Mantrap, Lady Betty Blackleg, the Countess of Sligo, Mrs. Langhorns, old Miss Biddy Buckskin, and your humble servant, keep up the spirit of the place.

Miss Hardcastle. Then it's a very merry place, I suppose.

Marlow. Yes, as merry as cards, suppers, wine, and old women can make us.

Miss Hardcastle. And their agreeable Rattle, ha! ha! ha!

Marlow. (*aside*) Egad! I don't quite like this chit. She looks knowing, methinks. You laugh, child!

Miss Hardcastle. I can't but laugh to think what time they all have for minding their work or their family.

Marlow. (*aside*) All's well, she don't laugh at me. (*to her*) Do *you* ever work, child?

Miss Hardcastle. Ay, sure. There's not a screen or a quilt in the whole house but what can bear witness to that.

Marlow. Odso! Then you must shew me your embroidery. I embroider and draw patterns myself a little. If you want a judge of your work you must apply to me.   [*seizing her hand.*

Miss Hardcastle. Ay, but the colours don't look well by candle light. You shall see all in the morning.   [*struggling.*

Marlow. And why not now, my angel? Such beauty fires beyond the power of resistance.——Pshaw! the father here! My old luck: I never nick'd seven that I did not throw ames ace[95] three times following.   [*Exit* MARLOW.

Enter HARDCASTLE, *who stands in surprize*

Hardcastle. So, madam! So I find *this* is your *modest* lover. This is your humble admirer that kept his eyes fixed on the ground, and only ador'd at humble distance. Kate, Kate, art thou not asham'd to deceive your father so?

Miss Hardcastle. Never trust me, dear papa, but he's still the modest man I first took him for, you'll be convinced of it as well as I.

Hardcastle. By the hand of my body, I believe his impudence is infectious! Didn't I see him seize your hand? Didn't I see him hawl you about like a milk maid? and now you talk of his respect and his modesty, forsooth!

Miss Hardcastle. But if I shortly convince you of his modesty, that he has only the faults that will pass off with time, and the virtues that will improve with age, I hope you'll forgive him.

Hardcastle. The girl would actually make one run mad! I tell you I'll not be convinced. I am convinced. He has scarcely been three hours in the house, and he has already encroached on all my prerogatives. You may like his impudence, and call it modesty. But my son-in-law, madam, must have very different qualifications.

Miss Hardcastle. Sir, I ask but this night to convince you.

Hardcastle. You shall not have half the time, for I have thoughts of turning him out this very hour.

Miss Hardcastle. Give me that hour then, and I hope to satisfy you.

Hardcastle. Well, an hour let it be then. But I'll have no trifling with your father. All fair and open, do you mind me?

Miss Hardcastle. I hope, Sir, you have ever found that I considered your commands as my pride; for your kindness is such that my duty as yet has been inclination.   [*Exeunt.*

ACT IV

Enter HASTINGS *and* MISS NEVILLE

Hastings. You surprise me! Sir Charles Marlow expected here this night? Where have you had your information?

Miss Neville. You may depend upon it. I just saw his letter to Mr. Hardcastle, in which he tells him he intends setting out a few hours after his son.

Hastings. Then, my Constance, all must be completed before he arrives. He knows me; and should he find me here, would discover my name, and perhaps my designs, to the rest of the family.

Miss Neville. The jewels, I hope, are safe.

Hastings. Yes, yes. I have sent them to Marlow, who keeps the keys of our baggage. In the meantime, I'll go to prepare matters for our elopement. I have had the Squire's promise of a fresh pair of horses; and, if I should not see him again, will write him further directions.   [*Exit.*

Miss Neville. Well! success attend you. In the meantime, I'll go amuse my aunt with the old pretence of a violent passion for my cousin.   [*Exit.*

Enter MARLOW, *followed by a* SERVANT

Marlow. I wonder what Hastings could mean by sending me so valuable a thing as a casket to keep for him, when he knows the only place I have is the seat of a post-coach at an Inn-door. Have you deposited the casket with the landlady, as I ordered you? Have you put it into her own hands?

Servant. Yes, your honour.

Marlow. She said she'd keep it safe, did she?

Servant. Yes, she said she'd keep it safe enough; she ask'd me how I came by it? and she said she had a great mind to make me give an account of myself.   [*Exit* SERVANT.

Marlow. Ha! ha! ha! They're safe however. What an unaccountable set of beings have we got amongst! This little barmaid though runs in my head most strangely and drives out the absurdities of all the rest of the family. She's mine; she must be mine, or I'm greatly mistaken.

Enter HASTINGS

Hastings. Bless me! I quite forgot to tell her that I intended to prepare at the bottom of the garden. Marlow here, and in spirits too!

Marlow. Give me joy, George! Crown me, shadow me with laurels! Well, George, after all, we modest fellows don't want for success among the women.

Hastings. Some women you mean. But what success has your honour's modesty been crowned with now, that it grows so insolent upon us?

Marlow. Didn't you see the tempting, brisk, lovely little thing that runs about the house with a bunch of keys to its girdle?

Hastings. Well! and what then?

Marlow. She's mine, you rogue you. Such fire, such motion, such eyes, such lips——but egad! she would not let me kiss them though.

Hastings. But are you sure, so very sure of her?

Marlow. Why man, she talk'd of shewing me her work above-stairs, and I am to improve the pattern.

Hastings. But how can *you*, Charles, go about to rob a woman of her honour?

Marlow. Pshaw! pshaw! we all know the honour of the bar-maid of an inn. I don't intend to *rob* her, take my word for it, there's nothing in this house, I shan't honestly *pay* for.

Hastings. I believe the girl has virtue.

Marlow. And if she has, I should be the last man in the world that would attempt to corrupt it.

Hastings. You have taken care, I hope, of the casket I sent you to lock up? It's in safety?

Marlow. Yes, yes. It's safe enough. I have taken care of it. But how could you think the seat of a post-coach at an Inn-door a place of safety? Ah! numbskull! I have taken better precautions for you than you did for yourself.——I have——

Hastings. What!

Marlow. I have sent it to the landlady to keep for you.

Hastings. To the landlady!

Marlow. The landlady.

Hastings. You did.

Marlow. I did. She's to be answerable for its forth-coming, you know.

Hastings. Yes, she'll bring it forth, with a witness.

Marlow. Wasn't I right? I believe you'll allow that I acted prudently upon this occasion?

Hastings. (*aside*) He must not see my uneasiness.

Marlow. You seem a little disconcerted though, methinks. Sure nothing has happened?

Hastings. No, nothing. Never was in better spirits in all my life. And so you left it with the landlady, who, no doubt, very readily undertook the charge?

Marlow. Rather too readily. For she not only kept the casket; but, thro' her great precaution, was going to keep the messenger too. Ha! ha! ha!

Hastings. He! he! he! They're safe however.

Marlow. As a guinea in a miser's purse.

Hastings. (*aside*) So now all hopes of fortune are at an end, and we must set off without it. (*to him*) Well, Charles,

I'll leave you to your meditations on the pretty bar-maid, and, he! he! he! may you be as successful for yourself as you have been for me.   [*Exit.*

Marlow. Thank ye, George! I ask no more. Ha! ha! ha!

Enter HARDCASTLE

Hardcastle. I no longer know my own house. It's turned all topsey-turvey. His servants have got drunk already. I'll bear it no longer, and yet, from my respect for his father, I'll be calm. (*to him*) Mr. Marlow, your servant. I'm your very humble servant. (*bowing low*)

Marlow. Sir, your humble servant. (*aside*) What's to be the wonder now?

Hardcastle. I believe, Sir, you must be sensible, Sir, that no man alive ought to be more welcome than your father's son, Sir. I hope you think so?

Marlow. I do from my soul, Sir. I don't want much intreaty. I generally make my father's son welcome wherever he goes.

Hardcastle. I believe you do, from my soul, Sir. But tho' I say nothing to your own conduct, that of your servants is insufferable. Their manner of drinking is setting a very bad example in this house, I assure you.

Marlow. I protest, my very good Sir, that's no fault of mine. If they don't drink as they ought *they* are to blame. I ordered them not to spare the cellar. I did, I assure you. (*to the side scene*) Here, let one of my servants come up. (*to him*) My positive directions were, that as I did not drink myself, they should make up for my deficiencies below.

Hardcastle. Then they had your orders for what they do! I'm satisfied!

Marlow. They had, I assure [you]. You shall hear from one of themselves.

Enter SERVANT, *drunk*

Marlow. You, Jeremy! Come forward, sirrah! What were my orders? Were you not told to drink freely, and call for what you thought fit, for the good of the house?

Hardcastle. (*aside*) I begin to lose my patience.

Jeremy. Please your honour, liberty and Fleet-street for ever! Tho' I'm but a servant, I'm as good as another man. I'll drink for no man before supper, Sir, dammy! Good liquor will sit upon a good supper, but a good supper will not sit upon ——hiccup——upon my conscience, Sir.

Marlow. You see, my old friend, the fellow is as drunk as he can possibly be. I don't know what you'd have more, unless you'd have the poor devil soused in a beer-barrel.

Hardcastle. Zounds! He'll drive me distracted if I contain myself any longer. Mr. Marlow, Sir; I have submitted to your insolence for more than four hours, and I see no likelihood of its coming to an end. I'm now resolved to be master here, Sir, and I desire that you and your drunken pack may leave my house directly.

Marlow. Leave your house!—Sure, you jest, my good friend? What, when I'm doing what I can to please you.

Hardcastle. I tell you, Sir, you don't please me; so I desire you'll leave my house.

Marlow. Sure you cannot be serious! At this time o'night, and such a night. You only mean to banter me?

Hardcastle. I tell you, Sir, I'm serious; and, now that my passions are rouzed, I say this house is mine, Sir; this house is mine, and I command you to leave it directly.

Marlow. Ha! ha! ha! A puddle in a storm. I shan't stir a step, I assure you. (*in a serious tone*) This your house, fellow! It's my house. This is my house. Mine, while I chuse to stay. What right have you to bid me leave this house, Sir? I never met with such impudence, curse me, never in my whole life before.

Hardcastle. Nor I, confound me if ever I did. To come to my house, to call for what he likes, to turn me out of my own chair, to insult the family, to order his servants to get drunk, and then to tell me *This house is mine, Sir.* By all that's impudent it makes me laugh. Ha! ha! ha! Pray, Sir, (*bantering*) as you take the house, what think you of taking the rest of the furniture? There's a pair of silver candlesticks, and there's a fire-screen, and here's a pair of brazen nosed bellows, perhaps you may take a fancy to them?

Marlow. Bring me your bill, Sir, bring me your bill, and let's make no more words about it.

Hardcastle. There are a set of prints too. What think you of the rake's progress for your own apartment?

Marlow. Bring me your bill, I say; and I'll leave you and your infernal house directly.

Hardcastle. Then there's a mahogany table, that you may see your own face in.

Marlow. My bill, I say.

Hardcastle. I had forgot the great chair, for your own particular slumbers, after a hearty meal.

Marlow. Zounds! bring me my bill, I say, and let's hear no more on't.

Hardcastle. Young man, young man, from your father's letter to me I was taught to expect a well-bred modest man as a visitor here, but now I find him no better than a coxcomb and a bully; but he will be down here presently and shall hear more of it.   [*Exit*.

Marlow. How's this! Sure, I have not mistaken the house! Every thing looks like an inn. The servants cry, coming. The attendance is aukward; the bar-maid too to attend us. But she's here and will further inform me. Whither so fast, child. A word with you.

Enter MISS HARDCASTLE

Miss Hardcastle. Let it be short then. I'm in a hurry. (*aside*) (I believe he begins to find out his mistake, but it's too soon quite to undeceive him.)

Marlow. Pray, child, answer me one question. What are you, and what may your business in this house be?

Miss Hardcastle. A relation of the family, Sir.

Marlow. What. A poor relation?

Miss Hardcastle. Yes, Sir. A poor relation appointed to keep the keys, and to see that the guests want nothing in my power to give them.

Marlow. That is, you act as the bar-maid of this inn.

Miss Hardcastle. Inn. O law—What brought that in your head. One of the best families in the county keep an inn. Ha! ha! ha! old Mr. Hardcastle's house an inn.

Marlow. Mr. Hardcastle's house! Is this house Mr. Hardcastle's house, child!

Miss Hardcastle. Ay, sure. Whose else should it be.

Marlow. So then all's out, and I have been damnably imposed on. O, confound my stupid head, I shall be laugh'd

at over the whole town. I shall be stuck up in caricatura in all
the print-shops. The Dullissimo Maccaroni.[96] To mistake this
house of all others for an inn, and my father's old friend for an
inn-keeper. What a swaggering puppy must he take me for.
What a silly puppy do I find myself. There again, may I be
hanged, my dear, but I mistook you for the bar-maid.

Miss Hardcastle. Dear me! dear me! I'm sure there's nothing in my *behaviour* to put me upon a level with one of that
stamp.

Marlow. Nothing, my dear, nothing. But I was in for a list
of blunders, and could not help making you a subscriber.
My stupidity saw every thing the wrong way. I mistook your
assiduity for assurance, and your simplicity for allurement. But
it's over—This house I no more shew *my* face in!

Miss Hardcastle. I hope, Sir, I have done nothing to dis-
oblige you. I'm sure I should be sorry to affront any gentleman who has been so polite, and said so many civil things to
me. I'm sure I should be sorry (*pretending to cry*) if he left
the family upon my account. I'm sure I should be sorry, people
said any thing amiss, since I have no fortune but my character.

Marlow. (*aside*) By heaven, she weeps. This is the first mark
of tenderness I ever had from a modest woman, and it touches
me. (*to her*) Excuse me, my lovely girl, you are the only part
of the family I leave with reluctance. But to be plain with you,
the difference of our birth, fortune and education, make an
honourable connexion impossible; and I can never harbour a
thought of seducing simplicity that trusted in my honour, or
bringing ruin upon one whose only fault was being too lovely.

Miss Hardcastle. (*aside*) Generous man! I now begin to
admire him. (*to him*) But I'm sure my family is as good as
miss Hardcastle's, and though I'm poor, that's no great misfortune to a contented mind, and, until this moment, I never
thought that it was bad to want fortune.

Marlow. And why now, my pretty simplicity?

Miss Hardcastle. Because it puts me at a distance from one
that if I had a thousand pound I would give it all to.

Marlow. (*aside*) This simplicity bewitches me, so that if
I stay I'm undone. I must make one bold effort, and leave
her. (*to her*) Your partiality in my favour, my dear, touches
me most sensibly, and were I to live for myself alone, I could

easily fix my choice. But I owe too much to the opinion of the world, too much to the authority of a father, so that—I can scarcely speak it—it affects me. Farewell.   [*Exit.*

Miss Hardcastle. I never knew half his merit till now. He shall not go, if I have power or art to detain him. I'll still preserve the character in which I stoop'd to conquer, but will undeceive my papa, who, perhaps, may laugh him out of his resolution.   [*Exit.*

Enter TONY, MISS NEVILLE

Tony. Ay, you may steal for yourselves the next time. I have done my duty. She has got the jewels again, that's a sure thing; but she believes it was all a mistake of the servants.

Miss Neville. But, my dear cousin, sure you won't forsake us in this distress. If she in the least suspects that I am going off, I shall certainly be locked up, or sent to my aunt Pedigree's, which is ten times worse.

Tony. To be sure, aunts of all kinds are damn'd bad things. But what can I do? I have got you a pair of horses that will fly like Whistlejacket,[97] and I'm sure you can't say but I have courted you nicely before her face. Here she comes; we must court a bit or two more, for fear she should suspect us.

                    [*they retire, and seem to fondle.*

Enter MRS. HARDCASTLE

Mrs. Hardcastle. Well, I was greatly fluttered, to be sure. But my son tells me it was all a mistake of the servants. I shan't be easy, however, till they are fairly married, and then let her keep her own fortune. But what do I see! Fondling together, as I'm alive. I never saw Tony so sprightly before. Ah! have I caught you, my pretty doves! What, billing, exchanging stolen glances, and broken murmurs. Ah!

Tony. As for murmurs, mother, we grumble a little now and then, to be sure. But there's no love lost between us.

Mrs. Hardcastle. A mere sprinkling, Tony, upon the flame, only to make it burn brighter.

Miss Neville. Cousin Tony promises to give us more of his company at home. Indeed, he shan't leave us any more. It won't leave us cousin Tony, will it?

Tony. O! it's a pretty creature. No, I'd sooner leave my horse in a pound than leave you when you smile upon one so. Your laugh makes you so becoming.

Miss Neville. Agreeable cousin! Who can help admiring that natural humour, that pleasant, broad, red, thoughtless, (*patting his cheek*) ah! it's a bold face.

Mrs. Hardcastle. Pretty innocence.

Tony. I'm sure I always lov'd cousin Con's hazle eyes, and her pretty long fingers that she twists this way and that over the haspicholls,[98] like a parcel of bobbins.

Mrs. Hardcastle. Ah, he would charm the bird from the tree. I was never so happy before. My boy takes after his father, poor Mr. Lumpkin, exactly. The jewels, my dear Con, shall be your's incontinently. You shall have them. Isn't he a sweet boy, my dear? You shall be married to-morrow, and we'll put off the rest of his education, like Dr. Drowsy's sermons, to a fitter opportunity.

Enter DIGGORY

Diggory. Where's the 'Squire? I have got a letter for your worship.

Tony. Give it to my mamma. She reads all my letters first.

Diggory. I had orders to deliver it into your own hands.

Tony. Who does it come from?

Diggory. Your worship mun ask that o' the letter itself.

Tony. I could wish to know, tho'. (*turning the letter, and gazing on it.*)

Miss Neville. (*aside*) Undone, undone. A letter to him from Hastings. I know the hand. If my aunt sees it, we are ruined for ever. I'll keep her employ'd a little if I can. (*to* MRS. HARD-CASTLE) But I have not told you, Madam, of my cousin's smart answer just now to Mr. Marlow. We so laugh'd—You must know, Madam—this way a little, for he must not hear us.

[*they confer.*

Tony. (*still gazing*) A damn'd cramp piece of penmanship as ever I saw in my life. I can read your print-hand very well. But here there are such handles, and shanks, and dashes, that one can scarce tell the head from the tail. *To Anthony Lumpkin, Esquire.* It's very odd, I can read the outside of my letters, where my own name is, well enough. But when I come to open it, it's all—buzz. That's hard, very hard; for the inside of the letter is always the cream of the correspondence.

Mrs. Hardcastle. Ha, ha, ha. Very well, very well. And so my son was too hard for the philosopher.

Miss Neville. Yes, Madam; but you must hear the rest, Madam. A little more this way, or he may hear us. You'll hear how he puzzled him again.

Mrs. Hardcastle. He seems strangely puzzled now himself, methinks.

Tony. (*still gazing*) A damned up and down hand, as if it was disguised in liquor. (*reading*) *Dear Sir.* Ay, that's that. Then there's an *M,* and a *T,* and an *S,* but whether the next be an *izzard* or an *R,* confound me, I cannot tell.

Mrs. Hardcastle. What's that, my dear. Can I give you any assistance?

Miss Neville. Pray, aunt, let me read it. No body reads a cramp hand better than I. (*twitching the letter from her*) Do you know who it is from?

Tony. Can't tell, except from Dick Ginger the feeder.

Miss Neville. Ay, so it is, (*pretending to read*) Dear 'Squire, Hoping that you're in health, as I am at this present. The gentlemen of the Shake bag club has cut the gentlemen of goose-green quite out of feather. The odds—um—odd battle—um long fighting—um here, here, it's all about cocks, and fighting; it's of no consequence, here, put it up, put it up.

[*thrusting the crumpled letter upon him.*

Tony. But I tell you, Miss, it's of all the consequence in the world. I would not lose the rest of it for a guinea. Here, mother, do you make it out. Of no consequence!

[*giving* MRS. HARDCASTLE *the letter.*

Mrs. Hardcastle. How's this! (*reads*) Dear 'Squire, I'm now waiting for Miss Neville, with a post-chaise and pair, at the bottom of the garden, but I find my horses yet unable to perform the journey. I expect you'll assist us with a pair of fresh horses, as you promised. Dispatch is necessary, as the *hag* (ay the hag) your mother will otherwise suspect us. Your's, Hastings. Grant me patience. I shall run distracted. My rage choaks me.

Miss Neville. I hope, Madam, you'll suspend your resentment for a few moments, and not impute to me any impertinence or sinister design that belongs to another.

Mrs. Hardcastle. (*curtesying very low*) Fine spoken, Madam, you are most miraculously polite and engaging, and quite the very pink of curtesy and circumspection, Madam. (*changing her tone*) And you, you great ill-fashioned oaf, with scarce sense enough to keep your mouth shut. Were you too join'd against me? But I'll defeat all your plots in a moment. As for you, Madam, since you have got a pair of fresh horses ready, it would be cruel to disappoint them. So, if you please, instead of running away with your spark, prepare, this very moment, to run off with *me*. Your old aunt Pedigree will keep you secure, I'll warrant me. You too, Sir, may mount your horse, and guard us upon the way. Here, Thomas, Roger, Diggory, I'll shew you, that I wish you better than you do yourselves. [*Exit.*

Miss Neville. So now I'm completely ruined.

Tony. Ay, that's a sure thing.

Miss Neville. What better could be expected from being connected with such a stupid fool, and after all the nods and signs I made him.

Tony. By the laws, Miss, it was your own cleverness, and not my stupidity, that did your business. You were so nice and so busy with your Shake-bags and Goose-greens, that I thought you could never be making believe.

Enter HASTINGS

Hastings. So, Sir, I find by my servant, that you have shewn my letter and betray'd us. Was this well done, young gentleman?

Tony. Here's another. Ask Miss there who betray'd you. Ecod, it was her doing, not mine.

Enter MARLOW

Marlow. So I have been finely used here among you. Rendered contemptible, driven into ill manners, despised, insulted, laugh'd at.

Tony. Here's another. We shall have old Bedlam broke loose presently.

Miss Neville. And there, Sir, is the gentleman to whom we all owe every obligation.

Marlow. What can I say to him, a mere boy, an ideot, whose ignorance and age are a protection.

Hastings. A poor contemptible booby, that would but disgrace correction.

Miss Neville. Yet with cunning and malice enough to make himself merry with all our embarrassments.

Hastings. An insensible cub.

Marlow. Replete with tricks and mischief.

Tony. Baw! damme, but I'll fight you both one after the other,——with baskets.[99]

Marlow. As for him, he's below resentment. But your conduct, Mr. Hastings, requires an explanation. You knew of my mistakes, yet would not undeceive me.

Hastings. Tortured as I am with my own disappointments, is this a time for explanations? It is not friendly, Mr. Marlow.

Marlow. But, Sir—

Miss Neville. Mr. Marlow, we never kept on your mistake till it was too late to undeceive you. Be pacified.

Enter SERVANT

Servant. My mistress desires you'll get ready immediately, Madam. The horses are putting to. Your hat and things are in the next room. We are to go thirty miles before morning.

[*Exit* SERVANT.

Miss Neville. Well, well; I'll come presently.

Marlow. (*to* HASTINGS) Was it well done, Sir, to assist in rendering me ridiculous? To hang me out for the scorn of all my acquaintance. Depend upon it, Sir, I shall expect an explanation.

Hastings. Was it well done, Sir, if you're upon that subject, to deliver what I entrusted to yourself, to the care of another, Sir?

Miss Neville. Mr. Hastings. Mr. Marlow. Why will you increase my distress by this groundless dispute? I implore, I entreat you——

Enter SERVANT

Servant. Your cloak, Madam. My mistress is impatient.

Miss Neville. I come. Pray be pacified. If I leave you thus, I shall die with apprehension.

Enter SERVANT

Servant. Your fan, muff, and gloves, Madam. The horses are waiting.

Miss Neville. O, Mr. Marlow! if you knew what a scene of constraint and ill-nature lies before me, I'm sure it would convert your resentment into pity.

Marlow. I'm so distracted with a variety of passions, that I don't know what I do. Forgive me, Madam. George, forgive me. You know my hasty temper, and should not exasperate it.

Hastings. The torture of my situation is my only excuse.

Miss Neville. Well, my dear Hastings, if you have that esteem for me that I think, that I am sure you have, your constancy for three years will but encrease the happiness of our future connection. If—

Mrs. Hardcastle. (*within*) Miss Neville. Constance, why Constance, I say

Miss Neville. I'm coming. Well, constancy. Remember, constancy is the word.   [*Exit.*

Hastings. My heart! How can I support this. To be so near happiness, and such happiness.

Marlow. (*to* TONY) You see now, young gentleman, the effects of your folly. What might be amusement to you is here disappointment, and even distress.

Tony (*from a reverie*). Ecod, I have hit it. It's here. Your hands. Yours and yours, my poor Sulky. My boots there, ho. Meet me two hours hence at the bottom of the garden; and if you don't find Tony Lumpkin a more good-natur'd fellow than you thought for, I'll give you leave to take my best horse, and Bet Bouncer into the bargain. Come along. My boots, ho!
                                    [*Exeunt.*

ACT V
SCENE *Continues*

Enter HASTINGS *and* SERVANT

Hastings. You saw the Old Lady and Miss Neville drive off, you say.

Servant. Yes, your honour. They went off in a post coach, and the young 'Squire went on horseback. They're thirty miles off by this time.

Hastings. Then all my hopes are over.

Servant. Yes, Sir. Old Sir Charles is arrived. He and the Old Gentleman of the house have been laughing at Mr. Marlow's mistake this half hour. They are coming this way.

Hastings. Then I must not be seen. So now to my fruitless appointment at the bottom of the garden. This is about the time.   [*Exit.*

Enter SIR CHARLES *and* HARDCASTLE

Hardcastle. Ha, ha, ha. The peremptory tone in which he sent forth his sublime commands.

Sir Charles. And the reserve with which I suppose he treated all your advances.

Hardcastle. And yet he might have seen something in me above a common inn-keeper, too.

Sir Charles. Yes, Dick, but he mistook you for an un-common innkeeper, ha, ha, ha.

Hardcastle. Well, I'm in too good spirits to think of any-thing but joy. Yes, my dear friend, this union of our families will make our personal friendships hereditary; and tho' my daughter's fortune is but small——

Sir Charles. Why, Dick, will you talk of fortune to *me*. My son is possessed of more than a competence already, and can want nothing but a good and virtuous girl to share his happi-ness and encrease it. If they like each other, as you say they do——

Hardcastle. If, man. I tell you they *do* like each other. My daughter as good as told me so.

Sir Charles. But girls are apt to flatter themselves, you know.

Hardcastle. I saw him grasp her hand in the warmest manner, myself; and here he comes to put you out of your *iffs,* I warrant him.

Enter MARLOW

Marlow. I come, Sir, once more, to ask pardon for my strange conduct. I can scarce reflect on my insolence without confusion.

Hardcastle. Tut, boy, a trifle. You take it too gravely. An hour or two's laughing with my daughter will set all to rights again. She'll never like you the worse for it.

Marlow. Sir, I shall be always proud of her approbation.

Hardcastle. Approbation is but a cold word, Mr. Marlow; if I am not deceived, you have something more than approbation thereabouts. You take me.

Marlow. Really, Sir, I have not that happiness.

Hardcastle. Come, boy, I'm an old fellow, and know what's what, as well as you that are younger. I know what has past between you; but mum.

Marlow. Sure, Sir, nothing has past between us but the most profound respect on my side, and the most distant reserve on her's. You don't think, Sir, that my impudence has been past upon all the rest of the family.

Hardcastle. Impudence! No, I don't say that—Not quite impudence—Though girls like to be play'd with, and rumpled a little too, sometimes. But she has told no tales, I assure you.

Marlow. I never gave her the slightest cause.

Hardcastle. Well, well, I like modesty in its place well enough. But this is over-acting, young gentleman. You *may* be open. Your father and I will like you the better for it.

Marlow. May I die, Sir, if I ever——

Hardcastle. I tell you, she don't dislike you; and as I'm sure you like her——

Marlow. Dear Sir—I protest, Sir——

Hardcastle. I see no reason why you should not be joined as fast as the parson can tie you.

Marlow. But hear me, Sir——

Hardcastle. Your father approves the match, I admire it, every moment's delay will be doing mischief, so——

Marlow. But why won't you hear me? By all that's just and true, I never gave Miss Hardcastle the slightest mark of my attachment, or even the most distant hint to suspect me of affection. We had but one interview, and that was formal, modest and uninteresting.

Hardcastle. (*aside*) This fellow's formal modest impudence is beyond bearing.

Sir Charles. And you never grasp'd her hand, or made any protestations!

Marlow. As heaven is my witness, I came down in obedience to your commands. I saw the lady without emotion, and parted without reluctance. I hope you'll exact no further proofs of my duty, nor prevent me from leaving a house in which I suffer so many mortifications.   [*Exit.*

Sir Charles. I'm astonish'd at the air of sincerity with which he parted.

Hardcastle. And I'm astonish'd at the deliberate intrepidity of his assurance.

Sir Charles. I dare pledge my life and honour upon his truth.

Hardcastle. Here comes my daughter, and I would stake my happiness upon her veracity.

Enter MISS HARDCASTLE

Hardcastle. Kate, come hither, child. Answer us sincerely, and without reserve; has Mr. Marlow made you any professions of love and affection?

Miss Hardcastle. The question is very abrupt, Sir! But since you require unreserved sincerity, I think he has.

Hardcastle. (*to* SIR CHARLES) You see.

Sir Charles. And pray, madam, have you and my son had more than one interview?

Miss Hardcastle. Yes, Sir, several.

Hardcastle. (*to* SIR CHARLES) You see.

Sir Charles. But did he profess any attachment?

Miss Hardcastle. A lasting one.

Sir Charles. Did he talk of love?

Miss Hardcastle. Much, Sir.

Sir Charles. Amazing! And all this formally?

Miss Hardcastle. Formally.

Hardcastle. Now, my friend, I hope you are satisfied.

Sir Charles. And how did he behave, madam?

Miss Hardcastle. As most profest admirers do. Said some civil things of my face, talked much of his want of merit, and the greatness of mine; mentioned his heart, gave a short tragedy speech, and ended with pretended rapture.

Sir Charles. Now I'm perfectly convinced, indeed. I know his conversation among women to be modest and submissive. This forward canting ranting manner by no means describes him, and I am confident, he never sate for the picture.

Miss Hardcastle. Then what, Sir, if I should convince you to your face of my sincerity? If you and my papa, in about half and hour, will place yourselves behind that screen, you shall hear him declare his passion to me in person.

Sir Charles. Agreed. And if I find him what you describe, all my happiness in him must have an end.   [*Exit.*

Miss Hardcastle. And if you don't find him what I describe —I fear my happiness must never have a beginning.

[*Exeunt.*

SCENE *changes to the Back of the Garden*

Enter HASTINGS

Hastings. What an ideot am I to wait here for a fellow who probably takes a delight in mortifying me. He never intended to be punctual, and I'll wait no longer. What do I see. It is he, and perhaps with news of my Constance.

Enter TONY, *booted and spattered*

Hastings. My honest 'Squire! I now find you a man of your word. This looks like friendship.

Tony. Ay, I'm your friend, and the best friend you have in the world, if you knew but all. This riding by night, by the bye, is cursedly tiresome. It has shook me worse than the basket of a stage-coach.

Hastings. But how? Where did you leave your fellow travellers? Are they in safety? Are they housed?

Tony. Five and twenty miles in two hours and a half is no such bad driving. The poor beasts have smoaked for it. Rabbet me, but I'd rather ride forty miles after a fox, than ten with such *varment.*

Hastings. Well, but where have you left the ladies? I die with impatience.

Tony. Left them? Why, where should I leave them, but where I found them?

Hastings. This is a riddle.

Tony. Riddle me this, then. What's that goes round the house, and round the house, and never touches the house?

Hastings. I'm still astray.

Tony. Why that's it, mon. I have led them astray. By jingo, there's not a pond or slough within five miles of the place but they can tell the taste of.

Hastings. Ha, ha, ha, I understand; you took them in a round, while they supposed themselves going forward. And so you have at last brought them home again.

Tony. You shall hear. I first took them down Feather-bed-lane, where we stuck fast in the mud. I then rattled them crack over the stones of Up-and-down Hill—I then introduc'd them to the gibbet on Heavy-tree Heath, and from that, with a circumbendibus, I fairly lodged them in the horsepond at the bottom of the garden.

Hastings. But no accident, I hope.

Tony. No, no. Only mother is confoundedly frightened. She thinks herself forty miles off. She's sick of the journey, and the cattle can scarce crawl. So if your own horses be ready, you may whip off with cousin, and I'll be bound that no soul here can budge a foot to follow you.

Hastings. My dear friend, how can I be grateful?

Tony. Ay, now its dear friend, noble 'Squire. Just now, it was all ideot, cub, and run me through the guts. Damn *your* way of fighting, I say. After we take a knock in this part of the country, we kiss and be friends. But if you had run me through the guts, then I should be dead, and you might go kiss the hangman.

Hastings. The rebuke is just. But I must hasten to relieve

Miss Neville; if you keep the old lady employed, I promise to take care of the young one. [*Exit* HASTINGS.

Tony. Never fear me. Here she comes. Vanish. She's got from the pond, and draggled up to the waist like a mermaid.

Enter MRS. HARDCASTLE

Mrs. Hardcastle. Oh, Tony, I'm killed. Shook. Battered to death. I shall never survive it. That last jolt that laid us against the quickset hedge has done my business.

Tony. Alack, mama, it was all your own fault. You would be for running away by night, without knowing one inch of the way.

Mrs. Hardcastle. I wish we were at home again. I never met so many accidents in so short a journey. Drenched in the mud, overturned in a ditch, stuck fast in a slough, jolted to a jelly, and at last to lose our way. Whereabouts do you think we are, Tony?

Tony. By my guess we should be upon Crackskull common, about forty miles from home.

Mrs. Hardcastle. O lud! O lud! the most notorious spot in all the country. We only want a robbery to make a complete night on't.

Tony. Don't be afraid, mama, don't be afraid. Two of the five that kept here are hanged, and the other three may not find us. Don't be afraid. Is that a man that's galloping behind us? No; it's only a tree. Don't be afraid.

Mrs. Hardcastle. The fright will certainly kill me.

Tony. Do you see any thing like a black hat moving behind the thicket?

Mrs. Hardcastle. O death!

Tony. No, it's only a cow. Don't be afraid, mama; don't be afraid.

Mrs. Hardcastle. As I'm alive, Tony, I see a man coming towards us. Ah! I'm sure on't. If he perceives us, we are undone.

Tony. (*aside*) Father-in-law,[100] by all that's unlucky, come to take one of his night walks. (*to her*) Ah, it's a highwayman, with pistils as long as my arm. A damn'd ill-looking fellow.

Mrs. Hardcastle. Good heaven defend us! He approaches.

Tony. Do you hide yourself in that thicket, and leave me to manage him. If there be any danger I'll cough and cry hem. When I cough be sure to keep close.

[MRS. HARDCASTLE *hides behind a tree in the back scene.*

Enter HARDCASTLE

Hardcastle. I'm mistaken, or I heard voices of people in want of help. Oh, Tony, is that you? I did not expect you so soon back. Are your mother and her charge in safety?

Tony. Very safe, Sir, at my aunt Pedigree's. Hem.

Mrs. Hardcastle. (*from behind*) Ah death! I find there's danger.

Hardcastle. Forty miles in three hours; sure, that's too much, my youngster.

Tony. Stout horses and willing minds make short journeys as they say. Hem.

Mrs. Hardcastle. (*from behind*) Sure he'll do the dear boy no harm.

Hardcastle. But I heard a voice here; I should be glad to know from whence it came?

Tony. It was I, Sir, talking to myself, Sir. I was saying that forty miles in four hours was very good going. Hem. As to be sure it was. Hem. I have got a sort of cold by being out in the air. We'll go in, if you please. Hem.

Hardcastle. But if you talk'd to yourself, you did not answer yourself. I am certain I heard two voices, and am resolved (*raising his voice*) to find the other out.

Mrs. Hardcastle. (*from behind*) Oh! he's coming to find me out. Oh!

Tony. What need you go, Sir, if I tell you? Hem. I'll lay down my life for the truth—hem—I'll tell you all, Sir.

[*detaining him.*

Hardcastle. I tell you I will not be detained. I insist on seeing. It's in vain to expect I'll believe you.

Mrs. Hardcastle. (*running forward from behind*) O lud, he'll murder my poor boy, my darling. Here, good gentleman, whet your rage upon me. Take my money, my life, but spare that young gentleman, spare my child, if you have any mercy.

Hardcastle. My wife! as I'm a Christian. From whence can she come, or what does she mean!

Mrs. Hardcastle. (*kneeling*) Take compassion on us, good

Mr. Highwayman. Take our money, our watches, all we have, but spare our lives. We will never bring you to justice, indeed we won't, good Mr. Highwayman.

Hardcastle. I believe the woman's out of her senses. What, Dorothy, don't you know *me?*

Mrs. Hardcastle. Mr. Hardcastle, as I'm alive! My fears blinded me. But who, my dear, could have expected to meet you here, in this frightful place, so far from home. What has brought you to follow us?

Hardcastle. Sure, Dorothy, you have not lost your wits! So far from home, when you are within forty yards of your own door! (*to him*) This is one of your old tricks, you graceless rogue you. (*to her*) Don't you know the gate, and the mulbery-tree; and don't you remember the horsepond, my dear?

Mrs. Hardcastle. Yes, I shall remember the horsepond as long as I live; I have caught my death in it. (*to* TONY) And is it to you, you graceless varlet, I owe all this? I'll teach you to abuse your mother, I will.

Tony. Ecod, mother, all the parish says you have spoil'd me, and so you may take the fruits on't.

Mrs. Hardcastle. I'll spoil you, I will.

[*Follows him off the stage. Exit.*

Hardcastle. There's morality, however, in his reply.

[*Exit.*

Enter HASTINGS *and* MISS NEVILLE

Hastings. My dear Constance, why will you deliberate thus? If we delay a moment, all is lost for ever. Pluck up a little resolution, and we shall soon be out of the reach of her malignity.

Miss Neville. I find it impossible. My spirits are so sunk with the agitations I have suffered, that I am unable to face any new danger. Two or three years patience will at last crown us with happiness.

Hastings. Such a tedious delay is worse than inconstancy. Let us fly, my charmer. Let us date our happiness from this very moment. Perish fortune. Love and content will encrease what we possess beyond a monarch's revenue. Let me prevail.

Miss Neville. No, Mr. Hastings; no. Prudence once more comes to my relief, and I will obey its dictates. In the moment of passion, fortune may be despised, but it ever produces a lasting repentance. I'm resolved to apply to Mr. Hardcastle's compassion and justice for redress.

Hastings. But tho' he had the will, he has not the power to relieve you.

Miss Neville. But he has influence, and upon that I am resolved to rely.

Hastings. I have no hopes. But since you persist, I must reluctantly obey you.   [*Exeunt.*

SCENE *Changes*

Enter SIR CHARLES *and* MISS HARDCASTLE

Sir Charles. What a situation am I in! If what you say appears, I shall then find a guilty son. If what he says be true, I shall then lose one that of all others I most wish'd for a daughter.

Miss Hardcastle. I am proud of your approbation, and to shew I merit it, if you place yourselves as I directed, you shall hear his explicit declaration. But he comes.

Sir Charles. I'll to your father, and keep him to the appointment.   [*Exit* SIR CHARLES.

Enter MARLOW

Marlow. Tho' prepar'd for setting out, I come once more to take leave, nor did I, till this moment, know the pain I feel in the separation.

Miss Hardcastle. (*in her own natural manner*) I believe these sufferings cannot be very great, Sir, which you can so easily remove. A day or two longer, perhaps, might lessen your uneasiness, by shewing the little value of what you now think proper to regret.

Marlow. (*aside*) This girl every moment improves upon me. (*to her*) It must not be, Madam. I have already trifled too long with my heart. My very pride begins to submit to my passion. The disparity of education and fortune, the anger of a parent, and the contempt of my equals, begin to lose their weight; and nothing can restore me to myself, but this painful effort of resolution.

Miss Hardcastle. Then go, Sir. I'll urge nothing more to detain you. Tho' my family be as good as her's you came down to visit, and my education, I hope, not inferior, what are these advantages without equal affluence? I must remain contented with the slight approbation of imputed merit. I must have only the mockery of your addresses, while all your serious aims are fix'd on fortune.

Enter HARDCASTLE *and* SIR CHARLES *from behind*

Sir Charles. Here, behind this screen.

Hardcastle. Ay, ay, make no noise. I'll engage my Kate covers him with confusion at last.

Marlow. By heavens, Madam, fortune was ever my smallest consideration. Your beauty at first caught my eye; for who could see that without emotion? But every moment that I converse with you, steals in some new grace, heightens the picture, and gives it stronger expression. What at first seem'd rustic plainness now appears refin'd simplicity. What seem'd forward assurance now strikes me as the result of courageous innocence and conscious virtue.

Sir Charles. What can it mean! He amazes me!

Hardcastle. I told you how it would be. Hush!

Marlow. I am now determined to stay, Madam, and I have too good an opinion of my father's discernment, when he sees you, to doubt his approbation.

Miss Hardcastle. No, Mr. Marlow, I will not, cannot detain you. Do you think I could suffer a connexion, in which there is the smallest room for repentance? Do you think I would take the mean advantage of a transient passion, to load you with confusion? Do you think I could ever relish that happiness which was acquired by lessening your's?

Marlow. By all that's good, I can have no happiness but what's in your power to grant me. Nor shall I ever feel repentance but in not having seen your merits before. I will stay, even contrary to your wishes; and tho' you should persist to shun me, I will make my respectful assiduities atone for the levity of my past conduct.

Miss Hardcastle. Sir, I must entreat you'll desist. As our acquaintance began, so let it end, in indifference. I might have given an hour or two to levity; but seriously, Mr. Marlow, do you think I could ever submit to a connexion where *I* must appear mercenary, and *you* imprudent? Do you think I could ever catch at the confident addresses of a secure admirer?

Marlow (*kneeling*) Does this look like security? Does this look like confidence? No, Madam, every moment that shews me your merit, only serves to encrease my diffidence and confusion. Here let me continue——

Sir Charles. I can hold it no longer. Charles, Charles, how hast thou deceived me! Is this your indifference, your uninteresting conversation!

Hardcastle. Your cold contempt; your formal interview. What have you to say now?

Marlow. That I'm all amazement! What can it mean!

Hardcastle. It means that you can say and unsay things at pleasure. That you can address a lady in private, and deny it in public; that you have one story for us, and another for my daughter.

Marlow. Daughter!—this lady your daughter!

Hardcastle. Yes, Sir, my only daughter. My Kate, whose else should she be?

Marlow. Oh, the devil.

Miss Hardcastle. Yes, Sir, that very identical tall squinting lady you were pleased to take me for. (*curtesying*) She that you addressed as the mild, modest, sentimental man of gravity, and the bold forward agreeable Rattle of the ladies club; ha, ha, ha.

Marlow. Zounds, there's no bearing this; it's worse than death.

Miss Hardcastle. In which of your characters, Sir, will you give us leave to address you? As the faultering gentleman, with looks on the ground, that speaks just to be heard, and hates hypocrisy; or the loud confident creature, that keeps it up with Mrs. Mantrap, and old Miss Biddy Buckskin, till three in the morning; ha, ha, ha.

Marlow. Oh, curse on my noisy head. I never attempted to be impudent yet that I was not taken down. I must be gone.

Hardcastle. By the hand of my body, but you shall not. I

see it was all a mistake, and I am rejoiced to find it. You shall not, Sir, I tell you. I know she'll forgive you. Won't you forgive him, Kate? We'll all forgive you. Take courage, man.

[*They retire, she tormenting him to the back Scene.*]

Enter MRS. HARDCASTLE, TONY

Mrs. Hardcastle. So, so, they're gone off. Let them go, I care not.

Hardcastle. Who gone?

Mrs. Hardcastle. My dutiful niece and her gentleman, Mr. Hastings, from town. He who came down with our modest visitor here.

Sir Charles. Who, my honest George Hastings? As worthy a fellow as lives, and the girl could not have made a more prudent choice.

Hardcastle. Then, by the hand of my body, I'm proud of the connexion.

Mrs. Hardcastle. Well, if he has taken away the lady, he has not taken her fortune; that remains in this family to console us for her loss.

Hardcastle. Sure, Dorothy, you would not be so mercenary?

Mrs. Hardcastle. Ay, that's my affair, not your's. But you know if your son, when of age, refuses to marry his cousin, her whole fortune is then at her own disposal.

Hardcastle. Ay, but he's not of age, and she has not thought proper to wait for his refusal.

Enter HASTINGS *and* MISS NEVILLE

Mrs. Hardcastle. (*aside*) What, returned so soon. I begin not to like it.

Hastings. (*to* HARDCASTLE) For my late attempt to fly off with your niece, let my present confusion be my punishment. We are now come back, to appeal from your justice to your humanity. By her father's consent I first paid her my addresses, and our passions were first founded in duty.

Miss Neville. Since his death I have been obliged to stoop to dissimulation to avoid oppression. In an hour of levity I was ready even to give up my fortune to secure my choice. But I'm now recovered from the delusion, and hope from your tenderness what is denied me from a nearer connexion.

Mrs. Hardcastle. Pshaw, pshaw, this is all but the whining end of a modern novel.

Hardcastle. Be it what it will, I'm glad they're come back to reclaim their due. Come hither, Tony boy. Do you refuse this lady's hand whom I now offer you?

Tony. What signifies my refusing? You know I can't refuse her till I'm of age, father.

Hardcastle. While I thought concealing your age boy was likely to conduce to your improvement, I concurred with your mother's desire to keep it secret. But since I find she turns it to a wrong use, I must now declare you have been of age these three months.

Tony. Of age! Am I of age, father?

Hardcastle. Above three months.

Tony. Then you'll see the first use I'll make of my liberty. (*taking* MISS NEVILLE's *hand*) Witness all men by these presents, that I, Anthony Lumpkin, Esquire, of BLANK place, refuse you, Constantia Neville, spinster, of no place at all, for my true and lawful wife. So Constance Neville may marry whom she pleases, and Tony Lumpkin is his own man again.

Sir Charles. O brave 'Squire.

Hastings. My worthy friend.

Mrs. Hardcastle. My undutiful offspring.

Marlow. Joy, my dear George, I give you joy sincerely. And could I prevail upon my little tyrant here to be less arbitrary, I should be the happiest man alive, if you would return me the favour.

Hastings. (*to* MISS HARDCASTLE) Come, madam, you are now driven to the very last scene of all your contrivances. I know you like him, I'm sure he loves you, and you must and shall have him.

Hardcastle. (*joining their hands*) And I say so too. And Mr. Marlow, if she makes as good a wife as she has a daughter, I don't believe you'll ever repent your bargain. So now to supper, to-morrow we shall gather all the poor of the parish about us, and the Mistakes of the Night shall be crowned with a merry morning; so boy take her; and as you have been mistaken in the mistress, my wish is, that you may never be mistaken in the wife.

EPILOGUE

Well, having stoop'd to conquer with success,
And gain'd a husband without aid from dress,
Still as a bar-maid, I could wish it too,
As I have conquer'd him to conquer you:
And let me say, for all your resolution,
That pretty bar-maids have done execution.
Our life is all a play, compos'd to please,
"We have our exits and our entrances."
The first act shews the simple country maid,
Harmless and young, of ev'ry thing afraid;
Blushes when hir'd, and with unmeaning action,
I hopes as how to give you satisfaction.
Her second act displays a livelier scene,—
Th' unblushing bar-maid of a country inn,
Who whisks about the house, at market caters,
Talks loud, coquets the guests, and scolds the waiters.
Next the scene shifts to town, and there she soars,
The chop-house toast of ogling connoissieurs.
On 'Squires and cits she there displays her arts,
And on the gridiron broils her lovers' hearts—
And as she smiles, her triumphs to compleat,
Even Common Councilmen forget to eat.
The fourth act shows her wedded to the 'Squire,
And Madam now begins to hold it higher;
Pretends to taste, at operas cries *caro*,
And quits her Nancy Dawson, for *Che Faro*.[101]
Doats upon dancing, and in all her pride,
Swims round the room, the *Heinel* of Cheapside:
Ogles and leers with artificial skill,
Till having lost in age the power to kill,
She sits all night at cards, and ogles at spadille.
Such, thro' our lives, the eventful history—
The fifth and last act still remains for me.
The bar-maid now for your protection prays,
Turns female barrister, and pleads for Bayes.[102]

NOTES

1. "A cloak, however coarse, to keep out the cold." Horace, *Satires*, I. iii. 14.
2. "He grieves in truth who grieves without a witness." Martial, *Epigrams*, I. xxxiii. 4.
3. Dr. John Hill, prolific miscellaneous writer, who for two years wrote what we should call a "column" in a daily newspaper, under the name of "The Inspector."
4. Arthur Murphy, actor and playwright, whose first tragedy, *The Orphan of China,* had been produced at Drury Lane in 1759.
5. Dr. Johnson, who regarded his dictionary with justifiable pride, but who thought that his *Rambler* essays had been too hastily written.
6. David Hume, whose skepticism had been revealed in essays recently published, was at this time writing his *History of England.* He had published the first volume, dealing with the reigns of the first Stuart kings, in 1754. The "last" volume referred to here, including the reign of Elizabeth, had appeared in 1759.
7. Tobias Smollett, the novelist. Goldsmith's review of his *History of England* is included in the present edition.
8. No further installment was published.
9. "Greed is more destructive than the sword."
10. The phrase, which Goldsmith has just translated, is from the opening section of Petronius's *Satyricon.*
11. Presumably Thomas Sheridan, who was at this time delivering lectures on elocution. He was the father of the famous dramatist.
12. A footnote referred the original reader to the first novel reviewed in the present edition, *The Impetuous Lover.*

13. This passage, which Goldsmith has translated for us, is from Boileau's *Art of Poetry,* iii. 401-2.

14. A fanatic who had attempted to assassinate Louis XV. See note 75.

15. An usher was an assistant to a schoolmaster. Goldsmith, whose face was scarred by small pox, had been an usher at an academy in the outskirts of London.

16. Two famous racehorses. In a letter written at the end of 1757 Goldsmith complained that in Ireland more was spent on "the Podareen mare" in one season than in rewards to learned men in a century.

17. The second half of this sentence is a revision of the relatively tame: "all men who have any character on their tombs have a good one."

18. The celebrated Stone of Scone, which medieval chroniclers identified as Jacob's pillow.

19. The "Seven Years' War" had begun in 1756.

20. Juffrouw, here translated as madam.

21. Goldsmith is thought to have had in mind Home's *Douglas,* which was first acted in London in 1757.

22. *The Oxford English Dictionary,* noting this form of the word, quotes Dickens: "The fire that warmed you when you were a babby."

23. This phrase is a revise, substituted for the original "at once."

24. An earlier version of these verses was sent by Goldsmith to his brother Henry in 1759. In part they reappear in ll. 229-238 of *The Deserted Village.* Brave Prince William was William Augustus, Duke of Cumberland, the military hero. The twelve rules of Charles I (the Royal Martyr) were: 1. Urge no healths. 2. Profane no divine ordinance. 3. Touch no state matters. 4. Reveal no secrets. 5. Pick no quarrels. 6. Make no comparisons. 7. Maintain no ill opinions. 8. Keep no bad company. 9. Encourage no vice. 10. Make no long meals. 11. Repeat no grievances. 12. Lay no wagers.

25. "From the toe-nail of Hercules," a variation of the proverbial "You may judge of Hercules from his foot," i.e., "You may judge of the whole from the part."

26. The tutor, who was responsible for the young man's education while on the Grand Tour.

27. A colloquialism for arm-in-arm. Spintria, used by Goldsmith as a plural, is the Latin word for a male prostitute.

28. In Letter XXII Lien Chi Altangi wrote that his son Hingpo, "incited by filial piety," decided to leave China to join his father. In Thibet he was captured by a band of Tartars, who sold him as a slave to a cruel Persian.

29. The Chinese phoenix, an ornament of gold and jewels worn in the hair.

30. An obsolete word, meaning "creature," with connotations at once unpleasant and supernatural. Compare Milton's lines on Satan (*Paradise Lost,* x, 279):

    So sented the grim Feature and upturn'd
    His Nostril wide into the murkie Air.

31. A fur hat. In the revised version Goldsmith substituted the word garter.

32. Tom D'Urfey, a merry poet and dramatist who flourished at the end of the seventeenth century and was one of those attacked by Jeremy Collier in his *Short View of the Immorality and Profaneness of the English Stage.* He was a favorite of Charles II.

33. Pope's *Second Satire of the Second Book of Horace Paraphrased,* ll. 79-80.

34. Goldsmith inserted the following note here: "This story bears a striking similitude to the real history of Miss S——d who accompanied Mrs. W——e in her retreat near Florence." No one has yet been able to identify Miss S——d, but Mrs. W——e, who in Goldsmith's revised note becomes Lady W——e, is without doubt Lady Walpole, wife of Horace Walpole's brother Robert. Her many amours in Italy were well advertised. Writing in 1752 to his friend George Montagu, who was apparently in Italy, Horace Walpole says that he will be "much obliged for the passion-flower, notwithstanding it comes out of a garden of Eden from which Eve my sister-in-law long ago gathered passion-fruit."

35. Austin Dobson in *Eighteenth Century Vignettes* gives a characteristically charming account of Vauxhall Gardens, the fashionable pleasure resort here described.

36. *The Gentleman's Magazine* for August 1765 describes the water-works as a "curious piece of machinery . . . representing a beautiful landscape in perspective, with a miller's house,

a water-mill, and a cascade. The exact appearance of water is seen flowing down a declivity; and turning the wheel of the mill, it rises up in a foam at the bottom, and then glides away."

37. The evening of the king's birthday was the occasion for fashionable parties, at which new clothes were worn.

38. The two theatres were Drury Lane and Covent Garden.

39. Rival productions of *The Beggar's Opera* held the stage in September 1760, when this letter was first published. At Covent Garden the part of Polly was taken by Miss Brent, at Drury Lane by Mrs. Vincent. The copper tail mentioned in the previous paragraph presumably refers to the actress's train. Compare lines 279-280 of *The Traveller:*

> Here vanity assumes her pert grimace,
> And trims her robes of frize with copper lace.

Lace of silver or gold was more costly.

40. A borrowing from Latin, defined as "pertaining to a wagon."

41. Another deliberately ponderous word, suggesting hanging, or the gallows.

42. "A factory of peoples." The phrase was applied in the sixth century to the Goths (Jordanes, *De Origine actibusque Getarum,* near the beginning). Johan Basilides is presumably Ivan IV, "the Terrible" (1530-1584), son of Basil III and the first to call himself Czar. But Goldsmith might be referring to Ivan III, "the Great" (1440-1505), son of Basil II, who by his many conquests and by his marriage established Moscow as the political center of Russia.

43. "What is pleasing and useful." Horace, *Art of Poetry,* line 334.

44. The text of this letter is based on the revised version, because I have not seen a copy of the newspaper in which it was first published.

45. In Letter XCIV Hingpo reported that while he and his beautiful companion were traveling from Terki towards Moscow their party was attacked by "Wolga" pirates. The women were sent off in one vessel, leaving the men to fight a three-day battle. On the fourth day the pirates were finally beaten off; the travelers then learned that the women had been wrecked on the banks of the Wolga and carried away by

peasants. The letter ended: "Need I paint the situation of my mind on this occasion? Need I describe all I feel when I despair of beholding the beautiful Zelis more? Fancy had dressed the future prospect of my life in the gayest colouring, but one unexpected stroke of fortune has robbed it of every charm. Her dear idea mixes with every scene of pleasure, and without her presence to enliven it the whole becomes tedious, insipid, insupportable. I will confess, now that she is lost, I will confess I loved her; nor is it in the power of time or of reason to erase her image from my heart."

46. Giovanni Francesco Gemelli, whose *Voyage Round the World* was published in Naples in 1699-1700.

47. Letter XCIX ended with the introduction of the Man in Black's niece, "a young lady of exquisite beauty. Her very appearance was sufficient to silence the severest satyrist of the sex; easy without pride and free without impudence, she seemed capable of supplying every sense with pleasure; her looks, her conversation were natural and unconstrained; she had neither been taught to languish nor ogle, to laugh without a jest or sigh without sorrow. I found that she had just returned from abroad and had been conversant in the manners of the world. Curiosity prompted me to ask several questions, but she declined them all. I own I never found myself so strongly prejudiced in favour of apparent merit before, and could willingly have prolonged our conversation, but the company after some time withdrew."

48. Goldsmith later added a note at this point: "Translation of a South American Ode."

49. In the original version the following words appeared in place of this bracketed passage: "A dispute however about carving one of the dishes."

50. One of the Inns of Court, existing for the study and practice of the law.

51. Tricked, cheated.

52. Those who are desperate. The phrase was used by gamblers to signify a desperate risk.

53. "We, whom neither the son of Tydeus nor Achilles of Larissa nor a ten-year war could master, succumbed to wiles." Vergil, *Aeneid,* ii. 197.

54. Various kinds of wigs worn from the time of Charles II until

Goldsmith's day. A bob had the bottom locks turned up into short curls; a major was a full wig, tied back in one curl; the back hair of a bag wig was enclosed in an ornamental bag; and a ramillie (from Marlborough's victory at Ramillies in 1706) had a long plait behind, tied with a bow at top and bottom.

55. A servant in the popular comedy by Richard Steele.

56. A servant who at the age of eighteen achieved notoriety early in 1753 by disappearing for a month. Her story upon her return was that she had been seized by two men who dragged her to a house near London, where she was confined until she managed to escape. Those who were supposedly the culprits were tried and found guilty, but the case was by no means clear. After a year of investigation she was herself found guilty of willful and corrupt perjury and was transported to New England. She is said to have there married a Quaker named Treat and to have died in Weathersfield, Connecticut, in 1773. To this day the true story of what happened to her during that mysterious month is not known.

57. "Hurried on with turbid flow." An apt quotation from Horace, *Satires*, i. 4. 11.

58. Chapter LV of Smollett's *Roderick Random*.

59. Mechanics.

60. Verse 25 of Psalm XXXVII.

61. A feeder was one who fattened animals that were to be slaughtered, but the word was humorously applied, as here, to a tutor.

62. In the slang of that time *to smoke* meant *to make fun of*.

63. Defoe's *Religious Courtship* (1722) is a series of dialogues urging the necessity of making a good Christian marriage. Thwackum and Square are the theologian and deist in Fielding's *Tom Jones*.

64. Hot spiced ale mixed with the pulp of roasted apples.

65. In the first edition Goldsmith wrote *Bangorean*. The Bangorian controversy (begun in 1717 by the Bishop of Bangor) dealt with the dilemma of strict churchmen when the House of Hanover supplanted that of the Stuarts. Because it provoked a spate of pamphlets written by well-meaning but pedantic clergymen, it is the sort of battle in which Dr. Primrose might have engaged with enthusiasm. But Goldsmith's

alteration narrows the Vicar's writings to those concerned with monogamy. See the second paragraph of Chapter Two.

66. A long riding-cloak.

67. John Newbery, the printer for whom Goldsmith did much of his writing.

68. See note 15.

69. A toy used to soothe infants who were cutting teeth. Richard Garnett has pointed out that by extension the soothing necklace can mean "a hangman's halter."

70. An Irish phrase, meaning to beat up a brothel.

71. With a siserary, i.e., at once.

72. The fact that George had sent a challenge meant that he was the first to break the law.

73. The reference is supposedly to Charles Churchill, the satirist.

74. In February 1758 Goldsmith published an article in *The Literary Magazine,* in which, speaking of the Dutch, he wrote: "France is not only now their neighbour but their master, prepared to pour in its myriads upon their little spot of ground, once saved from the sea, and now in danger of as formidable a deluge. No longer do we see there the industrious citizen planning schemes to defend his own liberty and the liberty of Europe, but the servile money-meditating miser, who desires riches to dissipate in luxury, and whose luxuries make him needy."

75. In 1514 two brothers, Luke and George Dosa, headed a revolt in Hungary. When it was suppressed, George (not Luke) was punished by having a red-hot crown put on his head. In 1757 a fanatic named Robert Francis Damien attempted to assassinate Louis XV. After being tortured, he was torn to pieces by horses. Compare the reference to Louis and Damien at the end of Letter V of *The Citizen of the World.*

76. Various enclosure bills were passed in the eighteenth century that enabled a lord of the manor to enclose common lands, thus depriving humbler folk of what they had considered their own. "Districts once covered with small arable farms were turned into immense pastures, and there were complaints that a single man monopolised a tract which had formerly supported twelve or fourteen industrious families. Whole villages, which had depended on free pasture land and fuel, dwindled

and perished, and a stream of emigrants passed to America. Macaulay, in an essay which is by no means among the most valuable of his productions, has censured Goldsmith's *Deserted Village* as wholly unnatural and incongruous. The village, he says, in its happy state could only have existed in England; the village in its deserted state could only have existed in Ireland. But there are contemporary pictures of the effects of enclosures in England which go far to refute the criticism." (W. E. H. Lecky, *England in the Eighteenth Century,* London, 1892, vii. 260.)

77. In 1733 General Oglethorpe, later a friend of Goldsmith's, founded the colony of Georgia as a refuge for paupers. The river Altama, or Altamaha, was the boundary which separated Georgia from the Spaniards in Florida.

78. An act against "Cutpurses and Pyckpurses" was passed in the eighth, not the fifth, year of Elizabeth's reign. Fielding, mentioned five lines earlier, was Sir John, who in 1754 had succeeded his half-brother Henry as justice of the peace for Westminster.

79. Dorothy Monroe was a celebrated beauty of the time.

80. Falstaff's remark (*1 Henry IV,* V.i.126) on the eve of battle.

81. Goldsmith's ironical criticism of the tastes of his genteel contemporaries, "grown of late too delicate." (Preface to *The Good Natur'd Man.*) The best commentary on this passage is Goldsmith's, printed in this edition on p. 70.

82. "Water Parted" is a song from Arne's opera *Artaxerxes;* the minuet is from Handel's opera *Ariadne.*

83. Very much.

84. *Hamlet,* I.v.125.

85. A few years before this play was written John Harrison had invented an instrument for determining the longitude at sea.

86. My colleague Aubrey Williams has unearthed evidence which shows that some of the prostitutes who frequented the theatre district assumed titles, such as "duchess." See "Pope's Duchesses and Lady Marys" in *Review of English Studies* for January, 1954.

87. "The names of considerably more than half the Commons of 1761 were in the books of the peerage and baronetage. The rest were almost all of gentry origin." (L. B. Namier, *Struc-*

ture of Politics at the Accession of George III, i.207.) As is clear from Letter CXII of *The Citizen of the World*, voters expected free drinks from the candidates.

88. Heyder Ally had recently usurped the throne of Mysore in India. Ally Khan was Subah of Bengal. Ally Croaker was the hero of a popular Irish ballad.

89. The Royal Marriage Act of 1772 provided that no descendant of George II could marry without the previous consent of the king. The act had been passed because two of the king's brothers had married without the royal consent. One of them, the Duke of Gloucester, was present at the opening performance of the play, and at this point was cheered by the audience.

90. *The Complete Housewife* and John Quincy's *Complete English Dispensatory* were well-known handbooks of medicine for the home.

91. "A noted sharper, swaggerer, and debauchee" in Restoration London.

92. A revolving piece of fireworks.

93. The innkeeper's daughter in Farquhar's comedy.

94. The rooms of an inn were given names, such as the Lamb, Dolphin, or Angel, instead of numbers.

95. A pair of aces, the lowest possible throw.

96. A fop. Caricatures of celebrities were sold in the print-shops.

97. A famous racehorse.

98. Tony's pronunciation of harpsichord.

99. A sword or stick with wickerwork protection for the hand.

100. Step-father.

101. The "correct" word at operas was the Italian *caro*, darling. *Nancy Dawson* was a popular ballad; *che faro* are the opening words of an aria in Gluck's *Orfeo*. Anna Frederica Heinel was a dancer who had captivated London audiences.

102. The dramatist ridiculed in Buckingham's *Rehearsal*. Goldsmith here ironically adopts the name for himself.